Safe sailing
from the author,

Bernard L. Gordon

MAN AND THE SEA

To Liza Barocas

From Fay Saranga

OTHER BOOKS BY *Bernard L. Gordon*

The Marine Fishes of Rhode Island (1960)

*Advisor's Handbook for Junior Chapters
of American Littoral Society* (1964)

A Guide to Historical Southern New England (1967)

MAN AND THE SEA

Classic Accounts
of Marine Explorations

EDITED BY *Bernard L. Gordon*
FOREWORD BY *Paul M. Fye*

PUBLISHED FOR
The American Museum of Natural History
THE DOUBLEDAY NATURAL HISTORY PRESS
GARDEN CITY, NEW YORK   1972

Except where otherwise noted, the line illustrations for this book were prepared by the Graphic Arts Division of The American Museum of Natural History.

MAN AND THE SEA was also published in a hardcover edition by the Natural History Press in December 1970.

ACKNOWLEDGMENTS

I want to express my appreciation for the help I received in the development of this volume from the following: Toni Strassman, Toni Werbel, Maureen Mahon, Tom Childs, Jr., Joseph Gordon, J. Rosson Overcash, David Wilmarth, William Newman, Richard Ruggles, Roger Charlier, Donald Zinn, Giles Mead, Richard Wolfe, Roland Moody, Sol Malkin, Irene Arman, and Esther Gordon.

Yonder is the sea, great and of wide extent;
Therein are moving things innumerable,
Living creatures both small and great.
There the ships make their course;
There is the great leviathan whom thou has formed to sport
therein.
These all wait upon thee,
That thou mayest give them food in due season . . .

PSALM 104
THE BOOK OF PSALMS

Bernard L. Gordon is an associate professor of earth sciences at Northeastern University in Boston, where he has been a member of the faculty since 1961. He received his B.S. and M.S. degrees at the University of Rhode Island and also studied at Brown University, the University of Massachusetts, and Boston University.

In 1966 Professor Gordon visited the Soviet Union to present a paper at the 2nd International Oceanographic Congress at Moscow University. In addition to writing numerous articles and papers for scientific journals and popular magazines, such as *Natural History*, he is the author of *The Marine Fishes of Rhode Island*, and *A Guide to Historical Southern New England*.

During the summer, Professor Gordon combines his academic career with his love of the sea as the proprietor of a unique shop in Watch Hill, Rhode Island, where he sells fishing tackle and rare books on natural science.

FOR JOE . . .

And all others . . .
Who share the joys of locomotion
Down within the depths of the ocean

CONTENTS

CONTRIBUTORS

~~~~~~

FOREWORD

The ocean has always played a vital role in man's life, sometimes bringing good, sometimes bad. For those living near its shores, it has been the dominant environmental factor—ever present, pervasive and awe inspiring. For others its influence has been more subtle, but only slightly less profound.

Today, it is clear that the influence of the oceans is felt by everyone living anywhere on the globe. As we understand more and more about ocean phenomena, we realize that these influences are constant and of vital importance to mankind everywhere.

Not only do the oceans continue to provide us, as they have for centuries, a great highway for transportation of the large fraction of the world's goods, an important source of food and an important arena for military operations, but they influence our lives in other and even more vital ways. The oceans now provide new sources of animal protein, increasing means of recreation, growing mineral resources—including a significant portion of our oil and gas—and even landing fields for our space ships.

Perhaps most important of all to young people and students are the new techniques becoming available for studying the oceans. Since oceanography is an interdisciplinary activity, many applications are made of new tools of science and technology which are developed in related fields. These range from the multiple use of satellites in precise navigation, in the study of ice cover and even the measurement of waves to the use of the latest in computers. But, more important, the student of the oceans today has many new sophisticated tools, which are uniquely designed for ocean study and available to him for the first time. The development of small research submersibles like *Alvin* and *Aluminaut* permit the oceanographer to descend into the deep ocean for visual observation. Every dive literally opens new vistas in a most exciting way. This past year has seen the development of drilling techniques which enable the geologist to obtain samples of the solid earth from below the deep ocean. The cruises of the *Glomar Challenger* in the North and South Atlantic have already produced new evidence in support of the theories of continental drift and sea-floor spreading.

But the studies of the oceans are no longer restricted to the natural phenomena observed by the oceanographer. Today the oceans are becoming of vital interest to the economist, the political scientist, the international lawyer and the diplomat. Evidence of this is plainly visible on the national and international scene.

Early in 1969 the Presidential Commission on Marine Science, Engineering and Resources, chaired by Dr. Julius A. Stratton, submitted its far reaching recommendations to the President. This report outlines a program of great significance for the United States. It is truly a national program. It suggests roles of increasing importance for the Federal Government, and the State and local governments, as well as for American industry. Leadership in the scientific studies of oceanography will continue to be in the university laboratories and private institutions. Leadership in the proposed development of an ocean technology will necessarily be in industry and in governmental organizations.

On the international scene, the General Assembly of the United Nations has established a major committee (composed of 42 member states) on the Peace Uses of the Sea-Bed and the Ocean Floor beyond the limits of National Jurisdiction. This action grew out of a high interest on the part of all member states, not just the 121 nations with ocean shores, and from earlier studies and resolutions from various parts of the United Nations organization.

This standing Sea-Bed Committee is charged with studying the entire range of problems relating to the peaceful and cooperative use of the deep sea-bed. The scope of the committee's assignments includes legal, technical and diplomatic problems which must be solved to ensure the wise use of the oceans' resources for the benefit of all peoples.

The seas truly are among the most challenging frontiers for students in the last third of the twentieth century. The lore and fascination of the seas goes back to the earliest written word in man's history. This rich tradition from the past must be integrated with exciting modern ocean activities.

Professor Gordon's selection of writings about the oceans should assist the student in his own personal evaluation of our rich heritage and our continually changing marine opportunities. It is also an inspiring collection for the seasoned oceanographer.

> Paul M. Fye
> President and Director
> Woods Hole Oceanographic Institution
> April 1969

The dynamic realm of the global ocean is constantly in flux. Since primitive man first cast eyes on waves breaking on the shore, he has searched for explanations of its awesome phenomena and mastery of its domain.

Historically, nations whose vessels mastered the seas rose to prominence through the exploitation of the underdeveloped areas of the globe. Portugal, Spain, England, Holland, and France ventured to the ends of the earth to claim the riches of colonial territories by virtue of their naval and merchant fleets.

Ocean currents and wind systems provided the propulsion for Columbus, da Gama, Dias, Drake, and Cook. These early explorers of distant shores obtained intimate knowledge of tidal fluctuation, wind and currents. It remained for the men of science, such as Newton, Ferrel, Ekman, and Bjerknes, to provide valid explanations of ocean movement.

Today, we find man has largely explored, populated, and exploited the dry land areas of our planet. Food and mineral resources from the continents are being utilized to the point of great depletion to meet the needs of the growing world population. Beneath the waters that cover seventy percent of the surface of the earth lies the promise for man's future.

The potential resources of the global seas are fantastic. Food, mineral and power resources exist in the oceans which render those on land miniscule by comparison. According to various authorities, potential food supply of the oceans is sufficient to provide every man, woman and child on this planet with one pound of nutrient rich food each day. There is enough common salt in the ocean to cover the earth's land surface to a depth of forty-two feet. If the gold and silver present in the ocean's waters could be extracted, there would be a ton for every person on earth of the former, and twenty tons for everyone of the latter.

The power resources of the oceans are also tremendous when we consider the quantity of heavy hydrogen in the seas or the magnitude of the tides. It has been estimated that all the rivers on land produce 850,000,000 kilowatts of power; whereas, the potential energy of the tides could produce 1,000,000,000 kilowatts.

This book has been prepared to give students of marine science historical and contemporary insights into the growth and development of oceanography. Having taught oceanography on the college level for over a decade, I have felt a growing need for this present volume as an aid to better understanding of the growth and direction of ocean science.

I wish to express my thanks for assistance received at the libraries of Harvard University, Northeastern University, the Boston Public Library, the Woods Hole libraries, and the Pell Library of the Graduate School of Oceanography of the University of Rhode Island. Thanks are also due to the many individuals whose advice and contributions helped to make this volume achieve its present form and significance especially to the *Antiquarian Bookman* and the antiquarian book dealers around the world who helped me obtain original copies of many of the significant papers in this volume.

Bernard L. Gordon
Associate Professor
Northeastern University
Boston, Massachusetts

"Yes; I love it! The sea is everything. It covers seven-tenths of the terrestrial globe. Its breath is pure and healthy. It is an immense desert, where man is never lonely, for he feels life stirring on all sides. The sea is only the embodiment of a supernatural and wonderful existence . . . Nature manifests herself in it by her three kingdoms, mineral, vegetable, and animal. The sea is the vast reservoir of Nature. The globe began with sea, so to speak; and who knows if it will not end with it? In it is supreme tranquility. The sea does not belong to despots. Upon its surface men can still exercise unjust laws, fight, tear one another to pieces, and be carried away with terrestrial horrors. But at thirty feet below its level, their reign ceases, their influence is quenched, and their power disappears. Ah! sir, live—live in the bosom of the waters! There only is independence! There I recognize no masters! There I am free."

Captain Nemo in Jules Verne's
Twenty Thousand Leagues Under the Sea

Page 71, 1875 edition, Published by
Donnelley, Loyd & Company, Chicago, Illinois

MAN AND THE SEA

Genesis:

1. *THE FLOOD**

(*8:vi 5–viii 22*)

VI 5 When Yahweh saw how great was man's wickedness on earth, and how every scheme that his mind devised was nothing but evil all the time, 6 Yahweh regretted that he had made man on earth, and there was sorrow in his heart. 7 And Yahweh said, "I will blot out from the earth the men that I created, man and beast, the creeping things, and the birds of the sky; for I am sorry that I made them." 8 But Noah found favor with Yahweh.

╱9 This is the line of Noah.—Noah was a righteous man; he was without blame in that age; Noah walked with God.—10 Noah begot three sons: Shem, Ham, and Japheth.

11 The earth was corrupt in the view of God, and it was full of lawlessness. 12 And God saw how corrupt the earth was, for all flesh had corrupted their ways on earth.

13 Then God said to Noah, "I have decided to put an end to all flesh, for the earth is filled with lawlessness because of them. So I am about to destroy both them and the earth. 14 Make yourself an ark of gopher wood; make it an ark with compartments, and cover it inside and out with pitch. 15 This is how you shall build it: the length of the ark shall be three hundred cubits, its width fifty cubits, and its height thirty cubits. 16 Make a sky light for the ark, terminating it within a cubit of the top. Put the entrance in the side of the ark, which is to be made with lower, second, and third decks.

17 For my part, I am about to bring on the Flood—waters upon the earth—to eliminate everywhere all flesh in which there is the breath of life: everything on earth shall perish. 18 But with you I will establish my covenant, and you shall enter the ark—you, your sons, your wife, and your sons' wives. 19 And of all else that is alive, of all flesh, you shall take two of each into the ark to stay alive

* From THE ANCHOR BIBLE (Genesis), E. A. Speiser, translator and editor. Copyright © 1965 Doubleday & Company, Inc., New York. Reprinted by permission of the Publisher.

with you; they must be male and female. 20 Of the birds of every
kind, cattle of every kind, every kind of creeping thing—two of each
shall come inside to you to stay alive. 21 For your part, provide yourself with all the food that is to be eaten, and store it away to serve as
provisions for you and for them."

22 This Noah did. Just as God commanded him, so he did./

VII 1 Then Yahweh said to Noah, "Go into the ark, you and
all your household, for you alone have I found to be truly righteous
in this age. 2 Of every clean animal take seven pairs, a male and its
mate; and of the animals that are unclean, one pair, a male and its
mate; 3 but seven pairs again of the birds of the sky, male and female, to preserve issue throughout the earth. 4 For in seven days' time
I will cause it to rain upon the earth for forty days and forty
nights; and I will blot out from the surface of the earth all existence
that I created."

5 Noah did just as Yahweh commanded him. /6 Noah was in his
six hundredth year when the Flood came—waters upon the earth./

7 Then Noah, together with his sons, his wife, and his sons'
wives, went inside the ark because of the waters of the Flood.
8 Of the clean animals and the animals that are unclean, the birds
of the sky and everything that creeps on earth, 9 [two of each][a],
male and female, came inside the ark to Noah, as God had commanded Noah. 10 As soon as the seven days were over, the waters
of the Flood were upon the earth.

/11 In the six hundredth year of Noah's life, in the second month,
on the seventeenth day of the month—on that day—

> All the fountains of the great deep burst forth
> And the sluices in the sky broke open./

12 Heavy rain fell upon the earth forty days and forty nights. /13
On the aforesaid day, Noah and his sons, Shem, Ham, and Japheth,
Noah's wife, and the three wives of his sons had entered the ark—
14 they as well as every kind of beast, every kind of creature that
creeps on earth, and every kind of bird, every[b] winged thing. 15
They came inside the ark to Noah, two each of all flesh in which
there was the breath of life. 16 Those that entered comprised male
and female of all flesh, as God had commanded Noah./Then Yahweh shut him in.

---

[a] Evidently a gloss.
[b] LXX, and others, read "and every winged bird."

/17 The Flood came down upon the earth/forty days. As the waters increased, they bore the ark aloft, so that it rose above the earth. /18 The waters swelled and increased greatly upon the earth, and the ark drifted on the surface of the water. 19 The waters continued to swell more and more, until all the highest mountains everywhere were submerged, 20 the crest reaching fifteen cubits above the submerged mountains. 21 And all flesh that had stirred on earth perished—birds, cattle, beasts, and all the creatures that swarmed on earth—and all mankind./ 22 All in whose nostrils was the faintest breath of life, everything that had been on dry land, died out. 23 All existence on earth was blotted out—man, cattle, creeping things, and birds of the sky; they were blotted out from the earth. Only Noah was left, and those that were with him in the ark.

/24 When the waters over the earth had maintained their crest one hundred and fifty days, **VIII** 1 God remembered Noah and all the beasts and cattle that were with him in the ark, and God caused a wind to sweep across the earth. The waters began to subside. 2 The fountains of the deep and the sluices in the sky were stopped up,/ and the heavy rain from the sky was held back. 3 Little by little the waters receded from the earth. /By the end of one hundred and fifty days the waters had diminished so that 4 in the seventh month, on the seventeenth day of the month, the ark came to rest on the Ararat range. 5 The waters went on diminishing until the tenth month. In the tenth month, on the first day of the month, the peaks of the mountains became visible./

6 At the end of forty days Noah opened the hatch of the ark that he had made, 7 and released a raven; it went back and forth waiting for the water to dry off from the earth. 8 Then he sent out a dove, to see if the waters had dwindled from the ground. 9 But the dove could not find a place for its foot to rest on, and returned to him in the ark, for there was water all over the earth; so putting out his hand, he picked it up, and drew it inside the ark toward him. 10 He waited another seven days and again released the dove from the ark. 11 The dove returned to him toward evening, and there in its bill was a plucked olive leaf! Noah knew then that the waters had dwindled from the ground. 12 He waited yet another seven days and released the dove once more; it did not return to him again.

13 /In the six hundred and first year [of Noah's life], on the first day of the month, the waters had begun to dry from the earth./ Noah removed the covering of the ark and saw that the surface of

the ground was drying. ╱14 In the second month, on the twenty-seventh day of the month, the earth was dry.

15 Then God spoke to Noah, saying, 16 "Come out of the ark, together with your wife, your sons, and your sons' wives. 17 Bring out with you every living being that is with you—all flesh, be it bird or cattle or any creature that creeps on earth—and let them swarm on earth, and breed and increase on it." 18 So Noah came out, with his sons, his wife, and his sons' wives. 19 And every animal, every creeping thing, and every bird—everything that stirs on earth —left the ark, group by group.╱

20 Then Noah built an altar to Yahweh and, choosing from every clean animal and every clean bird, offered burnt offerings on the altar. 21 As Yahweh smelled the soothing odor, he said to himself, "Never again will I doom the world because of man, since the devisings of man's heart are evil from the start; neither will I ever again strike down every living being, as I have done.

> 22 So long as the earth endures,
> Seedtime and harvest,
> Cold and heat,
> Summer and winter,
> And day and night
> Shall not cease."

COMMENT

The received biblical account of the Flood is beyond reasonable doubt a composite narrative, reflecting more than one separate source. One of the sources goes back to P, and is easy enough to identify except for a clause or two. But the identity of the narrator or narrators other than P has caused considerable trouble and debate. Nevertheless, if one is prepared to overlook a few highly technical details—as one must in a comprehensive study—it should not be too hazardous to accept *J* as the only other author involved.

More serious for our immediate purposes is the fact that the respective versions of P and *J* have not been handed down in connected form, as was the case, for example, with Sec. 1 (P) and Sec. 2 (*J*). Here the two strands have become intertwined, the end result being a skillful and intricate patchwork. Nevertheless—and this is indicative of the great reverence with which the components were handled—the underlying versions, though cut up and rearranged, were not altered in themselves. The upshot is that we are now faced not only with certain duplications (e.g., vi 13–22 : vii 1–5), but also with obvious internal contradictions, particularly in regard to the numbers of the various animals taken into the ark (vi 19–20, vii 14–15 : vii 2–3), and the timetable of the Flood (viii 3–5, 13–14 : vii 4, 10, 12, 17, viii 6, 10, 12).

To show the diverging accounts at a glance is not a simple task. A number of modern treatments resort to the expedient of reshuffling the text, but this does violence, in turn, to a tradition that antedates the LXX translation of twenty-two centuries ago. The arrangement followed here reproduces the exact order of the received ("Masoretic") text. At the same time, however, everything that can be traced to P has been placed between diagonals. This way the two components can be distinguished at a glance, or they may be followed consecutively if one wishes to do so. No attempt, however, has been made to mark in J the possible ministrations of R (edactor), in the few instances where such "joins" appear to be indicated, minimal remarks on this subject have been included in the NOTES.

That the biblical account as a whole goes back ultimately to Mesopotamian sources is a fact that is freely acknowledged by most modern scholars; see the detailed discussion in Heidel's *Gilgamesh Epic . . .* , pp. 224–89. But the actual ties are more complex than is generally assumed.

The primeval Flood is echoed in a variety of cuneiform sources; cf. S. N. Kramer, *From the Tablets of Sumer*, 1956, pp. 176 ff. The most extensive prototype, and the best known by far, is found in Tablet XI of the Gilgamesh Epic. It is with this celebrated narrative that the biblical account has most in common.

In both instances there is a Flood hero who has been singled out for deliverance from the impending universal catastrophe. Each is told to construct an ark according to detailed specifications. There follow related descriptions of the elemental cataclysm, the annihilation of all life outside the ark, and the eventual grounding of the strange vessel on top of a tall mountain. Both Noah and Utnapishtim, his Babylonian counterpart, release a series of birds at appropriate intervals to test the subsidence of the waters; each account mentions a dove and a raven. Lastly, when dry land has reappeared in the now desolate world, each principal gives expression to his boundless relief through a sacrifice of humble thanksgiving.

So much correspondence in over-all content is inescapable proof of basic interrelationship. There are, however, also significant differences in detail. The biblical Flood, as was noted earlier is given strong moral motivation, whereas the cuneiform version—at least the one that is incorporated in the Gilgamesh Epic—fails to suggest a plausible cause; one might ascribe the awesome interlude to mere whims of heaven. There are, furthermore, dissimilarities with respect to the occupants of the two arks (the Mesopotamian personnel includes "all the craftsmen") and the order of the test flights (raven–swallow–dove in Gilg.). Above all, there is the immediately apparent difference in names: Noah as against Utnapishtim; the mountains of Ararat as opposed to Mount Nisir. It is thus clear that Hebrew tradition must have received its material from some intermediate, and evidently northwesterly, source, and that it proceeded to adjust the data to its own needs and concepts.

The ultimate inspiration for the Mesopotamian cycle of Flood narratives can only be a matter of guesswork at this time. Perhaps the best chance of a likely solution lies in the recent disclosures concerning the geological background of Lower Mesopotamia (cf. J. M. Lees and N. L. Falcon, "The Geological History of the Mesopotamian Plains," *Geographical Journal* 118 [1952], 24–39). It now appears that not very long ago, as geological ages are reckoned, waters from the Persian Gulf submerged a large coastland area, owing probably to a sudden rise in the sea level. If that rise was precipitated by extraordinary undersea eruptions, the same phenomenon could also have brought on extremely heavy rains, the whole leaving an indelible impression on the survivors. All this, however, must remain in the realm of speculation.

COMMENTS ON THE FLOOD[*]
by Eduard Suess

1. The event known as the *Deluge* took place in the region of the Lower Euphrates, and was connected with an extensive and devastating inundation of the Mesopotamian plain.

2. The chief cause was an earthquake of considerable violence in the region of the Persian Gulf, or to the south of it, which was preceded by several smaller concussions.

3. It is most probable that during the period of the most violent shocks a cyclone came from the south out of the Persian Gulf.

4. The traditions of other races do not justify us in asserting

[*] From Suess, E., 1888. *Das Antlitz Der Erde*. Prag, Leipsiz, Wein. English from translation by H.B.C. Solas, 1904. Published at the Clarendon Press, Oxford.

that the flood extended over the whole earth, or indeed beyond the lower course of the Euphrates and Tigris.

It is this occurrence, after remaining impressed on the memory of man for thousands of years, which has, under the influence of an entirely different hypothesis and by a strange concatenation of circumstances, passed from the sacred books of antiquity into the science of geology and given birth to such terms as "diluvium", "diluvial formation" and "diluvial deposits." The flood was violent and destructive, but we have no proof that it was widely distributed. Its main features as they present themselves to the geologist are as follows:

In the course of a seismic period of some duration the water of the Persian Gulf was repeatedly driven by earthquake-shocks over the plain at the mouths of the Euphrates. Warned by these floods, a prudent man, Hasis-Adra, i.e. the god-fearing philosopher, builds a ship for the rescue of his family, and calks it with pitch, as is still the custom on the Euphrates. The movements of the earth increase; he flees with his family to the ship; the subterranean water bursts forth from the fissured plain; a great diminution in atmospheric pressure, indicated by fearful storm and rain, probably a true cyclone, approaches from the Persian Gulf, and accompanies the most violent manifestation of the seismic force. The sea sweeps in a devastating flood over the plain, raises the rescuing vessel, washes it far inland, and leaves it stranded on one of those Miocene foothills which bound the plain of the Tigris on the north and north-east below the confluence of the Little Zab.

~~~~~~~~~~~~~~~~

Plato:

2.   THE GREAT ISLAND OF ATLANTIS*

Translated by B. Jowett

Many great and wonderful deeds are recorded of your state in our histories. But one of them exceeds all the rest in greatness and valour. For these histories tell of a mighty power which unprovoked made an expedition against the whole of Europe and Asia, and to which your city put an end. This power came forth out of the Atlantic Ocean, for in those days the Atlantic was navigable; and there was an island situated in front of the straits which are by you called the pillars of Heracles; the island was larger than Libya and Asia put together, and was the way to other islands, and from these you might pass to the whole of the opposite continent which surrounded the true ocean; for this sea which is within the Straits of Heracles is only a harbour, having a narrow entrance, but that other is a real sea, and the surrounding land may be most truly called a boundless continent. Now in this island of Atlantis there was a great and wonderful empire which had rule over the whole island and several others, and over parts of the continent, and, furthermore, the men of Atlantis had subjected the parts of Libya within the columns of Heracles as far as Egypt, and of Europe as far as Tyrrhenia. This vast power, gathered into one, endeavoured to subdue at a blow our country and yours and the whole of the region within the straits; and then, Solon, your country shone forth, in the excellence of her virtue and strength, among all mankind. She was pre-eminent in courage and military skill, and was the leader of the Hellenes. And when the rest fell off from her, being compelled to stand alone, after having undergone the very extremity of danger, she defeated and triumphed over the invaders, and preserved from slavery those who were not yet subjugated, and

---

* From THE DIALOGUES OF PLATO, Jowett Translation. Copyright, February 12, 1892, by The Macmillan Company.

Plato was born *c.* 427 B.C. and died *c.* 347 B.C.
Although Greek scholar Benjamin Jowett, 1817–1893, is known primarily for his translation of the Dialogues, he is considered one of England's greatest educators as well.

generously liberated all the rest of us who dwell within the pillars. But afterwards there occurred violent earthquakes and floods; and in a single day and night of misfortune all your warlike men in a body sank into the earth, and the island of Atlantis in like manner disappeared in the depths of the sea. For which reason the sea in those parts is impassable and impenetrable, because there is a shoal of mud in the way; and this was caused by the subsidence of the island.

~~~~~~~~~~~~~~~~~~~

3.   *THE NATURAL HISTORY OF PLINY**

Translated by John Bostock and H. T. Riley

WONDERS OF THE SEA (Chapter 101 [98])

All seas are purified at the full moon[1]; some also at stated periods. At Messina and Mylae a refuse matter, like dung,[2] is cast up on the shore, whence originated the story of the oxen of the Sun having had their stable at that place. To what has been said above (not to omit anything with which I am acquainted) Aristotle adds, that no animal dies except when the tide is ebbing. The observation has been often made on the ocean of Gaul; but it has only been found true with respect to man.[3]

* From the London Edition of THE NATURAL HISTORY OF PLINY. Published by Henry G. Bohn, 1855.

Caius Plinius Secundus, A.D. 23–79, was a Roman naturalist, encyclopedist, and writer.

[1] It has been suggested, with some plausibility, that the greater height of the tides at this period will cause a greater quantity of matter to be cast on shore. This circumstance is referred to by Sencca, Nat. Quest. iii. 26; and by Strabo.

[2] Alexandre observes on this supposed fact, "Algarum molles quaedam species intelligendae sunt, quae convoluntae et marcidae in littus ejiciuntur." Lemaire, i. 432.

[3] It may cause some surprise to find that such an opinion has been entertained even in modern times; but more correct observation has shown it to be without foundation. Lemaire.

THE POWER OF THE MOON OVER THE LAND AND THE SEA
(Chapter 102 [99])

Hence we may certainly conjecture, that the moon is not un-justly regarded as the star of our life.[4] This it is that replenishes the earth[5]; when she approaches it, she fills all bodies, while, when she recedes, she empties them. From this cause it is that shell-fish grow with her increase,[6] and that these animals which are without blood more particularly experience her influence; also, that the blood of man is increased or diminished in proportion to the quantity of her light; also that the leaves and vegetables generally, as I shall describe in the proper place,[7] feel her influence, her power penetrating all things.

THE POWER OF THE SUN (Chapter 103 [100])

Fluids are dried up by the heat of the sun; we have therefore regarded it as a masculine star, burning up and absorbing every-thing.[8]

WHY THE SEA IS SALT (Chapter 104)

Hence it is that the widely-diffused sea is impregnated with the flavors of salt, in consequence of what is sweet and mild being evaporated from it, which the force of fire easily accomplishes; while all the more acrid and thick matter is left behind; on which account the water of the sea is less salt at some depth than at the surface. And this is a more true cause of the acrid flavour, than that the sea is the continued perspiration of the land,[9] or that the greater part of the dry vapour is mixed with it, or that the nature of the

---

[4] "Spiritus sidus"; "Quod vitalem humorem ae spiritus in corporibus rebusque omnibus varie temperet." Hardouin in Lemaire, i.433.

[5] "Terras saturet"; as Alexandre interprets it, "succo impleat"; Lemaire.

[6] This circumstance is alluded to by Cicero, De Divin. ii.33, and by Horace, Sat.ii.4, 30. It is difficult to conceive how an opinion so totally unfounded, and so easy to refute, should have obtained general credence.

[7] Lib. xviii. chap 75.

[8] Aristotle, Meteor. ii.1, remarks, that as the sun is continually evaporating the water of the sea, it must eventually be entirely dried up. But we have reason to believe, that all the water which is evaporated by the solar heat, or any other natural process, is again deposited in the form of rain or dew.

[9] "Terrae sudor"; according to Aristotle, Meteor. ii.4: this opinion was adopted by some of the ancients. VOL. I.

earth is such that it impregnates the waters, and, as it were, medicates them.[10] Among the prodigies which have occurred, there is one which happened when Dionysius, the tyrant of Sicily, was expelled from his kingdom; that, for the space of one day, the water in the harbour became sweet.

(101) The moon, on the contrary, is said to be a feminine and delicate planet, and also nocturnal; also that it resolves humours and draws them out, but does not carry them off. It is manifest that the carcases of wild beasts are rendered putrid by its beams, that, during sleep, it draws up the accumulated torpor into the head, that it melts ice, and relaxes all things by its moistening spirit.[11] Thus the changes of nature compensate each other, and are always adequate to their destined purpose; some of them congealing the elements of the stars and others dissolving them. The moon is said to be fed by fresh, and the sun by salt water.

WHERE THE SEA IS THE DEEPEST (Chapter 105 [102])

Fabianus[12] informs us that the greatest depth of the sea is 15 stadia.[13] We learn from others, that in the Euxine, opposite to the nation of the Coraxi, at what is called the Depths of the Euxine,[14] about 300 stadia[15] from the mainland, the sea is immensely deep, no bottom having been found.

---

[10] The commentators discuss at considerable length the relative merits of the three hypotheses here proposed, to account for the saltness of the ocean; all of which are equally unfounded. See Hardouin in Lemaire, i.434, 435. Aristotle's opinion on this subject is contained in his Meteor.

[11] It is not easy to ascertain the origin of the very general opinion respecting the peculiar physical action of the moon. The alleged facts are, for the most part, without foundation, and I am not aware of any circumstance which could, originally, have made them a part of the popular creed of so many nations, ancient as well as modern. Perhaps some of the effects which have been ascribed to the specific action of the moon, may be explained by the lower temperature and greater dampness of the air, during the absence of the sun.

[12] There appears to be some doubt respecting the history of the person here referred to: according to the account of Hardouin, Fabianus was a naturalist, who enjoyed a high reputation; he lived in the time of Tiberius: see Lemaire, i. 188.

[13] This would be a depth of 3,250 yards, not very far short of two miles.

[14] "Boca Ponti"; Aristotle refers to this as one of those parts where the sea is unfathomable; Meteor. i.13.

[15] A distance of nearly nine and a half miles. [The stadium of Eratosthenes equaled about 520 ft. The stadium at Athens was between 603 and 610 feet.]

~~~~~~~~~~~~~~~~

Leonardo Da Vinci:

4.   *WAVES, SEAS AND DEVICES**

Translated by Edward MacCurdy

OF THE WAVES

Sometimes the waves are swifter than the wind, and sometimes the wind is much swifter than the wave; the ships prove this upon the sea. The waves can be swifter than the wind through having been commenced by the great winds, the wind then having ceased and the wave having still preserved a great impetus.

OF THE CONSUMPTION OR EVAPORATION OF THE WATER OF THE MEDITERRANEAN SEA

The Mediterranean Sea a vast river interposed between Africa Asia and Europe gathers within itself about three hundred principal rivers, and in addition to these it receives the rains which fall upon it over a space of three thousand miles. It gives back to the mighty ocean its own waters and the others that it has received, and without doubt it gives less back to the sea than those it receives; for from it descend many springs which flow through the bowels of the earth and vivify this terrestrial machine. This is necessary by reason of the fact that the surface of this Mediterranean is more remote from the centre of the world than the surface of this ocean, as is proved by my second [rule]; and in addition to this the heat of the sun is continually evaporating a portion of the water of the Mediterranean, and as a consequence this sea can acquire but little increase from the aforesaid rains, and is but little diminished through the water that has been added to it being poured into the ocean, or from it being evaporated by the heat of the sun or the course of the parching winds.

* From THE NOTEBOOKS OF LEONARDO DA VINCI, Edited and translated by Edward MacCurdy, Reynal & Hitchcock, New York, 1939. Reprinted by permission of Harcourt, Brace & World and Jonathan Cape Ltd.

The genius of Leonardo Da Vinci, 1452–1519, is evidenced in his work as painter, sculptor, architect, musician, engineer, and scientist.

UNDERWATER DEVICE

How by an appliance many are able to remain for some time under water. How and why I do not describe my method of remaining under water for as long a time as I can remain without food; and this I do not publish or divulge on account of the evil nature of men who would practice assassinations at the bottom of the seas, by breaking the ships in their lowest parts and sinking them together with the crews who are in them; and although I will furnish particulars of others they are such as are not dangerous, for above the surface of the water emerges the mouth of the tube by which they draw in breath, supported upon wine-skins or pieces of cork.

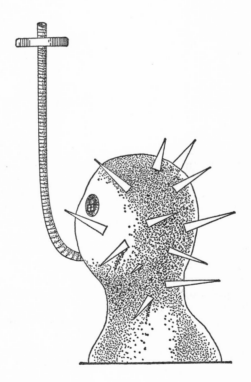

Fig. 4–1. Breathing tube and underwater mask (with spikes) designed by Leonardo Da Vinci.

A breastplate of armour together with hood, doublet and hose, and a small wine-skin for use in passing water, a dress for the armour, and the wine-skin to contain the breath, with half a hoop of iron to keep it away from the chest. If you have a whole wine-skin with a valve from the [?ball MS. *da pal* . . . *?palla*], when you deflate it, you will go to the bottom, dragged down by the sacks of sand; when you inflate it, you will come back to the surface of the water.

A mask with the eyes protruding made of glass, but let its weight be such that you raise it as you swim.

Carry a knife which cuts well so that a net does not hold you prisoner.

~~~~~~~~~~~~~~~

Hugo Grotius:

5.   *THE FREEDOM OF THE SEAS**

NEITHER THE INDIAN OCEAN NOR THE RIGHT OF NAVIGATION
THEREON BELONGS TO THE PORTUGUESE BY TITLE OF
OCCUPATION

If therefore the Portuguese have acquired no legal right over the nations of the East Indies, and their territory and sovereignty, let us consider whether they have been able to obtain exclusive jurisdiction over the sea and its navigation or over trade. Let us first consider the case of the sea.

Now, in the legal phraseology of the Law of Nations, the sea is called indifferently the property of no one (*res nullius*), or a common possession (*res communis*), or public property (*res publica*). It will be most convenient to explain the signification of these terms if we follow the practice of all the poets since Hesiod, of the philosophers and jurists of the past, and distinguish certain epochs, the divisions of which are marked off perhaps not so much by intervals of time as by obvious logic and essential

* First published November 1608 in Latin as *Mare Liberum*. The following excerpt is from *The Freedom of the Seas* or *The Right Which Belongs to the Dutch to Take Part in the East Indian Trade* by Hugo Grotius, Oxford University Press, translated by Ralph Van Deman Magoffin, Copyright © 1916 by the Carnegie Endowment for International Peace, Washington, D.C.

Hugo Grotius, 1583–1645, was a Dutch jurist and statesman.

character. And we ought not to be criticised if in our explanation of a law deriving from nature, we use the authority and definition of those whose natural judgment admittedly is held in the highest esteem.

It is therefore necessary to explain that in the earliest stages of human existence both sovereignty and common possession had meanings other than those which they bear at the present time.[1] For nowadays sovereignty means a particular kind of proprietorship, such in fact that it absolutely excludes like possession by any one else. On the other hand, we call a thing 'common' when its ownership or possession is held by several persons jointly according to a kind of partnership or mutual agreement from which all other persons are excluded. Poverty of language compels the use of the same words for things that are not the same. And so because of a certain similarity and likeness, our modern nomenclature is applied to that state of primitive law. Now, in ancient times, 'common' meant simply the opposite of 'particular'; and 'sovereignty' or 'ownership', meant the privilege of lawfully using common property. This seemed to the Scholastics[2] to be a use in fact but not in law, because what now in law is called use, is a particular right, or if I may use their phraseology, is, in respect to other persons, a privative right.

In the primitive law of nations, which is sometimes called Natural Law, and which the poets sometimes portray as having existed in a Golden Age, and sometimes in the reign of Saturn or of Justice, there was no particular right. As Cicero says: 'But nothing is by nature private property'. And Horace[3]: 'For nature has decreed to be the master of private soil neither him, nor me, nor any-one else'. For nature knows no sovereigns. Therefore in this sense we say that in those ancient times all things were held in common, meaning what the poets do when they say that primitive men acquired everything in common, and that Justice maintained a community of goods by means of an inviolable compact. And to make this clearer, they say that in those primitive times the fields were not delimited by boundary lines, and that there was no commercial intercourse. Avienus says[4]: 'It seemed that all lands without distinction were common to all'.

Water, is classed by the jurists among the things common to all

[1] Paul de Castro on Digest I, 1, 5; Dist. I, C. VII.
[2] Vasquius, Controversiae illustres, c. 1, n. 10; Lib. VI, V, 12, 3; Clem. V, 11.
[3] Satires II, 2, 129–130.
[4] Aratus 302–303.

mankind; as is done also by Ovid[5]: 'Why do you deny me water? Its use is free to all. Nature has made neither sun nor air nor waves private property; they are public gifts'.

He says that these things are not by nature private possession, but that, as Ulpian claims,[6] they are by nature things open to the use of all, both because in the first place they were produced by nature, and have never yet come under the sovereignty of any one, as Neratius says[7]; and in the second place because, as Cicero says, they seem to have been created by nature for common use. But the poet uses 'public', in its usual meaning, not of those things which belong to any one people, but to human society as a whole; that is to say, things which are called 'public' are, according to the laws of the Law of Nations, the common property of all, and the private property of none.

The air belongs to this class of things for two reasons. First, it is not susceptible of occupation; and second its common use is destined for all men. For the same reasons the sea is common to all, because it is so limitless that it cannot become a possession of any one, and because it is adapted for the use of all, whether we consider it from the point of view of navigation or of fisheries. Now, the same right which applies to the sea applies also to the things which the sea has carried away from other uses and made its own, such for example as the sands of the sea, of which the portion adjoining the land is called the coast or shore.[8] Cicero therefore argues correctly[9]: 'What is so common as the sea for those who are being tossed upon it, the shore for those who have been cast thereon'. Vergil also says that the air, the sea, and the shore are open to all men.

These things therefore are what the Romans call 'common' to all men by natural law,[10] or as we have said, 'public' according to the Law of Nations; and indeed they call their use sometimes common, sometimes public. Nevertheless, although those things are with reason said to be *res nullius*, so far as private ownership is concerned, still they differ very much from those things which,

[5] Metamorphoses VI, 349–351.
[6] Digest VIII, 4, 13.
[7] Digest XLI, 1, 14; Comines, Memoirs III, 2; Donellus IV, 2; Digest XLI, 3, 49. [Philippe de Comines (1445–1509), a French historian, and one of the negotiators of the treaty of Senlis (1493).]
[8] Digest I, 8, 10.
[9] De officiis I, 52.
[10] Institutes II, 1, 1 and 5; Digest I, 8, 1, 2, 10; XLI, 1, 14 and 50; XLVII, 10, 13; XLIII, 8, 3, and 4–7.

though also *res nullius*, have not been marked out for common use, such for example as wild animals, fish, and birds. For if any one seizes those things and assumes possession of them, they can become objects of private ownership, but the things in the former category by the consensus of opinion of all mankind are forever exempt from such private ownership on account of their susceptibility to universal use; and as they belong to all they cannot be taken away from all by any one person any more than what is mine can be taken away from me by you. And Cicero says that one of the first gifts of Justice is the use of common property for common benefit. The Scholastics would define one of these categories as common in an affirmative, the other in a privative sense. This distinction is not only familiar to jurists, but it also expresses the popular belief. In Athenaeus for instance the host is made to say that the sea is the common property of all, but that fish are the private property of him who catches them. And in Plautus' Rudens when the slave says[11]: 'The sea is certainly common to all persons', the fisherman agrees; but when the slave adds: 'Then what is found in the common sea is common property', he rightly objects, saying: 'But what my net and hooks have taken, is absolutely my own'.

Therefore the sea can in no way become the private property of any one, because nature not only allows but enjoins its common use.[12] Neither can the shore become the private property of any one. The following qualification, however, must be made. If any part of these things is by nature susceptible of occupation, it may become the property of the one who occupies it only so far as such occupation does not affect its common use. This qualification is deservedly recognized. For in such a case both conditions vanish through which it might eventuate, as we have said, that all of it would pass into private ownership.

Since therefore, to cite Pomponius, building is one kind of occupation, it is permissible to build upon the shore, if this can be done without inconvenience to other people[13]; that is to say (I here follow Scaevola) if such building can be done without hindrance to public or common use of the shore. And whoever shall have constructed a building under the aforesaid circumstances will become the owner of the ground upon which said building

[11] Act IV, Scene 3 (975, 977, 985).
[12] Donellus IV, 2.
[13] Digest XXXIX, 2, 24.

is; because this ground is neither the property of any one else, nor is it necessary to common use. It becomes therefore the property of the occupier, but his ownership lasts no longer than his occupation lasts, inasmuch as the sea seems by nature to resist ownership. For just as a wild animal, if it shall have escaped and thus recovered its natural liberty, is no longer the property of its captor, so also the sea may recover its possession of the shore.

We have now shown that whatever by occupation can become private property can also become public property, that is, the private property of a whole nation.[14] And so Celsus considered the shore included within the limits of the Roman Empire to be the property of the Roman people. There is not therefore the least reason for surprise that the Roman people through their emperors or praetors was able to grant to its subjects the right of occupying the shore. This public occupation, however, no less than private occupation, was subject to the restriction that it should not infringe on international rights. Therefore the Roman people could not forbid any one from having access to the seashore,[15] and from spreading his fishing nets there to dry, and from doing other things which all men long ago decided were always permissible.

The nature of the sea, however, differs from that of the shore, because the sea, except for a very restricted space, can neither easily be built upon, nor inclosed; if the contrary were true yet this could hardly happen without hindrance to the general use. Nevertheless, if any small portion of the sea can be thus occupied, the occupation is recognized. The famous hyperbole of Horace must be quoted here: "The fishes note the narrowing of the waters by piers of rock laid in their depths."[16]

Now Celsus holds that piles driven into the sea belong to the man who drove them.[17] But such an act is not permissible if the use of the sea be thereby impaired. And Ulpian says that whoever builds a breakwater must see to it that it is not prejudicial to the interests of any one; for if this construction is likely to work an injury to any one, the injunction 'Nothing may be built on public property' would apply. Labeo, however, holds that in case any such construction should be made in the sea, the following injunction is to be enforced: 'Nothing may be built in

[14] Donellus IV, 2 and 9.
[15] Digest I, 8, 4; XLIII, 8, 3.
[16] Odes III, i, 33–34 [Bennett's (Loeb) translation, page 171].
[17] Digest XLIII, 8, 3; 8, 2.

the sea whereby the harbor, the roadstead, or the channel be rendered less safe for navigation'.[18]

Now the same principle which applies to navigation applies also to fishing, namely, that it remains free and open to all. Nevertheless there shall be no prejudice if any one shall by fencing off with stakes an inlet of the sea make a fish pond for himself, and so establish a private preserve. Thus Lucullus once brought the water of the sea to his villa by cutting a tunnel through a mountain near Naples.[19] I suspect too that the seawater reservoirs for fish mentioned by Varro and Columella were of this sort. And Martial had the same thing in mind when he says of the Formian villa of Apollinaris[20]: 'Whenever Nereus feels the power of Aeolus, the table safe in its own resources laughs at the gale'. Ambrose also has something to say on the same subject.[21] 'You bring the very sea into your estates that you may not lack for fish'. In the light of all this the meaning of Paulus is clear when he says[22] that if any one has a private right over the sea, the rule *uti possidetis* applies. This rule however is applicable only to private suits, and not to public ones, among which are also to be included those suits which can be brought under the common law of nations. But here the question is one which concerns the right of use arising in a private suit, but not in a public or common one. For according to the authority of Marcianus whatever has been occupied and can be occupied[23] is no longer subject to the law of nations as the sea is. Let us take an example. If any one had prevented Lucullus or Apollinaris from fishing in the private fish ponds which they had made by inclosing a small portion of the sea, according to the opinion of Paulus they would have the right of bringing an injunction, not merely an action for damages based on private ownership.[24]

Indeed, if I shall have staked off such an inclosure in an inlet of the sea, just as in a branch of a river, and have fished there, especially if by doing so continuously for many years I shall have given proof of my intention to establish private ownership, I shall certainly prevent any one else from enjoying the same rights.

[18] Digest XLIII, 12, 1.
[19] Pliny, Natural History IX, 54, 170.
[20] Epigrams X, 30, 19–20.
[21] De Nabuthe, cap. 3.
[22] Digest XLVII, 10, 14.
[23] See note 15.
[24] Digest XLIV, 3, 7.

I gather from Marcianus that this case is identical with that of the ownership of a lake, and it is true however long occupation lasts, as we have said above about the shore. But outside of an inlet this will not hold, for then the common use of the sea might be hindered.[25]

Therefore if any one is prevented from fishing in front of my town house or country seat, it is a usurpation, but an illegal one, although Ulpian, who rather makes light of this usurpation, does say that if any one is so prevented he can bring an action for damages.[26] The Emperor Leo, whose laws we do not use, contrary to the intent of the law, changed this, and declared that the entrances, or vestibules as it were, to the sea, were the private property of those who inhabited the shore, and that they had the right of fishing there.[27] However he attached this condition, that the place should be occupied by certain jetty or pile constructions, such as the Greeks call ἐποχαί, thinking doubtless that no one who was himself allowed to fish anywhere in the sea would grudge any one else a small portion of it. To be sure it would be an intolerable outrage for any one to snatch away, even if he could do so, from public use a large area of the sea; an act which is justly reprehended by the Holy Man,[28] who says: 'The lords of the earth claim for themselves a wide expanse of sea by *jus mancipii*, and they regard the right of fishing as a servitude over which their right is the same as that over their slaves. That gulf, says one, belongs to me, and that gulf to some one else. They divide the very elements among themselves, these great men'!

Therefore the sea is one of those things which is not an article of merchandise,[29] and which cannot become private property. Hence it follows, to speak strictly, that no part of the sea can be considered as the territory of any people whatsoever. Placentinus seems to have recognized this when he said: 'The sea is a thing so clearly common to all, that it cannot be the property of any one save God alone'. Johannes Faber[30] also asserts that the sea has been left *sui juris*, and remains in the primitive condition where

25 Digest XLI, 3, 45.
26 Digest XLVII, 10, 13.
27 Novels of Leo, 102, 103, 104; See also Cujas XIV, 1.
28 Hexameron V, 10, 27 [St. Ambrose (c. 333–397), Bishop of Milan, is meant].
29 Donellus IV, 6.
30 On Institutes II, 1; Digest XIV, 2, 9 [Johannes Faber (c. 1570–c. 1640) was Bishop of Vienna, and Court preacher to Emperor Ferdinand. He was known popularly as 'Malleus Haereticorum'].

all things were common. If it were otherwise there would be no difference between the things which are 'common to all', and those which are strictly termed 'public'; no difference, that is, between the sea and a river. A nation can take possession of a river, as it is inclosed within their boundaries, with the sea, they cannot do so.

Now, public territory arises out of the occupation of nations, just as private property arises out of the occupation of individuals. This is recognized by Celsus, who has drawn a sharp distinction between the shores of the sea,[31] which the Roman people could occupy in such a way that its common use was not harmed, and the sea itself, which retained its primitive nature. In fact no law intimates a contrary view.[32] Such laws as are cited by writers who are of the contrary opinion apply either to islands, which evidently could be occupied, or to harbors, which are not 'common', but 'public', that is, 'national'.

Now those who say that a certain sea belonged to the Roman people explain their statement to mean that the right of the Romans did not extend beyond protection and jurisdiction; this right they distinguish from ownership. Perchance they do not pay sufficient attention to the fact that although the Roman People were able to maintain fleets for the protection of navigation and to punish pirates captured on the sea, it was not done by private right, but by the common right which other free peoples also enjoy on the sea. We recognize, however, that certain peoples have agreed that pirates captured in this or in that part of the sea should come under the jurisdiction of this state or of that, and further that certain convenient limits of distinct jurisdiction have been apportioned on the sea. Now, this agreement does bind those who are parties to it,[33] but it has no binding force on other nations, nor does it make the delimited area of the sea the private property of any one. It merely constitutes a personal right between contracting parties.

This distinction so conformable to natural reason is also confirmed by a reply once made by Ulpian. Upon being asked whether the owner of two maritime estates could on selling either of them impose on it such a servitude as the prohibition of fishing in a

---

[31] Digest XLIII, 8, 3.

[32] Digest V, 1, 9; XXXIX, 4, 15; Glossators on Digest I, 8, 2; Institutes II, 1; Baldus on L. Quaedam, in Digest I, 8, 2.

[33] Baldus, Quibus modis feudi amittuntur, chapter beginning In principio, second column; Code XI, 13, 1; Angeli on Digest XLVII, 10, 14; Digest VIII, 4, 13 and 4.

particular part of the sea, he replied that the thing in question, evidently the sea, could not be subjected to a servitude, because it was by nature open to all persons; but that since a contract made in good faith demands that the condition of a sale be respected, the present possessors and those who succeed to their rights were bound to observe that condition. It is true that the jurist is speaking of private estates and of private law, but in speaking here of the territory of peoples and of public law the same reasoning applies, because from the point of view of the whole human race peoples are treated as individuals.

Similarly, revenues levied on maritime fisheries are held to belong to the Crown, but they do not bind the sea itself or the fisheries, but only the persons engaged in fishing.[34] Wherefore subjects, for whom a state or a ruler is by common consent competent to make laws, will perhaps be compelled to bear such charges, but so far as other persons are concerned the right of fishing ought everywhere to be exempt from tolls, lest a servitude be imposed upon the sea, which is not susceptible to a servitude.

The case of the sea is not the same as that of a river,[35] for as a river is the property of a nation, the right to fish in it can be passed or leased by the nation or by the ruler, in such a way (and the like is true with the ancients) that the lessee enjoys the operation of the injunction *de loco publico fruendo* by virtue of the clause 'He who has the right to lease has leased the exclusive right of enjoyment'.[36] Such a condition cannot arise in respect to the sea. Finally those who count fishing among the properties of the Crown have not examined carefully enough the very passage which they cite to prove their contention, as Isernia* and Alvotus† have noticed.

It has therefore been demonstrated[37] that neither a nation nor an individual can establish any right of private ownership over the sea itself (I except inlets of the sea), inasmuch as its occupation is not permissible either by nature or on grounds of public utility. The discussion of this matter has been taken up for this reason, namely, that it may be seen that the Portuguese have not established private ownership over the sea by which people go to the East Indies. For the two reasons that stand in the way of ownership

* [Andrea d'Isernia (c. 1480–1533), an Italian commentator, called often Feudistarum Patriarcha.]

† [Probably a misprint for Alvarus (Alvarez).]

[34] C. Quae sing Regalia, in Feudis.

[35] Balbus, De praescriptionibus IV, 5; 1, q. 6, n. 4.

[36] Digest XLVII, 10, 13; XLIII, 9, 1.

[37] See note 34.

are in this case infinitely more powerful than in all others. That which in other cases seems difficult, is here absolutely impossible; and what in other cases we recognize as unjust is here most barbarous and inhuman.

The question at issue then is not one that concerns an INNER SEA, one which is surrounded on all sides by the land and at some places does not even exceed a river in breadth, although it is well known that the Roman jurists cited such an inner sea in their famous opinions condemning private avarice. No! the question at issue is the OUTER SEA, the OCEAN, that expanse of water which antiquity describes as the immense, the infinite, bounded only by the heavens, parent of all things; the ocean which the ancients believed was perpetually supplied with water not only by fountains, rivers, and seas, but by the clouds, and by the very stars of heaven themselves; the ocean which, although surrounding this earth, the home of the human race, with the ebb and flow of its tides, can be neither seized nor inclosed; nay, which rather possesses the earth than is by it possessed.

~~~~~~~~~~~~~~~~

Isaac Newton:

6.   *TIDES**

Translated by Andrew Mott

The ocean must flow twice and ebb twice, each day, and the highest water occurs at the third hour after the approach of the luminaries to the meridian of the place.

And from the diurnal motion and the attractions of the sun and moon our sea ought twice to rise and twice to fall every day, as well lunar as solar, and the greatest height of the water

* From Isaac Newton, PRINCIPIA: *Mathematical Principles of Natural Philosophy and His System of the World,* translated by Andrew Mott, University of California Press. Copyright © 1934 by the Regents of the University of California.

English physicist and philosopher Sir Isaac Newton, 1642–1727, is probably best known for his formulation of the law of gravity and the laws of motion; in addition, he invented a reflecting telescope, served in Parliament and was President of the Royal Society from 1703.

to happen before the sixth hour of either day and after the twelfth hour preceding. By the slowness of the diurnal motion the flood is retracted to the twelfth hour; and by the force of the motion of reciprocation it is protracted and deferred till a time nearer to the sixth hour. But until that time will be more accurately determined by the phenomena, why should we not choose the middle between those extremes, and conjecture the greatest height of the water to happen at the third hour? In this manner the water will rise all that time in which the force of the luminaries to raise it is greater, and will fall all that time in which their force is less; namely, from the ninth to the third hour when that force is greater, and from the third to the ninth when it is less. The hours I reckon from the approach of each luminary to the meridian of the place, as well under as above the horizon; and by the hours of the lunar day I understand the twenty-fourth parts of that time which the moon spends before it comes about again by its apparent diurnal motion to the meridian of the place which it left the day before.

The tide is greatest in the syzygies of the luminaries and least in their quadratures, and at the third hour after the moon reaches the meridian; outside of the syzygies and quadratures the tide deviates somewhat from that third hour towards the third hour after the solar culmination.

But the two motions which the two luminaries raise will not appear distinct, but will make a certain mixed motion. In the conjunction or opposition of the luminaries their forces will be conjoined, and bring on the greatest flood and ebb. In the quadratures the sun will raise the waters which the moon depresses, and depress the waters which the moon raises; and from the difference of their forces the smallest of all tides will follow. And because (as experience tells us) the force of the moon is greater than that of the sun, the greatest height of the water will happen about the third lunar hour. Outside of the syzygies and quadratures, the greatest tide which by the single force of the moon should take place at the third lunar hour, and by the single force of the sun at the third solar hour, by the combined forces of both must happen at an intermediate time that approaches nearer to the third hour of the moon than to that of the sun; and, therefore, while the moon is passing from the syzygies to the quadratures, during which time the third hour of the sun precedes the third of the moon, the greatest tide will precede the third lunar hour, and that by the greatest interval a little after the octants of the moon; and by like intervals the greatest tide will follow the third lunar hour, while the moon is passing from the quadratures to the syzygies.

The tides are greatest when the luminaries are nearest the earth.

But the effects of the luminaries depend upon their distances from the earth; for when they are less distant their effects are greater, and when more distant their effects are less, and that as the third power of their apparent diameters. Therefore it is that the sun in the winter time, being then in its perigee, has a greater effect, and makes the tides in the syzygies somewhat greater, and those in the quadratures somewhat less, other things being equal, than in the summer season; and every month the moon, while in the perigee, raises greater tides than at the distance of fifteen days before or after, when it is in its apogee. Hence it comes to pass that two highest tides do not follow one the other in two immediately succeeding syzygies.

The tides are greatest about the equinoxes.

The effect of either luminary likewise depends upon its declination or distance from the equator; for if the luminary were placed at the pole, it would constantly attract all the parts of the waters, without any increase or remission of its action, and could cause no reciprocation of motion; and, therefore, as the luminaries decline from the equator towards either pole, they will by degrees lose their force, and on this account will excite lesser tides in the solstitial than in the equinoctial syzygies. But in the solstitial quadratures they will raise greater tides than in the quadratures about the equinoxes; because the effect of the moon, then situated in the equator, most exceeds the effect of the sun; therefore the greatest tides take place in those syzygies, and the least in those quadratures, which happen about the time of both equinoxes; and the greatest tide in the syzygies is always succeeded by the least tide in the quadratures, as we find by experience. But because the sun is less distant from the earth in winter than in summer, it comes to pass that the greatest and least tides more frequently appear before than after the vernal equinox, and more frequently after than before the autumnal.

~~~~~~~~~~~~~~~~~~~~~~~~~

Edmund Halley:

7.   A NEW CONTRIVANCE FOR DIVING*

Many methods have been proposed, and many Engines contriv'd, for
enabling Men to abide a competent while under Water: And the
respiring fresh air being absolutely necessary to maintain Life in
all that breathe, several Ways have been thought of for carrying
this down to the diver, who must, without being supply'd therewith,
return very soon or perish.

We have heard of Divers for Spunges in the Archipelago, help-
ing themselves by carrying down spunges dipp'd in Oil in their
Mouths; but considering how small a Quantity of Air can be sup-
pos'd to be contain'd in the interstices of a Spunge, and how
much that little will be contracted by the Pressure of the incumbent
Water, it cannot be believ'd that a supply, by this Means obtain'd,
can long subsist a Diver. Since by Experiment it is found that a
Gallon of Air included in a Bladder, and by a pipe reciprocally
inspir'd and expir'd by the Lungs of a Man, will become unfit
for any further Respiration, in little more than one Minute of
Time; and though its Elasticity be not much alter'd, yet in passing
the Lungs, it loses its vivifying Spirit, and is render'd effete, not
unlike the Medium found in Damps, which is present Death to
those that breathe it; and which, in an Instant, extinguishes the
brightest Flame, or the shining of glowing Coals, or red hot Iron,
if put into it. I shall not go about to shew what it is the Air loses
by being taken into the lungs, or what it communicates to the
Blood by the extreme Ramifications of the Aspera Arteria, so intimately interwoven with the Capillary Blood-Vessels; much less to
explain how it is performed, since no Discovery has been made to
prove that the ultimate Branches of the Veins and Arteries there,
have any Anastomoses with those of the Trachea; as by the Micro-

---

* From Edmund Halley. 1716. "A New Contrivance for Diving." THE ROYAL
SOCIETY OF LONDON. PHILOSOPHICAL TRANSACTIONS. No. 349 Pp. 492 *et seq.*

Edmund Halley, English astronomer and mathematician, was born in 1656
and died in 1742.

scope they are found to have with one another. But I leave this
to the Anatomists; and only conclude from the aforesaid Experiment,
that a naked Diver, without a spunge, cannot be above a Couple
of Minutes inclos'd in Water, (as I once saw a Florida-Indian at
Bermudas) nor much longer with a Spunge, without suffocating;
and not near so long without great Use and Practise: Ordinary
Persons generally begining to stifle in about half a Minute of Time.
Besides, if the Depth be considerable, the Pressure of the Water
on the Vessels is found by Experience to make the Eyes Blood-
shot, and frequently to occasion spitting of Blood.

When therefore there has been Occasion to continue long under
Water, some have contriv'd double flexible Pipes to circulate Air
down into a Cavity enclosing the Diver, as with Armour, to bear
off this Pressure of the Water, and to give leave to his Breast to dilate
upon Inspiration: The fresh Air being forc'd down by one of the
Pipes with Bellows, or otherwise, and returning by the other of
them, not unlike to an Artery and Vein. This has indeed been
found sufficient for small depths, not exceeding twelve or fifteen
Foot: But when the Depth surpasses three Fathoms, Experience
teaches us, that this Method becomes impracticable; For though
the Pipes and the rest of the Apparatus may be contriv'd to perform
their Office duly, yet the Water (its Weight being now become considerable) does too closely embrace the Limbs that are bare, or
cover'd with a flexible Covering, that it obstructs the Circulation
of the Blood in them; and presses with so much Force on all the
Junctures, where the Armour is made tight with Leather, Skins, or
such like, that if there be the least Defect in any of them, the
whole Engine will instantly fill with Water, which will rush in
with so much Violence, as to endanger the Life of the Man below,
who may be drown'd before he can be drawn up. Upon both these
Accounts, the Danger encreases with the Depth. Besides, a Man
thus shut up in a weighty Case, as this must needs be, cannot but
be very unwieldy and unactive, and therefore unfit to execute what
he is design'd to do at the Bottom.

To remedy these Inconveniences, the Diving-Bell was next thought
of; wherein the Diver is safely convey'd into any reasonable Depth,
and may stay more or less Time under Water, according as the Bell
is of greater or lesser Capacity. This is most conveniently made in
the Form of a Truncate Cone, the smaller Basis being closed, and
the larger open; and ought to be so poiz'd with Lead, and so suspended, that the Vessel may sink full of air, with its greater or open
Basis downwards, and as near as may be in a Situation parallel
to the Horizon, so as to close with the Surface of the Water all

Fig. 7–1. Halley's diving-bell.

at once. Under this Couvercle the Diver setting, sinks down together with the included Air; and if the Cavity of the Vessel may
contain a Tun of Water, a single Man may remain therein at least
an Hour, without much Inconvenience, at five or six Fathoms deep.
But this included Air, as it descends lower, does contract itself
according to the Weight of the Water that compresses it; so that
at thirty three Feet deep or thereabouts, the Bell will be half full
of Water, the Pressure of it being then equal to that of the whole
Atmosphere. And at all other Depths, the Space occupied by the
compress Air in the upper Part of the Bell, will be to the under
Part of its Capacity fill'd with Water, as thirty three feet to the

Depth of the Surface of the Water in the Bell below the common Surface thereof. And this condens'd Air, being taken in with the Breath, soon insinuates itself into all the Cavities of the Body, and has no sensible Effect, if the Bell be permitted to descend so slow as to allow Time for that Purpose. The only Inconvenience is found in the Ears, within which there are Cavities opening only outwards, and that by Pores so small as not to give admission even to the Air itself, unless they be dilated and distended by a considerable Force. Hence on, the first Descent of the Bell, a Pressure begins to be felt on each Ear, which by Degrees grows painful, like as if a Quill were forcibly thrust into the hole of the Ear; till at length the Force overcoming the Obstacle, that which constringes these Pores yields to the Pressure, and letting some condens'd Air slip in, present Ease ensues. But the Bell descending still lower, the Pain is renew'd, and again eas'd after the same Manner. But when the Engine is drawn up again, the condens'd Air finds a much easier Passage out of those Cavities, and even without Pain. This Force on the auditory Passages might be suspected to be prejudicial to the Organs of Hearing, but that Experience teaches otherwise. But what is more inconvenient in this Engine, is, the Water entering into it, so as to contract the Bulk of Air (according to the aforesaid Rule) into so small a Space, as that it soon heats and becomes unfit for Respiration, for which reason it must be often drawn up to recruit it: And besides the Diver being almost cover'd with the Water thus entering into his Receptacle, will not be long able to endure the Cold thereof.

To obviate these Difficulties which attend the Use of the common Diving-Bell, I have thought of Means to convey Air down to it, whilst below; whereby not only the Air included therein, would be refresh'd and recruited, but also the Water wholly driven out, in whatever Depth it is; and will furnish Air at the Bottom of the Sea in any Quantity desir'd. The Description of my Apparatus take as follows:

The Bell I made use of was of Wood, containing about sixty Cubic Feet in its Concavity, and was of the Form of a truncate Cone, whose Diameter at Top was three Feet, and at Bottom five. This I coated with Lead so heavy, that it would sink empty, and I distributed the Weight so about its Bottom, that it would go down in a perpendicular Situation, and no other. In the Top, I fix'd a strong, but clear Glass, to let in the Light from above; and likewise a Cock to let out the hot Air that had been breath'd and below, about a Yard under the Bell, I plac'd a Stage which hung by three ropes, each of which was charg'd with about one hundred

Weight, to keep it steady. This Machine, I suspended from the Mast of a Ship, by a Spritt, which was sufficiently secur'd by Stays to the Mast-head, and was directed by Braces to carry it over board clear of the Ship-side, and to bring it again within board.

To supply Air to this Bell when under Water, I caused a couple of Barrels, of about 36 Gallons each, to be cas'd with Lead, so as to sink empty, each having a Bung-hole in its lowest Part, to let in the Water, as the Air in them condens'd on their descent; and to let it out again, when they were drawn up full from below. And to a Hole in the uppermost Part of these Barrels, I fix'd a Leathern Trunk or Hose, well liquor'd with Bees-Wax and Oil, and long enough to fall below the Bung-hole, being kept down by a Weight appended; so that the Air in the upper Part of the Barrels could not escape, unless the lower Ends of these Hole were first lifted up.

I fitted these Air-Barrels with Tackle proper to make them rise and fall alternately, after the Manner of two Buckets in a Well; which was done with so much ease, that two men, with less than half their Strength, could perform all the Labour; and in their Descent they were directed by Lines fasten'd to the under Edge of the Bell, which pass'd through Rings plac'd on both Sides the Leathern Hose in each Barrel; so that sliding down by those Lines, they came readily to the Hand of a Man, who stood on the Stage on purpose to receive them, and to take up the Ends of the Hose into the Bell. Through these Hose, as soon as these Ends came above the Surface of the Water in the Barrels, all the Air that was included in the upper Parts of them, was blown with great Force into the Bell, whilst the Water enter'd at the Bung-holes below, and fill'd them: And as soon as the Air of one Barrel had been thus receiv'd, upon a signal given, that was drawn up, and at the Same time the other descended; and by an alternate Succession furnish'd Air so quick, and in such Plenty, that I myself have been one of five, who have been together at the Bottom, in nine or ten Fathoms Water, for about an Hour and half at a Time, without any Sort of ill Consequence: And I might have continu'd there as long as I pleas'd for any Thing that appear'd to the contrary. Besides the whole Cavity of the Bell was kept entirely free from Water, so that I sat on a Bench, which was diametrically plac'd near the Bottom, with all my Cloaths on. I only observ'd, that it was necessary to be let down gradually at first, as about 12 Feet at a Time; and then to stop and drive out the Water that enter'd, by receiving three or four barrels of fresh Air, before I descended farther. But being arriv'd at the Depth design'd, I then let out as much of the hot Air that had been breath'd, as each Barrel would replenish with cool, by means of the Cock at the Top of the Bell; through whose Aperture, though very small, the Air would rush with so great Violence, as to make the Surface of the Sea boil, and to cover it with a white Foam, notwithstanding the great Weight of Water over us.

Thus I found I could do any Thing that was requir'd to be done just under us; and that, by taking off the Stage, I could, for a Space as wide as the Circuit of the Bell, lay the Bottom of the Sea so far dry, as not to be over Shoes thereon. And by the Glass Window so much light was transmitted; that, when the Sea was clear, and especially when the Sun Shone, I could see perfectly well to write or read, much more to take up any Thing that was under us: And by the Return of the Air-Barrels, I often sent up Orders, written with an Iron Pen on small Plates of Lead, directing how to move us from Place to Place. At other times, when the Water was troubled and thick, it would be as dark as Night below; but in such a Case, I have been able to keep a Candle burning in the Bell as long as I pleas'd, notwithstanding the great Expence of Air requisite to maintain Flame.

I take this Invention to be applicable to various Uses; such as fishing for pearl, Diving for Coral, Spunges, and the like, in far greater Depths than has hitherto been thought possible: Also for the fitting and planning of the Foundations of Moles, Bridges, etc. upon rocky Bottoms; and for the cleaning and scrubbing of Ship's Bottoms when foul, in calm Weather at Sea.

By an additional Contrivance, I have found it not impracticable for a Diver to go out of this Engine to a good Distance from it, the Air being convey'd to him with a continu'd Stream, by small flexible Pipes; which Pipes may serve as a Clue to direct him back again, when he would return to the Bell.

~~~~~~~~~~~~

Benjamin Franklin:

8.   ON *THE GULF STREAM**

Vessels are sometimes retarded, and sometimes forwarded in their voyages, by currents at sea, which are often not perceived. About the year 1769 or 70, there was an application made by the board of customs at Boston, to the lords of the treasury in London, complaining that the packets between Falmouth and New-York, were generally a fortnight longer in their passages, than merchant ships from London to Rhode-Island, and proposing that for the future they should be ordered to Rhode-Island instead of New York. Being then concerned in the management of the American post-office, I happened to be consulted on the occasion; and it appearing strange to me that there should be such a difference between two places, scarce a day's run asunder, especially when the merchant ships are generally deeper laden, and more weakly manned than the packets, and had from London the whole length of the river and channel to run before they left the land of England, while the packets had only to go from Falmouth, I could not but think the fact misunderstood or misrepresented. There happened then to be in London, a Nantucket sea-captain of my acquaintance, to whom I communicated the affair. He told me he believed the fact might be true; but the difference was owing to this, that the Rhode-Island captains were acquainted with the gulf stream, which those of English packets were not. We are well acquainted with that stream, says he, because in our persuit of whales, which keep near the sides of it, but are not to be met with in it, we run down along the sides, and frequently cross it to change our side: and in crossing it have sometimes met and spoke with those packets, who were in the middle of it, and stemming it. We have informed them that they were stemming a current, that was against them to the value of three miles an hour; and advised them to cross it and get

* From *Transactions of the American Philosophical Society* (1786). Volume 2, Pp 314–317.

When he was ten years old, Benjamin Franklin, 1706–90, left school to work for his father. From these humble beginnings he rose to distinction as statesman, printer, scientist, and writer.

out of it; but they were too wise to be counselled by simple American fishermen. When the winds are but light, he added, they are carried back by the current more than they are forwarded by the wind: and if the wind be good, the subtraction of 70 miles a day from their course is of some importance. I then observed that it was a pity no notice was taken of this current upon the charts, and requested him to mark it out for me, which he readily complied with, adding directions for avoiding it in sailing from Europe to North-America. I procured it to be engraved by order from the general post-office, on the old chart of the Atlantic, at Mount and Page's, Tower-hill; and copies were sent down to Falmouth for the captains of the packets, who slighted it however; but it is since printed in France, of which edition I hereto annex a copy.

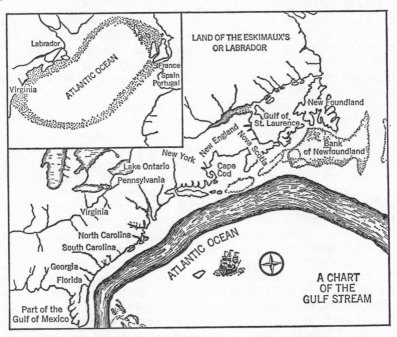

Fig. 8–1. Adapted from Benjamin Franklin's first chart of the Gulf Stream, published between pages 316 and 317 in the 1786 edition of *Transactions of the American Philosophical Society*. Philadelphia.

This stream is probably generated by the great accumulation of water on the eastern coast of America between the tropics, by the trade winds which constantly blow there. It is known that a large piece of water ten miles broad and generally only three feet deep, has by a strong wind had its waters driven to one side and sustained so as to become six feet deep, while the windward side was laid dry. This may give some idea of the quantity heaped up on the American coast, and the reason of its running down in a strong current through the islands into the bay of Mexico, and from thence issuing through the gulph of Florida, and proceeding along the coast to the banks of Newfoundland, where it turns off towards and runs down through the Western islands. Having since crossed this stream several times in passing between America and Europe, I have been attentive to sundry circumstances relating to it, by which it is interspersed, I find that it is always warmer than the sea on each side of it, and that it does not sparkle in the night: I annex hereto the observations made with the thermometer in two voyages, and possibly may add a third. It will appear from them, that the thermometer may be an useful instrument to a navigator, since currents coming from the northward into southern seas, will probably be found colder than the water of those seas, as the currents from southern seas into northern are found warmer. And it is not to be wondered that so vast a body of deep warm water, several leagues wide, coming from between the tropics and issuing out of the gulph into the northern seas, should retain its warmth longer than the twenty or thirty days required to its passing the banks of Newfoundland. The quantity is too great, and it is too deep to be suddenly cooled by passing under a cooler air. The air immediately over it, however, may receive so much warmth from it as to be rarified and rise, being rendered lighter than the air on each side of the stream; hence those airs must flow in to supply the place of the rising warm air, and meeting with each other, form those tornados and warm-spouts frequently met with, and seen near and over the stream; and as the vapour from a cup of tea in a warm room, and the breath of an animal in the same room, are hardly visible, but become sensible immediately when out in the cold air, so the vapour from the gulph stream, in warm latitudes is scarcely visible, but when it comes into the cool air from Newfoundland, it is condensed into the fogs, for which those parts are so remarkable.

The power of wind to raise water above its common level in the sea, is known to us in America, by the high tides occasioned in all our sea-ports when a strong northeaster blows against the gulph stream.

The conclusion from these remarks is, that a vessel from Europe to North-America may shorten her passage by avoiding to stem the stream, in which the thermometer will be very useful; and a vessel from America to Europe may do the same by the same means of keeping in it. It may often happened accidentally, that voyages have been shortened by these circumstances. It is well to have the command of them.

~~~~~~~~~~~~~~~~

Alexander von Humboldt:

9.   SEAWEED AND FLYING-FISH*

To the north of the Cape Verd Islands we met with great masses of floating seaweeds. They were the tropic grape, (*Fucus natans*), which grows on submarine rocks, only from the equator to the fortieth degree of north and south latitude. These weeds seem to indicate the existence of currents in this place, as well as to south-west of the banks of Newfoundland. We must not confound the latitudes abounding in scattered weeds with those banks of marine plants, which Columbus compares to extensive meadows, the sight of which dismayed the crew of the *Santa Maria* in the forty-second degree of latitude. I am convinced, from the comparison of a great number of journals, that in the basin of the Northern Atlantic there exist two banks of weeds very different from each other. The most extensive is a little west of the meridian of Fayal, one of the Azores, between the twenty-fifth and thirty-sixth degrees of latitude.[1] The temperature of the Atlantic in those latitudes is from sixteen to twenty degrees, and the north winds, which sometimes rage there very tempestuously, drive floating isles of seaweed into the low

---

* From Alexander von Humboldt, NARRATIVE OF TRAVELS TO THE EQUINOCTIAL REGIONS OF AMERICA (1799–1804). H. G. Bohn, London. 1852. Friedrich Heinrich Alexander von Humboldt, German scientist, explorer and writer, was born in 1769 and died in 1859.

[1] It would appear that Phoenician vessels came "in thirty days' sail with an easterly wind," to the *weedy sea*, which the Portuguese and Spaniards call *mar de zargasso*. I have shown, in another place ("Views of Nature," Bohn's edition, p. 46) that the passage of Aristotle, *De Mirabil*, (ed. Duval, p. 1157), can scarcely be applied to the coasts of Africa, like an analogous passage of the Periplus of Scylax. Supposing that this sea, full of weeds, which impeded the course of the Phoenician vessels, was the *mar de zargasso*, we need not admit that the ancients navigated the Atlantic beyond thirty degrees of west longitude from the meridian of Paris.

latitudes as far as the parallels of twenty-four and even twenty degrees. Vessels returning to Europe, either from Monte Video or the Cape of Good Hope, cross these banks of Fucus, which the Spanish pilots consider as at an equal distance from the Antilles and Canaries; and they serve the less instructed mariner to rectify his longitude. The second bank of Fucus is but little known; it occupies a much smaller space, in the twenty-second and twenty-sixth degrees of latitude, eighty leagues west of the meridian of the Bahama Islands. It is found on the passage from the Caiques to the Bermudas.

Though a species of seaweed[2] has been seen with stems eight hundred feet long, the growth of these marine cryptogamia being extremely rapid, it is nevertheless certain, that in the latitudes we have just described, the Fuci, far from being fixed to the bottom, float in separate masses on the surface of the water. In this state, the vegetation can scarcely last longer than it would in the branch of a tree torn from its trunk; and in order to explain how moving masses are found for ages in the same position, we must admit that they owe their origin to submarine rocks, which, lying at forty or sixty fathoms' depth, continually supply what has been carried away by the equinoctial currents. This current bears the tropic grape into the high latitudes, toward the coasts of Norway and France; and it is not the Gulf-stream, as some mariners think, which accumulates the Fucus to the south of the Azores.

The causes that unroot these weeds at depths where it is generally thought the sea is but slightly agitated, are not sufficiently known. We learn only, from the observations of M. Lamouroux, that if the fucus adhere to the rocks with the greatest firmness before its fructification, it separates with great facility after that period, or during the season which suspends its vegetation like that of the terrestrial plants. The fish and mollusca which gnaw the stems of the seaweeds no doubt contribute also to detach them from their roots.

From the twenty-second degree of latitude, we found the surface of the sea covered with flying-fish,[3] which threw themselves up into the air, twelve, fifteen, or eighteen feet, and fell down on the deck. I do not hesitate to speak on a subject of which voyagers discourse as frequently as of dolphins, sharks, sea-sickness, and the phosphorescence of the ocean. None of these topics can fail to

[2] The *baudreux* of the Falkland Islands, *Fucus giganteus*, Forster; *Laminaria pyrifera*, Lamour.
[3] *Exoceotus volitans.*

afford interesting observations to naturalists, provided they make them their particular study. Nature is an inexhaustible source of investigation, and in proportion as the domain of science is extended, she presents herself to those who know how to interrogate her, under forms which they have never yet examined.

I have named the flying-fish, in order to direct the attention of naturalists to the enormous size of their natatory bladder, which, in an animal of 6·4 inches, is 3·6 inches long, 0·9 of an inch broad, and contains three cubic inches and a half of air. As this bladder occupies more than half the size of the fish, it is probable that it contributes to its lightness. We may assert that this reservoir of air is more fitted for flying than swimming; for the experiments made by M. Provenzal and myself have proved, that, even in the species which are provided with this organ, it is not indispensably necessary for the ascending movement to the surface of the water. In a young flying-fish, 5·8 inches long, each of the pectoral fins, which serve as wings, presented a surface to the air of $3\frac{7}{16}$ square inches. We observed, that the nine branches of nerves, which go to the twelve ways of these fins, are almost three times the size of the nerves that belong to the ventral fins. When the former of these nerves are excited by galvanic electricity, the rays which support the membrane of the pectoral fin extend with five times the force with which the other fins move when galvanised by the same metals. Thus, the fish is capable of throwing itself horizontally the distance of twenty feet before retouching the water with the extremity of its fins. This motion has been aptly compared to that of a flat stone, which, thrown horizontally, bounds one or two feet above the water. Notwithstanding the extreme rapidity of this motion, it is certain, that the animal beats the air during the leap; that is, it alternately extends and closes its pectoral fins. The same motion has been observed in the flying scorpion of the rivers of Japan: they also contain a large air-bladder, with which the great part of the scorpions that have not the faculty of flying are unprovided. The flying-fish, like almost all animals which have gills, enjoy the power of equal respiration for a long time, both in water and in air, by the same organs; that is, by extracting the oxygen from the atmosphere as well as from the water in which it is dissolved. They pass a great part of their life in the air; but if they escape from the sea to avoid the voracity of the Dorado, they meet in the air the Frigate-bird, the Albatross, and others, which seize them in their flight. Thus, on the banks of the Orinoco, herds of the Cabiai, which rush from the water to escape the crocodile, become the prey of the jaguar, which awaits their arrival.

I doubt, however, whether the flying-fish spring out of the water merely to escape the pursuit of their enemies. Like swallows, they move by thousands in a right line, and in a direction constantly opposite to that of the waves. In our own climates, on the brink of a river, illumined by the rays of the sun, we often see solitary fish fearlessly bound above the surface as if they felt pleasure in breathing the air. Why should not these gambols be more frequent with the flying-fish, which from the strength of their pectoral fins, and the smallness of their specific gravity, can so easily support themselves in the air? I invite naturalists to examine whether other flying-fish, for instance the *Cypselurus exsilens*, the *Exocaetus volitans*, and the *Trigla hirundo*, have as capacious an air-bladder as the flying-fish of the tropics. This last follows the heated waters of the Gulf-stream when they flow northward. The cabin-boys amuse themselves with cutting off a part of the pectoral fins, and assert, that these wings grow again.

Nathaniel Bowditch:

10.   *CURRENTS**

A current is a progressive motion of the water, causing all floating bodies to move that way towards which the stream is directed. The *set of a current*, is that point of the compass towards which the waters run, and its *drift* is the rate it runs per hour. The most usual way of discovering the set and drift of an unknown current, is thus:

Let three or four men take a boat a little way from the ship: and by a rope fastened to the boat's stern, let down a heavy iron pot or loaded kettle to the depth of 80 or 100 fathoms; then heave the log, and the number of knots run out in half a minute will be the miles the current sets per hour, and the bearing of the log will show the set of it.

There is a very remarkable current, called the GULF STREAM, which sets in a north-east direction along the coast of America,

*From Nathaniel Bowditch, THE NEW AMERICAN PRACTICAL NAVIGATOR, E. & G. W. Blunt, New York. 1832.

Nathaniel Bowditch, an American mathematician, astronomer and navigator, was born in 1773 and died in 1838.

from Cape Florida towards the Isle of Sables, at unequal distances from the land, being about 75 miles from the shore of the southern states, but more distant from the shore of the northern states; the width of the stream is about 40 or 50 miles, widening towards the north; the velocity is various from one to three knots per hour, or more, being greatest in the channel between Florida and the Bahamas, and gradually decreasing in passing to the northward; but is greatly influenced by the winds both in drift and set.

We are chiefly indebted to Doctor Franklin, Commodore Truxton, and Mr. Jonathan Williams, for the knowledge we possess of the direction and velocity of this stream; its general course, as given by them, is marked on the chart affixed to this work. They all concur in recommending the use of the thermometer, as the best means of discovering when in, or near the stream. For, it appears by their observations, that the water is warmer than the air when in the stream; and that at leaving it, and approaching towards the land, the water will be found six or eight degrees colder than in the stream, and six or eight degrees colder still, when on soundings. Vessels coming from Europe to America, by the northern passage, should keep a little to the northward of the stream, where they may probably be assisted by a counter current, as is observed by Commodore Truxton. When bound from America to Europe, a ship may generally shorten her passage by keeping in the gulf. By steering N.W. you will generally cross the gulf in the shortest time, as the direction of the stream is nearly N.E. Those who wish for further information on this subject, may consult an ingenious treatise on "Thermometrical Navigation," published by Mr. Jonathan Williams, at Philadelphia, in 1799, and re-published by Edm. M. Blunt, to accompany his Chart of the Western Ocean, in 1819.

In other parts of the Atlantic ocean the currents are variable, but are generally south-easterly, along the coast of Spain, Portugal and Africa, from the Bay of Biscay towards Madeira and the Cape de Verds. Between the tropics there is generally a current setting to the westward.

There is also a remarkable current which sets through the Mozambique channel, between the Island of Madagascar and the main continent of Africa, in a south-westerly direction: in proceeding towards Cape Lagullas the current takes a more westerly course, and then tends round the Cape towards St. Helena. Ships bound to the westward from India, may generally shorten their passage, by taking advantage of this current. On the contrary, when bound to the eastward, round the Cape of Good Hope, they ought to keep far to the southward of it. However, there appears to be a great difference in the velocity of this current at different times; for some ships have been off this Cape several days endeavouring to get to the westward, and have found no current; others have experienced it setting constantly to the westward during their passage from the Cape towards St. Helena, Ascension and the West India Islands.

Besides the imaginary divisions [latitude, longitude, etc.] of the earth, there are various natural divisions of its surface, formed by nature, such as continents, oceans, islands, seas, rivers, &c.

A *Continent* is a large tract of land, wherein are several empires, kingdoms, and countries conjoined—as Europe, Asia, Africa, and America.

An *Island* is a part of the earth that is environed or encompassed round by the sea, as Long Island, Block Island, &c.

A *Peninsula* is a portion of land surrounded with water, save one narrow neck which joins it to the continent, as the Morea.

An *Isthmus* is a narrow neck of land joining a peninsula to the adjacent land, by which the people may pass from one to the other, as the isthmus of Darien.

A *Promontory* is a high part of land stretching itself into the sea, the extremity of which is called a Cape or Headland.

A *Mountain* is a rising of dry land, overtopping the adjacent country, and appearing first at a distance.

An *Ocean* is a vast collection of water, separating continents from one another, and washing their borders or shores, as the Atlantic and Pacific Oceans.

A *Sea* is part of the ocean, to which we must sail through some strait, as the Mediterranean and Baltic seas. This term is sometimes used for the whole body of salt water on the globe.

A *Strait* is a narrow part of the ocean lying between two shores, and opening a way into some sea, as the Straits of Gibraltar that lead into the Mediterranean Sea.

A *Creek* is a small narrow part of the sea or river, that goes up but a little way into the land.

A *Bay* is a great inlet of the land, as the Bay of Biscay, and the Bay of Mexico; otherwise a bay is a station or road for ships to anchor in.

A *River* is a considerable stream of water issuing out of one or various springs, and continually gliding along in one or more channels, till it discharges itself into the ocean: the lesser streams are called rivulets.

A *Lake* is a large collection of waters in an inland place, as the lakes Superior and Huron in America.

A *Gulf* is a part of the ocean or sea, nearly surrounded by the land, except where it communicates with the sea, as the Gulf of Venice.

~~~~~~~~~~~~

William Scoresby:

11.   CAPTURING THE WHALE*

Whenever a whale lies on the surface of the water, unconscious of the approach of its enemies, the hardy fisher rows directly upon it; and an instant before the boat touches it, buries his harpoon in its back. But if, while the boat is yet at a little distance, the whale should indicate his intention of diving, by lifting his head above its common level and then plunging it under water, and raising his body, until it appear like the large segment of a sphere,—the harpoon is thrown from the hand, or fired from a gun, the former of which, when skilfully practised, is efficient at the distance of eight or ten yards, and the latter at the distance of thirty yards, or upward. The wounded whale, in the surprise and agony of the moment, makes a convulsive effort to escape. Then is the moment of danger. The boat is subjected to the most violent blows from its head, or its fins, but particularly from its ponderous tail, which sometimes sweeps the air with such tremendous fury, that both boat and men are exposed to one common destruction.

The head of the whale is avoided, because it cannot be penetrated with the harpoon; but any part of the body, between the head and the tail, will admit of the full length of the instrument,

---

* From William Scoresby, Jr., ACCOUNT OF THE ARCTIC REGION WITH A HISTORY AND DESCRIPTION OF THE NORTHERN WHALE FISHERY. Archibald Constable and Co., Edinburgh, 1820.

Before entering the Anglican ministry in 1822, William Scoresby, 1789–1857, was an arctic explorer and scientist.

without danger of obstruction. The harpoon, therefore, is always struck into the back, and generally well forward towards the fins, thus affording the chance, when it happens to drag and plough along the back, of retaining its hold during a longer time than when struck in closer to the tail.

The moment that the wounded whale disappears, or leaves the boat, a jack or flag, elevated on a staff, is displayed; on sight of which, those on watch in the ship, give the alarm, by stamping on the deck, accompanied by a simultaneous and continued shout of "a fall."[1] At the sound of this, the sleeping crew are roused, jump from their beds, rush up on deck, with their clothes tied by a string in their hands, and crowd into the boats. With a temperature of Zero, should a *fall* occur, the crew would appear upon deck, shielded only by their drawers, stockings, and shirts, or other habiliments in which they sleep. They generally, contrive to dress themselves, in part at least, as the boats are *lowered* down; but sometimes they push off in the state in which they rise from their beds, row away towards the "fast boat," and have no opportunity of clothing themselves for a length of time afterwards. The alarum of "a fall," has a singular effect on the feelings of a sleeping person, unaccustomed to the whale-fishing business. It has often been mistaken as a cry of distress. A landsman, in a Hull ship, seeing the crew, on an occasion of a fall, rush upon deck, with their clothes in their hands, and leap into the boats, when there was no appearance of danger, thought the men were all mad; but, with another individual, the effect was totally different. Alarmed with the extraordinary noise; and still more so, when he reached the deck, with the appearance of all the crew seated in the boats in their shirts, he imagined the ship was sinking. He therefore endeavoured to get into a boat himself, but every one of them being fully manned, he was always repulsed. After several fruitless endeavours to gain a place among his comrades, he cried out, with feelings of evident distress, "What shall I do?—Will none of you take me in?"

The first effort of a "fast-fish," or whale that has been struck, is to escape from the boat, by sinking under water. After this, it pursues its course directly downward, or re-appears at a little distance and swims with great celerity, near the surface of the water, towards

---

[1] The word *fall*, as well as many others used in fishery, is derived from the Dutch language. In the original it is written *val*, implying jump, drop, fall, and is considered as expressive of the conduct of the sailors, when *manning* the boats on an occasion requiring extreme dispatch.

any neighbouring ice, among which it may obtain an imaginary shelter; or it returns instantly to the surface, and gives evidence of its agony, by the most convulsive throes, in which its fins and tail are alternately displayed in the air, and dashed into the water with tremendous violence. The former behaviour, however, that is, to dive towards the bottom of the sea, is so frequent, in comparison of any other, that it may be considered as the general conduct of a fast-fish.

PROCEEDING IN CAPTURING THE WHALE

A whale, struck near the edge of any large sheet of ice, and passing underneath it, will sometimes run the whole of the lines out of one boat, in the space of eight or ten minutes of time. This being the case, when the "fast-boat" is at a distance, both from the ship and from any other boat, it frequently happens that the lines are all withdrawn before assistance arrives, and, with the fish, entirely lost. In some cases, however, they are recovered. To retard, therefore, as much as possible, the flight of the whale, it is usual for the harpooner, who strikes it, to cast one, two, or more turns of the line round a kind of post called a *bollard*; which is fixed within ten or twelve inches of the stem of the boat, for the purpose. Such is the friction of the line, when running round the bollard, that it frequently envelopes the harpooner in smoke; and if the wood were not repeatedly wetted, would probably set fire to the boat. During the capture of one whale, a groove is sometimes cut in the bollard near an inch in depth; and, were it not for a plate of brass, iron, or a block of lignum-vitae, which covers the top of the stem where the line passes over, it is apprehended that the action of the line on the material of the boat, would cut it down to the water's-edge, in the course of one season of successful fishing. The approaching distress of a boat, for want of line, is indicated by the elevation of an oar, in the way of a mast, to which is added a second, a third, or even a fourth, in proportion to the nature of the exigence. The utmost care and attention are requisite, on the part of every person in the boat, when the lines are running out; fatal consequences having been sometimes produced by the most trifling neglect. When the line happens "to run foul," and cannot be cleared on the instant, it sometimes draws the boat under water; on which, if no auxiliary boat, or convenient piece of ice, be at hand, the crew are plunged into the sea, and are obliged to trust to the buoyancy of their oars or to their skill in swimming, for supporting themselves on the surface. To provide against such an accident, as well as to be ready to furnish an additional supply of lines, it is usual, when boats are sent in pursuit, for two to go out in company; and when a whale has been struck, for the first assisting boat which approaches, to join the fast-boat, and to stay by it, until the fish reappears. The other boats likewise make towards the one carrying a flag, and surround it at various distances, awaiting the appearance of the wounded whale.

On my first voyage to the whale-fishery, such an accident as above alluded to, occurred. A thousand fathoms of line were already out, and the fast-boat was forcibly pressed against the side of a piece of ice. The harpooner, in his anxiety to retard the flight of the whale, applied too many turns of the line round the bollard, which, getting entangled, drew the boat beneath the ice. Another boat, providentially was at hand, into which the crew, including myself, who happened to be present, had just time to escape. The whale, with near two miles length of line, was, in consequence of the accident, lost, but the boat was recovered. On a subsequent occasion, I underwent a similar misadventure, but with a happier result; we escaped with a little wetting into an accompanying boat, and the whale was afterwards captured, and the boat with its lines recovered.

When fish have been struck by myself, I have on different occasions estimated their rate of descent. For the first 300 fathoms, the average velocity was usually after the rate of eight to ten miles *per* hour. In one instance, the third line of 120 fathoms was run out in 61 seconds; that is, at the rate of 8⅙ English miles, or 7⅛ nautical miles *per* hour.

By the motions of the fast-boat, the simultaneous movements of the whale are estimated. The auxiliary boats, accordingly, take their stations, about the situation where the whale, from these motions, may reasonably be expected to appear.

The average stay under water, of a wounded whale, which steadily descends after being struck, according to the most usual conduct of the animal, is about 30 minutes. The longest stay I ever observed was 56 minutes; but in shallow water, I have been informed, it has sometimes been known to remain an hour and a half at the bottom after being struck, and yet has returned to the surface alive. The greater the velocity, the more considerable the distance to which it descends, and the longer the time it remains under water, so much greater in proportion is the extent of its exhaustion, and the consequent facility of accomplishing its capture. Immediately that it re-appears, the assisting boats make for the place with their utmost speed, and as they reach it, each harpooner plunges his harpoon into its back, to the amount of three, four, or more, according to the size of the whale, and the nature of the situation. Most frequently, however, it descends for a few minutes after receiving the second harpoon, and obliges the other boats to await its return to the surface, before any further attack can be made. It is afterwards actively plied with lances, which are thrust into its body, aiming at its vitals. At length, when exhausted by numerous wounds and the loss of blood, which flows from the huge animal in copious streams, it indicates the approach of its dissolution, by discharging from its "blow-holes," a mixture of blood along with the air and mucus which it usually expires, and finally jets of blood alone. The sea, to a great extent around, is dyed with its blood, and the ice, boats, and men, are sometimes drenched with the same. Its track is likewise marked by a broad pellicle of oil, which exudes from its wounds, and appears on the surface of the sea. Its final capture is sometimes preceded by a convulsive and energetic struggle, in which its tail, reared, whirled, and violently jerked in the air, resounds to the distance of miles. In dying, it turns on its back or on its side; which joyful circumstance is announced by the capturers with the striding of their flags, accompanied with three lively huzzas!

The remarkable exhaustion observed on the first appearance of a wounded whale at the surface, after a descent of 700 or 800 fathoms perpendicular, does not depend on the nature of the wound it has received; for a hundred superficial wounds received from harpoons, could not have the effect of a single lance penetrating the vitals, but is the effect of the almost incredible pressure to which the animal must have been exposed. The surface of the body of a large whale, may be considered as comprising an area of 1540 square feet. This, under the common weight of the atmosphere only, must sustain a pressure of 3,104,640 lb., or 1386 tons. But at the depth of 800 fathoms, where there is a column of water equal in weight to about 154 atmospheres, the pressure on the animal must be equal to 211,200 tons.[2] This is a degree of pressure of which we can have but an imperfect conception. It may assist our

---

[2] From experiments made with sea water taken up near Spitzbergen, I find that 35 cubical feet weigh a ton. Now, supposing a whale to descend to the depth of 800 fathoms, or 4800 feet, which I believe, is not uncommon, we have only to divide 4800 feet, the length of the column of water pressing upon the whale, by 35 feet, the length of a column of sea-water, a foot square, weighing a ton, the quotient 137½ shows the pressure per square foot upon the whale, in tons; which, multiplied by 1540, the number of square feet of surface exposed by the animal, affords a product of 211,200 tons, besides the usual pressure of the atmosphere.

comprehension, however, to be informed, that it exceeds in weight sixty of the largest ships of the British navy, when manned, provisioned, and fitted for a six months cruise.

Every boat fast to a living whale carries a flag, and the ship to which such boats belong, also wears a flag, until the whale is either killed or makes its escape. These signals serve to indicate to surrounding ships, the exclusive title of the "fast-ship" to the entangled whale, and to prevent their interference, excepting in the way of assistance, in the capture.

A very natural inquiry connected with this subject, is, What is the length of time requisite for capturing a whale? This is a question which can only be answered indirectly; for I have myself witnessed the capture of a large whale, which has been effected in twenty-eight minutes; and have also been engaged with another fish which was lost, after it had been entangled about sixteen hours. Instances are well authenticated, in which whales have yielded their lives to the lances of active fishers, within the space of fifteen minutes from the time of being struck; and in cases where fish have been shot with a harpoon-gun, in a still shorter period; while other instances are equally familiar and certain, wherein a whale having gained the shelter of a pack or compact patch of ice, has sustained or avoided every attack upon it, during the space of forty or fifty hours. Some whales have been captured when very slightly entangled with a single harpoon, while others have disengaged themselves, though severely wounded with lances, by a single act of violent and convulsive distortion of the body, or tremendous shake of the tail, from four or more harpoons; in which act, some of the lines have been broken with apparent ease, and the harpoons to which other lines were attached, either broken or torn out of the body of the vigorous animal. Generally, the speedy capture of a whale depends on the activity of the harpooners, the favourableness of situation and weather, and, in no inconsiderable degree, on the peculiar conduct of the whale attacked. Under the most favourable circumstances; namely, when the fishermen are very active, the ice very open, or the sea free from ice, and the weather fine—the average length of time occupied in the capture of a whale, may be stated as not exceeding an hour.[3] The general average, including all sizes of

[3] Twelve large whales taken in different voyages, memoranda of whose capture I have preserved, were killed, on an average, in 67 minutes. The shortest time expended in the taking of one of the 12 whales, was 28 minutes; the longest time 2 hours. One of these whales, we believed, descended 670 fathoms perpendicular; another 720; and a third 750. One descended 1400 fathoms obliquely, and another 1600 fathoms.

fish and all circumstances of capture, may probably be two or three hours.

The method practised in the capture of whales, under favourable circumstances, is very uniform with all the fishers, both Britains and foreigners. The only variation observable in the proceedings of the different fishers, consisting in the degree of activity and resolution displayed, in pursuance of the operations of harpooning and lancing the whale, and in the address manifested in improving by any accidental movement of the fish, which may lay it open to an effectual attack—rather than in anything different or superior in the general method of conducting the fishery. It is true, that with some the harpoon-gun is much valued, and used with advantage, while with others, it is held in prejudiced aversion; yet, as this difference of opinion affects only the first attack and entanglement of the whale, the subsequent proceedings with all the fishers, may still be said to be founded on equal and unanimous principles. Hence, the mode described in the preceding pages, of conducting the fishery for whales under favourable circumstances, may be considered as the general plan pursued by the fishers of all the ports of Britain, as well as those of other nations who resort to Spitzbergen. Neither is there any difference in the plan of attack, or mode of capture between fish of large size, and those of lesser growth; the proceedings are the same, but, of course, with the smaller whales less force is requisite; though it sometimes happens, that the trouble attached to the killing of a very small whale, exceeds that connected with the capture of one of the largest individuals. The progress or flight of a large whale cannot be restrained; but that of an under-size fish may generally be confined within the limits of 400 to 600 fathoms of line. A full grown fish generally occupies the whole, or nearly the whole, of the boats belonging to one ship in its capture; but three, four, and sometimes more small fish, have been killed at the same time, by six or seven boats. It is not unusual for small whales to run downward, until they exhaust themselves so completely, that they are not able to return to the surface, but are suffocated in the water. As it is requisite that a whale that has been *drowned* should be drawn up by the line, which is a tedious and troublesome operation, it is usual to guard against such an event, by resisting its descent with a tight strain on the line, and also by hauling upon the line the moment its descent is stopped, with a view of irritating the wound, and occasioning such a degree of pain, as may induce it to return to the surface, where it can be killed and secured without farther trouble. Seldom more than two harpoons are struck into an under-size whale.

The ease with which some whales are subdued, and the slight-ness of the entanglement by which they are taken, is truly sur-prising; but with others it is equally astonishing, that neither line nor harpoon, nor any number of each, is sufficiently strong to effect their capture. Many instances have occurred where whales have escaped from four, five, or even more harpoons, while fish equally large have been killed through the medium of a single harpoon. Indeed, whales have been taken in consequence of the entanglement of a line, without any harpoon at all; though, when such a case has occurred, it has evidently been the result of accident.

Jacob Bigelow:

12.   *DIVING BELLS**

The diving bell is an inverted vessel, containing air, and used for the purpose of enabling persons to descend with safety to great depths under water. It is made tight at the top and sides, but is entirely open at bottom. Its principle is the same with that of a gasometer, and may be familiarly illustrated by immersing an inverted tumbler in a vessel of water. The air cannot escape from the inside of the vessel, being necessitated by the order of specific gravities, to occupy the upper part of the cavity.

Diving bells appear to have been first introduced in the beginning of the sixteenth century. They were first known as objects of curiosity only, but have been since applied to the recovery of valuable articles from wrecks, the blasting and mining of rocks at the bottom of the sea, and the practice of submarine architecture. They may be made of almost any shape, but the common form has been that of a bell, or hollow cone, made of wooden staves, and

* From J. Bigelow M.D., 1829. *Elements of Technology,* Boston, Hilliard, Gray, Little, and Wilkins.

Jacob Bigelow, 1786–1879, was an American physician and botanist who made several important contributions to medical theory and practice. He was associated with Harvard University from 1815 to 1855. He originated the word 'technology.'

strongly bound with hoops, having seats for the occupants on the inside. It is suspended with ropes from a vessel above, and is ballasted with heavy weights at bottom, which serve to sink it, and to prevent it from turning over. More recently diving bells have been made of cast iron. The kind of bell used at Howth, near Dublin,[1] is an oblong iron chest, six feet long, four broad, and five high, thicker at bottom than at top, and weighing four tons. It has a seat at each end, and is capable of holding four persons. The upper part is pierced with eight or ten holes, in which are fixed the same number of strong convex glasses, which transmit the light. As the air in the bell becomes contaminated by breathing, it is renewed by letting down barrels, or small bells, of fresh air, which are transferred to the large bell; or else by keeping up a constant supply through a pipe, by means of a forcing pump, which is worked by men at the surface.

Persons who descend in diving bells, often experience a pain in the ears, and a sense of pressure, occasioned by the condensation of the air within the cavity of the bell. These symptoms gradually pass off, or habit renders the body indifferent to them, so that workmen remain under water, at the depth of twenty feet or more, for seven or eight hours in a day, without detriment to the health.

Submarine Navigation.—A machine was invented during the American revolution, by Mr. Bushnell of Connecticut, which was capable of containing a person in safety under water, and of being governed and steered in any direction at pleasure. It is described[2] as being a hollow vessel of a spheroidal form, composed of curved pieces of oak, fitted together and bound with iron hoops, the seams being caulked and covered with tar to render them tight. A top or head, was closely fitted to the vessel, and served the purpose of a door. In this were inserted several strong pieces of glass to admit the light. The machine contained air enough to render it buoyant, and to support respiration. A quantity of lead was attached to the bottom for ballast. The vessel was made to sink by admitting water, and to rise, by detaching a part of the leaden ballast, or by expelling water with a forcing pump. It was propelled horizontally, by means of revolving oars placed obliquely like the sails of a windmill, on an axis which entered the boat through a tight collar, or water joint, and was turned with a crank within. A rudder was also employed for steering the vessel. When fresh air was required, the vessel rose to the surface and took in

---

[1] Edinburgh Philosophical Journal, vol. v. p. 8.
[2] Silliman's Journal, vol. ii. p. 94.

air through apertures at the top. The intention of this machine was to convey a magazine of powder under ships of war for the purpose of blowing them up. Several experiments were made with it, which, though unsuccessful in their object, nevertheless proved the practicability of this species of locomotion.

The late Mr. Fulton, made various experiments on submarine navigation, in a boat large enough to contain several persons, furnished with masts and sails so as to be capable of proceeding at the surface of the water, and also of plunging, when required, below the surface.[3] While under water, its motions were governed by two machines, one of which caused it to advance horizontally, while the other regulated its ascent and descent, its depth below the surface being known by the pressure on a barometer. A supply of fresh air was carried down in the boat, condensed into a strong copper globe, by which the air of the boat was replaced when it became unfit for respiration. Mr. Fulton's object was the destruction of ships of war, by bringing underneath them an explosive engine called a torpedo.

~~~~~~~~~~~~~~~~

Charles Darwin:

13.   PLANKTON AND PHOSPHORESCENCE*

DECEMBER 1833

During our different passages south of the Plata, I often towed astern a net made of bunting, and thus caught many curious animals. Of Crustacea there were many strange and undescribed genera. One, which in some respects is allied to the Notopods (or those crabs which have their posterior legs placed almost on their backs, for the purpose of adhering to the under side of rocks), is very remarkable from the structure of its hind pair of legs. The penultimate joint, instead of terminating in a simple claw, ends in

---

* From: C. R. Darwin, THE VOYAGE OF THE *Beagle, December 1831– October 1836*, Anchor edition, Doubleday & Company, New York. Charles Darwin was born in 1809 and died in 1882. It was his five year cruise as official naturalist on the *Beagle* which started Darwin on the career of exploration, investigation and written correlation of facts which led to his conception of evolution.

[3] See Colden's Life of Fulton, 8vo. New York, 1810.

three bristle-like appendages of dissimilar lengths—the longest equalling that of the entire leg. These claws are very thin, and are serrated with the finest teeth, directed backwards: their curved extremities are flattened, and on this part five most minute cups are placed which seem to act in the same manner as the suckers on the arms of the cuttle-fish. As the animal lives in the open sea, and probably wants a place of rest, I suppose this beautiful and most anomalous structure is adapted to take hold of floating marine animals.

In deep water, far from the land, the number of living creatures is extremely small: south of the latitude 35°, I never succeeded in catching anything besides some beroe, and a few species of minute entomostracous crustacea. In shoaler water, at the distance of a few miles from the coast, very many kinds of crustacea and some other animals are numerous, but only during the night. Between latitudes 56° and 57° south of Cape Horn, the net was put astern several times; it never, however, brought up anything besides a few of two extremely minute species of Entomostraca. Yet whales and seals, petrels and albatross, are exceedingly abundant throughout this part of the ocean. It has always been a mystery to me on what the albatross, which lives far from the shore, can subsist; I presume that, like the condor, it is able to fast long; and that one good feast on the carcass of a putrid whale lasts for a long time. The central and intertropical parts of the Atlantic swarm with Pteropoda, Crustacea, and Radiata, and with their devourers the flying-fish, and again with their devourers the bonitos and albacores; I presume that the numerous lower pelagic animals feed on the Infusoria, which are now known, from the researches of Ehrenberg, to abound in the open ocean: but on what, in the clear blue water, do these Infusoria subsist?

While sailing a little south of the Plata on one very dark night, the sea presented a wonderful and most beautiful spectacle. There was a fresh breeze, and every part of the surface, which during the day is seen as foam, now glowed with a pale light. The vessel drove before her bows two billows of liquid phosphorus, and in her wake she was followed by a milky train. As far as the eye reached, the crest of every wave was bright, and the sky above the horizon, from the reflected glare of these livid flames, was not so utterly obscure as over the vault of the heavens.

As we proceed further southward the sea is seldom phosphorescent; and off Cape Horn I do not recollect more than once having seen it so, and then it was far from being brilliant. This circumstance probably has a close connection with the scarcity of organic beings in that part of the ocean. After the elaborate paper,[1] by Ehrenberg, on the phosphorescence of the sea, it is almost superfluous on my part to make any observations on the subject. I may however add, that the same torn and irregular particles of gelatinous matter, described by Ehrenberg, seem in the southern as well as in the northern hemisphere, to be the common cause of this phenomenon. The particles were so minute as easily to pass through fine gauze; yet many were distinctly visible by the naked eye. The water when placed in a tumbler and agitated, gave out sparks, but a small portion in a watch-glass scarcely ever was luminous. Ehrenberg states that these particles all retain a certain degree of irritability. My observations, some of which were made directly after taking up the water, gave a different result. I may also mention, that having used the net during one night, I allowed it to become partially dry, and having occasion twelve hours afterwards to employ it again, I found the whole surface sparkled as brightly as when first taken out of the water. It does not appear probable in this case, that the particles could have remained so long alive. On one occasion having kept a jelly-fish of the genus Dianæa till it was dead, the water in which it was placed became luminous. When the waves scintillate with bright green sparks, I believe it is generally owing to minute crustacea. But there can be no doubt that very many other pelagic animals, when alive, are phosphorescent.

On two occasions I have observed the sea luminous at considerable depths beneath the surface. Near the mouth of the Plata some circular and oval patches, from two to four yards in diameter, and with defined outlines, shone with a steady but pale light; while the surrounding water only gave out a few sparks. The appearance resembled the reflection of the moon, or some luminous body; for the edges were sinuous from the undulations of the surface. The ship, which drew thirteen feet of water, passed over, without disturbing these patches. Therefore we must suppose that some animals were congregated together at a greater depth than the bottom of the vessel.

Near Fernando Noronha the sea gave out light in flashes. The appearance was very similar to that which might be expected from a large fish moving rapidly through a luminous fluid. To this cause the sailors attributed it; at the time, however, I entertained some doubts, on account of the frequency and rapidity of the flashes. I have already remarked that the phenomenon is very much more

[1] An abstract is given in No. IV. of the Magazine of Zoology and Botany.

common in warm than in cold countries; and I have sometimes imagined that a disturbed electrical condition of the atmosphere was most favourable to its production. Certainly I think the sea is most luminous after a few days of more calm weather than ordinary, during which time it has swarmed with various animals.

~~~~~~~~~~~~~~~~

Louis Agassiz:

14. DIRECTIONS FOR COLLECTING FISHES AND OTHER OBJECTS OF NATURAL HISTORY* (*New Edition, with Several Additions*)

The following letter was written and privately printed by the author and distributed to scientists, educators, and explorers around the United States.

Dear Sir,

Having been engaged for several years in the preparation of a *Natural History of the Fishes of the United States,* I wish, before beginning the printing of my work, to collect as extensive materials as possible, respecting the geographical distribution of these animals. It has occurred to me, that by means of a circular containing directions for collecting fishes I might obtain the information required. I should, indeed, like to secure separate collections of our fishes from every bay and inlet along the coast, and from every stream, river, creek, lake, and pond upon the mainland, throughout the whole country, and am satisfied that such collections would furnish invaluable information respecting the geographical distribution of our aquatic animals. I would thank you for any assistance and contribution you can furnish from your quarter of the country, and since I extend my investigations to all the branches of Natural History, any specimens besides fishes, which may be obtained,

---

* John Louis Rodolphe Agassiz, Swiss-American zoologist and geologist, was born in 1807 and died in 1873. Through his efforts the Harvard Museum of Comparative Zoology was established in 1859.

would be equally acceptable, including geological specimens and fossil remains. In return I would propose exchanges of other specimens if desired, or reciprocate the favor in any other way in my power, and pay the expenses incurred in making collections for me. Specimens from foreign countries are also solicited, especially when their origin is satisfactorily ascertained. Any person into whose hands this circular may come, feeling inclined to correspond with me upon these subjects, is requested to address me under the following direction:

L. Agassiz
*Professor of Zoology and Geology in the
Lawrence Scientific School, at
Harvard University*
Cambridge, Massachusetts

DIRECTIONS FOR COLLECTING FISHES AND OTHER OBJECTS OF NATURAL HISTORY

The present condition of our science requires collections made in a very different spirit from those gathered in former years. The naturalist must not only know all the different kinds of animals; he must also become acquainted with the changes they undergo while growing, and with their geographical range. To arrive at this knowledge, it is necessary to obtain, separately, complete collections from every district upon the mainland, from every inlet along the sea-shores, and from every distinct fresh-water basin, and to select a number of specimens of every kind, if possible so as to include the young, as well as the adults, males and females.[1] The number and diversity of species found in our fresh waters especially, is much greater than is usually supposed by accidental observers. A variety of little fishes, sometimes belonging even to different families, are almost everywhere used for bait by fishermen, and frequently mistaken under one common name, Minnows, or supposed to be simply the young of larger kinds. Among these, most valuable discoveries may be made. There are still districts in our country where a naturalist may fish half a dozen new species and more of these small nondescripts, in a single creek, within a few hours.[2] A small hand-net is very useful to collect these smallest kinds of fishes, and I have generally found that I could more easily obtain this small fry from

---

[1] There are many species of our fishes in which the sexes differ as much as among our fowls.

[2] It actually happened to me last winter, at Mobile, Alabama, and at St. Louis, Mo., to discover six and even eight new species of fishes in a single day.

boys, than from either fishermen or anglers. Again, scores of fishes are indiscriminately called Bass, Perch, Sunfish, Suckers, &c., in different parts of the country, which, when compared side by side, prove as different from one another as a robin and a crow. It is, therefore, a matter of great importance for the naturalist to get every species of fish from every water-basin, that he may have an opportunity of ascertaining for himself how far they agree, and how far they differ, in different watercourses. Anglers and professional fishermen generally know the fishes of their own fishing-grounds much better than naturalists, and from them most valuable information may be obtained respecting the species inhabiting their neighborhood. There is, on that account, no difficulty in ascertaining from them whether a complete collection of all the fishes of any given locality has been obtained. But the difficulty begins when it is attempted to identify the fishes of distant places, relying upon their names for comparison. Such is the confusion of these names in different sections of the country, arising from the use of the same names for different objects, and of different names for the same objects, that nothing short of complete collections obtained *separately* from every important locality will prevent the naturalist from making gross mistakes in his identification of species from remote localities. Few men not trained in the study of Natural History are prepared to believe that even the fishes living in the headwaters of a river may differ entirely from those living in its middle and lower course, and that it may therefore be necessary to make separate collections in different parts of one and the same waterbasin. This is still more important respecting distinct water-systems. But a complete survey ought to cover the whole ground as soon as possible. It would not be too much to have one collection for every hundred miles upon our large streams, and one for every fifty and even for every twenty miles upon smaller rivers.

The preservation of fishes requires but little care and attention. Any vessel, jar, can, keg, or barrel, fit to hold alcohol, is also fit for collecting fishes, which may be heaped up in it like herrings in salt. The alcohol used must be of about the strength of that of .88 specific gravity[3] for most fishes; for suckers and brook-trouts, however, it ought to be stronger, about .80, their flesh being either

[3] Common whiskey of .90 to .92 specific gravity may be used by adding strong alcohol, in the proportion of one gallon of alcohol to one gallon of whiskey. Highly rectified whiskey, as it is prepared in some parts of the country, may occasionally do by itself, especially if it has nearly the specific gravity of .88. It is, however, always safer to err by using too strong than too weak spirits. Specimens may be contracted by too strong alcohol, and lose to some extent their form; they will certainly spoil entirely in too weak a mixture.

soft or very fat, and more readily decomposed. In *summer or in warm climates* it is advisable to use always strong alcohol to obviate the effects of evaporation. Suppose it is intended to make a complete collection from one of the larger tributaries of some of our great rivers. All that is wanted will be a few jars, such as are used to keep preserves, a barrel of about fifteen or twenty gallons, and a supply of whiskey and alcohol. These may be kept in a cool place, a cellar, or a sheltered recess, ready to receive the fishes. The smallest fishes are best kept by themselves in jars, and the larger ones in a barrel. The barrel ought to be put upon one head, the other being removed and used as a cover. It will be well to see that the fishes are placed in it in as natural a position as possible, that is to say, stretched out with the fins closed against the body, or at least not un-naturally bent. It is equally desirable to exclude specimens *the fins of which are bruised, and* the scales rubbed off, unless they be rare species. When the fishes are too long to be stretched across the barrel, they may be gently bent upon their flatter side, and if too stiff to allow this, put in, head foremost, in an upright or slanting position, and then slightly bent against the sides of the barrel. It is useless at first to pour more alcohol over the fishes than is necessary to cover them. While cruising at sea, it will be well to throw some rags over the specimens to prevent their jarring, until the vessel in which they are contained is quite full, and headed up. *Of the smaller kinds of fishes, at least a dozen of each would be required for a full and satisfactory examination.* Where they may easily be caught, more would be very acceptable. Of those of medium size, about half that number; and of the larger ones, as may be most convenient, one, two, or three. It will secure a better state of preservation, and afford fuller means of study, if a cut is made into the belly of the larger fishes to allow the alcohol to penetrate the intestines. At all events, these ought never to be removed. The knowledge of the local names is very desirable. To rectify the errors of nomenclature now spread over the whole country, the simplest way of recording the name of a fish is to write it with a black hard pencil upon a piece of stiff paper, or with indelible ink upon cloth, and to place such a label under the gill-cover of the specimen to which it belongs. Specimens too small to be labelled in that way may be rolled in a piece of cotton cloth upon which the name is written. Delicate fishes, with very deciduous scales, would keep better if they were wrapped up singly in this way in cloth. Any other notice respecting the habits, uses, &c. of such specimens may be preserved in the same manner, or referred to a No. inscribed upon the label of the fish. It would be very important to record as far as possible the date at which the specimens preserved were caught. *This may often enable an anatomist to determine the spawning season of the species.* Also the depth at which they are known to live. Should any collector be sufficiently familiar with painting to draw colored figures of any of these fishes, or so situated as to have some of them drawn by an artist, it would be an invaluable contribution to Natural History.

When collections have to travel over great distances, or to be for many months on a journey, it is desirable that every specimen should be wrapped up singly in a piece of cloth; but this is not necessary, generally speaking, for collections which are likely to be taken care of after a short journey.

Those unaccustomed to making collections may occasionally suppose from their smell that they are spoiling, the mixture of alcohol with dead animal matter being rather disagreeable; but unless there is actual putrefaction, no apprehension need be had respecting the safety of a collection, and the removal of decayed specimens is all that is required for the preservation of the remainder, *provided the alcohol has the necessary strength of at least twenty-eight degrees of Beaumé, or .88 specific gravity.* To avoid losses, it is prudent never to use kegs of more than twenty to twenty-five gallons, save in exceptional cases, where very large and highly valuable specimens are to be preserved. As a general rule, a twenty-five gallon keg will contain any desirable specimen collected even in our largest rivers, there being always an opportunity now and then to obtain a moderately large specimen of our largest fishes, which when full grown are at any rate too bulky to be preserved in alcohol. Upon small watercourses, or small ponds, an ordinary jar may be sufficient to contain complete separate collections of all their natural productions. Of very large fishes, especially of sharks and skates, the skin may be preserved, leaving the whole head attached to it, and rolled up, preserved like other specimens, in alcohol. A longitudinal cut upon one side, in preference the right side, will afford sufficient facility for removing the intestines and all the flesh and bones of the body. Skeletons would be also very desirable. To obtain them it is simply necessary to boil the animal, either whole or in parts, and to gather and clean all the bones and preserve them together in a sack. A naturalist will readily put up the loose parts in their natural connection.

This method of collecting may apply to almost all animals, it being now very desirable to obtain specimens even of quadrupeds and birds in alcohol, for the sake of making anatomical preparations. Such specimens require, however, to be injected with alcohol through the mouth and anus, and also into the abdominal cavity. Reptiles may be treated like fishes, as also most of the lower animals. I may say here, that insects, and all brittle objects of Natural History, especially when small, must be preserved in comparatively small jars; whilst shell-fishes, crabs and lobsters, sea-urchins, star-fishes, corals, &c., protected as they are by their solid envelopes, need no special care after being put into alcohol, except, perhaps, to be wrapped up in soft paper or in cloth. All kinds of insects, even butterflies, may be collected in strong alcohol, provided they are divided off into comparatively small jars and not allowed to shake. Such specimens answer best for anatomical examination. It requires a peculiar skill to make good collections of dried specimens of insects, and to pin and spread them properly, though specimens preserved in this manner are the most valuable for exhibition. The preservation of shells in alcohol, without removing the soft parts of the animal, is particularly desirable. Small shells are better packed first in small boxes, and these packed like larger specimens. Geological specimens and fossils require to be wrapped up carefully in several layers of soft paper, and packed closely to prevent any friction.

As soon as a collection is supposed to be complete, it is best to send it off at once, that it may be taken care of properly, and examined whilst the specimens are in the best state of preservation. Not to multiply the packages, it is desirable to put everything in one barrel or in one box; but to secure their perfect preservation, under such circumstances, a few precautions are required. In the first place, assort somewhat the alcoholic specimens, in tubs, before packing them, so that the larger ones may be placed side by side and not crush the more delicate ones. After selecting an appropriate keg, placing it upon one head, the other being removed, or taking, for packing, the barrel used for collecting, the larger specimens are first put in, in the manner described above; smaller tough ones, such as perches, being placed in the empty intervals, and so on, until all the larger and coarser specimens are disposed of, and covered with alcohol, which is poured in gradually. Upon these, a layer of rags or soft paper is placed, to protect the next layer of smaller fishes, between each of which a layer of rags is to be added to prevent the too close contact of such a bulk of flesh, avoiding, however, all presssure upon the specimens, and allowing them simply to rest upon one another with their natural weight. In this way, a whole barrel of fishes may be packed with perfect safety, like sardines, and travel for thousands of miles, with a comparatively small quantity of alcohol between them. Finally, the smallest specimens, already

packed by themselves in small jars, in the same manner as the larger
ones in the barrel, may be also packed in the barrel, being wrapped
up in rags, and in that condition placed among the larger specimens;
or the small jars containing the small fishes may be packed in a box
by themselves. Before closing up the barrel, it is necessary to see that
no empty space is left; otherwise, even when full of alcohol, the
solid contents may move; and for their preservation nothing is
more important than to prevent the specimens from jarring when
travelling. This applies equally to the small jars. However, before
heading the barrel, it is necessary to draw, through the bunghole, so
much of the alcohol as may be necessary to allow the head to be
secured without losing any liquid. After heading the barrel, it is to
be completely filled with alcohol either through the bunghole or
through a small hole in the upper head. The liquor used in collecting may be used again in packing, provided it be strenthened
by some additional alcohol that may give it at least the strength
required, as stated above. In packing dried specimens, the same
care must be taken to pack first the heavy ones together, and next
to protect the delicate ones by packing them beforehand in small
boxes before allowing them to go among the larger ones.

After having mentioned all the preparations necessary to obtain
perfect collections, I may add, that any rough gathering of a few
specimens, taken up accidentally, may be also quite welcome, and
highly valuable as a first indication of what might be obtained from
a locality the natural productions of which have not yet been
studied. A mere catalogue of all the fishes known to the anglers and
fishermen of your vicinity, giving their vernacular names, would
be very acceptable.

A notice of the physical character of the localities where specimens have been collected would be a valuable addition to the
collection itself. Respecting the land it should mention: the height
above the level of the sea, if known, the nature of the soil, whether
dry, moist or swampy, muddy, sandy or rocky, &c. Respecting the
water: the mean and extreme temperatures, if ascertained, whether
clear or muddy, and of what color, deep or shallow, stagnant or
current; of rivers especially, the rapidity of the current, and also
whether subject to great rise and fall.

*When despatching such collections to their final destination, it is
important to mark each barrel or box with a conspicuous sign, that
there should be no possibility of mistaking them; the chief value of
specimens in Natural History arising in our days from a correct
identification of their origin.*

Any parcel directed to me, care of *Stratton's Cambridge Express*,

Boston, will reach me safely, and be taken care of, even in case I should be absent from Cambridge. To save you any further trouble, you may deliver your parcels to a commission merchant of your place, and request him when forwarding to send me a bill of lading, mentioning the sign marked upon the parcels. Small packages may be sent by express, larger ones by the ordinary freight lines.

CAMBRIDGE 1853

Matthew F. Maury:

15.   THE PHYSICAL GEOGRAPHY OF THE SEA*

THE GULF STREAM

There is a river in the ocean. In the severest droughts it never fails, and in the mightiest floods it never overflows. Its banks and its bottoms are of cold water, while its current is of warm. The Gulf of Mexico is its fountain, and its mouth is in the Arctic Seas. It is the Gulf Stream. There is in the world no other such majestic flow of waters. Its current is more rapid than the Mississippi or the Amazon, and its volume more than a thousand times greater.

Its waters, as far out from the Gulf as the Carolina coasts, are of indigo blue. They are so distinctly marked that their line of junction with the common sea-water may be traced by the eye. Often one half of the vessel may be perceived floating in Gulf Stream water, while the other half is in common water of the sea; so sharp is the line, and such the want of affinity between those waters, and such, too, the reluctance, so to speak, on the part of those of the Gulf Stream to mingle with the common water of the sea.

At the salt-works in France, and along the shores of the Adriatic, where the *"salines"* are carried on by the process of solar evaporation, there is a series of vats or pools through which the water is

---

* Harper & Brothers, first edition, 1855.

Matthew Fontaine Maury, 1806–73, was an American hydrographer and naval officer who wrote widely on navigation and naval reform. PHYSICAL GEOGRAPHY OF THE SEA was the first classical work of modern oceanography.

passed as it comes from the sea, and is reduced to the briny state. The longer it is exposed to evaporation, the salter it grows, and the deeper is the hue of its blue, until crystallization is about to commence, when the now deep blue water puts on a reddish tint. Now the waters of the Gulf Stream are salter than the waters of the sea through which they flow, and hence we can account for the deep indigo blue which all navigators observe off the Carolina coasts.

These salt-makers are in the habit of judging of the richness of the sea-water in salt by its color—the greener the hue, the fresher the water. We have in this, perhaps, an explanation of the contrasts which the waters of the Gulf Stream present with those of the Atlantic, as well as of the light green of the North Sea and other Polar waters; also of the dark blue of the trade-wind regions, and especially of the Indian Ocean, which poets have described as the "black waters."

What is the cause of the Gulf Stream has always puzzled philosophers. Many are the theories and numerous the speculations that have been advanced with regard to it. Modern investigations and examinations are beginning to throw some light upon the subject, though all is not yet clear.

Early writers maintained that the Mississippi River was the father of the Gulf Stream. Its floods, they said, produce it; for its velocity, it was held, could be computed by the rate of the current of the river.

Captain Livingston overturned this hypothesis by showing that the volume of water which the Mississippi River empties into the Gulf of Mexico is not equal to the three thousandth part of that which escapes from it through the Gulf Stream.

Moreover, the water of the Gulf Stream is salt—that of the Mississippi, fresh; and those philosophers forgot that just as much salt as escapes from the Gulf of Mexico through this stream, must enter the Gulf through some other channel from the main ocean; for, if it did not, the Gulf of Mexico, in process of time, unless it had a salt bed at the bottom, or was fed with salt springs from below—neither of which is probable—would become a fresh water basin.

The above quoted argument of Captain Livingston, however, was held to be conclusive; and upon the remains of the hypothesis which he had so completely overturned, he set up another, which, in turn, has been upset. In it he ascribed the velocity of the Gulf Stream as depending "on the motion of the sun in the ecliptic, and the influence he has on the waters of the Atlantic."

But the opinion that came to be the most generally received and deep-rooted in the mind of seafaring people was the one repeated by Dr. Franklin, and which held that the Gulf Stream is the escaping of the waters that have been *forced* into the Caribbean Sea by the trade-winds, and that it is the pressure of those winds upon the water which forces up into that sea a head, as it were, for this stream.

We know of instances in which waters have been accumulated on one side of a lake, or in one end of a canal, at the expense of the other. The pressure of the trade-winds may *assist* to give the Gulf Stream its initial velocity, but are they of themselves adequate to such an effect? To my mind, the laws of Hydrostatics, as at present expounded, appear by no means to warrant the conclusion that it is, unless the aid of other agents also be brought to bear.

Admiral Smyth, in his valuable memoir on the Mediterranean (p. 162), mentions that a continuance in the Sea of Tuscany of *"gusty gales"* from the southwest has been known to raise its surface no less than twelve feet above its ordinary level. This, he says, occasions a strong surface drift through the Strait of Bonifaccio. But in this we have nothing like the Gulf Stream; no deep and narrow channel-way to conduct these waters off like a miniature river even in that sea, but a mere surface flow, such as usually follows the piling up of water in any pond or gulf above the ordinary level. The Bonifaccio current does not flow like a *"river in the sea"* across the Mediterranean, but it spreads itself out as soon as it passes the Straits, and, like a circle in the water, loses itself by broad spreading as soon as it finds sea room.

Supposing the pressure of the waters that are *forced* into the Caribbean Sea by the trade-winds to be the *sole* cause of the Gulf Stream, that sea and the Mexican Gulf should have a much higher level than the Atlantic. Accordingly, the advocates of this theory require for its support "a great degree of elevation." Major Rennell likens the stream to "an immense river descending from a higher level into a plain." Now we know very nearly the average breadth and velocity of the Gulf Stream in the Florida Pass. We also know, with a like degree of approximation, the velocity and breadth of the same waters off Cape Hatteras. Their breadth here is about seventy-five miles against thirty-two in the "Narrows" of the Straits, and their mean velocity is three knots off Hatteras against four in the "Narrows." This being the case, it is easy to show that the depth of the Gulf Stream off Hatteras is not so great as it is in the "Narrows" of Bemini by nearly 50 per cent., and that, consequently, instead of *descending*, its bed represents the surface of an inclined plane, with its descent inclined from the north toward the south, *up* which plane the lower depths of the stream *must* ascend. If we assume its depth off Bemini* to be two hundred fathoms, which are thought to be within limits, the above rates of breadth and velocity will give one hundred and fourteen fathoms for its depth off Hatteras. The waters, therefore, which in the Straits are below the level of the Hatteras depth, so far from *descending*, are actually forced up an inclined plane, whose submarine ascent is not less than ten inches to the mile.

The Niagara is an "immense river descending into a plain." But instead of preserving its character in Lake Ontario as a distinct and well-defined stream for several hundred miles, it spreads itself out, and its waters are immediately lost in those of the lake. Why should not the Gulf Stream do the same? It gradually enlarges itself, it is true; but, instead of mingling with the ocean by broad spreading, as the "immense rivers" descending into the northern lakes do, its waters, like a stream of oil in the ocean, preserve a distinctive character for more than three thousand miles.

Moreover, while the Gulf Stream is running to the north from its supposed elevated level at the south, there is a cold current coming down from the north; meeting the warm waters of the Gulf midway the ocean, it divides itself, and runs by the side of them right back into those very reservoirs at the south, to which theory gives an elevation sufficient to send out entirely across the Atlantic a jet of warm water said to be more than three thousand times greater in volume than the Mississippi River. This current from Baffin's Bay has not only no trade-winds to give it a head, but the prevailing winds are unfavorable to it, and for a great part of the way it is below the surface, and far beyond the propelling reach of any wind. And there is every reason to believe that this, with other polar currents, is quite equal in volume to the Gulf Stream. Are they not the effects of like causes? If so, what have the trade-winds to do with the one more than the other?

It is a custom often practiced by seafaring people to throw a bottle overboard, with a paper, stating the time and place at which it is done. In the absence of other information as to currents, that afforded by these mute little navigators is of great value. They leave no tracks behind them, it is true, and their

---

* Professor Bache reports that the officers of the Coast Survey have sounded with the deep sea lead, and ascertained its depth here to be 370 fathoms (January, 1856).

routes can not be ascertained. But knowing where they were cast, and seeing where they are found, some idea may be formed as to their course. Straight lines may at least be drawn, showing the shortest distance from the beginning to the end of their voyage, with the time elapsed. Admiral Beechey, R.N., has prepared a chart, representing, in this way, the tracks of more than one hundred bottles. From it, it appears that the waters from every quarter of the Atlantic tend toward the Gulf of Mexico and its stream. Bottles cast into the sea midway beween the Old and the New Worlds, near the coasts of Europe, Africa, and America, at the extreme north or farthest south, have been found either in the West Indies, on the British Isles, or within the well-known range of Gulf Stream waters.

Of two cast out together in south latitude on the coast of Africa, one was found on the island of Trinidad; the other on Guernsey, in the English Channel.

When facts are wanting, it often happens that hypothesis will serve, in their stead, the purposes of illustration. Let us, therefore, suppose a globe of the earth's size, having a solid nucleus, and covered all over with water two hundred fathoms deep, and that every source of heat and cause of radiation be removed, so that its fluid temperature becomes constant and uniform throughout. On such a globe, the equilibrium remaining undisturbed, there would be neither wind nor current.

Let us now suppose that all the water within the tropics, to the depth of one hundred fathoms, suddenly becomes oil. The aqueous equilibrium of the planet would thereby be disturbed, and a general system of currents and counter currents would be immediately commenced—the oil, in an unbroken sheet on the surface, running toward the poles, and the water, in an under current, toward the equator. The oil is supposed, as it reaches the polar basin, to be reconverted into water, and the water to become oil as it crosses Cancer and Capricorn, rising to the surface in the intertropical regions and returning as before.

Thus, *without wind*, we should have a perpetual and uniform system of tropical and polar currents. In consequence of diurnal rotation of the planet on its axis, each particle of oil, were resistance small, would approach the poles on a spiral turning to the east, with a relative velocity greater and greater, until, finally, it would reach the pole, and whirl about it at the rate of nearly a thousand miles the hour. Becoming water and losing its velocity, it would approach the tropics by a similar, but inverted spiral, turning toward the west. Owing to the principle here alluded to, all currents from the equator to the poles should have an eastward tendency, and all from the poles toward the equator a westward.

The hottest water in the Gulf Stream is also the lightest; as it rises to the top, it is cooled both by evaporation and exposure, when the surface is replenished by fresh supplies of hot water from below. Thus, in a winter's day, the waters at the surface of the Gulf Stream off Cape Hatteras may be at 80°, and at the depth of five hundred fathoms—three thousand feet—as actual observations show, the thermometer will stand at 57°. Following the stream thence off the Capes of Virginia, one hundred and twenty miles, it will be found—the water-thermometer having been carefully noted all the way—that it now stands a degree or two less at the surface, while all below is cooler. In other words, the stratum of water at 57°, which was three thousand feet below the surface off Hatteras, has, in a course of one hundred and twenty or one hundred and thirty miles in a horizontal direction, ascended, vertically, six hundred feet; that is, this stratum has run up hill with an ascent of five or six feet to the mile.

As a rule, the hottest water of the Gulf Stream is at or near the surface; and as the deep-sea thermometer is sent down, it shows that these waters, though still far warmer than the water on either side at corresponding depths, gradually become less and less warm until the bottom of the current is reached. There is reason to believe that the warm waters of the Gulf Stream are nowhere permitted, in the oceanic economy, to touch the bottom of the sea. There is everywhere a cushion of cool water between them and the solid parts of the earth's crust. This arrangement is suggestive, and strikingly beautiful. One of the benign offices of the Gulf Stream is to convey heat from the Gulf of Mexico, where otherwise it would become excessive, and to dispense it in regions beyond the Atlantic for the amelioration of the climates of the British Islands and of all Western Europe. Now cold water is one of the best non-conductors of heat, and if the warm water of the Gulf Stream was sent across the Atlantic in contact with the solid crust of the earth—comparatively a good conductor of heat—instead of being sent across, as it is, in contact with a cold, non-conducting cushion of cool water to fend it from the bottom, all its heat would be lost in the first part of the way, and the soft climates of both France and England would be as that of Labrador, severe in the extreme, and ice-bound.

~~~~~~~~~~~~~~

William Ferrel:

16.   AN ESSAY ON THE WINDS AND THE
CURRENTS OF THE OCEAN*

Introduction. The earth is surrounded on all sides by an exceedingly rare and elastic body called the atmosphere, extending with
a diminishing density to an unknown distance into space, but
pressing upon the earth with a force equal to that of a homogeneous atmosphere 5½ miles high. It is also partially surrounded
by the ocean, which is of a very variable depth, and known to
be, in many places, more than 4 miles. If the specific gravity of
the atmosphere and of the ocean, were everywhere the same, all
the forces of gravity and of pressure which act upon any part of
them, would be in exact equilibrium, and they would forever
remain at rest. But as some parts of the earth are much warmer
than others, and air and water expand and become rare as their
temperature is increased, their specific gravities are not the same
in all parts of the earth, and hence the equilibrium is destroyed,
and a system of winds and currents is produced. It is proposed
in this essay to inquire into the effects which are produced, both
in the atmosphere and in the ocean, by this disturbance of
equilibrium, and by means of a new force which has never been
taken into account in any theory of winds and currents, to endeavor
to account for certain phenomena in their motions, which have always been a puzzle in Meteorology and Hydrology. As there are some
uncertain data connected with this subject, such as the amount of the
disturbing force, the effects of continents, friction, etc., which render
a complete solution of the problem impracticable, we shall aim
at giving a popular explanation of observed phenomena rather than
a complete solution of the problem, yet we shall give the result
of some calculations, based upon known data, or at least upon

* From NASHVILLE JOURNAL OF MEDICINE AND SURGERY, Volume XI, No. 4,
October, 1856.

William Ferrel, 1817–91, was an American meteorologist who did valuable
research on tides, currents, winds, and storms and wrote extensively on his
findings.

very reasonable hypotheses, which will show that the causes which we have given, are adequate to the effects which are attributed to them.

The general motions of the Ocean. Inasmuch as the atmosphere and the ocean are both fluids somewhat similarly situated, except that the latter only partially surrounds the earth, and are both subject to the same disturbing influences of a difference of temperature between the equator and the poles, it is reasonable to suppose that there is a similarity in their general motions. This is known from observation to be the case, except that the continents interfere more with the motions of the ocean than with those of the atmosphere. The general motion of the ocean in the torrid zone, where it is not interrupted by continents, is toward the west with an average velocity of about ten miles in twenty-four hours. Towards the poles the motion, in general, is towards the east, which is a necessary consequence of the preservation of areas; for if one part have a western motion, another part must have an eastern one, as was shown with regard to the atmosphere. If, then, there were no continents, there would be a general flowing of all the tropical parts of the ocean westward, and of the remaining parts towards the east. But when the tropical or equatorial current impinges against the eastern sides of the continents, as in the Atlantic, a part is turned along the eastern side towards each pole. Likewise, when the eastern flow towards the poles, strikes against the western side of a continent, it is deflected towards the equator. Hence the northern parts of both the Atlantic and the Pacific, have a tendency to a vorticular motion, their tropical parts moving westward, and then turning northward on the eastern sides of the continents and joining the eastern flow, and south again towards the equator on the western sides of the continents. And it is evident from observation, that the southern parts of these oceans, and also the Indian ocean, have a tendency, in some measure, to the same kind of motions, except that the continents do not extend so far south, and consequently only a part of the eastern flow, is turned toward the equator, the rest flowing on and producing the general eastern motion of the waters observed in the Southern ocean.

The forces which produce the motions of the Ocean. The *primum mobile* of the motions of the ocean, as of the atmosphere, depends principally upon the difference of temperature between the equatorial and polar regions. The temperature of the ocean, on the surface at the equator, is about 80°, and it has a temperature above the mean temperature of the earth, which is 39.5°, to the depth of 7200 feet.[1] Towards the poles it is below the freezing point, and continues below the mean temperature at the parallel of 70°, to the depth of 4500 feet. As water expands about 0.000455 of its bulk for every degree of increasing temperature, and sea-water contracts down to the temperature of 28°, calculations based upon these data, supposing the temperature to increase or decrease in proportion to the depth, make the specific gravity of the part at the equator, so much less than that at the poles, that it would have to rise about ten feet above the general level at the equator to be in equilibrium, at the bottom of the sea, with the part at the poles. But then the equilibrium at the surface would be destroyed, and the waters would flow there towards the poles, where the superior pressure at the bottom over that of the equator, would cause a current to flow back, at the bottom of the sea, towards the equator. Hence, if this cause of disturbance existed alone, there would be a current at the bottom of the sea from the poles towards the equator, moved by a force equal to the pressure of a stratum of water of about five feet, and one at the surface from the equator towards the poles, moved by an equal force. But this motion, combined with the rotatory motion of the earth, gives rise to other forces, just as in the case of the atmosphere, which greatly modify these motions, as will be shown hereafter.

The preceding are the principal forces concerned in giving motion to the waters of the ocean. Lieutenant MAURY, however, lays little stress upon these, and seems to think that the principal agencies concerned in these motions, arise from evaporation, the saltness of the ocean, galvanism, etc.[2] But we think it may be shown that these agencies can have no perceptible effect.

First, Lieutenaut MAURY supposes excessive evaporation to take place within the tropics, and this vapor to be carried away and precipitated in extra-tropical regions, and infers that this would have, at least, a very sensible effect in producing the currents of the ocean. He puts the amount of evaporation equal to the evaporation of a stratum of one half of an inch per day. Now if a stratum of water one half of an inch in thickness, is evaporated in twenty-four hours in one place, and precipitated in another, it produces a difference of level of one inch between the two places, and the currents which it produces, must be such as are sufficient to restore this level in the same space of time. Now we may judge how ex-

[1] Mrs. Somervill's Physical Geography, p. 202.
[2] See Physical Geography of the Sea. §§ 26, 34 and 300.

ceedingly small a current this would produce, when we consider that there is a rise of about two feet in the open ocean, at one place, and a fall of the same amount at another, every six hours, caused by the tides, and yet the flowing of the water from the one place to the other to produce this rise at the one place, and fall at the other, it is well known, does not produce any sensible currents in the open sea. Again, this matter can be easily reduced to calculation. If a stratum of water one half of an inch in thickness, were taken up by evaporation from the torrid zone, and none of it precipitated there, but all conveyed to the temperate and polar zones, it may be demonstrated, upon the supposition that the ocean is four miles in-depth, that the flow of water towards the equator to restore the equilibrium in the same time, would not amount to a velocity of one foot per hour.

We think it may be likewise shown by calculations, based upon reasonable hypotheses, if not entirely upon well known data, that the salts of the sea also can have but little influence in producing currents. Lieutenant MAURY makes a similar hypothesis, with regard to evaporation, in treating of the influence of the salt of the ocean, which he does in treating of the influence of evaporation, and supposes that the excess of salt left in the torrid zone, by the excess of evaporation there, and the great precipitation in the temperate and polar regions, produces such a difference in the specific gravity, as to destroy the equilibrium of the sea and to have a very sensible influence in producing currents, and especially the Gulf stream. With regard to the latter, he supposes that the water of the Gulf of Mexico, has a much greater specific gravity than the water in the Atlantic, on account of the great evaporation to which it has been exposed in its passage from the coast of Africa across the Atlantic and through the Caribbean sea, and that, consequently, it is forced out into the Atlantic by its greater pressure. Now suppose it takes the water a year, which is about the actual time, to pass from the coast of Africa to the Gulf of Mexico; in this time, according to the hypothesis of the evaporation of a stratum of a half an inch daily, it loses by evaporation a stratum of water fifteen feet in depth, and as the salt contained in this stratum, can not be evaporated, it remains in the part left, and increases its saltness. But sea-water contains only about three per cent. of saline matter, and consequently the amount of salt contained in this stratum of fifteen feet, only increases the weight of the rest to an amount equal to the weight of a stratum of water about six inches deep. Hence it only gives the water of the Gulf a tendency to flow out into the Atlantic with a force equal to the force with which a homogeneous fluid would flow out with its surface six inches above the general level of the Atlantic. This is much less than the opposing force arising from the great specific gravity of the water in the northern part of the Atlantic on account of its lower temperature, as we have shown by calculations. The same reasoning may be applied to any other part of the ocean. For if the salt of the ocean has any influence in producing currents, it must be to produce an under current from the torrid zone, where evaporation is supposed to be in excess, towards the poles, and consequently a counter-current at the surface from the poles toward the equator. But, upon any reasonable hypothesis, the water at the surface can not lose by evaporation, in passing from the poles to the equator, a stratum of water of such a depth, that the amount of salt contained in it, can increase the specific gravity at the equator, as much as the lower temperature increases it towards the poles. Hence, if the salt of the sea has any sensible influence, it is only in opposition to a greater influence, and consequently it has a tendency to diminish, rather than increase, the currents of the ocean. We think it is therefore manifest, that neither evaporation nor the salts of the sea, can have much influence in producing currents, even upon Lieutenant MAURY's hypothesis, that evaporation is greatly in excess of precipitation in the torrid zone. But is this a true hypothesis? Although there is a great evaporation in the torrid zone, there is also great precipitation, for with few exceptions more rain falls at the equator than in any other part of the earth, and it is only the amount of evaporation over precipitation that should be taken into account, which we have reason to think, is very small, and if Professor ESPY's theory is correct, it cannot be anything; for, according to this theory, no vapor can pass from the torrid to the temperate zones and produce rain, since the current bearing it there, would be a descending current, and consequently could not produce it.

The Ocean not level. As it has been shown in the case of the atmosphere, that the resultant of the forces causes an accumulation about the parallels of 28°, so, as the motions of the ocean are somewhat similar, and it is acted upon by the same forces, it may be shown that there must be a slight accumulation, about those parallels, in the ocean also. Whatever may be the causes of the motions of the ocean, we know that in the torrid zone it has a small western motion, and in other parts a slight motion towards the east. The great equatorial current of the Atlantic moves about ten miles in twenty-four hours, but if we suppose that the average motion of the water in the torrid zone, is five miles only per day, and that the maximum velocity of the water eastward, in the extra-tropical regions is the same, using the same hypothesis which we did with regard to the atmosphere, the forces which result from these motions, must cause an accumulation of more than forty feet, about the parallels of 28°, above the level of the sea at the poles, and about five feet above the level of the equator. This, however, would be the amount of accumulation to produce an equilibrium of the forces at the surface, but as this accumulation would then produce a greater pressure there upon the bottom than towards the poles and at the equator, it would produce, as in the case of the atmosphere, a flowing out from beneath this accumulation towards the poles and the equator, and a settling down of the surface above, below this state of equilibrium, sufficient to cause a counter-current at the surface from the poles and the equator to supply the currents below. The accumulation then would be only about one-half that stated above, and there would be a flowing of water at the surface from both sides *towards* the parallels of 28°, and below, a current in both directions *from* these parallels, similar to the motions of the atmosphere.

That the water of the ocean has such a motion as has been stated, appears from observations of its motions, and other circumstances. Says Lieutenant MAURY, "there seems to be a larger flow of polar waters into the Atlantic than of waters from it, and I cannot account for the preservation of the equilibrium of this ocean by any other hypothesis than that which calls in the aid of under currents." It is well known, that in Baffin's bay there is a strong surface-current running south, and a strong counter-current beneath running north. Another evidence of this general tendency of the waters, is, that icebergs, in both hemispheres, are drifted from the poles towards the equator, and in the south Atlantic sometimes reach the parallel of 37°. It is also evident from the fact that, in both the North Atlantic and Pacific oceans, there are large collections of drift and sea-weed about the parallels of 28°, so thickly matted that vessels are retarded in passing through them.[3] These collections can only be formed by the flowing of the water at the surface from both sides to these parallels. It has been supposed that these collections are owing to the slight vorticular motions of these oceans, it being supposed that any floating substances on the surface would have a tendency to collect at the vortex. This, however, would not be the case;

---

[3] Humboldt's Cosmos, Vol. 2, p. 278.

for on account of friction at the bottom, the surface would have a greater vorticular motion than the bottom, and consequently the water would be driven very slowly at the surface by the centrifugal force towards the sides, where it would cause a slight elevation and increase of pressure, which would cause the water to return towards the vortex at the bottom, and not at the top; and hence floating substances at the surface, could have no tendency to collect at the vortex.

We have corroborated these deductions from theory by numerous experiments made with a vessel of water with light substances on the surface. When the vessel is first receiving the vorticular motion, the substances collect in the middle; for, as it is the vessel which give motion to the water by means of the friction, the vessel, and consequently the bottom of the water, has then a greater motion than the top; and hence the reverse of what is stated above takes place; but if the vessel is not stopped, and the water within allowed to continue its motion, the vorticular motion at the bottom is retarded faster than at the top, and soon has a slower motion there, when the light substances on the surface are seen to recede from the vortex towards the sides, and if there are any light substances on the bottom, they collect in the center, all of which proves that the water recedes from the middle at the surface and returns to it at the bottom, and exactly agrees with the deductions from theory. These collections of sea-weed, then, cannot be caused by the vorticular motions of the ocean, but must be the result of a general tendency of the surface water to flow from both the equator and the poles towards these parallels; and as it is prevented from collecting on these parallels near either side on account of the slight vorticular motion of the ocean, it collects only in the middle.

Explanation of the Gulf Stream. We come now to the Gulf stream, which has been a puzzle to philosophers ever since it was first discovered. Many explanations have been given, and all known forces which can have any influence, have been brought in to account for this wonderful phenomenon. The most usual explanation is, that it is the escaping of the waters which have been forced into the Caribbean sea and the Gulf of Mexico by the trade winds, which have been supposed to raise their surface above the general level, and thus afford a head, as it were, for this stream. This, without doubt, has a very considerable effect, but it has not generally been deemed adequate alone to account for the phenomenon, nor does it, in connection with all other known influences, afford a satisfactory explanation. "What is the cause of the Gulf stream," says Lieutenant MAURY, "has always puzzled philosophers. Modern investigations and examinations are beginning to throw some light upon the subject, though all is not yet clear."

We shall now endeavor to show, that the additional force which we have taken into account in explaining both the winds and the currents of the ocean, and which seems to have been overlooked heretofore, will at least throw much additional light upon the subject, if not afford a complete explanation. We have shown that this force, which results from the eastward flow of the water in the extra-tropical regions, and from the western motion within the tropics, has a tendency to drive the water from the poles towards the equator, and also slightly from the equator towards the poles, and to produce an accumulation of at least twenty feet on the parallel of 28°, above the level at the poles, upon the supposition that the maximum of this east and west flow, is only five miles per day. But if, from any cause, the force which results from this eastward flow, should be cut off at any place, the water would flow northward at that place with a force equal to that which would result from a head on the parallel of 28°, at least twenty feet above the level towards the poles. Now it may be seen from the configuration of the coast of the United States, that this force is actually cut off along that coast; for this force depends upon the eastward flow of the water there, which it cannot have inasmuch as it must flow in both ways along the coast to fill up the vacuum which such a motion would produce. As the Gulf of Mexico, therefore, and the adjacent part of the Atlantic, lie in the parallel of greatest accumulation, the water must flow from these parts along the coast with a force equal to that stated above. In addition to this, the momentum of the water flowing westward in the torrid zone, with a motion depending upon the prime moving cause due to a difference of specific gravity between the poles and the equator, in connection with the rotatory motion of the earth, and being independent of the effect of the trade winds, must force the water in the Caribbean sea and the Gulf of Mexico, considerably above the general level, and add to the preceding force. When we consider that the motion of the water which produces the tides on our coasts, is in general imperceptible in the open ocean, and yet, on account of the sloping bottom of the ocean, which causes a smaller volume of water to receive the momentum of a larger one, it causes considerable rise of the water along the coast, we have reason to think that the general tendency of the water westward in the torrid zone, may keep the water in the Gulf considerably above the general level, since its water and that in the Caribbean sea, if the bottom of the ocean be sloping, must in a great measure receive the momentum of the whole body of water moving westward in the adjacent part of the Atlantic. The eastern tendency of the water in the northern part of the North Atlantic, due to the prime moving force mentioned above, and independent of the winds which prevail there, causes the surface of the ocean in the latitude of Newfoundland to be somewhat depressed below the general level next to the coast, which also adds to the force of the Gulf stream. All these forces, taken in connection with the influence of the trade winds, to which this phenomenon has been mainly attributed, we think, furnish a complete and satisfactory explanation of that great wonder and mystery of the ocean, the Gulf stream.

The Greenland and other currents. The general eastward motion of the waters of the ocean in the northern part of the Atlantic, and consequent depression next the coast of North America, also furnish an explanation of the cold current of water flowing between the Gulf stream and the coast of the United States, called the Greenland current. On account of the rotatory motion of the earth, the water of the Gulf stream in flowing northward, tends to the east, and for the same reason the water flowing from Greenland and Baffin's bay to supply the eastern flow, tends towards the west, and consequently flows in between the Gulf stream and the coast of the United States.

There must be a motion of the waters somewhat similar to that of the Gulf stream and the Greenland current, wherever the great equatorial current impinges against a continent, and the eastward flow towards the poles is cut off. Hence, on the eastern coast of South America, there is the warm Brazilian current towards Cape Horn, and on the eastern coast of Africa, the Mozambique current, which at the cape of Good Hope is called the Lagullas current. Also, on the eastern coast of Asia, there is the warm China current, flowing towards the north, similar to the Gulf stream, and the cold Asiatic current, insinuating itself between it and the coast, like the Greenland current.

On the western sides of the continents a motion somewhat the reverse of this must take place. Hence, instead of a warm stream flowing towards the north, there is a cold current flowing towards the equator. On the west of Portugal, and the northern part of Africa, there is a flow of colder water towards the equator, and west of the southern part of Africa, is the cold Atlantic current, also tending towards the equator, both to join the great equatorial current flowing across the Atlantic. On the west coast of North America, also, there is a flow of colder water along the coast from the north, and on the west coast of South America, is Humboldt's current, 8° or 10° colder than the rest of the ocean in the same latitude, both tending towards the equator to join the great western current there across the Pacific, and to fill up, as it were, the vacuum which this current has a tendency to leave about the equator, on the western coast of America.

Nashville, October 4, 1856.

A. Cialdi and P. A. Secchi:

17.　　ON THE TRANSPARENCY OF THE SEA*

Translated by Albert Collier, Gale M. Finlayson, and Edwin W. Cake

PREFATORY NOTE

[The following translation was submitted by Prof. Albert Collier of Florida State University. The "work now in press" referred to in the second paragraph is "Sul moto ondoso del mare e su le correnti di esso specialmente su quelle littorali," by Comdr. Alessandro Cialdi, containing a 30-page scientific diary by Prof. P. A. Secchi entitled "Relazione delle esperienze fatte a bordo della pontificia Pirocorvetta l'Immacolata Concezione per determinare la trasparenza del mare." John E. Tyler, Visibility Laboratory, Scripps Institution of Oceanography, has kindly supplied these notes based on the latter.]

According to Secchi's scientific diary, *L'Immacolata Concezione* was made ready at Civitavecchia. The morning of 20 April 1865 they were

* From LIMNOLOGY and OCEANOGRAPHY, April 1968, Vol. 13, No. 2, pps. 391–394. Reprinted by permission of the publisher and the translators. (Originally published: Comptes Rendu de L'Academie des Sciences, Paris, 1865, 61: 100–104.)

Alessandro Cialdi was Commander of the ship *L'Immacolata Concezione,* on which the above experiments took place.

Pietro Angelo Secchi, 1818–73, a Jesuit priest, was an Italian astronomer and a pioneer in classifying stars by their spectra.

hosts to His Excellency Monsignor Randi, papal delegate of Civitavecchia, and other prelates, and at 1400 hours departed on their expedition.

With respect to his preparation for the experimental work, Secchi
says,

For my part I had set up various optical accessories, hoping that they would
prove useful to me, and among them a pair of good binoculars, various polari-
scopes, a Nicol prism, a tourmaline and a pile of crystal sheets, which equipment
was indicated by Arago as quite useful in diminishing the reflected light of the
ocean and therefore to better observe the bottom and to aid penetration of
visual sight in the water. I added a spectrometer and a Hipp recording aneroid
barometer, taking advantage of this occasion to see what usefulness could be
offered by this instrument at sea.

The experiments apparently lasted until 1 June 1865. Secchi's report
is dated 10 June 1865.

Part II of Secchi's report is entitled "Conclusions derived from the
preceding experiments." In this part he devotes sections to 1) influence
of size of the disc; 2) influence of shade; 3) influence of height
of the observer above the water; 4) influence of altitude of the sun;
5) influence of clearness of the sky; 6) influence of color.

Following Secchi's report there is a short but grandiose conclusion
by Comdr. Cialdi in which he seems to be trying to settle some
argument about the color of the water over Agullas Bank. He then
closes with a passage from Virgil's *Aeneid*, Book I, which supports his
argument.

[Both the Cialdi work and the volume of Arago are cited in ONI
Translation A-655, U.S. Hydrographic Office, 1955.—EDITOR.]

Among the subjects which Arago recommended to sailors for
study is the transparency of the sea and its color.[1] The depth
at which one sees objects in the sea is most interesting, but
unfortunately there are few direct observations. I mean, of course,
direct experiments, and not more or less conjectural observations
in which it is "believed" that the bottom of the sea has been
seen. These direct experiments are limited (as much as we have
been able to ascertain) to those of Captain Bérard, who, while
cruising among the Mulgrave Islands and Wallis Island, saw a
streak of light from a cowrie bed at a depth of 40 m. But neither
the height of the sun nor the state of the sky were mentioned.

I believe it will be of some interest to the academy to record
a résumé of the results of the experiments which have been made
on this subject by Mr. Cialdi on board the ship *L'Immacolata
Concezione* under his command. Mr. Cialdi was kind enough to
entrust me with the direction and discussion of the optical aspects

[1] See Arago, *Works*, Vol. VIII; Paris.

of his work. The details of these observations will appear in the near future in a work now in press. Here I will limit myself to a simple narrative of the principal results.

The bodies selected for submersion in the sea were discs of different colors and sizes: a system of ropes and weights was arranged to hold them horizontal in the water and graduated lines served to determine the depth.

The first was a large disc of 3.73 m in diameter, formed of an iron circle covered with oiled sailcloth, and varnished with white lead. The others were little discs of only 0.40 m in diameter but of diverse substances. One was a pure white earthenware plate held by iron wire in an iron circle; the others were cloth discs supported by iron circles, also 0.40 m in diameter, but of different colors: white, yellow, and the color of sea mud.

Experimental immersions were made in the sea, opposite the coast of Civitavecchia, at a distance from land of 6 to 12 nautical miles and at depths which varied between 90 and 300 m. The sea, in these parts, was perfectly clear, of a beautiful color and of a great purity. The time was the end of April, on a very calm sea which for a long time had not been strongly agitated. The tranquility of the sea during these experiments was such that one could go down in small boats and make observations as if one had been in a port. The third day the sky was of an extraordinary purity. Such favorable conditions are not easy to encounter simultaneously and for that reason I believe these observations to be important. At the time of each observation the altitude of the sun was determined with a sextant. Here are the results.

The maximum depth at which the large disc (3.75 m) was visible was 42.5 m, the elevation of the sun being 60° 17'. Its visibility was approximately equal from the side of the shadow of the ship and from the side of the sun, provided that the solar rays reflected by the water were prevented from reaching the eye. The length of the shadow projected on the water does, however, provide a little advantage. Since observations were made at different solar heights, it was possible, according to existing photometric laws, to determine the depth at which one could see the disc by a vertical illumination of the sun. The result was that one could see it at 44 m, or at the most at 45.

We found the large surface to have an advantage over the smaller ones: because the images of the latter, when they have reached a certain depth, are deformed in all directions by refraction, and become so diffused that it is impossible to recognize the object exactly, even when it is still sufficiently clear. Thus, the earthenware disc was visible at a maximum of 35 m, the sun's altitude being 59° 48', and only in exceptionally favorable circumstances. We once saw it at 42 m, the sun being at 38° 42', even though the white of the plate was clearly more brilliant than that of the cloth. The little discs in white cloth disappeared sooner. This disappearance, as I have said, depends especially on the diffusion of the image, which is broken in all directions, and becomes impossible to recognize.

The large disc, on the other hand, still remained large enough and regular enough in its form to remain perfectly recognizeable, even though it appeared to be no more than a small cloud. At first its color became light green, then it changed progressively through light blue to a dark blue as its depth increased. Finally the color darkened until visibility was lost. It must be noted that in each experiment the disappearance happened in rather narrow limits of depth, varying rarely from one meter in the same circumstances. The discs painted yellow and the color of the sea slime disappeared at depths representing hardly half of those of the white ones, that is to say, between 17 and 24 m.

Some attempts were made to recognize the different circumstances favoring visibility. Thus it was determined that by placing the eye as near as possible to the water the depth increases: between the measurements taken on the deck of the ship and in the smaller craft there was a difference of one to 2 m, but this advantage was more noticeable for the little discs than for the large ones.

In order to destroy the reflection of the light on the water which greatly impaired distinct vision, polarizers proposed by Arago were used, but without any advantageous result. The absorption of the light produced by all these instruments, and the necessity of using a single eye, certainly counterbalanced any expected gain in control of light reflections. Moreover, the removal of reflected light is never complete, because the movement of the water presents a liquid surface under angles different from those of complete polarization. The best means to see well is to project a wide shadow over the water at the point of observation, and to place the eye as near to the water as possible.

The most important factors are the height of the sun and the clearness of the sky. Under a sky covered with light clouds, although very white and very thin, one had 4 m less of depth than under a sky perfectly clear. It is difficult to calculate the visibility which one would obtain with a vertical sun, because the authors who have written on photometry do not agree on the law of absorption of the terrestrial atmosphere. The figure given here, approximately 45 m, results from observations made in very varied circumstances, and can not be too far from the truth. It is to be noted that the result obtained for the earthenware plate is rather close to the observation of Captain Bérard.

These experiments give us only the depth at which objects disappear when the light reflected by them equals in color and intensity that of the surrounding environment. This does not imply that there is an absolute extinction of light; but on the contrary proves that light restricted of certain rays can penetrate great depths. Bouguer had concluded from his observations that at the depth of 83.03 m seawater no longer allowed light to pass. This isn't true: we see that after passing through 90 m of water that is to say 45 while descending and 45 while rising, light is merely reduced to the rays which constitute the true color of the sea.

When the light, reflected by white discs is analyzed with a spectroscope, the first colors to disappear are red and yellow; these two colors are rapidly absorbed by immersion. After them comes the absorption of green, especially in a zone which surrounds the B lines of Frauenhofer. Blue, indigo, and violet remain completely unaltered and rather sharp. That explains the color of the seawater, which is of a lovely blue darkening to violet. This luminous absorption is also perfectly in accord with the absorption of thermal and chemical radiations: the first of these being less refractable, is stopped by the water, which is athermonous, while the other passes well enough through because water is very diactinic.

The total absorption of light, therefore, cannot be concluded from these experiments but for our goal, which was to establish the limit of visibility of submerged objects, they are sufficient. Indeed, an object disappears necessarily when it reflects no other light than that which is partly equal to that of the surrounding environment. The question might arise as to the possible advantage in visibility of an object having a very large surface, as for example the sea bottom itself. It certainly would not be denied that there would be some advantage resulting from multiple reflections in water; but from the manner in which our large disc behaved, this advantage appears to me to be very small. After the disc was reduced in visibility to the shape of a small whitish cloud, we increased the depth by two or three meters and it disappeared as the surrounding waters took on a darker shade. Thus, even if we utilize a vast surface, it could, at a certain depth, reflect only the filtered rays which seawater can transmit; and we have seen that that happens at about 45 m. Supposing the most favorable of conditions, I believe that in seas like our Mediterranean, one could reach at the most only 50 m and, with great difficulty, 60 m. [It is interesting to compare this with the maximum depth of 67 m calculated by Tyler (Limnol. Oceanog., 13:1–6).] It would be interesting to repeat these experiments in other seas.

From these results, it may be doubted that one has actually seen the sea bottom at depths of 100 and 200 m; it is much more reasonable to suppose that one has perceived only mud raised to great heights by the waves. This doubt is all the more reasonable since sea bottoms are not as reflective as white lead, and, as we have observed, the shades of color most similar to those of the true ocean floors disappear at less than half the depth.

~~~~~~~~~~~~~~~~~~~~

John Tyndall:

18.   *OCEANIC DISTILLATION**

The sun, you know, is never exactly overhead in England. But at the equator, and within certain limits north and south of it, the sun at certain periods of the year is directly overhead at noon. These limits are called the Tropics of Cancer and of Capricorn. Upon the belt comprised between these two circles the sun's rays fall with their mightiest power; for here they shoot directly downwards, and heat both earth and sea more than when they strike slantingly.

When the vertical sunbeams strike the land they heat it, and the air in contact with the hot soil becomes heated in turn. But when heated the air expands, and when it expands it becomes lighter. This lighter air rises, like wool plunged into water, through the heavier air overhead.

When the sunbeams fall upon the sea the water is warmed, though not so much as the land. The warmed water expands, becomes thereby lighter, and therefore continues to float upon the

* From John Tyndall. THE FORMS OF WATER, D. Appleton & Co., 1872, New York.

John Tyndall, born in Ireland in 1820, was a physicist whose chief researches were in the fields of light, sound, and radiant heat. He died in 1893.

top. This upper layer of water warms to some extent the air in contact with it, but it also sends up a quantity of aqueous vapour, which being far lighter than air, helps the latter to rise. Thus both from the land and from the sea we have ascending currents established by the action of the sun.

When they reach a certain elevation in the atmosphere, these currents divide and flow, part towards the north and part towards the south: while from the north and the south a flow of heavier and colder air sets in to supply the place of the ascending warm air.

Incessant circulation is thus established in the atmosphere. The equatorial air and vapour flow above toward the north and south poles, while the polar air flows below towards the equator. The two currents of air thus established are called the upper and the lower trade winds.

But before the air returns from the poles great changes have occurred. For the air as it quitted the equatorial regions was laden with aqueous vapour, which could not subsist in the cold polar regions. It is there precipitated, falling sometimes as rain, or more commonly as snow. The land near the pole is covered with this snow, which gives birth to vast glaciers in a manner hereafter to be explained.

It is necessary that you should have a perfectly clear view of this process, for great mistakes have been made regarding the manner in which glaciers are related to the heat of the sun.

It was supposed that if the sun's heat were diminished, greater glaciers than those now existing would be produced. But the lessening of the sun's heat would infallibly diminish the quantity of aqueous vapour, and thus cut off the glaciers at their source. A brief illustration will complete your knowledge here.

In the process of ordinary distillation, the liquid to be distilled is heated and converted into vapour in one vessel, and chilled and reconverted into liquid in another. What has just been stated renders it plain that the earth and its atmosphere constitute a vast distilling apparatus in which the equatorial ocean plays the part of the boiler, and the chill regions of the poles the part of the condenser. In this process of distillation *heat* plays quite as necessary a part as *cold*, and before Bishop Heber could speak of "Greenland's icy mountains," the equatorial ocean had to be warmed by the sun.

~~~~~~~~~~~

Thomas H. Huxley:

19.   *THE PROBLEMS OF THE DEEP SEA* *

Thus, though it is true that sea-water steadily contracts as it cools down to its freezing point, instead of expanding before it reaches its freezing point as fresh water does, the truth has been steadily ignored by even the highest authorities in physical geography, and the erroneous conclusions deduced from their erroneous premises have been widely accepted as if they were ascertained facts. Of course, if sea-water, like fresh water, were heaviest at a temperature of 39° F. and got lighter as it approached 32° F., the water of the bottom of the deep sea could not be colder than 39°. But one of the first results of the careful ascertainment of the temperature at different depths, by means of thermometers specially contrived for the avoidance of the errors produced by pressure, was the proof that, below 1000 fathoms in the Atlantic, down to the greatest depths yet sounded, the water has a temperature always lower than 38° Fahr., whatever be the temperature of the water at the surface. And that this low temperature of the deepest water is probably the universal rule for the depths of the open ocean is shown, among others, by Captain Chimmo's recent observations in the Indian ocean, between Ceylon and Sumatra; where, the surface water ranging from 85°—81° Fahr., the temperature at the bottom, at a depth of 2270 to 2656 fathoms, was only from 34° to 32° Fahr.

As the mean temperature of the superficial layer of the crust of the earth may be taken at about 50° Fahr., it follows that the bottom layer of the deep sea in temperate and hot latitudes, is, on the average, much colder than either of the bodies with which it is in contact; for the temperature of the earth is constant, while that of the air rarely falls so low as that of the bottom water in the latitudes in question; and even when it does, has time to affect

* From Thomas H. Huxley, DISCOURSES: *Biological and Geological Essays,* D. Appleton & Co., New York and London, 1895.

Thomas Henry Huxley, 1825–95, was an English biologist and an exponent of Darwinism. He was the grandfather of Julian and Aldous Huxley.

only a comparatively thin stratum of the surface water before the return of warm weather.

How does this apparently anomalous state of things come about? If we suppose the globe to be covered with a universal ocean, it can hardly be doubted that the cold of the regions towards the poles must tend to cause the superficial water of those regions to contract and become specifically heavier. Under these circumstances, it would have no alternative but to descend and spread over the sea bottom, while its place would be taken by warmer water drawn from the adjacent regions. Thus, deep, cold, polar-equatorial currents, and superficial, warmer, equatorial-polar currents, would be set up; and as the former would have a less velocity of rotation from west to east than the regions towards which they travel, they would not be due southerly or northerly currents, but south-westerly in the northern hemisphere, and north-westerly in the southern; while, by a parity of reasoning, the equatorial-polar warm currents would be north-easterly in the northern hemisphere, and south-easterly in the southern. Hence, as a north-easterly current has the same direction as a south-westerly wind, the direction of the northern equatorial-polar current in the extra-tropical part of its course would pretty nearly coincide with that of the anti-trade winds. The freezing of the surface of the polar sea would not interfere with the movement thus set up. For, however bad a conductor of heat ice may be, the unfrozen sea-water immediately in contact with the undersurface of the ice must needs be colder than that further off; and hence will constantly tend to descend through the subjacent warmer water.

In this way, it would seem inevitable that the surface waters of the northern and southern frigid zones must, sooner or later, find their way to the bottom of the rest of the ocean; and there accumulate to a thickness dependent on the rate at which they absorb heat from the crust of the earth below, and from the surface water above.

If this hypothesis be correct, it follows that, if any part of the ocean in warm latitudes is shut off from the influence of the cold polar underflow, the temperature of its deeps should be less cold than the temperature of corresponding depths in the open sea. Now, in the Mediterranean, Nature offers a remarkable experimental proof of just the kind needed. It is a landlocked sea which runs nearly east and west, between the twenty-ninth and forty-fifth parallels of north latitude. Roughly speaking, the average temperature of the air over it is 75° Fahr. in July and 48° in January.

This great expanse of water is divided by the peninsula of Italy (including Sicily), continuous with which is a submarine elevation carrying less than 1,200 feet of water, which extends from Sicily to Cape Bon in Africa, into two great pools—an eastern and a western. The eastern pool rapidly deepens to more than 12,000 feet, and sends off to the north its comparatively shallow branches, the Adriatic and the Ægean Seas. The western pool is less deep, though it reaches some 10,000 feet. And, just as the western end of the eastern pool communicates by a shallow passage, not a sixth of its greatest depth, with the western pool, so the western pool is separated from the Atlantic by a ridge which runs between Capes Trafalgar and Spartel, on which there is hardly 1,000 feet of water. All the water of the Mediterranean which lies deeper than about 150 fathoms, therefore, is shut off from that of the Atlantic, and there is no communication between the cold layer of the Atlantic (below 1,000 fathoms) and the Mediterranean. Under these circumstances, what is the temperature of the Mediterranean? Everywhere below 600 feet it is about 55° Fahr.; and consequently, at its greatest depths, it is some 20° warmer than the corresponding depths of the Atlantic.

It seems extremely difficult to account for this difference in any other way, than by adopting the views so strongly and ably advocated by Dr. Carpenter, that, in the existing distribution of land and water, such a circulation of the water of the ocean does actually occur, as theoretically must occur, in the universal ocean, with which we started.

It is quite another question, however, whether this theoretic circulation, true cause as it may be, is competent to give rise to such movements of sea-water, in mass, as those currents, which have commonly been regarded as northern extensions of the Gulf-stream. I shall not venture to touch upon this complicated problem; but I may take occasion to remark that the cause of a much simpler phenomenon—the stream of Atlantic water which sets through the Straits of Gibraltar, eastward, at the rate of two or three miles an hour or more, does not seem to be so clearly made out as is desirable.

The facts appear to be that the water of the Mediterranean is very slightly denser than that of the Atlantic (1·0278 to 1·0265), and that the deep water of the Mediterranean is slightly denser than that of the surface; while the deep water of the Atlantic is, if anything, lighter than that of the surface. Moreover, while a rapid superficial current is setting in (always, save in exceptionally violent easterly winds) through the Straits of Gibraltar, from the Atlantic to the Mediterranean, a deep undercurrent (together with variable side currents) is setting out through the Straits, from the Mediterranean to the Atlantic.

Dr. Carpenter adopts, without hesitation, the view that the cause of this indraught of Atlantic water is to be sought in the much more rapid evaporation which takes place from the surface of the Mediterranean than from that of the Atlantic; and thus, by lowering the level of the former, gives rise to an indraught from the latter.

But is there any sound foundation for the three assumptions involved here? Firstly, that the evaporation from the Mediterranean, as a whole, is much greater than that from the Atlantic under corresponding parallels; secondly, that the rainfall over the Mediterranean makes up for evaporation less than it does over the Atlantic; and thirdly, supposing these two questions answered affirmatively: Are not these sources of loss in the Mediterranean fully covered by the prodigious quantity of fresh water which is poured into it by great rivers and submarine springs? Consider that the water of the Ebro, the Rhine, the Po, the Danube, the Don, the Dnieper, and the Nile, all flow directly or indirectly into the Mediterranean; that the volume of fresh water which they pour into it is so enormous that fresh water may sometimes be baled up from the surface of the sea off the Delta of the Nile, while the land is not yet in sight; that the water of the Black Sea is half fresh, and that a current of three or four miles an hour constantly streams from it Mediterraneanwards through the Bosphorus;—consider, in addition, that no fewer than ten submarine springs of fresh water are known to burst up in the Mediterranean, some of them so large that Admiral Smyth calls them "subterranean rivers of amazing volume and force"; and it would seem, on the face of the matter, that the sun must have enough to do to keep the level of the Mediterranean down; and that, possibly, we may have to seek for the cause of the small superiority in saline contents of the Mediterranean water in some condition other than solar evaporation.

Louis Agassiz, Alexander Agassiz:

20. THE ORGANIZATION AND PROGRESS OF
THE ANDERSON SCHOOL OF NATURAL
HISTORY: Report of the Trustees for 1873*

REPORT

On the 14th of December, 1872, Professor [Louis] Agassiz printed
the accompanying circular:—

MUSEUM OF COMPARATIVE ZOÖLOGY, CAMBRIDGE, MASS.,

December 14, 1872.

*Programme of a Course of Instruction in Natural History, to
be delivered by the Seaside, in Nantucket, during the Summer
Months, chiefly designed for Teachers who propose to introduce
the Study into their Schools, and for Students preparing to
become Teachers.*

Zoölogy in general, and Embryology of the Vertebrates, by L.
AGASSIZ, Director of the Museum.

The Extinct Animals of Past Ages, compared with those now living,
and the Methods of identifying them, by N. S. SHALER, Professor
of Palæontology in the Lawrence Scientific School.

Comparative Anatomy and Physiology of the Vertebrates, by DR. B.
G. WILDER, Professor of Anatomy and Physiology in Cornell University, Ithaca, N.Y.

The Animals and Plants living in Deep Waters, and the peculiar
Conditions of their Existence, by L. F. DE POURTALÈS, Assistant
in the United States Coast Survey.

---

* From: *The Organization and Progress of the Anderson School of Natural
History at Penikese Island*, Welch, Bigelow, and Company, University Press,
1874. The Report was written by the Trustees for 1873: Louis Agassiz (President
and Director), Thomas G. Cary, of Cambridge, (Treasurer), Alexander Agassiz,
of Cambridge, Martin Brimmer, of Boston, Theodore Lyman, of Brookline.

While Louis Agassiz spent most of his career teaching (at Harvard) and
training a generation of scientists, his son Alexander participated in extensive
oceanographic expeditions to the West Indies, Hawaii, Australia and the west
coast of South America, later publishing his findings in a number of books.

Embryology of the Radiates, by A. AGASSIZ, Assistant in the Museum of Comparative Zoölogy.

Natural History and Embryology of the Mollusks, by. . . .

How to make Biological Collections to illustrate the History of Insects injurious to Vegetation, by DR. H. A. HAGEN, Professor of Entomology in Harvard University.

Natural History and Embryology of the Articulates, by DR. A. S. PACKARD, Professor of Entomology in the Massachusetts Agricultural College.

Natural History of the Fishes and Reptiles, by F. W. PUTNAM, General Secretary of the American Association for the Advancement of Science.

Natural History of Birds and Mammals, by J. A. ALLEN, Assistant in the Museum of Comparative Zoölogy.

On Breeding, and Nests and Eggs of Birds, by. . . .

Practical Exercises in the Use of the Microscope, by. . . .

Instruction in Drawing and Painting of Animals, by PAULUS ROETTER, Artist in the Museum of Comparative Zoölogy.

On Fisheries and their Management, by PROFESSOR SPENCER F. BAIRD, Assistant Secretary of the Smithsonian Institution.

On Fish Breeding, by THEODORE LYMAN, Assistant in the Museum of Comparative Zoölogy.

The Faunæ of the North Atlantic, compared with one another, and with those of other Parts of the World, by. . . .

The Plants of the Sea, by. . . .

The Physics of the Sea, by. . . .

Physical Hydrography, by PROFESSOR W. MITCHELL, Assistant in the United States Coast Survey.

Chemistry of Feeding and Breathing, by PROFESSOR W. GIBBS, Rumford Professor of Physics in Harvard University.

Chemistry of the Sea and Air, by PROFESSOR JAMES CRAFTS, Professor of Chemistry in the Technological Institute in Boston.

The terms of admission, and the day of opening the course, will be advertised as soon as all the necessary arrangements in Nantucket can be made, including information concerning board, etc. A number of aquariums and the necessary apparatus to dredge in deep water will be provided. The Superintendent of the United States Coast Survey and the United States Commissioner of Fisheries have promised their co-operation to the extent of their ability, without interfering with the regular service of their departments. PROFESSORS SHALER, WILDER, PACKARD, and PUTNAM, and perhaps others, may spend the whole, or nearly the whole, season in Nantucket, with a view to superintend the laboratory work, while the other gentlemen will stay there only part of the time, or as long as required by the share they are able to take in the course of instruction.

In behalf of the Faculty of the Museum of
Comparative Zoölogy in Cambridge, Mass.,

L. AGASSIZ.

This plan was subsequently referred to by Professor Agassiz in his appeal to the Legislature for State aid. His remarks were extensively circulated in the daily papers, and met the eye of Mr. Anderson, who at once telegraphed to Professor Agassiz to take no further steps in the matter till he had heard from him. A few days afterwards his friend Mr. W. Girod came to Cambridge, bringing a letter to Professor Agassiz, in which Mr. Anderson formally offered him the island of Penikese as a site for the proposed Summer School of Natural History.

A few days later Mr. Anderson, with characteristic liberality, met some of the practical difficulties of the organization by an endowment of fifty thousand dollars for the equipment and running expenses of the School.

The following extracts from a circular issued by Professor Agassiz, and from his address to the students on the opening day, will show his views regarding the organization and purposes of the School. We quote from the circular:—

"I must make hard work a condition of a continued connection with the School, and desire particularly to impress it upon the applicants for admission that Penikese Island is not to be regarded as a place of summer resort for relaxation. I do not propose to give much instruction in matters which may be learned from books. I want, on the contrary, to prepare those who shall attend and *observe for themselves.* I would therefore advise all those who wish only to be taught natural history in the way in which it is generally taught, by recitations, to give up their intention of joining the School."

In his address Professor Agassiz said:—

"Our object is to study nature, and I hope I may lead you in this enterprise so that you may learn to read for yourselves. We should make nature our text-book; whenever we read books we are removed from the things we could be better acquainted with; instead of the things themselves we appropriate the interpretation of some one else; and, however correctly we may have done this, we invariably return to the study of the things themselves, whenever we wish to make real progress; and I hope to live long enough to make text-books useless and hateful, without even implying a reflection upon the services text-books may have rendered in past times. . . . . From the method of teaching adopted, only a limited number of pupils could be received, and the advantages you enjoy to-day have given you greater facilities for work, better appliances than I had myself, not merely when commencing my career, but when making some of my most important investigations."

The applications for admission have been considered in accordance with the annexed circular:—

MUSEUM OF COMPARATIVE ZOÖLOGY, CAMBRIDGE, MASS.

The applications for admission to the ANDERSON SCHOOL OF NATURAL HISTORY are so numerous, that it has been decided that the successful pupils of a preceding year should have the first claim to admission the following season; next, the principals and professors of colleges and of high and normal schools; next, teachers in other public institutions; and, finally, teachers in private schools. Beginners cannot be admitted until after the applications of these several classes of pupils have been met. You are therefore requested to send me your claims to admission, before an answer to your application can be given.

Respectfully yours,
L. AGASSIZ.

In spite of the difficulties attending such a novel undertaking, Professor Agassiz decided if possible to open the School in 1873. Nothing could of course be done till the spring was sufficiently advanced, but in the mean time he made his plans for the summer campaign. The island was formally presented to him, on the 22d of April, by the representative of Mr. John Anderson, Mr. Girod. On the 20th of the same month Count Pourtalès, with the architect, Mr. R. H. Slack, visited the island, selected a suitable site for the buildings, and arranged a general plan. The plans were at once completed, and by the 16th of May the contract was made for the buildings. On the 28th of May the timber arrived from Maine in New Bedford. There the building was framed. On the 5th of

June the first cargo reached Penikese, and the first building was raised on the 14th of June. Before the 8th of July, that is, in little more than three weeks from the day it was raised, not only must this building be ready for the reception of fifty persons, but it must include the possibility of laboratories, where the work of students and professors could be carried on. The architect, the carpenters, indeed all experts connected with the undertaking, declared the thing impracticable, and friends advised the postponement of the opening, if not the renunciation of the scheme, for that year. Professor Agassiz was inflexible. He felt, perhaps, that for him at least that year was the only year. A commencement was actually made on the appointed day; and, whatever the difficulties and privations, they were met both by professors and pupils with the utmost cheerfulness and good-humor.

During the summer the second building, with the connecting lecture-room, was nearly completed, and the interior arrangements of the buildings already erected were completed. At the time of writing this Report but little remained to be done to complete the proposed equipment of the School.

The plates accompanying this Report need no special explanation. They give, 1. A general view of the buildings; 2. The geographical position of Penikese in Buzzard's Bay; 3. A plan of the island; 4, 5. Plans of the work-rooms and dormitories.

During the first session (1873) Professor Agassiz lectured nearly every day. His principal topics were the Glaciers, Methods of studying Natural History, Radiates, and General Embryology.

The yacht *Sprite*, the donation of C. W. Galloupe, Esq., of Boston, was sent to Penikese Island at his own expense, and turned over to Count Pourtalès at New Bedford on the 7th of July, who kindly took charge of the dredging parties during the whole session. In accordance with an arrangement between Professor Agassiz and the Superintendent of the United States Coast Survey, the crew were mustered into the United States service, and the dredging outfit was supplied by the Coast Survey. During the session of the Anderson School the yacht took out daily, weather permitting, from eight to ten of the pupils on a dredging excursion, giving them thus instruction in the use of the implements, and at the same time obtaining a variety of specimens for study which could not be procured from the shore. On account of the lectures generally, delivered in the morning and evening, the excursions could not be extended far from the island, and were chiefly made in the space between Penikese Island and the light-ships on the Sow and Pigs, and Hen and Chicken Reefs. After the close of the school session the *Sprite* went to Casco Bay, by direction of Professor Agassiz, to obtain specimens in large numbers for the use of the students, particularly of Brachiopods and of such Echinoderms as could not be procured in Buzzard's Bay. Whilst in Casco Bay she was in charge of Mr. S. W. Garman, assisted by Mr. J. F. Hooper, and very good collections were obtained.

The services of Captain R. Delano, as sailing-master, contributed much to the success of the work.

Dr. A. S. Packard, Jr., remained on the island for five weeks. During that time he delivered fifteen lectures on Articulates, and superintended the laboratory work of his department. He also took charge of several dredging parties. Mr. Bicknell superintended the microscopic work of the students. Professor Jordan assisted those who devoted themselves to marine algae. Messrs. Hawkins and Roetter gave instruction in Natural-History Drawing.

Dr. Brewer delivered three lectures upon Birds. Professor Guyot gave a short course on Physical Geography with special reference to climatology as related to organic life and to the individual features of the great geographical regions.

Professor Wilder passed the whole session on the island, and took special charge of the instruction in Vertebrates. He delivered over twenty lectures, illustrated by a large series of diagrams brought by him from Cornell University.

Dr. Nichols kindly took charge of the business of the School. Mr. Garman undertook the general care of the laboratories.

The Smithsonian Institution, Mr. Thomas G. Appleton, Messrs. Scribner & Co., as well as several of the teachers, have presented a number of books to the School. It would be very desirable to have a library of reference at Penikese. The difficulty, however, of keeping the books on the island in good condition during the winter must limit the library to the most necessary works.

It is, of course, too early to speculate upon the effect of the advantages to be derived from the Anderson School. That its privileges are fully appreciated by those who have enjoyed them for one season is shown by the fact that the majority have applied for readmission. Indeed, it meets a demand which must be very urgent, as there are no less than ninety applications beyond the capacity of the School. With the general introduction of instruction in science into our common schools, the demand for well-qualified teachers has become very great. The summer is the only time of the year during which teachers can avail themselves of the oppor-tunity they have for the practical study of natural history. At first, of course, their whole time must be devoted to a thorough mastery of what they will be called upon to teach, and to making small collections to illustrate their own lessons. But it is not too much to hope that after a time the more advanced students at Penikese, having advantages which few naturalists have enjoyed during the days of their apprenticeship, may be able to enter upon original investigations, to carry them on from year to year, and make eventually valuable contributions to science.

After the death of Professor Agassiz the accompanying circular was sent to the superintendents of public instruction of the several States, with the hope of obtaining their co-operation in carrying on the School:—

ANDERSON SCHOOL OF NATURAL HISTORY AT PENIKESE ISLAND,
CAMBRIDGE, MASS., JANUARY 15, 1874.

DEAR SIR,—The School for Natural History established by Professor Agassiz upon the island of Penikese, presented to him for that purpose by Mr. John Anderson of New York, has been in operation one summer. During this first session instruction has been given in various branches of natural history, in geology, in physical geography, and especially in zoölogy. The class of students was composed of applicants from various States, and included seventeen female teachers and twenty-six male teachers from the public schools of Maine, New Hampshire, Massachusetts, New York, New Jersey, Pennsylvania, Ohio, Indiana, Illinois, Wisconsin, and Missouri. These teachers are now scattered throughout the country, and are engaged in teaching natural history as a part of their regular duty. Their letters, constantly received by Professor Agassiz, since the opening of the School terms, show how strong and beneficial a stimulus our public education has already received through this institution.

For the session of 1874 the applications exceed by some forty or fifty* the accommodations provided on the island. Twenty female teachers and twenty-six male teachers, gathered from thirteen States, will receive instruction at the Anderson School during the coming summer; a part of these are students of the last session, a certain proportion of room being reserved for those who could most profitably pursue a second annual course.

To organize the School, in the first instance, Professor Agassiz drew largely upon the fund given by Mr. Anderson. His own failing health warned him that his time was short, and he felt the importance of establishing the School on a broad and com-

* At the time the circular was issued.

prehensive basis before he left it. For this reason he gave the institution at once the proportions he meant it to retain, and provided simple but ample accommodations, both scientific and personal, for professors and students. The buildings consist of dormitories and laboratories for the use of fifty students, with the necessary lecture-room, dining-room and kitchen, the accommodations for the professors being found in Mr. Anderson's former house. All the economy consistent with permanence and solidity of structure has been exercised in this first outlay, and yet the time will soon come when the School must close, not only from the impossibility of paying the professors, but also for want of means to meet the necessary expenses of an institution which can only be partially self-supporting.

The peculiar relations existing between the younger naturalists of the country and the late Director of the School enabled him to secure not only their good-will, but also their grateful, efficient, and gratuitous services. He has gone from among us; and while I have no doubt that the same spirit will animate his former associates, if the occasion require it, yet I feel that it would be unfair to ask further sacrifices from those who have so nobly done their share in initiating the enterprise.

This School, so successfully conducted for one session, has not only exercised already a powerful influence in America, but is recognized abroad wherever an interest is felt in the progress of culture as an original and very valuable experiment in education. Even the seaside laboratories, lately established or projected in Europe, have never aimed at the vital and wide-spread connection with the education of the people which lies at the very foundation of the Anderson School. Institutions of the kind, so far as they have existed hitherto, have been intended for the professional few. This is intended to teach the children, throughout the length and breadth of the land, how to study nature. It meets also a demand already felt. All who know anything of our public, normal, and training schools say that there is a very earnest and general desire to introduce a larger, more liberal, and above all a more natural method of instruction in the different branches of natural history, but that the teachers are wanting. The Anderson School is simply a normal school for the preparation of such teachers, with all the necessary outfit of buildings, apparatus, aquariums, ready to our hand. In fact, nowhere else can such opportunities be found for a cheap and thorough training in natural history.

Under these circumstances I have no hesitation in appealing to you for aid in obtaining a permanent endowment for its support.

The expenses of the School will always be kept down to a minimum, the rate of board and some other items depending mainly upon the students themselves. But the professors must be paid, and certain provision for transportation, necessary waste of material, etc., etc., must be made. For this object I ask your co-operation in obtaining from the Legislature of your State, or from other means at the disposal of your State Board of Education, a moderate appropriation, say, of five thousand dollars, or an annual grant of three hundred and fifty dollars, as a contribution towards the permanent support of the Anderson School. Every such share would entitle your State to the admission of two teachers annually as students at Penikese, the teachers to be selected for their aptitude in natural history in such a manner as you think best. Considering the scarcity of efficient teachers in natural history, it would certainly be an economy to obtain for so small a sum the privilege of training in this manner the teachers already in your employ.

Hoping you will give the matter your cordial consideration,

I remain, very respectfully yours,

ALEX. AGASSIZ,
Director of the Anderson School.

ADDENDUM

The Report for 1873 of the Anderson School was the only one ever published, and there is nothing else relating to it. It was closed after the second session and has left no successor nor representatives.

A. AGASSIZ
November 20, 1879

~~~~~~~~~~~~~~~~~~

John Murray:

21.   ON OCEANIC DEPOSITS AND NODULES*

Valparaiso, Chili,
  9th December, 1875.

> 1. *Preliminary Report on Specimens of the Sea-bottoms ob-
> tained in the Soundings, Dredgings, and Trawlings of H.M.S.
> 'Challenger,' in the years 1873–75, between England and Val-
> paraiso.*

Method of Work.—During the first six months of the expedition
the sounding-apparatus in use on board was provided with a very
narrow cylinder, which brought up only a very small quantity of the
bottom.

In July 1873 Capt. Nares had a much larger cylinder fitted to the
instrument, one with a 2-inch bore; and later on he caused the
weights to be so arranged with respect to the cylinder that the latter
projected some 18 inches beneath the former.

This arrangement, the cylinder of which is always provided with
the common butterfly-valve, usually gives us a very large quantity of
the bottom in each sounding. Sometimes the tube has been forced
fully 18 inches into the bottom, and has brought up frequently
as much as a quart of the ooze, mud, or clay. When the tube
arrives on board the contents are carefully removed, and the colour,
extent, and arrangement of the section is noted. A portion is washed
several times in distilled water and dried, a portion is submitted
to a rough analysis, and the remainder, if any, is preserved in
spirit.

The analysis consists in determining so far as possible:—

---

* From Proceedings of the Royal Society 1876. "Preliminary Reports to
Professor WYVILLE THOMSON, F.R.S., Director of the Civilian Scientific Staff,
on Work done on board the 'Challenger.'" By JOHN MURRAY, Esq., Naturalist
to the Expedition. (Published by permission of the Lords of the Admiralty.)
Received Feb. 14, 1876. Read March 16, 1876.

Sir John Murray, 1841–1914, was a Canadian born oceanographer and marine
naturalist who devised an apparatus for sounding and registering the temperature
of great depths.

1. The kinds of organisms present, and their relative abundance, whether carbonate of lime or siliceous, and whether alive or dead.

2. The kind and quantity of amorphous and mineral matter, and its ratio to the remains of the above organisms.

This is accomplished by decanting the finer from the coarser particles, and examining each with the microscope. When carbonate of lime is present this is removed by weak acid, and the specimen is again examined. When manganese is present in great quantity this is removed by strong hydrochloric acid, and again an examination is made. Very frequently portions of the upper layers are placed in colouring solutions (as carmine, magenta, &c.), for the purpose of rendering more distinct any organized material, should any be present.

When the dredge or trawl brings up mud, a considerable quantity is preserved for future work, and what remains is carefully sifted. The siftings are examined and preserved.

Lately it has been the custom to send down tow-nets loosely attached to the trawl or dredge and at the weights in front of the trawl. These often bring up specimens of the bottom when the trawl fails to do so. As these nets do not probably sink deep into the ooze, they give us a surer idea of the nature of the surface-layers than previously obtained by the trawl alone.

Red and Grey Clays.—By far the most abundant oceanic deposits are the deep-sea clays. These are of a grey, red, or dark chocolate-colour, and are found at depths greater than 2000 fathoms. The red and chocolate-colours of many of these clays is due to the presence of the oxide of iron in the first and of oxide of manganese in the latter instance. Most of them contain some carbonate of lime in the form of *Globigerina*-shells; in one or two instances, however, I have not been able to find a single shell, nor has acid caused the least bubble of effervescence. The remains of siliceous organisms occur also in great numbers in the clays of some regions—so much so that, as I have stated, some of those soundings in the North-west Pacific which have been classed as clays might have been called Radiolarian ooze. In most places, however, they are nearly or quite absent. These clays are not amorphous in the true sense of the word —not amorphous in the sense in which a chemical precipitate is amorphous. They all contain small white and other coloured mineral particles in great abundance—exceedingly small particles, so as to be recognized only under the high powers of the microscope. They contain amorphous matter, it is true; but it is doubtful if this ever makes up so much as a half of any sample in bulk. They also contain larger mineral particles, as quartz, mica, pumice, scoria, peroxide of manganese, and other mineral particles. Quartz and mica particles appear to be present only in some localities, as the North Atlantic and elsewhere. Peroxide of manganese is perhaps always present in the form of grains or nodules, sparingly distributed in some regions, in others making up nearly a half of the deposit or formation.

Pumice (the common felspathic or the highly vesicular augitic variety) and scoria appear to be universally distributed over the bottom of the ocean, and to be abundant in most of the deep-sea clays and present in them all. In those clays furthest from continents and islands sharks' teeth, ear-bones of whales, other bones of whales, and bones of turtles (?) are very frequently found, all these having usually a more or less thick coating of peroxide of manganese.

Globigerina-ooze.—After the deep-sea clays, this is the most abundant deep-sea deposit. It has occurred at all depths from 250 fathoms to 2900 fathoms. The *Globigerinæ*, which give at once the name and the chief characteristic to this deposit, are really found all over the bottom of the ocean. Even in our deepest clays, if the surface-layers be selected and all the amorphous matter be washed away, one or two shells of some variety of pelagic Foraminifera can usually be detected. By pursuing this method I have only failed on one or two occasions. They appear to be quite absent in the Arafura Sea. It is, however, when they occur in vast numbers that they form the deposit known by this name; at least such is the sense in which it is here used.

We did not find a *Globigerina-*ooze in any of the enclosed seas, in the Southern Ocean south of lat. 50° S., nor in the North Pacific north of lat. 10° N.

In the Southern Ocean only one small species of *Globigerina* was found in the surface-waters; but in the North Pacific many varieties of pelagic Foraminifera abound near the surface of the ocean.

In other parts of the preceding oceans, and in the other oceans we have visited, it occurs in irregular patches, being always present in the open ocean when we have depths of less than 1800 fathoms. Its presence or absence at depths beyond 1800 fathoms is, however, determined by conditions at present unknown. A number of varieties occur both as to colour and composition. Some specimens are nearly pure white, others have a rose-colour, and others are red or dark brown. The red and brown colour arises from the presence of the oxides of iron and manganese. In the white varieties the sediment, after dissolving away the carbonate of lime, is in some specimens abundant, in others not abundant, and is either of a red or slate-blue colour. We find the former colour to prevail in those soundings far from continents and large islands, and the sediment is not abundant except where pumice or scoria is present. The latter, or slate-blue colour, is found in those soundings more or less near continents and large islands; and it is suspected that this sediment has its source chiefly from the disintegration of these adjacent lands.

Mica, quartz, pumice, scoria, and other mineral particles are met with; but in those soundings furthest from land a little piece of pumice or scoria may be the only trace of mineral particles.

In some specimens there are very many remains of organisms with siliceous shells, as Radiolaria, Diatoms, and Challengerias; but in others these remains are almost entirely wanting. In three soundings in mid-Atlantic between the Canary and Virgin Islands, and in several soundings in the South Pacific, manganese in the forms of grains and nodular concretions is very abundant. As a rule, however, this substance occurs rather sparingly in *Globigerina*-ooze. In some instances we get little nodules of these bottoms, the shells as it were being run together by a siliceous cement. Many small pieces of cherty-like mineral also occur, which are angular and soft, and do not look as if they had been transported. Manganese nodules occurring in the *Globigerina*-ooze have often a nucleus of a yellow and green colour, in which *Globigerina*-shells can be seen; but their carbonate of lime has been entirely removed, and replaced by a silicate.

Diatomaceous Ooze.—South of the latitude of the Crozets, on our southern trip, we found Diatoms abundant, both in the surface-waters and in the bottom.

About the Crozets, Kerguelen, M'Donald's Islands, and close to the ice-barrier, the frustules of these organisms were very abundant in the soundings, but were masked by much land-débris. Between the parallels of 53° and 63° S., *i.e.* between the north edge of the ice and the latitude of M'Donald's Islands, we got in three soundings a pale straw-coloured deposit, composed principally of the frustules of Diatoms and their broken-down parts. In addition, they contained a good many Radiolarian remains, a few specimens of one small species of *Globigerina*, a few particles of mica, quartz, and granitic pebbles, also a little amorphous blue clayey matter. No manganese particles were noticed. The one of these soundings which is nearest to the ice contains much amorphous clayey matter and larger mineral particles than the other two. When dried this deposit is of a white colour, and is very light.

Radiolarian Ooze.—Organisms with the siliceous skeletons abound in the surface-waters, and apparently also in the deepest waters, of all the oceans and seas we have visited.[1] The skeletons of these organisms are found in all, or almost all, the sea-bottoms. Even in those cases where at first sight they would seem to be quite absent, a more careful examination (by dissolving away a large quantity of carbonate of lime where this exists, and examining the sediment by careful washing in the case of clays, &c.) will usually reveal a Radiolarian skeleton, a Diatom frustule, or broken portions of these.

It is, however, only in some limited areas that these exuviæ rise into such prominence as to be characteristic of the deposit taking place. Such is the case in the Antarctic, where we have a Diatom-ooze, and in the Western and Middle Pacific, where we have the above deposit.

Our deepest sounding (4475 fathoms or 4575) was a Radiolarian ooze; with the exception of a little amorphous matter, manganese particles, a few yellow cherty-like particles, and some pumice pieces, this bottom was entirely composed of the exuviæ of organisms with siliceous skeletons—as Radiolaria, one or two Diatoms, and some organisms which seem to be undescribed (Challengerias), but which are numerous in the deeper waters of the Pacific (see notes on surface animals, p. 536).

A section of about 3 inches came up. The upper two were of a red colour, due to the presence of much manganese; the lower one was a pale straw-colour, and contained relatively few manganese grains.

In our trip from the Sandwich Islands to the Society Islands we again met with Radiolarian ooze. Between 7° and 12° north of the equator we came on a patch represented by four soundings, some of these containing not a single *Globigerina;* then just on the equator, in two soundings, one at a depth of 2925 fathoms, we got a *Globigerina*-ooze containing a good many Radiolaria. Between 2° and 10° south we again had a patch of Radiolarian ooze represented by three soundings, and containing only a few pelagic Foraminifera or their broken parts. The occurrence of this patch of *Globigerina*-ooze in the position indicated (see map, Plate 20),

---

[1] They are, however, much more numerous in the Pacific than in the Atlantic, especially in the equatorial waters.

and the comparative or total absence of the *Globigerina*-shells in the deposits a little to the north and south of it, is sufficiently curious and significant. It will be well to note that, in the *Globigerina*-patch, manganese and other mineral particles are much less abundant than in the adjacent Radiolarian. Note also the presence of the south equatorial current and the dip of some isotherms over the *Globigerina*-patch. One or two soundings to the east of Japan might have been classed under this head; but in them the siliceous remains do not make up over one third of the sample in bulk. Generally it may be said that in the Western and Middle Pacific the siliceous remains of Radiolaria and Diatoms are abundant in the deposits, whereas in the South Pacific and Atlantic they are much less so, or absent in the bottoms.

The Manganese in Deposits.

The peroxide of manganese, in the form of minute grains, concretions, nodules, aggregations, or incrustations, occurs widely distributed in ocean-deposits. It has been met with most frequently in the deep-sea clays; indeed it seems to be present in all of them, sparingly in some localities, abundantly in others.

It is, however, not confined to these clays; it has been found in most of the other deposits and at all depths greater than 500 fathoms. In the *Globigerina*- and Radiolarian ooze and in the clays it usually assumes the forms of minute grains, pellets, and nodules. In those bottoms to which it gives a chocolate-colour, the higher powers of the microscope show small, round, red-brown grains of manganese, often with a dark spot in the centre.

The nodules vary from little pellets to masses of a large size and of several pounds in weight. In some regions every thing at the bottom, even the bottom itself, would appear to be overlaid by and impregnated with this substance. In the foregoing list, as at No. 318 and elsewhere, some of the nodules have been described with a little detail. The varieties which are most commonly procured may be here mentioned:—

Nodules of a black-brown colour throughout, the manganese being laid down in concentric layers, which are evident from their enclosing lines of red clay.

Nodules having a nucleus of pumice which is surrounded by concentric layers, the original nucleus being often very deeply impregnated by spider-like ramifications of the manganese, or nearly the whole pumice may be replaced by manganese. When pieces of bone have formed the nucleus we have much the same state of things. The compact bone of the tympanics of cetaceans does not, however, appear to alter so rapidly as other bone; and hence it may be that we get ear-bones in such great numbers.

Sharks' teeth of all sizes (one was 4 inches across the base) are frequent, and are sometimes surrounded by concentric layers of nearly an inch in thickness. A siliceous sponge (*Farrea*) was found imbedded in two inches.

A mass of red clay may occupy the centre of the nodule. The nucleus is occasionally a mottled yellow-and-green substance, with agate bands in some parts, and *Globigerina*, the carbonate of lime being replaced by silicate in these last. This nucleus can be cut with a knife, like new cheese, or it is hard and brittle, breaking with a conchoidal fracture.

Large flat aggregations occur which seem to have been formed on hardened flat portions of the bottom.

The *Globigerina*-shells and Radiolaria are at times covered by small specks of the manganese; and in the former these are deposited in the substance of the shell.

In several soundings and dredgings to the south-west of the Canaries we got very many large pieces of a branching Gorgonoid which were deeply coated and impregnated with manganese. This was in a depth of from 1100 to 1575 fathoms.

In 670 fathoms, off the Desertas, the dead shells, pieces of coral, Polyzoa, &c. were all coated with a thin film of the peroxide of manganese; and we have had indications of the same thing in still shallower water.

In some of the Radiolarian oozes, and in other deposits, we have found the manganese more abundant in the upper layers than in the lower, and *vice versa*.

The following are the localities where we have met the manganese in greatest quantities:—

Off the Canary Islands.

Mid-Atlantic, between Canary and Virgin Islands.

South-west of Australia.

North and south of the Sandwich Islands.

North of Tahiti.

Generally in the South Pacific in our course between Tahiti and Valparaiso.

~~~~~~~~~~~~~~~~

J. W. Judd:

22.   ON THE PHENOMENA OF THE VOLCANIC
ERUPTION OF THE KRAKATOA*

During the closing days of the month of August, 1883, the tele-
graph-cable from Batavia carried to Singapore, and thence to every
part of the civilised world, the news of a terrible subterranean convulsion—one which in its destructive results to life and property,
and in the startling character of the world-wide effects to which it
gave rise, is perhaps without a parallel in historic times.

As is usual in such cases, the first reports of this tremendous
outburst of the volcanic forces appear to have been quite misleading
and altogether unworthy of credence. Nor is this to be wondered at.
The towns and villages along the shores of the Sunda Strait were,
during the crisis of the eruption, enveloped in a terrible darkness,
which lasted for many hours, and, while thus obscured, were over-
whelmed by a succession of great sea-waves; those who succeeded in
saving their lives amid these appalling incidents were, it need
scarcely be added, not in a position to make trustworthy observations upon the wonderful succession of phenomena occurring around
them.

For some time after the eruption, the Sunda Strait was almost impassable; lighthouses had been swept away, all the old familiar
landmarks on the shores were obscured by a vast deposit of volcanic
dust; the sea itself was encumbered with enormous masses of floating pumice, in many places of such thickness that no vessel could
force its way through them; and for months after the eruption one
of the principal channels was greatly obstructed by two new islands
which had arisen in its midst.

The first accounts brought to Europe stated that Thwart-way

* From Report of the Krakatoa Committee of the Royal Society, "The
Eruption of Krakatoa, and Subsequent Phenomena" edited by G. J. Symons.
Trübner & Co., London, 1888.

John Wesley Judd, 1840–1916, was an English geologist recognized for his
brilliant demonstrations of relationships of apparently different strata in England
and on the continent.

Island, situated at the eastern entrance of the Strait, had been split into five portions; that the Cape of Anjer had been sundered by a great fissure; that a number of small islands had subsided; and that no fewer than sixteen volcanoes had burst into eruption within the Strait. Subsequently, however, it was found that those who had first made their way into the Strait after the great convulsion, had been altogether misled by the hasty and imperfect glimpses which they had obtained of the desolated district, and that the real centre of the volcanic disturbance was at Krakatoa, the actual eruptions being confined to that island and the district immediately surrounding it.

The first efforts of the Dutch Indian Government were, of course, directed to taking measures for the safety and relief of the survivors of this terrible catastrophe, and for restoring the navigation of the great marine highway between Java and Sumatra. A man-of-war was despatched to the Strait to visit the ports, and penetrate as far as possible into the great bays on both sides of the Strait; while a surveying vessel was ordered to make first a preliminary and then a detailed examination of the changes which had taken place, and which had rendered the existing charts almost useless. But no sooner was this accomplished, than the Government determined to undertake a complete scientific investigation into the effects of the eruption, and of the phenomena which accompanied it, as far as these could be ascertained by the inquiries of a Commission visiting the whole of the district chiefly affected by it. The Dutch Indian Government were fortunate in having at their disposal the services of the eminent geologist, Mr. R. D. M. VERBEEK, whose surveys of Java, Sumatra, and of the actual scene of the outbreak, are widely known to the scientific world. The Dutch Scientific Commission, for inquiry into the nature and results of the Krakatoa eruption, was appointed on October the 4th, 1883; a preliminary report of its proceedings appeared on February the 19th, 1884[1]; and subsequently, the complete report, illustrated by an atlas of plates, and containing a very valuable permanent record of the event, was published in both the Dutch and the French languages.[2]

At the commencement of 1884, the French Minister of Public Instruction, on the motion of the "Commission des Voyages et Missions," directed MM. RENÉ BRÉON and W. C. KORTHALS to visit

[1] 'Kort verslag over de uitbarsting van Krakatau,' door R. D. M. VERBEEK.
[2] 'Krakatau, par R. D. M. VERBEEK, Ingénieur en chef des Mines, Chevalier du Lion Néerlandais. Publié par ordre de son Excellence le Gouverneur-Général des Indes Néerlandaises.' Batavia. The first part of the Dutch edition appeared in 1884, and of the French in 1885. The second part appeared in Dutch in 1885, and in French in 1886.

the scene of the eruption, and to make a report as to the result of their enquiries upon the spot. Only a preliminary report of this Commission, dated May the 30th, 1884, has yet been published,[3] but an interesting account of the proceedings of its members, from the pen of M. BRÉON, has appeared in a French periodical.[4]

The Sunda Strait, where this great convulsion occurred, connecting, as it does, the China Seas with the Indian Ocean, is one of the most important commercial highways of the globe, and many hundreds of vessels pass through it every year. During the time that the eruption of Krakatoa was in progress, a number of ships passed within sight of the volcano, and even at the crisis of the eruption several vessels were actually within the Strait, while others were in its immediate proximity. The observations made by captains or passengers in these vessels, as well as in others at greater distances, and recorded in log-books, diaries, letters to journals, &c., are of very great value and interest; for, those on shipboard were not exposed to the dangers incurred by the witnesses on the land, seeing that the destructive sea-waves passed harmlessly, and in some cases unobserved, by them. Inasmuch, however, as many months had to elapse before these ships could reach the various ports of Europe and America to which they were bound, it was long before all the facts and observations could be collected and compared. The members of the Krakatoa Committee of the Royal Society are under great obligations to the numerous captains and owners of merchant vessels, who, in response to an appeal made by them through the 'Times' and other newspapers, have furnished them with copies of logs and other documents, and with specimens of pumice and dust collected at a great number of different points.

To those who, like Herr METZGER, of Stuttgart, and Dr. KLOOS, of Carlsruhe, have collected from Dutch and other newspapers statements bearing upon the eruption, and to journals which have opened their columns to correspondence on the subject, the Committee is likewise indebted for many interesting details which might otherwise have been lost. Very great value attaches to the mass of useful materials collected in the pages of 'Nature' during the months which followed the eruption. To Mr. H. O. FORBES, also, who was at Batavia after the commencement of the eruption, and who took much pains in collecting information bearing on the subject,[5] the Committee's thanks are largely due.

[3] 'Comptes Rendus,' tom. xcix., p. 395.
[4] 'La Nature,' April 4 and 25, and May 16, 1885.
[5] 'Proceedings of the Royal Geographical Society,' vol. vi. (1884), p. 129.

The whole of the circumstances attending the great catastrophe of the Sunda Strait have been so carefully investigated, and so faithfully recorded by Mr. VERBEEK, in his able and comprehensive work, 'Krakatau,' that it will only be necessary in the present part of this report to give a general summary of the order of events, dwelling especially upon those questions a right understanding whereof is necessary for the interpretation of the remarkable phenomena displayed in distant countries, which in the following parts of the report are shown to have been more or less directly connected with the volcanic disturbance at Krakatoa.

The constant augmentation of tension beneath Krakatoa in the end gave rise to a series of tremendous explosions, on a far grander scale than those resulting directly from the influx of the sea-water into the vent; the four principal of these occurred, according to the careful investigations of Mr. VERBEEK, at 5.30, 6.44, 10.2,[6] and 10.52, Krakatoa time, on the morning of August the 27th. Of these, the third, occurring shortly after 10 o'clock, was by far the most violent, and was productive of the most wide-spread results.

Although no one was near enough to Krakatoa during these paroxysmal outbursts to witness what took place there, a comparison of the condition of the volcano and of the surrounding seas before and after these terrible manifestations of the subterranean forces, leaves little doubt as to the real nature of the action.

In the first place, we find that the whole of the northern and lower portion of the Island of Krakatoa disappeared, with the exception of a bank of pumice and one small isolated rock, about 10 yards square, which was left standing above the ocean with deep water all round it. This rock consists of solid pitchstone, and probably represents a dyke or plug filling the throat of one of the volcanic cones that formerly occupied the old crater. At the same time a large portion of the northern part of the basaltic cone of Rakata was destroyed and a nearly vertical cliff formed, giving rise to a magnificent section which afforded a perfect insight into the internal structure of the volcano. The depth of the great crateral hollow which was produced, where the northern part of Krakatoa formerly rose to heights of from 300 to 1,400 feet above the sea level, in some places exceeds 1,000 feet below that same level. (See Fig. 22–1.)

In attempting to judge of the effects produced around the flanks of the great crater of Krakatoa, we have the two new and very

[6] Corresponding to the wave mentioned on p. 69 as 9 h. 58 m. Krakatoa time=2 h. 56 m. G.M.T.

S.E.

Fig. 22–1. Outline of the crater of Krakatoa as it is at the present time. The dotted line indicates the portions blown away in the paroxysmal outburst of August 1883, and the changes in form of the flanks of the mountain by the fall of ejected materials upon them.

detailed charts prepared by the Royal Dutch surveying vessel *Hydrograaf,* under Commandant C. VAN DOORN. The first of these was the result of a careful survey made immediately after the eruption, and was published on October the 26th, 1883, while the second appeared somewhat later, after the new Islands of Steers and Calmeyer had been reduced to sandbanks.

Certain it is that the portion of the Island of Krakatoa which disappeared during the eruption was equal to about two-thirds of the original area, the part that remained consisting only of the southern moiety of the volcanic cone of Rakata. Of this fragment the southern outline, according to the new charts, differs considerably from that of the southern shore of the original island, and its height, if the old charts can be depended upon, was increased from 2,623[7] to 2,750 feet. But the top and sides of this fragment of the cone of Rakata are so covered by masses of ejected materials that the alteration in its form and height are, it appears to me, sufficiently accounted for without requiring us to call in any theory of general upheaval of the mass.

Of the other islands of the group, Poolsche Hoedje (Polish Hat) has entirely disappeared; Lang Island has been increased by an addition to its northern extremity, and its height above the sea seems to have been augmented, the whole of the vegetation that formerly covered it being deeply buried by ejected matters; and lastly, Verlaten Island has, by accretions on the side farthest away from the central crater, been enlarged to more than three times its former area, while a considerable addition has been made to its height.

In judging of the alterations in the form of the sea-bottom around the Krakatoa group, we have to rely upon the few and not very accurate soundings in the old chart of the Strait. From a compari-

[7] According to VERBEEK, the height previous to the eruption was 2,697 feet. After the eruption he says the height was 2,730 feet, but was reduced by June, 1886, to 2,677 feet.

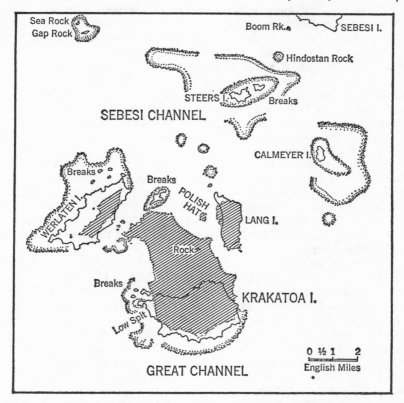

Fig. 22–2. Map of Krakatoa and the surrounding islands, from the chart prepared immediately after the eruption. Later charts show the islands of Steers and Calmeyer reduced to sandbanks. The shaded areas show the form of the islands according to the old chart. Much of the discrepancy between the southern limit of Krakatoa in the two maps is due to the imperfection of the old survey. Dotted lines show sandbanks and lines of breakers.

son of these with the depths given in the new chart, we can scarcely doubt that over a circle with a radius of 10 or 12 miles from the centre of the Krakatoa volcano, the sea-bottom outside the great crater has been raised by an amount which varies from 10 to 60 feet. Mr. VERBEEK concluded however, that along a line 8 or 9 miles in length, and extending westward from the great crater, an *increase* of depth has taken place, and this is not improbably due to the opening of a fissure on the flanks of the submerged cone.

In the so-called New or Sebesi Channel, between Krakatoa and Sebesi Islands, the original depth of water was much less than on the other sides of the Krakatoa group, seldom, indeed, exceeding 20 fathoms; and several rocks in this channel rose above the sea-level. After the eruption it was found that this channel was completely blocked by banks composed of volcanic materials, and two portions of these banks rose above the sea as islands, which received the name of Steers Island and Calmeyer Island. By the action of the waves, however, these islands were, in the course of a few months, completely washed away, and their materials distributed over the sea bottom.

The changes which took place in the forms of the islands and in the depth of the sea around them, have been supposed by some to indicate a general elevation of the islands of the Krakatoa group, accompanied by a great subsidence of the central or crateral area. A careful study of these changes in the light of what is known to have taken place at other volcanic centres leads me to adopt a wholly different conclusion.

The action going on within a volcanic vent during eruption is in all essential features identical with that which takes place in the throat of a geyser. In both cases we have a mass of heated liquid, in the midst of which large quantities of gaseous materials are being disengaged so as to escape into the atmosphere as the pressure is relieved, and these escaping gases carry up with them portions of the liquid in which they have been confined. Now just as the throwing of sods and earth into the tube of a geyser, by causing a check in the escape of steam and water and thereby leading to an augmentation of the tension of the elastic fluids below, gives rise to a more than usually violent explosion, so the interruption to the regular ejections going on at Krakatoa, consequent on the chilling of the surface of the lava in the vent by inrushes of sea-water, caused *a check and then a rally* of the pent-up force of gases seeking to escape from the molten mass. The serious catastrophic outbursts that produced such startling effects both in the air and in the ocean appear to me to have been the direct consequences of this "check and rally" of the subterranean forces.

In these last terrible outbursts, in which the volcano rapidly expended its remaining force, we are evidently dealing with the breaking up and ejection of solid lava constituting the framework of the volcano, and not with the simple dissipation of the lava-froth (pumice) as during all the earlier stages of the eruption. That the materials were not carried far from the centre of ejection is shown by the fact that no falls of coarse materials are recorded from any of the vessels that were within or near the Strait at the time, but the bulk of the solid fragments thrown out during these great explosions must have fallen back into the sea, upon and immediately around the flanks of the volcano itself. This is proved by the alteration in the forms of the islands of the Krakatoa group, and by the change in the height of the floor of the surrounding ocean. By these grand explosive outbursts the old crater was completely eviscerated, and a cavity formed, more than 1,000 feet in depth, while the solid materials thrown out from the crater were spread over the flanks of the volcano, causing the alterations in their form which have been noticed.[8]

It was the rush of the great sea-waves over the land, caused by the violent evisceration of the crater of Krakatoa aided by the impact upon the water of the Strait of the enormous masses of falling material, that caused the great destruction of life and property in the Strait of Sunda. By the inrush of these waves on to the land, all vessels near the shore were stranded, the towns and villages along the coast devastated, two of the lighthouses swept away, and the lives of 36,380 of the inhabitants, among whom were 37 Europeans, sacrificed. The first waves reached both the Javan and the Sumatran coasts between 6 and 7 on the evening of August the 26th, and these probably mark the time of the first influx of water into the igneous focus. A succession of small oscillations of the sea continued all night, but the waves that followed the four great explosions of 5.30, 6.44, 10.2, and 10.52 in the morning of August the 27th, were undoubtedly the highest and most destructive of all.

Early on the morning of August the 27th, another phenomenon began to manifest itself. The vast quantity of watery vapour thrown into the atmosphere during the afternoon of the 26th and the night of the 26th and 27th of August, had reached an excessive height. This height has been estimated by Mr. JOLY at 17 and possibly even 23 miles, and by M. FLAMMARION at 12½ miles. This mass of vapour and dust, as so graphically described by Captain WOOL-DRIDGE, of the *Sir R. Sale*, on reaching the limit of its elevation spread itself out laterally, giving rise to the "pine-tree" appearance so familiar to the Italians, who are in the habit of watching the paroxysmal outbursts of Vesuvius. All night long this great cloud spread itself laterally, the particles of dust slowly descending through the atmosphere. Between 10 and 11 a.m. the three vessels then at the eastern entrance of the Strait encountered the fall of mingled

---

[8] It is probable that lateral eruptions contributed to the alterations produced by the ejection of materials from the central crater.

dust and water, which soon darkened the air and covered their decks and sails with a thick coating of mud. Some of the pieces of pumice falling on the *Sir R. Sale* were said to have been of the size of a pumpkin.

Between 10 and 10.30 a.m. the same state of things is reported in Lampong Bay, the G. G. *Loudon* being compelled at the latter hour to come to anchor on account of the darkness.

At Batavia, situated about 100 English miles from Krakatoa, the sky was clear at 7 a.m., but began to darken between that hour and 10 a.m.; at 10.15 the sky became lurid and yellowish, and lamps began to be required in the houses; about 10.30 the first falls from the overhanging clouds took place in the form of fine watery particles, and this was succeeded by a few grains of dust; at 11 a.m. this increased to a regular dust-rain, becoming heavier till 11.20, when complete darkness fell on the city. This heavy dust-rain continued till 1, and afterwards less heavily till 3 p.m. The dust fell in small rounded accretions, containing about 10 per cent. of water. A similar phenomenon is recorded as having been observed during the recent eruptions of Tarawera in New Zealand.

At Buitenzorg, a little farther from the volcano, similar phenomena were recorded but were of shorter duration. The dust-fall commenced at 11, but darkness did not begin till noon, and it passed away as the dust-fall ceased at 2 p.m. The darkness, however, extended in the country eastward as far as Tjandjer, about 130 English miles, and Bandong, nearly 150 miles from the volcano.

The air-waves produced by the great explosions appear to have been of three kinds. Those which were of sufficient rapidity of alternation to give rise to sounds, are recorded as being heard as far away as Rodriguez and Diego Garcia, which are respectively 3,080 and 2,375 English miles distant from the volcano. Other waves of larger dimensions caused the bursting in of windows, and even the cracking of walls 100 miles away at Batavia and Buitenzorg. Lamps were thrown down, gas-jets extinguished, and a gasometer, under the influence of one of these great waves, leaped out of its well, causing the gas to escape. Even at much greater distances cracks were produced in walls, and all accounts agree in ascribing the result to air-vibrations and not to earthquakes.

Eruptive action appeared to continue in the neighbourhood of Krakatoa during the whole of Monday, the 27th, though the darkness which prevailed over the Strait of Sunda prevented the exact nature of the operations going on there from being determined. Three vessels, the *Charles Bal*, the *Sir R. Sale*, and the *Norham Castle*, were all day beating about in the darkness at the eastern entrance of the Strait, the pumice-dust falling upon them in such quantities as to employ the crews for hours in shovelling it from the decks and in beating it from the sails and rigging. On board the G. G. *Loudon*, anchored in Lampong Bay, it is recorded that, after the rain of pumice-stone in the early morning, only dust and water fell in the form of mud, which accumulated on the deck at the rate of 6 inches in 10 minutes. Frequent explosions and vivid lightning in the neighbourhood of Krakatoa are recorded. After the great outbursts of the early morning of the 27th, however, it appears that there was a lull for a time, as at Buitenzorg no explosions were heard during the afternoon till 7 p.m. At this latter hour the explosions, as heard from Buitenzorg, recommenced, increasing in violence till 10 or 11 p.m., when they again declined, and finally ceased to be heard at 2.30 a.m. on Tuesday, the 28th of August.

On Wednesday, the 29th of August, the G. G. *Loudon* forced her way through the pumice-laden seas passing from the Bay of Lampong through the Strait of Lagoendie, and then sailed round the west, south, and east sides of Krakatoa, and thence on to Anjer, which place was reached at 4 p.m. They found that the whole of the northern part of the island of Krakatoa had disappeared, and that no smoke was at that time issuing from it.

William Dittmar:

23.   SEA WATER

*The Principal Saline Components.**

Sea water has long been known to consist in the main of a solution of the chlorides and sulphates of sodium, magnesium, potassium, and calcium. A quantitative analysis which correctly reports these few acids and bases, gives almost as close an approximation to the proportion of total solids as it is possible to obtain. And yet, from the fact of the ocean being what it is, it follows almost of necessity that there must be numerous minor components. Perhaps no

---

* From REPORT ON THE SCIENTIFIC RESULTS OF THE VOYAGE OF H.M.S. CHALLENGER (Physics and Chemistry) Volume 1, 1884.

William Dittmar was, in 1884, Professor of Chemistry, Anderson College, Glasgow.

element is entirely absent from sea-water; but according to Forchhammer only the following (in addition to the predominating components already named) have been proved to be present:

Bromine: easily detected in the mother-liquor obtained in the preparation of sea-salt by crystallisation.

Iodine: this element is present only in very minute traces; its presence until lately was only inferred, from its relatively abundant occurrence in the ashes of sea-weeds.

Fluorine: detected directly; also found in the boiler crusts of transatlantic steamers.

Phosphorus: in phosphate

Nitrogen: in ammonia, and in the organic matter necessarily diffused throughout the ocean.

Carbon: in carbonates and free carbonic acid, which, as we shall see, are by no means subordinate components; also as part of the organic matter.

Silicon: in silicates.

Boron: directly detectable; found also in the ashes of *Zostera maritima* and *Fucus vesiculosus.*

Silver: found by Malaguti in the copper bottoms of ocean-going ships. Forchhammer found 1/3,000,000th in a coral called *Pocillopora alcicornis.*

Lead: more abundant than silver; the coral just named gave to Forchhammer eight parts of lead to one of silver.

Copper: found in the ash of *Fucus vesiculosus,* and of other sea-weeds. The coral *Pocillopora* contains 1/500,000th, the coral *Heteropora* 1/350,000th, of the metal.

Zinc: proved to be present only indirectly by the analysis of the ashes of sea-plants. The ash of *Zostera maritima* contains .035% of ZnO.

Cobalt and *Nickel:* found in the ash of sea-plants.

Iron: easily detected directly.

Manganese: readily detected in the residue left on re-dissolving sea-water solids in water. Five hundred parts of dry *Zostera maritima* gave, to Forchhammer, 81.4 of an ash which contained about 4% of manganese.

Aluminum: in alumina, which can be detected by the ordinary methods.

Barium and *Strontium:* can be detected directly, and besides have been found in the ashes of marine plants and in oceanic boiler-crusts.

Arsenic: detected by Daubré.

Lithium: found by Bizio in the water of the Adriatic, by spectrum analysis.

Caesium, Rubidium, and *Gold:* discovered by Sonstadt. C. Schmidt succeeded in determining the rubidium even quantitatively.

The configuration of the ocean, broadly speaking, must have been the same as it is now for thousands of years. Hence its bed may be regarded by this time as having been almost deprived of all the more soluble components. No mineral, it is true, is absolutely insoluble in water; the ocean, consequently, must still be presumed to continue taking up soluble matter from the volcanic and other minerals with which it is in contact on the floor of the ocean, and what it thus gains is probably in excess over what it contributes towards the matter of new deposits. It must be granted also that it is continuously taking in large masses of dissolved mineral matter from rivers, and that what it receives from these two sources in a single year, if measured by ordinary standards, amounts to an immense quantity. But the gain even in a century is a mere trifle in comparison with what it already contains—far less no doubt than the relative errors in our most exact methods of measurement.

The ocean, of course, takes in gases from the air as well as solids from the earth's crust; but this is a case of mutual exchange, in which the gain and loss, on either side, must long since have arrived at a state of equilibrium.

Hence the absolute composition of the ocean as a whole, meaning the total number of kilograms of water, chloride of sodium, &c., &c., present in it, though subject probably to an extremely slow increase in the dissolved saline matter, is practically constant and invariable. The percentage composition of a given sample of ocean-water is, of course, liable to variation according to the place where and the time when it was collected. This holds true more especially of the volatile components, viz, for the dissolved nitrogen and oxygen, the merely dissolved part of the carbonic acid, and last, and not least, of the water which forms the bulk (some 96 percent or more) of the whole.

Water, even at the lowest temperatures occurring on the surface of the globe, is appreciably volatile, and its volatility, as part of the sea, is not very materially diminished by the salts dissolved in it. Hence, from the whole of the area of the ocean, myriads of molecules of vapour of water are continuously being given out into the atmosphere; at the same time molecules previously given out are returning whence they came, the tendency, however, in every portion of atmosphere touching the ocean being to establish the maximum vapour-tension corresponding to the prevailing temperature. This vapour-tension is the greater the higher the temperature, and it increases more rapidly than does the temperature. Hence the rate at which the air takes up water from the sea is very great in the tropics, less in our latitudes, and far less in the circumpolar regions. On the basis of some law of distribution of temperatures, it would be a matter of calculation to inquire what this would lead to if the atmosphere were in a state of stagnation. But the atmosphere is not in such a state, and cannot be. The moist air in the equatorial regions, being relatively warm and consequently light, ascends, while relatively cold and dry air streams into its place from the north and south: a corresponding part of the uppermost stratum of the aerial ocean wells over and flows towards the poles. The consequence is that the greater part of the moisture taken up by the warm air of the tropics is not recondensed there, but is deposited as rain in the colder latitudes. Hence the sea must be less saline there than in the lower latitudes; but the permanence of a great excess of salinity anywhere is precluded by the oceanic currents.

To map these currents accurately and determine their velocities is the most important problem of general oceanography, and the solution of this problem would obviously be greatly facilitated if we had a correct and complete representation of the contour surfaces of equal salinity. As a means towards this end, Mr. Buchanan, in the course of the Expedition, collected thousands of samples of ocean-water from a great variety of places and depths, and defined their salinity by determining their specific gravity at known temperatures. His results are detailed and discussed by himself in his Report on the Specific Gravity of Ocean-Water.[1] My own connection with this part of his work is but slight. All I did was—firstly, to work out experimentally the mathematical relation between salinity and temperature on the one hand, and specific gravity on the other, so that Mr. Buchanan's numbers might be reduced to a standard temperature, and be translated into salinities; and secondly, to determine the salinities of some 160 of Mr. Buchanan's water samples by a more direct (chemical) method, and compare the resulting values with those computed from Buchanan's specific gravities by my formula. This comparison led to the very satisfactory result, that the "probable error" in any one of Mr. Buchanan's specific gravities is rather less than±0.1; that of pure water being taken as =1000.

A little reflection shows that no number of analyses will enable one to calculate with any degree of exactitude the mean salinity of the ocean as a whole; but even by 160 salinity determinations,

[1] Phys. Chem. Chall. Exp., part ii.

since they correspond to a great variety of places, suffice to give an idea of the limits between which the quantity fluctuates. Expressing the salinity in "parts of total salts per 1000 parts of sea-water," I find that (of the 160 values)

The lowest (from the southern part of the Indian Ocean, south of 66° latitude) is 33.01.

The greatest (from the middle of the North Atlantic, at about 23° latitude) is 37.37.

(Some few samples from narrow straits or close to certain coasts are omitted, as being probably diluted to an abnormal extent with fresh water.)

So much as to the ratio of the water to the sum total of the salts dissolved in it. Let us now inquire into the percentage composition of the salt mixture itself.

A *priori*, we should say that this composition cannot be subject to any great variation; because, if there were no chemical changes going on in the ocean, and no gain or loss of dissolved individual salts, this composition would now, after thousands of years' constant intermixture, be absolutely the same everywhere; and what is going on in the shape of reactions and importation or exportation of individual salts, really amounts only to an extremely minute fraction of the whole, even in the course of a century. This conclusion is confirmed by the analyses of several hundred samples of surface-waters, which were carried out by Forchhammer in connection with a great research which he published in 1864.[2] According to his results, if we confine ourselves to the open ocean, we find that everywhere the ratios to one another of the quantities of chlorine, sulphuric acid, lime, magnesia, and total salts, exhibit practically constant values. With the view chiefly of supplementing Forchhammer's work, I have made exact determinations of the chlorine, sulphuric acid, lime, magnesia, potash, and soda in 77 samples of water collected by the *Challenger* from very different parts of the ocean:

12 from the surface.

10 from depths of 25 to 100 fathoms.

21 from depths of over 100 to 1000 fathoms.

34 from greater depths.

The results, while fairly agreeing with Forchhammer's, were in still closer accordance with one another, and thus showed that Forchhammer's proposition may be extended from surface-waters to ocean-waters obtained from all depths.

[2] Phil. Trans., 1865, vol. clv. p. 203.

Fridtjof Nansen:

24.   THE DRIFT OF THE FRAM*

What, then, are the results of the Norwegian Polar Expedition? This is a question which the reader might fairly expect to find answered here; but the scientific observations brought back are so varied and voluminous that it will be some time yet before they can be dealt with by specialists and before any general estimate of their significance can be formed. It will, therefore, be necessary to publish these results in separate scientific publications; and if I now attempted to give an idea of them, it would necessarily be imperfect, and might easily prove misleading. I shall, therefore, confine myself to pointing out a few of their more important features.

In the first place, we have demonstrated that the sea in the immediate neighborhood of the Pole, and in which, in my opinion, the Pole itself in all probability lies, is a deep basin, not a shallow one, containing many expanses of land and islands, as people were formerly inclined to assume. It is certainly a continuation of the deep channel which extends from the Atlantic Ocean northward between Spitzbergen and Greenland. The extent of this deep sea is a question which it is not at present easy to answer; but we at least know that it extends a long way north of Franz Josef Land, and eastward right to the New Siberian Islands. I believe that it extends still farther east, as, I think, may be inferred from the fact that the more the *Jeannette* expedition drifted north, the greater depth of sea did they find. For various reasons, I am led to believe that in a northerly direction also this deep sea is of considerable extent. In the first place, nothing was observed, either during the drift of the *Fram* or during our sledge expedition to the north, that would point to the proximity of any considerable expanse of land; the ice

* From F. Nansen, FARTHEST NORTH, Volume 2, pp. 707–713, Harper and Brothers, 1897.

In addition to his great achievements as an arctic explorer and scientist, Norwegian born Fridtjof Nansen, 1861–1930, was internationally renowned as a statesman and humanitarian. For this latter role, Nansen received the 1922 Nobel Peace Prize.

seemed to drift unimpeded, particularly in a northerly direction. The way in which the drift set straight to the north as soon as there was a southerly wind was most striking. It was with the greatest difficulty that the wind could head the drift back towards the southeast. Had there been any considerable expanse of land within reasonable distance to the north of us, it would have blocked the free movement of the ice in that direction. Besides, the large quantity of drift-ice, which drifts southward with great rapidity along the east coast of Greenland all the way down to Cape Farewell and beyond it, seems to point in the same direction. Such extensive ice-fields must have a still larger breadth of sea to come from than that through which we drifted. Had the *Fram* continued her drift instead of breaking loose to the north of Spitzbergen, she would certainly have come down along the coast of Greenland; but probably she would not have got close in to that coast, but would have had a certain quantity of ice between her and it; and that ice must come from a sea lying north of our route. On the other hand, it is quite probable that land may exist to a considerable extent on the other side of the Pole between the Pole and the North American archipelago. It appears to me only reasonable to assume that this multitude of islands must extend farther towards the north.

As a result of our expedition, I think we can now form a fairly clear idea of the way in which the drift-ice is continually moving from one side of the polar basin north of Bering Strait and the coast of Siberia, and across the regions around the Pole, and out towards the Atlantic Ocean. Where geographers at one time were disposed to locate a solid, immovable, and massive ice-mantle, covering the northern extremity of our globe, we now find a continually breaking and shifting expanse of drift-ice. The evidence which even before our expedition had induced me to believe most strongly in this theory is supplied by the Siberian drift-wood that is continually being carried to Greenland, as well as the mud found on the ice, as it could scarcely be of other than Siberian origin. We found several indications of this kind during our expedition, even when we were as far north as 86°, furnishing valuable indications as to the movement of the ice.

The force which sets this ice in motion is certainly for the most part supplied by the winds; and as in the sea north of Siberia the prevailing winds are southeasterly or easterly, whereas north of Spitzbergen they are northeasterly, they must carry the ice in the direction in which we found the drift. From the numerous observations I made I established the existence of a slow current in the water under the ice, travelling in the same direction. But it will be some time before the results of these investigations can be calculated and checked.

The hydrographic observations made during the expedition furnished some surprising data. Thus, for instance, it was customary to look upon the polar basin as being filled with cold water, the temperature of which stood somewhere about —1.5° C. Consequently our observations showing that under the cold surface there was warmer water, sometimes at a temperature as high as +1° C., were surprising. Again, this water was more briny than the water of the polar basin has been assumed to be. This warmer and more strongly saline water must clearly originate from the warmer current of the Atlantic Ocean (the Gulf Stream), flowing in a north and northeasterly direction off Novaya Zemlya and along the west coast of Spitzbergen, and then diving under the colder, but lighter and less briny, water of the Polar Sea, and filling up the depths of the polar basin. As I have stated in the course of my narrative, this more briny water was, as a rule, warmest at a depth of from 200 to 250 fathoms, beyond which it would decrease in temperature, though not uniformly, as the depth increased. Near the bottom the temperature rose again, though only slightly. These hydrographic observations appear to modify to a not inconsiderable extent the theories hitherto entertained as to the direction of the currents in the northern seas; but it is a difficult matter to deal with, as there is a great mass of material, and its further treatment will demand both time and patience. It must therefore be left to subsequent scientific publications.

Still less do I contemplate attempting to enter here into a discussion on the numerous magnetic, astronomical, and meteorological observations taken. At the end of this work I merely give a table showing the mean temperatures for each month during the drift of the *Fram* and during our sledging expedition.

On the whole, it may probably be said that, although the expedition has left many problems for the future to solve in connection with the polar area, it has, nevertheless, gone far to lift the veil of mystery which has hitherto shrouded those regions, and we have been put in a position to form a tolerably clear and reasonable idea of a portion of our globe that formerly lay in darkness, which only the imagination could penetrate. And should we in the near future get a bird's-eye view of the regions around the Pole as seen from a balloon, all the most material features will be familiar to us.

But there still remains a great deal to be investigated, and this can only be done by years of observation, to which end a new drift, like that of the *Fram,* would be invaluable. Guided by our experience, explorers will be in a position to equip themselves still better; but a more convenient method for the scientific investigation of unknown regions cannot easily be imagined. On board a vessel of this kind explorers may settle themselves quite as comfortably as in a fixed scientific station. They can carry their laboratories with them, and the most delicate experiments of all kinds can be carried out. I hope that such an expedition may be undertaken ere long, and if it goes through Bering Strait and thence northward, or perhaps slightly to the northeast, I shall be very much surprised if observations are not taken which will prove of far greater scope and importance than those made by us. But it will require patience: the drift will be more protracted than ours, and the explorers must be well equipped.

There is also another lesson which I think our expedition has taught—namely, that a good deal can be achieved with small resources. Even if explorers have to live in Eskimo fashion and content themselves with the barest necessaries, they may, provided they are suitably equipped, make good headway and cover considerable distances in regions which have hitherto been regarded as almost inaccessible.

MEAN TEMPERATURES (FAHR.) FOR EVERY MONTH DURING THE DRIFT OF THE "FRAM"

Months	1893	1894	1895	1896
	°	°	°	°
January	—	32.3	—28.1	—35.3
February	—	—32.1	—34.2	—30.5
March	—	—35.1	—30.6	— 1.7
April	—	— 6.1	—19.7	— 0.6
May	—	+13.8	+10.2	+12.6
June	—	+29.3	+28.0	+28.9
July	—	+32.4	+32.5	+31.8
August	—	+30.2	+27.3	+34.1
September	+29.1	+17.1	+14.9	—
October	— 1.1	— 8.5	— 6.2	—
November	—11.6	—23.4	—23.6	—
December	—20.6	—30.8	—27.2	—

CONTINUOUS PERIODS OF TEMPERATURE UNDER —40°

	Dates				
Years	January	February	March	November	December
1894	11 to 12	3 to 7	5 to 15	14 to 15	8 to 10
	14 to 15	11 to 19	17 to 19	—	17 to 18
	27 to 29	23 to 24	25 to 26	—	30 to 1*
1895	14 to 18	9 to 10	19 to 23	20 to 23	7 to 8
	23 to 26	13 to 16	26 to 28	—	—
	—	18 to 22	—	—	—
1896	29† to 18	4 to 9	4 to 5	—	—
	—	11 to 20	—	—	—

* January
†December

William A. Herdman:

25.   OCEANOGRAPHY, BIONOMICS, AND
AQUICULTURE*

We include in our subject-matter speciography and systematic zoology, which has been cultivated by the great classifiers and monographers from Linnæus to Hæckel, and has culminated in our times in the magnificent series of fifty quarto volumes, setting forth the scientific results of the *Challenger* expedition; a voyage of discovery comparable only in its important and wide-reaching results with the voyages of Columbus, Gama, and Magellan at the end of the fifteenth century. It is now so long since the *Challenger* investigations commenced that few, I suppose, outside the range of professional zoologists are aware that although the expedition took place in 1872 to 1876, the work resulting therefrom has been going on actively until now—for nearly a quarter of a century in all—and

* Opening address at the Ipswich meeting of the British Association for the Advancement of Science, 1895. Printed in Report of the British Association, 1895, No. 1351, volume 52, September 19, 1895.

William Abbott Herdman, 1858–1924, was a Scottish marine naturalist who, through his research, became interested in co-ordinating the fishing industry with scientific research.

in a sense, and a very real one, will never cease, for the *Challenger* has left an indelible mark upon science, and will remain through the ages exercising its powerful, guiding influence, like the work of Aristotle, Newton, and Darwin.

Most of the authors of the special memoirs on the sea and its various kinds of inhabitants have interpreted in a liberal spirit the instruction they received to examine and describe the collections intrusted to them, and have given us very valuable summaries of the condition of our knowledge of the animals in question, while some of the reports are little less than complete monographs of the groups. I desire to pay a tribute of respect to my former teacher and scientific chief, Sir Wyville Thomson, to whose initiative, along with Dr. W. B. Carpenter, we owe the first inception of our now celebrated deep-sea dredging expeditions, and to whose scientific enthusiasm, combined with administrative skill, is due in great part the successful accomplishment of the *Lightning*, the *Porcupine*, and the *Challenger* expeditions. Wyville Thomson lived long enough to superintend the first examination of the collections brought home, their division into groups, and the allotment of these to specialists for description. He enlisted the services of his many scientific friends at home and abroad, he arranged the general plan of the work, decided upon the form of publication, and died in 1882, after seeing the first ten or twelve zoological reports through the press.

Within the last few months have been issued the two concluding volumes of this noble series, dealing with a summary of the results, conceived and written in a masterly manner by the eminent editor of the reports, Dr. John Murray. An event of such first-rate importance in zoology as the completion of this great work ought not to pass unnoticed at this zoological gathering. I desire to express my appreciation and admiration of Dr. Murray's work, and I do not doubt that the section will permit me to convey to Dr. Murray the congratulations of the zoologists present, and their thanks for his splendid services to science. Murray, in these "Summary" volumes, has given definiteness of scope and purpose and a tremendous impulse to that branch of science—mainly zoological—which is coming to be called oceanography.

OCEANOGRAPHY

Oceanography is the meeting ground of most of the sciences. It deals with botany and zoology, "including animal physiology"; chemistry, physics, mechanics, meteorology, and geology all contribute, and the subject is of course intimately connected with geography, and has an incalculable influence upon mankind, his distribution, characteristics, commerce, and economics. Thus oceanography, one of the latest developments of marine zoology, extends into the domain of, and ought to find a place in, every one of the sections of the British Association.

Along with the intense specialization of certain lines of zoology in the last quarter of the nineteenth century, it is important to notice that there are also lines of investigation which require an extended knowledge of, or at least make use of the results obtained from, various distinct subjects. One of these is oceanography, another is bionomics, which I have referred to above, a third is the philosophy of zoology, or all those studies which bear upon the theory of evolution, and a fourth is the investigation of practical fishery problems, which is chiefly an application of marine zoology. Of these four subjects—which, while analytic enough in the detailed investigation of any particular problem are synthetic in drawing together and making use of the various divergent branches of zoology and the neighboring sciences—oceanography, bionomics, and the fisheries investigation are most closely related, and I desire to devote the remainder of this address to the consideration of some points in connection with their present position.

Dr. Murray, in a few only too brief paragraphs at the end of his detailed summary of the results of the *Challenger* expedition, which I have alluded to above, states some of the views, highly suggestive and original, at which he has himself arrived from his unique experience. Some of his conclusions are very valuable contributions to knowledge, which will no doubt be adopted by marine zoologists. Others, I venture to think, are less sound and well founded, and will scarcely stand the test of time and further experience. But for all such statements, or even suggestions, we should be thankful. They do much to stimulate further research; they serve, if they can neither be refuted nor established, as working hypotheses; and even if they have to be eventually abandoned, we should bear in mind what Darwin has said as to the difference in their influence on science between erroneous facts and erroneous theories: "False facts are highly injurious to the progress of science, for they often endure long; but false views, if supported by some evidence, do little harm, for everyone takes a salutary pleasure in proving their falseness; and when this is done, one path toward error is closed, and the road to truth is often at the same time opened." (Darwin: *The Descent of Man,* second edition, 1882, p. 606).

Probably no group of animals in the sea is of so much importance from the point of view of food as the Copepoda. They form a great part of the food of whales, and of herrings and many other useful fish, both in the adult and in the larval state, as well as of innumerable other animals, large and small. Consequently, I have inquired somewhat carefully into their distribution in the sea, with the assistance of Professor Brady, Mr. Scott, and Mr. Thompson. These experienced collectors all agree that Copepoda are most abundant, both as to species and individuals, close round the shore, amongst seaweeds, or in shallow water in the Laminarian zone over a weedy bottom. Individuals are sometimes extremely abundant on the surface of the sea amongst the plankton, or in shore pools near high water, where, amongst *Enteromorpha*, they swarm in immense profusion; but for a gathering rich in individuals, species, and genera, the experienced collector goes to the shallow waters of the Laminarian zone. In regard to the remaining, higher groups of the Crustacea, my friend Mr. Alfred O. Walker tells me that he considers them most abundant at depths of from o to 20 fathoms.

I hope no one will think that these are detailed matters interesting only to the collector, and having no particular bearing upon the great problems of biology. The sea is admittedly the starting point of life on this earth, and the conclusions we come to as to the distribution of life in the different zones must form and modify our views as to the origin of the faunas—as to the peopling of the deep sea, the shallow waters, and the land. Murray supposes that life started in Pre-Cambrian times on the mud, and from there spread upward into shallower waters, outward on to the surface, and, a good deal later, downward to the abysses by means of the cold Polar waters. The late Professor Moseley considered the pelagic, or surface life of the ocean, to be the primitive life from which all the others have been derived. Prof. W. K. Brooks (The Genus Salpa, 1893, p. 156, etc.) considers that there was a primitive pelagic fauna, consisting of the simplest microscopic plants and animals, and "that pelagic life was abundant for a long period during which the bottom was uninhabited."

I consider that the Laminarian zone close to low-water mark is at present the richest in life, that it probably has been so in the past, and that if one has to express a more definite opinion as to where, in Pre-Cambrian times, life in its simplest forms first appeared, I see no reason why any other zone should be considered as having a better claim than what is now the Laminarian to this distinction. It is there, at present, at any rate, in the upper edge of the Laminarian zone, at the point of junction of sea, land, and air, where there is a profusion of food, where the materials brought down by streams or worn away from the land are first deposited, where the animals are able to receive the greatest amount of light and heat, oxygen and food, without being exposed periodically to the air, rain, frost, sun, and other adverse conditions of the Littoral zone. It is there that life—it seems to me—is most abundant, growth most active, competition most severe. It is there, probably, that the surrounding conditions are most favorable to animal life; and, therefore, it seems likely that it is from this region that, as the result of overcrowding, migrations have taken place downward to the abysses, outward on the surface, and upward on to the shore. Finally, it is in this Laminarian zone, probably, that under the stress of competition between individuals and between allied species evolution of new forms by means of natural selection has been most active. Here, at any rate, we find, along with some of the most primitive of animals, some of the most remarkably modified forms, and some of the most curious cases of minute adaptation to environment. This brings us to the subject of

BIONOMICS,

which deals with the habits and variations of animals, their modifications, and the relations of these modifications to the surrounding conditions of existence.

It is remarkable that the great impetus given by Darwin's work to biological investigation has been chiefly directed to problems of structure and development, and not so much to bionomics until lately. Variations amongst animals in a state of nature is, however, at last beginning to receive the attention it deserves. Bateson has collected together, and classified in a most useful book of reference, the numerous scattered observations on variation made by many investigators, and has drawn from some of these cases a conclusion in regard to the discontinuity of variation which many field zoologists find it hard to accept.

Weldon and Karl Pearson have recently applied the methods of statistics and mathematics to the study of individual variation. This method of investigation, in Professor Weldon's hands, may be expected to yield results of great interest in regard to the influence of variations in the young animal upon the chance of survival, and so upon the adult characteristics of the species. But while acknowledging the value of these methods, and admiring the skill and care with which they have been devised and applied, I must emphatically protest against the idea which has been suggested, that only by such mathematical and statistical methods of study can we successfully determine the influence of the environment on species, gauge the utility of specific characters, and throw further light upon the origin of species. For my part, I believe we shall gain a truer insight into those mysteries which still involve variations and species by a study of the characteristic features of individuals, varieties, and species in a living state in relation to their environment and habits.

The mode of work of the old field naturalists, supplemented by the apparatus and methods of the modern laboratory, is, I believe, not only one of the most fascinating, but also one of the most profitable fields of investigation for the philosophical zoologist. Such studies must be made in that modern outcome of the growing needs of our science, the Zoological Station, where marine animals can be kept in captivity under natural conditions, so that their habits may be closely observed, and where we can follow out the old precept—first, observation and reflection; then experiment.

The biological stations of the present day represent, then, a happy union of the field work of the older naturalists with the laboratory work of the comparative anatomist, histologist, and embryologist. They are the culmination of the "Aquarium" studies of Kingsley and Gosse, and of the feeling in both scientific men and amateurs, which was expressed by Herbert Spencer when he said: "Whoever at the seaside has not had a microscope and an aquarium has yet to learn what the highest pleasures of the seaside are." Moreover, I feel that the biological station has come to the rescue, at a critical moment, of our laboratory worker who, without its healthy, refreshing influence, is often in these latter days in peril of losing his intellectual life in the weary maze of microtome methods and transcendental cytology. The old Greek myth of the Libyan giant, Antæus, who wrestled with Hercules and regained his strength each time he touched his mother earth, is true at least of the zoologist. I am sure he derives fresh vigor from every direct contact with living nature.

In our tanks and artificial pools we can reproduce the Littoral and the Laminarian zones; we can see the methods of feeding and breeding—the two most powerful factors in influencing an animal. We can study mimicry, and test theories of protective and warning coloration.

The explanations given by these theories of the varied forms and colors of animals were first applied by such leaders in our science as Bates, Wallace, and Darwin, chiefly to insects and birds, but have lately been extended, by the investigations of Giard, Garstang, Clubb, and others, to the case of marine animals. I may mention very briefly one or two examples. Amongst the Nudibranchiate

Mollusca—familiar animals around most parts of our British coasts—
we meet with various forms which are edible, and, so far as we
know, unprotected by any defensive or offensive apparatus. Such
forms are usually shaped or colored so as to resemble more or less
their surroundings, and so become inconspicuous in their natural
haunts. *Dendronotus arborescens*, one of the largest and most
handsome of our British Nudibranchs, is such a case. The large,
branched processes on its back, and its rich purple-brown and
yellow markings, tone in so well with the masses of brown and
yellow zoophytes and purplish red seaweeds, amongst which we
usually find *Dendronotus*, that it becomes very completely protected
from observation; and, as I know from my own experience, the
practiced eye of the naturalist may fail to detect it lying before him
in the tangled forests of a shore pool.

Other Nudibranchs, however, belonging to the genus *Eolis*, for
example, are colored in such a brilliant and seemingly crude manner
that they do not tone in with any natural surroundings, and so
are always conspicuous. They are active in their habits, and seem
rather to court observation than to shun it. When we remember
that such species of *Eolis* are protected by the numerous stinging
cells in the enidophorous sacs placed on the tips of all the dorsal
processes, and that they do not seem to be eaten by other
animals, we have at once an explanation of their fearless habits
and of their conspicuous appearance. The brilliant colors are in
this case of a warning nature, for the purpose of rendering the
animal provided with the stinging cells noticeable and recognizable.
But it must be remembered that in a museum jar, or in a laboratory
dish, or as an illustration in a book or on the wall, *Dendronotus*
is quite as conspicuous and striking an animal as *Eolis*. In order
to interpret correctly the effect of their forms and colors we
must see them alive and at home, and we must experiment upon
their edibility or otherwise in the tanks of our biological stations.[1]

Let me give you one more example of a somewhat different
kind. The soft, unprotected mollusk, *Lamellaria perspicua*, is not
uncommonly found associated (as Giard first pointed out) with
colonies of the compound Ascidian *Leptoclinum maculatum*, and
in these cases the *Lamellaria* is found to be eating the *Leptoclinum*,
and lies in a slight cavity which it has excavated in the Ascidian
colony, so as to be about flush with the general surface. The integu-
ment of the mollusk is, both in general tint, and also in surface mark-

[1] See my experiments on fishes with Nudibranchs, in Trans. Biol. Soc.,
Liverpool, Vol. IV, p. 150; and Nature for June 26, 1890.

ings, very like the Ascidian colony with its scattered ascidiozooids. This is clearly a good case of protective coloring. Presumably, the *Lamellaria* escapes the observation of its enemies through being mistaken for a part of the *Leptoclinum* colony; and the *Leptoclinum* being crowded like a sponge with minute, sharp-pointed spicules is, I suppose, avoided as inedible by carnivorous animals, which might devour such things as the soft, unprotected mollusk. But the presence of the spicules evidently does not protect the *Leptoclinum* from *Lamellaria*, so that we have, if the above interpretation is correct, the curious result that the *Lamellaria* profits by a protective characteristic of the *Leptoclinum*, for which it has itself no respect, or, to put it another way, the *Leptoclinum* is protected against enemies to some extent for the benefit of the *Lamellaria*, which preys upon its vitals.

It is to my mind no sufficient objection to theories of protective and warning coloration that careful investigation may from time to time reveal cases where a disguise is penetrated, a protection frustrated, an offensive device supposed to confer inedibility apparently ignored. We must bear in mind that the enemies, as well as their prey, are exposed to competition, are subject to natural selection, are undergoing evolution; that the pursuers and the pursued, the eaters and the eaten, have been evolved together, and that it may be of great advantage to be protected from *some* even if not from all enemies. Just as on land, some animals can browse upon thistles whose "nemo me impune lacessit" spines are supposed to confer immunity from attack, so it is quite in accord with our ideas of evolution by means of natural selection to suppose that some marine animals have evolved an indifference to the noxious sponge or to the bristling Ascidian, which are able, by their defensive characteristics, like the thistle, to repel the majority of invaders.

Although we can keep and study the Littoral and Laminarian animals at ease in our zoological stations, it may perhaps be questioned how far we can reproduce in our experimental and observational tanks the conditions of the Coralline and the Deep-mud zones. One might suppose that the pressure—which we have no means as yet for supplying[2]—and which at 30 fathoms amounts

[2] Following up M. Regnard's experiments, some mechanical arrangement whereby water could be kept circulating and aerated under pressure in closed tanks might be devised, and ought to be tried at some zoological station. I learn from the director at the Plymouth Station that some of the animals from deep water, such as Polyzoa, do not expand in their tanks.

to nearly 100 pounds on the square inch, and at 80 fathoms to about 240 pounds, or over 2 hundred-weight on the square inch, would be an essential factor in the life conditions of the inhabitants of such depths, and yet we have kept half a dozen specimens of *Calocaris macandreæ*, dredged from 70 to 80 fathoms, alive at the Port Erin Biological Station for several weeks; we have had both the red and the yellow forms of *Sarcodictyon catenata*, dredged from 30 to 40 fathoms, in a healthy condition with the polypes freely expanded for an indefinite period; and Mr. Arnold Watson has kept the Polynoid worm, *Panthalis oerstedi*, from the deep mud at over 50 fathoms, alive, healthy, and building its tube under observation, first for a week at the Port Erin Station, and for many months at Sheffield, in a comparatively small tank with no depth of water. Consequently, it seems clear that with ordinary care almost any marine animals from such depths as are found within the British area may be kept under observation and submitted to experiment in healthy and fairly natural conditions. The biological station, with its tanks, is in fact an arrangement whereby we bring a portion of the sea with its rocks and bottom deposits and seaweeds, with its inhabitants and their associates, their food and their enemies, and place it for continuous study on our laboratory table. It enables us to carry on the bionomical investigations to which we look for information as to the methods and progress of evolution; in it lie centered our hopes of a comparative physiology of the invertebrates—a physiology not wholly medical—and finally to the biological station we confidently look for help in connection with our coast fisheries. This brings me to the last subject which I shall touch upon, a subject closely related both to oceanography and bionomics, and one which depends much for its future advance upon our biological stations—that is the subject of

AQUICULTURE,

or industrial ichthyology, the scientific treatment of fishery investigations, a subject to which Professor McIntosh has first in this country directed the attention of zoologists, and in which he has been guiding us for the last decade by his admirable researches. What chemistry is to the aniline, the alkali, and some other manufactures, marine zoology is to our fishing industries.

Although zoology has never appealed to popular estimation as a directly useful science having industrial applications in the same way that chemistry and physics have done, and consequently has never had its claims as a subject of technical education sufficiently recognized; still, as we in this section are well aware, our subject has many technical applications to the arts and industries. Biological principles dominate medicine and surgery. Bacteriology, brewing, and many allied subjects are based upon the study of microscopic organisms. Economic entomology is making its value felt in agriculture. Along all these and other lines there is a great future opening up before biology, a future of extended usefulness, of popular appreciation, and of value to the nation—and not the least important of these technical applications will, I am convinced, be that of zoology to our fishing industries. When we consider their enormous annual value—about eight millions sterling at first hand to the fisherman, and a great deal more than that by the time the products reach the British public, when we remember the very large proportion of our population who make their living, directly or indirectly (as boat builders, net makers, etc.), from the fisheries, and the still larger proportion who depend for an important element in their food supply upon these industries; when we think of what we pay other countries—France, Holland, Norway—for oysters, mussels, lobsters, etc., which we could rear in this country if our sea shores and our sea bottom were properly cultivated; and when we remember that fishery cultivation or aquiculture is applied zoology, we can readily realize the enormous value to the nation which this direct application of our science will one day have—perhaps I ought rather to say, we can scarcely realize the extent to which zoology may be made the guiding science of a great national industry.

The flourishing shellfish industries of France, the oyster culture at Arcachon and Marennes, and the mussel culture by bouchots in the Bay of Aiguillon, show what can be done as the result of encouragement and wise assistance from Government, with constant industry on the part of the people, directed by scientific knowledge. In another direction the successful hatching of large numbers (hundreds of millions) of cod and plaice by Captain Dannevig in Norway, and by the Scottish fishery board at Dunbar, opens up possibilities of immense practical value in the way of restocking our exhausted bays and fishing banks, depleted by the overtrawling of the last few decades.

The demand for the produce of our seas is very great, and would probably pay well for an increased supply. Our choicer fish and shellfish are becoming rarer and the market prices are rising. The great majority of our oysters are imported from France, Holland, and America. Even in mussels we are far from being able to meet the demand. In Scotland alone the long-line fishermen use nearly a hundred millions of mussels to bait their hooks every time the lines are set, and they have to import annually many tons of these mussels at a cost of from £3 to £3 10s. a ton.

Whether the wholesale introduction of the French method of mussel culture, by means of bouchots, on to our shores would be a financial success is doubtful. Material and labor are dearer here, and beds, scars, or scalps seem, on the whole, better fitted to our local conditions; but as innumerable young mussels all around our coast perish miserably every year for want of suitable objects to attach to, there can be no reasonable doubt that the judicious erection of simple stakes or plain bouchots would serve a useful purpose, at any rate in the collection of seed, even if the further rearing be carried on by means of the bed system.

All such aquicultural processes require, however, in addition to the scientific knowledge, sufficient capital. They can not be successfully carried out on a small scale. When the zoologist has once shown, as a laboratory experiment in the zoological station, that a particular thing can be done—that this fish can be hatched or that shellfish reared—under certain conditions which promise to be an industrial success, then the matter should be carried out by the Government[3] or by capitalists on a sufficiently large scale to remove the risk of results being vitiated by temporary accident or local variation in the conditions. It is contrary, however, to our English traditions for Government to help in such a matter, and if our local sea fisheries committees have not the necessary powers nor the available funds, there remains a splendid opportunity for opulent landowners to erect sea-fish hatcheries on the shores of their estates, and for the rich merchants of our great cities to establish aquiculture in their neighboring estuaries, and by so doing instruct the fishing population, resuscitate the declining industries, and cultivate the barren shores—in all reasonable probability to their own ultimate profit.

In addition to the farming of our shores, there is a great deal to be done in promoting the fishing industries on the inshore and offshore grounds along our coast, and in connection with such work the first necessity is a thorough scientific exploration of our British seas by means of a completely fitted dredging and trawling expedition. Such exploration can only be done in little bits, spasmodically, by private

[3] We require in England a central board or Government department of fisheries, composed in part of scientific experts, and that not merely for the purpose of imposing and enforcing regulations, but still more, in order that research into fisheries problems may be instituted and aquicultural experiments carried out.

enterprise. From the time of Edward Forbes it has been the delight of British marine zoologists to explore, by means of dredging from yachts or hired vessels during their holidays, whatever areas of the neighboring seas were open to them. Some of the greatest names in the roll of our zoologists, and some of the most creditable work in British zoology, will always be associated with dredging expeditions. Forbes, Wyville Thomson, Carpenter, Gwyn Jeffreys, McIntosh, and Norman—one can scarcely think of them without recalling—

> "Hurrah for the dredge, with its iron edge,
>   And its mystical triangle,
> And its hided net, with meshes set,
>   Odd fishes to entangle!"[4]

Much good pioneer work in exploration has been done in the past by these and other naturalists, and much is now being done locally by committees or associations—by the Dublin Royal Society on the west of Ireland, by the Marine Biological Association at Plymouth, by the Fishery Board in Scotland, and by the Liverpool Marine Biology Committee in the Irish Sea; but few zoologists or zoological committees have the means, the opportunity, the time to devote, along with their professional duties, to that detailed, systematic survey of our whole British sea area which is really required. Those who have not had experience of it can scarcely realize how much time, energy, and money it requires to keep up a series of dredging expeditions, how many delays, disappointments, expensive accidents, and real hardships there are, and how often the naturalist is tempted to leave unprofitable grounds, which ought to be carefully worked over, for some more favored spot where he knows he can count upon good spoil. And yet it is very necessary that the whole ground—good or bad though it may be from the zoological point of view—should be thoroughly surveyed, physically and biologically, in order that we may know the conditions of existence which environ our fishes on their feeding grounds, their spawning grounds, their "nurseries," or whatever they may be.

The British Government has done a noble piece of work, which will redound to its everlasting credit, in providing for and carrying out the *Challenger* expedition. Now that that great enterprise is completed, and that the whole scientific world is united in appreciation of the results obtained, it would be a glorious consequence,

---

[4] The Dredging Song. (See "Memoir of Edward Forbes," p. 247).

and surely a very wise action in the interests of the national
fisheries, for the Government to fit out an expedition, in charge
of two or three zoologists and fisheries experts, to spend a couple
of years in exploring more systematically than has yet been done,
or can otherwise be done, our British coasts from the Laminarian
zone down to the deep mud. No one could be better fitted to
organize and direct such an expedition than Dr. John Murray.

Such a detailed survey of the bottom and the surface waters, of
their conditions and their contents, at all times of the year for a
couple of years, would give us the kind of information we require
for the solution of some of the more difficult fishery problems—
such as the extent and causes of the wanderings of our fishes, which
"nurseries" are supplied by particular spawning grounds, the reason
of the sudden disappearance of a fish, such as the haddock, from
a locality, and in general the history of our food fishes throughout
the year. It is creditable to our Government to have done the pioneer work in exploring the great ocean, but surely it would be at
least equally creditable to them—and perhaps more directly and
immediately profitable, if they look for some such return from
scientific work—to explore our own seas and our own sea fisheries.

There is still another subject connected with the fisheries which
the biologist can do much to elucidate—I mean the diseases of
edible animals and the effect upon man of the various diseased
conditions. It is well known that the consumption of mussels taken
from stagnant or impure water is sometimes followed by severe
symptoms of irritant poisoning which may result in rapid death.
This "musselling" is due to the presence of an organic alkaloid or
ptomaine, in the liver of the mollusk, formed doubtless by a
microorganism in the impure water. It is clearly of the greatest
importance to determine accurately under what conditions the
mussel can become infected by the microorganism, in what stage
it is injurious to man, and whether, as is supposed, steeping in
pure water with or without the addition of carbonate of soda will
render poisonous mussels fit for food.

During this last year there has been an outcry, almost amounting
to a scare, and seriously affecting the market,[5] as to the supposed
connection between oysters taken from contaminated water and
typhoid fever. This, like the musselling, is clearly a case for scientific investigation, and, with my colleague, Professor Boyce, I have
commenced a series of experiments and observations, partly at the

[5] I am told that between December and March the oyster trade decreased 75
per cent.

Port Erin Biological Station, where we have oysters laid down on different parts of the shore under very different conditions, as well as in dishes and tanks, and partly at University College, Liverpool.

Our object is to determine the effect of various conditions of water and bottom upon the life and health of the oyster, the effect of the addition of various impurities to the water, the conditions under which the oyster becomes infected with the typhoid bacillus, and the resulting effect upon the oyster, the period during which the oyster remains infectious, and, lastly, whether any simple practicable measures can be taken (1) to determine whether an oyster is infected with typhoid, and (2) to render such an oyster innocuous to man. As Professor Boyce and I propose to lay a paper upon this subject before the section, I shall not occupy further time now by a statement of our methods and results.

I have probably already sufficiently indicated to you the extent and importance of the applications of our science to practical questions connected with our fishing industries. But if the zoologist has great opportunities for usefulness, he ought always to bear in mind that he has also grave responsibilities in connection with fisheries investigations. Much depends upon the results of his work. Private enterprise, public opinion, local regulations, and even imperial legislation, may all be affected by his decisions. He ought not lightly to come to conclusions upon weighty matters. I am convinced that of all the varied lines of research in modern zoology, none contains problems more interesting and intricate than those of bionomics, oceanography, and the fisheries, and of these three series the problems connected with our fisheries are certainly not the least interesting, not the least intricate, and not the least important in their bearing upon the welfare of mankind.

~~~~~~~~~~

V. *Walfrid Ekman:*

26.   ON DEAD-WATER*

The following description is based entirely upon verbal and written accounts which I have received from a great number of sailors having experience on the subject. Special weight is laid on such statements as have been unanimously given by several authorities, or as may, for other reasons, be considered trustworthy.

Dead-water only appears near to coasts, in those places where a suitable layer of fresh or brackish water rests upon the heavier sea-water. A vessel, moving in such a place at slight or moderate speed, may happen to feel the influence of this phenomenon; it is then said that *the vessel "has taken dead-water"* or *"got into dead-water".* It is a very troublesome matter indeed. A sailing-vessel in this plight, generally refuses to answer her helm and becomes unmanageable; steamers, at times sailing-vessels also, keep their steerage, but nevertheless the dead-water is a great hindrance, causing the ship to lose her speed almost entirely. The *Fram,* for instance, though generally capable of making 4–5 knots, along the Siberian coast when heavily loaded, had her speed reduced to about 1 knot in dead-water; and a similar reduction of speed seems to be a common effect of this phenomenon. If, in addition, the vessel has to move up a river or against even a moderate current, her progress may be altogether stopped.

When dead-water is present, the sea-surface around the vessel presents a peculiar appearance, varying under different conditions. When the phenomenon takes place regularly, *a set of stripes will*

* From PROCEEDINGS OF THE NORWEGIAN NORTH POLAR EXPEDITION, 1893–1896, Vol. 5 Edited by F. Nansen. Published by the Fridtjof Nansen Fund for the Advancement of Science, Longman, Green, and Co. London, 1906. Reprinted by permission of Odd Nansen.

Vagn Walfrid Ekman (1874–1954), a Swedish oceanographer, is known for his explanation of "dead water" in relation to ship movement. In a 1905 paper "On the Influence of the Earth's Rotation on Ocean Currents" he developed the major ocean concepts now known as Ekman transport and the Ekman spiral. Ekman also invented several varieties of widely used current meters which bear his name.

be observed astern crossing the wake, or a couple of stripes stretch obliquely aft from the sides of the ship. They are described as "rips" or whirling "current backs"[1]; also as stripes of hopping wavelets. These stripes often stretch far away from the ship. Prof. NANSEN himself does not speak of any such rips or stripes but he observed *very long and low waves*, stretching across the wake of the *Fram*.

Round the ship's stern a wake is formed of unrippled, eddying water, which is said to follow the ship and even to advance towards her, so that *a boat in tow will be carried in close up under her stern*. The stripes issuing from the sides of the vessel seem to form the boundary line between the water following the vessel and the water outside. It is commonly believed that a bulk of water is clinging to the vessel; and this proceeds through the water outside, with a roar. It draws off from the vessel with increase of wind, and *vice versâ*. Likewise the stripes crossing the wake are said to come nearer to the stern, the more the wind slackens.

It is a peculiarity of dead-water, that *it always appears quite suddenly*. Its influence upon the steering of a ship, or the appearance of the sea-surface may, in some cases, be subject to gradual modifications; its effect upon the speed of the ship always take place, however, quite suddenly, the speed being at once reduced from its ordinary magnitude to a small fraction thereof. It very often happens, moreover, that the ship has dead-water at the very outset. Just as suddenly does the ship recover her ordinary speed when she gets rid of the dead-water—"as if cut away from a mooring astern". Sometimes she soon gets free, but on particular occasions vessels may remain helpless in the dead-water for a whole day or even longer.

Usually it is only vessels in tow and sailing vessels in a light breeze (vessels with comparatively small motive power), that are influenced by dead-water. It has happened, however, that steamers have been caught by it. It is said that vessels do not run the risk of falling into dead-water when moving at above a certain speed, *e. g.* 3, 4, or 5 knots according to conditions prevailing.

The phenomenon shows its simplest phase, when a *steamer* or a *ship in tow* takes dead-water. There is, however, a difference in steering, between screw-steamers and ships in tow; thanks to the influence of the screw the former are able to maintain their course; towed ships on the other hand, do not answer their helm at all, and often in narrow waterways, the tow-rope must be shortened,

---

[1] Smooth or agitated streaks often seen on the sea, denoting the boundary between two currents with different motions.

to prevent the ship from sheering off, with the consequent risk of running ashore.

If the engine be stopped, a ship in dead-water does not lose her motion gradually, as under ordinary circumstances, but she *stops short,* and may perhaps be sucked astern. In navigating the mouth of the river Glommen similar and still more remarkable effects of dead-water have been observed. The vessel is followed by a long train of the dead-water stripes described above. When the tug-boat is stopped and the towed ship in consequence stops short, the dead-water stripes overtake her, *and, as they pass, the ship swings backwards and forwards, once for each stripe that passes.* In the same way, vessels made fast to the shore, will be pushed up and down the river when a ship in dead-water has been towed past them; the power of the stripes being at times so violent as to tear a vessel away from her moorings.

Sailing-vessels, when caught by dead-water, usually do not answer their helm and, in spite of the rudder and various manoeuvres with the sails, take a certain course depending on the direction of the wind; often they run up in the wind with sails shivering. Therefore, the loss of steerage is generally the most troublesome effect of the dead-water on sailing-vessels, although in particular cases, the vessel may be kept to her course with more or less effort. Owing to the wind the aspect of the sea is often asymmetrical, the stripe issuing from the windward side being best developed. When the sea is rippled by the breeze the stripe on the windward side may be invisible, whereas on the leeward side where the sea is smoother, it may still be seen. Often, however, the dead-water appears in its regular aspect.

In the Kattegat the phenomenon is sometimes less regular. As long as the ship's course is between two certain points she may answer her helm quite willingly, but she cannot be made to head a course beyond either of these two limits. The wake and the "dead-water stripes" have often an asymmetric direction. The cause of this is, no doubt, to be ascribed to the lighter brackish water running as a narrow surface-current on the top of the heavier sea-water, so that the upper and the lower parts of the ship's body move in water of different velocities. Such surface-currents were directly observed in two cases mentioned below. It is evident that the two currents—especially if the ship draws more water aft than forward—tend to turn her head in a certain direction. To both sides of this direction she may be made to head, though within certain limits, depending on the strength and direction of the surface and under-currents, and of the wind. Thus the currents in the sea are able to considerably modify the effects of the dead-water. It is very probable that particular accidents mentioned by the mariners as "dead-water" are mainly caused by such surface- and under-currents. Some Scandinavian mariners apparently give the name of dead-water to various effects upon their vessels, which cause them to lose their steerage. Thus, for instance, when a vessel in a light wind, is affected by a whirl-pool or when she is brought out of her course by the influence of currents of different directions, she is sometimes said to have got into "dead-water" although the cause of the mishap has nothing in common with this peculiar phenomenon.

It was mentioned above (p. 135) that vessels run the risk of getting into dead-water if moving at below a certain speed depending on the conditions prevailing, but not when proceeding at higher speeds. In particular cases even steamers have "taken dead-water", whereas, in certain places, only sailing-vessels, in a very faint breeze, are exposed to it. It is therefore evident that dead-water may be of varying *strength* in different places and under different conditions. Without further defining this notion, I will give a summary of *the experiences of several Scandinavian mariners as to the strength of dead-water under different conditions.*

First of all, dead-water seems less effective the smaller be *the difference of density* between the surface layer and the sea-water below, or the more the former has mingled with the latter. In one of the strongest cases of dead-water that we know of—the experience of the *Fram* at Taimur—this difference of density was about as great as possible (fresh drinking water on the sea-surface, and pure sea-water on a level with the bottom-cock of the engine-room). In the Norwegian fjords, where the conditions are unusually good for river-water spreading almost unmixed over pure sea-water, most marked cases of dead-water are quite general. In the Kattegat, the density of the sea-water is not so great, and the river-water, before flowing out over the sea, becomes much mixed with sea-water. Dead-water appears there only with a light breeze, after some days of fine weather, and not at all when the water-layers are stirred by previous storms. (In the neighbourhood of the mouth of the Göta River, however, strong dead-water has been experienced.) In the Baltic, where the specific gravity is less than 1.006 or 1.007, dead-water is only exceptionally observed, and then only with very feeble wind.

Furthermore, *the relation between the thickness of the surface-layer and the draught of the vessel* is of great importance as regards the effect of dead-water. At the mouth of the Glommen, for instance, small craft experience dead-water farther out at sea, where the surface-layer has less thickness, than large vessels, by which it is again felt higher up the river. According as the outflow of fresh water increases, the region where dead-water appears withdraws from the river mouths seawards, and *vice versâ.* In winter, when there is little water in the Glommen, dead-water principally appears in the river proper, between the town and the Sarp rapids; but in summer its region is *below* the town and extends as far as the outermost rocks of the Kristiania Fjord.

Another fact, probably connected with the one stated above, is that dead-water is generally stronger in a moderate sea-breeze, than when a land-breeze is blowing. For, as a result of the sea-breeze, the fresh water is retained at the coast and its depth becomes in concequence greater, while the land-breeze carries most of it out to sea. On the Glommen the dead-water is said to be stronger at flood-tide, than at ebb—possibly owing to the tidal currents or to variations in the depth of the fresh-water layer.

Some of the narrators attribute importance to *the shape of the vessel:* it is said that a sharp built vessel is more exposed to dead-water than one of bluff design. One of my authorities has stated the contrary. Those that are laden or of deep draught are always more liable than are light ones.

Even after taking into account all the above circumstances, there is nevertheless something highly capricious about the appearance of dead-water; and it is often impossible to understand why, in a certain case, a vessel has not "taken dead-water", and in another case, why she did not escape its influence. A ship may, for instance, be towed without difficulty from one place to another, but another similar or smaller ship being shortly after towed the same way, will be so forcibly held by dead-water as scarcely to be moveable from the spot. On another occasion a sailing-vessel or a vessel in tow may be held by the dead-water, while other similar vessels, with less or equal moving power, may pass quite near to her without being in the least troubled by the phenomenon.

Vessels apparently often "take dead-water" on account of the wind slackening or as a result of the vessel entering water-layers of a different character; sometimes the cause of getting free may likewise be put down to a similar influence. But often the change cannot be explained by any perceivable external cause. Often a vessel gets into dead-water while tacking, or on account of bad steering, or when her speed is from any cause temporarily slackened. If a sailing-vessel takes dead-water on account of the wind slackening to below a certain strength, the wind, as a rule, must freshen to *above* this strength to free the ship again. In general, when a vessel's speed is temporarily slackened and she gets into dead-water, she may be unable to recover her head-way for some shorter or longer time, even when the conditions for full speed are present again.

Mariner's opinions of dead-water and its causes vary somewhat, and to judge from their explanations of the phenomenon they generally acknowledge they do not understand it. Most of my authorities, nevertheless agree in the observation, that it depends on the existence of a surface layer of fresh or brackish water. It is a general opinion, that "the fresh water sticks to the vessel" and is dragged along with it on the top of the salt water, thus impeding the speed—the fresh water on account of its forward motion, has no influence upon the rudder. Other narrators declare that the phenomenon is owing to the fresh water running as a surface-current above the salt water; if a ship moves at a slow speed, the rudder becomes too much influenced by the currents, so that the vessel loses her steerage. Another of my correspondents has advanced an explanation somewhat more correct. Mr. M. Leegaard, harbour engineer, explains the phenomenon as owing to the turning effect of currents on the ship's body itself, and, as already mentioned, this is sometimes the case.

With a view to *removing the dead-water*, seamen have made use of all sorts of odd means, which they believed would "loosen" or "rub away" the "dead-water crust", that is, the fresh water. Such means are:

Sheering off from the course,
Running the whole crew forward and aft on deck,
Pumping violently,
Scooping up a quantity of water on deck,
Pouring out petroleum ahead of the ship,
Dragging a hawser under the ship's bottom from stem to stern,
Working the rudder rapidly,
Firing guns into the water (on men of war),
Cutting and beating the water alongside with oars or handspikes etc.,
Dragging a seine along the ship's side, and so on.

Sometimes the two last mentioned methods are said to have been successful, but in most cases all of them are by the narrators themselves, declared to have been of no use. I may mention now, that on account of the explanation of the phenomenon which will be given later they must be expected to be of no appreciable effect, although several of them are not quite unreasonable.

Tug-boats, when their vessels in tow get into dead-water, have more effective means of getting them loose again, and these are said to often succeed. The simplest method is to let the tug stop for a while, until the dead-water stripes have passed by, and then to go full speed ahead again. Another effective way is said to be, to have the tow-rope as short as possible so that the screw violently stirs up the water around the towed vessel: or for the tug-boat to go to and fro along the sides of the ship and then to make full speed again. It is a singular experience, recorded by several observers, that a ship in dead-water may get free if passed by a steamer, even at a distance of several ship's lengths.

It is a difficult thing to state anything certain concerning *the frequency of "dead-water"*; the accounts are much too scanty and incomplete. It must of course, be expected *a priori* that the greatest numbers of accounts should be received from those fjords and other waters [of Scandinavia] that are most frequented, and that accounts should be altogether wanting from several small places with very little traffic, or where Prof. Nansen's request in the newspapers did not become known. Taking these circumstances into account, it seems probable that dead-water occurs in all Norwegian fjords into which any considerable quantity of fresh water flows and, although with less strength, in the Kattegat as well. As a general rule the phenomenon seems to appear in particular cases, only when circumstances are favourable, but yet not so very infrequently. In the environs of the mouth of the Glommen it is constantly feared; the towing masters must take it into account and not take too great a load at the risk of sticking in dead-water. Several narrators declare they have been out in dead-water on many occasions that they do not think it necessary to mention specially. All these cases, not specially described, are left out of account.

Still more difficult would it be to draw any reliable conclusions as to *the occurrence of dead-water beyond Scandinavia.* To my appeal published in at least 36 foreign newspapers,[2] I have not received more than 18 answers, of which number half are of decidedly negative import. *Only two narrators have certainly experienced dead-water themselves,* one in the Kristiania Fjord and the other inside Vancouver Island (Canada). It is not probable, therefore, that dead-water is at all as decided or as common on other seas as in Scandinavia; for one cannot assume that a phenomenon so troublesome and so characteristic should escape the attention of seamen. On the other hand, four of my Scandinavian authorities mention dead-water in the Mediterranean and off the

[2] 6 British, 1 German, 2 Dutch, 1 Belgian, 11 French, 2 Italian, 2 Chinese, 2 Brazilian, 1 in Argentina, 4 in United States of America and 4 Canadian.

great river-mouths of North and South America. Some old stories also tell us about certain strange adventures on the Mediterranean which doubtless were cases of dead-water, although owing to the narrators' modes of explanation, they would rather seem to be myths. Vessels propelled by oars or running before a fair wind were suddenly stopped in their course by a strong, unknown force. It was commonly believed that this was caused by a small fish the *Remora*, sucking itself fast to the ship's body, and it was said that but *one* of these fishes was required to hold a ship immovably. The belief in this power of the *Remora* seems to have survived far into later times, and for that reason it seems probable that the phenomena in question have appeared occasionally.

From all these circumstances I conclude that dead-water may occur at every place where fresh-water flows out over the sea, but that from some reason or other it is comparatively seldom met with beyond Scandinavia or appears in a less decided manner than in the Norwegian fjords.

Vilhelm F. K. Bjerknes:

27.   MOTIONS IN THE SEA*

Distribution of Mass. Every motion consists in the displacement of masses. Only in certain definite distributions of mass will the causes of motion cease to act. As introductory to the investigation of the conditions of equilibrium and motion of the atmosphere and the hydrosphere, we will therefore have to consider the distribution of mass in general, and the methods of finding and representing it.

For the numerical representation of the distribution of mass in a continuous medium, such as air or water, we have two methods: We can specify the volume occupied by the different unit-masses, or we can specify the masses present in the different units of volume. In the first case we register the *specific volume*, in the

* From V. Bjerknes, DYNAMIC METEOROLOGY AND HYDROGRAPHY, the Carnegie Institution, Washington, D.C. 1910. By permission of the publisher.

Vilhelm Friman Koren Bjerknes, 1862–1951, was a Norwegian physicist whose polar front theory of cyclones formed the basis of modern weather forecasting.

second the *density* of the medium. The number representing one of these quantities is the reciprocal of that representing the other. These quantities are completely equivalent in representing the distribution of mass. But which to choose is a question of importance, as it leads to one or the other of two different methods already referred to of formulating the conditions of equilibrium and motion of the medium. Theoretically neither of these methods has any advantage over the other, but they supplement each other in a convenient manner. We shall therefore develop both side by side.

Specific volume or density of atmospheric air or of sea-water are as a rule not observed directly. Generally they will have to be calculated from other quantities, more easily observed with sufficient precision. These quantities are pressure, temperature, and humidity in the case of the atmosphere; depth, temperature, and salinity in the case of the sea.

Remarks on Hydrographic Observations. Oceanographic observations are not yet organized systematically. But the general principles for their organization will be the same as for the meteorological observations. Hydrographic expeditions going out occasionally can only contribute to the knowledge of the average state, *i. e.*, to the climatology of the sea. But the final aim must be that of investigating the actual states and their variations. The organization must then be governed by the principle of simultaneity. The investigations will have to be performed not by one luxuriously fitted ship, passing months or years at sea, but by the cooperation of small ships going out simultaneously.

The demands regarding the degree of simultaneity and the intervals between the epochs of observation will depend upon the rapidity of the changes. There are indications both for rapid changes (among which the tidal phenomena in the deeper strata will play an important part) as well as for slow seasonal changes and changes from year to year. The problem will be to organize observations so as to separate from each other the changes of different rapidity and to investigate them as much as possible independently of each other. But a serious discussion on the suitable method of organization will only be possible by and by, as our knowledge of the oceanic phenomena advances.

Investigations of the Physical Properties of Sea-Water.—The physical properties of sea-water have been subject to elaborate investigations in connection with the international exploration of the northern European waters.[1]

---

[1] MARTIN KNUDSEN: Berichte über die Konstantenbestimmungen zur Aufstellung der hydrographischen Tabellen von Carl Forch, Martin Knudsen, und

The specific volume of sea-water and its reciprocal value, the density, depend upon three variables—pressure, temperature, and salinity. Generally the salinity is not determined directly, but deduced from the content of chlorine found by titration, s denoting the salinity and Cl the quantity of chlorine, both expressed in per milles ($^0/_{00}$) of weight. s and Cl are, according to Martin Knudsen, connected by the equation

$$s = 0.030 + 1.8050 \; Cl$$

By this equation, which is tabulated in Martin Knudsen's tables, we can pass from the independent variable Cl used by Martin Knudsen to the independent variable s, which we shall use consistently.

To express the results obtained for the specific volume or the density of sea-water, we shall introduce the following notations: a_{srp} means the specific volume and ρ_{srp} the density of sea-water of salinity $s^0/_{00}$, temperature τ° C., and sea-pressure of ρ decibars. By sea-pressure we then mean the total pressure diminished by the pressure exerted by the atmosphere against the surface of the sea. The decibar is employed as a practical unit instead of the unit centibar belonging to the m.t.s. system, because the pressure increases approximately by 1 decibar for every meter increase of depth.

Instead of writing the whole number representing a value of the density ρ, say the number 1.02674, practical hydrographers usually write the four last figures 26.74. This quantity being denoted by σ, we have thus

$$\sigma_{srp} = (\rho_{srp} - 1) \cdot 1000$$

On the Observations of the Sea-Motions. If the observations of the air-motions are too scarce, this is still more the case with those

S. P. L. Sörensen. Mémoires de l'Academie Royale des Sciences de Danemark. Copenhague, 1902.

MARTIN KNUDSEN: Berechnung der hydrographischen Tabellen und Diskussion der Ergebnisse. Wissenschaftliche Meeresuntersuchungen herausgegeben von der Komission zur Untersuchung der deutschen Meere in Kiel, Band 2, 1903.

MARTIN KNUDSEN: Hydrographical Tables according to the measurings of Carl Forch, J. P. Jacobsen, Martin Knudsen, and S. P. L. Sörensen. Copenhagen and London, 1901.

V. WALFRID EKMAN: Die Zusammendrückbarkeit des Meerwassers, etc. Conseil permanent International pour L'Exploration de la Mer. Publication de Circonstance N° 43. Copenhague, 1908.

of oceanic motions. Quantitative measurements are only to be had exceptionally. The motions of the sea's surface is in many cases known qualitatively from the drift of floating objects or of bottles thrown out for the purpose of investigation. Qualitative conclusions as to the motions in the deeper sheets can be drawn from the measurements of the salinity, this giving information as to the origin of the waters. Similar conclusions can be made also on the basis of the examination of the organisms contained in the water. But none of these observations are of the quantitative nature which can give rise to a closer kinematic analysis.

For this reason we can work out no example of a kinematic diagnosis of the sea-motions. But the principle of the methods to be employed in the case of the sea, as soon as serviceable material of observations is produced, will be sufficiently illustrated by the example worked out for the case of the atmosphere. We shall therefore only make occasional references to the sea.

The most important point to emphasize is the necessity of producing sufficient data of direct observations of the sea-motions from the surface as well as from all depths. Suitable instruments for doing it have already been invented.[2] It remains only to bring them into application on a sufficiently large scale and according to rational principles.

[2] V. W. *Ekman:* Kurze Beschreibung eines Propell-Strommessers. Conseil Permanent International pour l'Exploration de la Mer. Publications de Circonstance No. 24. Copenhague, 1905.

Otto Pettersson: Beschreibung des Bifilarstrommessers. Publications de Circonstance No. 25, Copenhague, 1905.

A. M. *van Roosendaal und C. H. Wind:* Prüfung von Strommessern und Strommessungsversuche in der Nordsee. Publications de Circonstance No. 26. Copenhague, 1905.

Fridtjof Nansen: Methods for measuring Direction and Velocity of Currents in the Sea. With an Appendix by V. W. *Ekman:* Current Measurements by means of buoy and releasing clock-work. Publications de Circonstance No. 34. Copenhague, 1906.

Helland-Hansen: Current Measurements in Norwegian fjords, the Norwegian Sea, and the North Sea in 1906. Bergens Museums Aarbog No. 15. Bergen, 1907.

Otto Pettersson: Strömstudier vid Östersjöns portar. Svenska hydrografisk-biologiska Kommissionens, Skrifter III. Gotenburg, 1908.

B. *Helland-Hansen and Fridtjof Nansen:* The Norwegian Sea. Report on Norwegian fishery and marine investigations, Vol. II, No. 2. Christiania, 1909.

~~~~~~~~~~~~~~~~~~~~~

Alfred Wegener:

28.   CONTINENTAL DRIFT*

He who examines the opposite coasts of the South Atlantic Ocean must be somewhat struck by the similarity of the shapes of the coast-lines of Brazil and Africa. Not only does the great right-angled bend formed by the Brazilian coast at Cape San Roque find its exact counterpart in the re-entrant angle of the African coast-line near the Cameroons, but also, south of these two corresponding points, every projection of the Brazilian side corresponds to a similarly shaped bay in the African, and conversely each indentation in the Brazilian coast has a complementary protuberance on the African. Experiment with a compass on a globe shows that their dimensions agree accurately.

This phenomenon was the starting-point of a new conception of the nature of the earth's crust and of the movements occurring therein; this new idea is called the theory of the displacement of continents, or, more shortly, the displacement theory, since its most prominent component is the assumption of great horizontal drifting movements which the continental blocks underwent in the course of geological time and which presumably continue even to-day.

According to this idea, to take a particular case, millions of years ago the South American continental plateau lay directly adjoining the African plateau, even forming with it one large connected mass. This first split in Cretaceous time into two parts, which then, like floating icebergs drifted farther and farther apart. Similarly, North America was close to Europe; and, at least from Newfoundland and Ireland northward, they formed with Greenland

---

* From THE ORIGINS OF CONTINENTS AND OCEANS by Alfred Wegener, Dover Publications, Inc. New York, 1966. By permission of the Publisher. Originally published in Germany in 1915.

Alfred Lothar Wegener, 1880–1930, was a German geologist, meteorologist, and arctic explorer who made several expeditions to Greenland where he established meteorological stations. Wegener lost his life while on his last expedition.

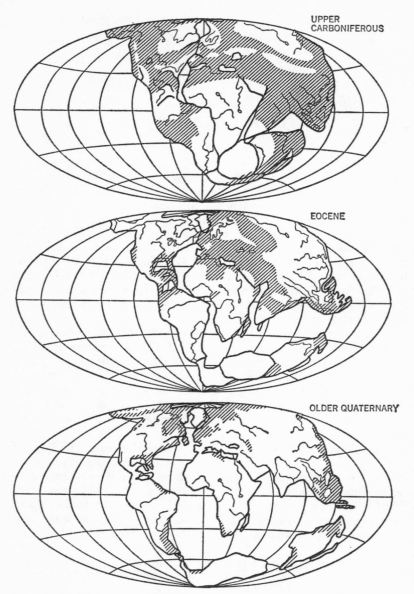

Fig. 28–1. Reconstructions of the map of the world for three periods according to the Displacement Theory. Shaded areas represent shallow seas; present-day outlines and rivers only for the purpose of identification.

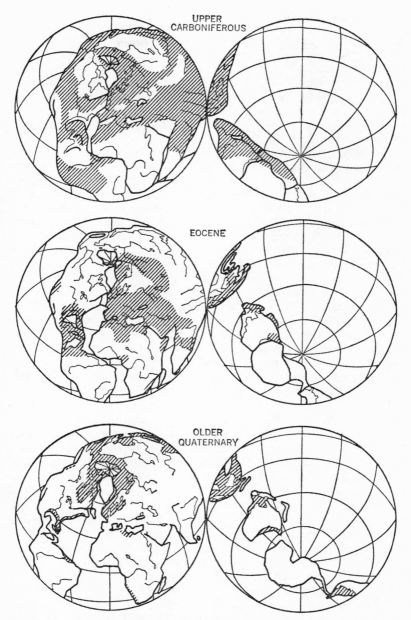

Fig. 28–2. The same reconstructions as in Fig. 28–1, but in another projection.

one connected block, which broke up by a forked rift near Greenland at the end of Tertiary time and farther north even in the Quaternary era; whereupon the constituent blocks moved apart from one another. The shelves, the portions of the continental masses overflowed by shallow seas, will always be considered in this book as parts of the blocks, the boundaries of which for great distances are not given by the coast-lines, but by the steep descent to the deep sea floor.

Similarly, it will be assumed that Antarctica, Australia and India lay adjoining South Africa, and with the latter and South America formed, until the beginning of the Jurassic period, a single large—even if partly submerged at times by shallow water—continental area, which in the course of Jurassic, Cretaceous and Tertiary time split and crumbled into smaller blocks which drifted away from each other in all directions. The three maps of the earth reproduced in Figs. 28–1 and 28–2 show these developments during the Upper Carboniferous, Eocene and Lower Quaternary periods. The case of India is somewhat different: it was originally connected by a long continental tract, mostly, it is true, covered by shallow seas, to the Asiatic continent. After, the separation of India from Australia on one side (in the Lower Jurassic) and from Madagascar on the other (during the transition from the Chalk to Tertiary) this long connecting portion was more and more folded together through the continuous gradual approach of India to Asia and constitutes to-day the mightiest mountain folds of the earth, the Himalayas and the numerous folded ranges of the high lands of Asia.

In other regions also the displacement of the blocks occurs in causal connection with the origin of the mountain systems. By the westward drift of the two Americas their anterior margin was folded together to form the mighty range of the Andes (which stretches from Alaska to Antarctica) as a result of the opposition of the ancient well-cooled and therefore resistant floor of the Pacific. A similar case is that of the Australian block, which includes New Guinea since it is only separated therefrom by a shelf. The recent high ranges of New Guinea occur on the side which is anterior with reference to the movement; as our map shows, this direction of movement was different before the break from Antarctica, for the present east coast was then the front side. Next the mountains of New Zealand lying immediately in front of this coast were folded, later becoming detached as festoons of islands by the altered direction of movement and then lagging behind. The present cordilleras of East Australia originated in a still older period; they were formed (at the same time as the more ancient folds, "Precordilleras," in South and North America, which are the foundations of the Andes) on the front margin of the continental masses, which were drifting as a whole before the separation.

Besides this westward wandering we also see to a large extent a striving towards the equator of the continental blocks. With this is connected the formation of the great Tertiary belt of folding stretching from the Himalayas to the Alps and Atlas mountains which were then in the equatorial zone.

The previously mentioned separation from the Australian block of the former coastal ranges of New Zealand, forming later a festoon of islands, leads us up to the phenomenon that smaller portions of the blocks are left behind by the westward wandering of the larger blocks. In this manner the marginal ranges of the East Asiatic continental coast separated as festoons of islands. The Lesser and Greater Antilles lag behind the movement of the Central American block, and similarly the so-called arc of the South Antilles between Patagonia and West Antarctica. Indeed all blocks tapering in a meridional direction show a curve of their points towards the east on account of this lag. The latter is well shown in the south point of Greenland, the submarine shelf of Florida, Tierra del Fuego and Graham Land, and the manner in which Ceylon has broken away from India.

It will easily be seen that this complete and extensive conception of the displacement theory must emanate from a definite acceptance of the relation of the oceans to the continental blocks. In fact, it is assumed that these two phenomena are fundamentally distinct, that the continental blocks with a thickness of about 100 km. swim in a magma out which they only project about 5 km. and which is uncovered in the floor of the oceans.

Thus the outermost lithosphere no longer completely covers the entire earth (whether it ever did can be left undecided), but has become smaller and smaller by continued folding and compression during the course of geological time, thereby increasing in thickness and splitting ultimately into more and more separated smaller continental blocks. The latter to-day cover but a quarter of the earth. The floors of the oceans form the free surface of the next layer of the body of the earth which is also assumed to exist under the continental blocks. The existence of this involves the geophysical side of the displacement theory.

The detailed establishment of this new hypothesis will form the major part of the book. Some historical remarks, however, should be given beforehand.

The first notion of the displacement of continents came to me in 1910 when, on studying the map of the world, I was impressed by the congruency of both sides of the Atlantic coasts, but I disregarded it at the time because I did not consider it probable. In the autumn of 1911 I became acquainted (through a collection of references, which came into my hands by accident) with the palæontological evidence of the former land connection between Brazil and Africa, of which I had not previously known. This induced me to undertake a hasty analysis of the results of research in this direction in the spheres of geology and palæontology, whereby such important confirmations were yielded, that I was convinced of the fundamental correctness of my idea. I first brought forward the idea on January 6th, 1912, in a lecture to the Geological Association of Frankfort-on-Main entitled "Die Herausbildung der Grossformen der Erdrinde (Kontinente und Ozeane) auf Geophysikalischer Grundlage." This lecture was followed on January 10th by a second on "Horizontalverschiebungen der Kontinente" to the Society for the Advancement of Science of Marburg. In the same year (1912), also, both of the first publications on the theory took place.[1]

Afterwards the participation in the traverse of Greenland under J. P. Koch of 1912/13 and later war-service hindered me from further elaboration of the theory. In 1915, however, I was able to use a long sick-leave to give a somewhat detailed description of the theory in the Vieweg series under the title of this book.[2] As a second edition of this was necessary after the close of the war, the publishers generously consented to transfer the book from the Vieweg to the Wissenschaft series, whereby the possibility was given for a considerably enlarged work.[3] The present edition is again virtually rewritten, as the process of the grouping of the data which affect the question according to the view-point of the new theory has meanwhile made further progress and an extensive recent literature about the subject has appeared.

During the above-mentioned work of examining the literature I several times chanced on views concordant with my own by older authors. Thus a rotation of the entire crust of the earth—but whose parts, however, did not alter their relative positions—had already been assumed by many authors, as Löffelholz von

[1] A. Wegener, "Die Entstehung der Kontinente," *Peterm. Mitt.*, 1912, pp. 185–195, 253–256, 305–309, and in a somewhat abbreviated form under the same title in *Geol. Rundsch.*, 3, Part 4, pp. 276–292, 1912.

[2] A. Wegener, *Die Entstehung der Kontinente und Ozeane*, Samml. Vieweg. No. 23, pp. 1–94. Brunswick, 1915.

[3] Second edition, *Die Wissenschaft*, No. 66, pp. 1–135. Brunswick, 1920.

Colberg,[4] Kreichgauer,[5] Sir John Evans and others. H. Wettstein has written a remarkable book,[6] in which, however, among many absurdities, a leaning towards great relative horizontal displacements of the continents is shown. The continents, (the submarine shelves of which however he did not consider) undergo, according to him, not only displacement but also deformation; they wander collectively westwards drawn by the tidal forces of the sun on the viscous body of the earth (as also E. H. L. Schwarz assumed in the *Geogr. Journ.*, 1912, pp. 284–299). But the oceans were considered by him as sunken continents, and he expressed fantastic ideas about the so-called geographical homologies and other problems of the face of the earth, which we will pass over. Like the present writer, Pickering in a work on the similarities of the South Atlantic coasts[7] has expressed the supposition that America was torn off from Europe-Africa and was dragged across the breadth of the Atlantic Ocean. But he did not consider that all the facts of the geological history of both these continents necessitated the assumption of an earlier connection up to the Cretaceous period, and thus he places the connection in the very remote past, and thought that the breaking away was connected with the theory of G. H. Darwin that the moon was thrown off the earth. Traces of this he believed are still to be seen in the Pacific basin.[8]

[4] Carl, Baron Löffelholz von Colberg, *Die Drehung der Erdkruste in geologischen Zeitäumen*, pp. 1–62; Münich, 1886. Second, much enlarged edition, pp. 1–247, Münich, 1895.

[5] D. Kreichgauer, *Die Äquatorfrage in der Geologie*, pp. 1–248. Steyl, 1902.

[6] H. Wettstein, *Die Strömungen des Festen, Flüssigen und Gasförmigen und ihre Bedeutung für Geologie, Astronomie, Klimatologie und Meteorologie*, pp. 1–406. Zürich, 1880.

[7] *Journal of Geology*, **15**, pp. 23–38, 1907: also *Gæa*, **43**, p. 385, 1907, and *Scot. Geogr. Mag.*, **23**, pp. 523–535, 1907.

[8] This theory of Darwin's, popular with many geologists, is pure hypothesis, and is held to be untenable by Schwarzschild, Liapunow, Rudzki, See and others. My own views on the origin of the moon, which are on totally different lines, may be found in A. Wegener, *Die Entstehung der Mondkrater*, Samml. Vieweg, No. 55, pp. 1–48. Brunswick, 1921.

~~~~~~~~~~~~~~~

John Murray and Johan Hjort:
29.   THE DEPTHS OF THE OCEAN*

The phenomena displayed at the surface of the ocean have been the object of observation from the earliest ages,—waves, currents, winds, tides, and the temperature of the water were matters of very great importance and concern to the earliest navigators. It was not, however, till about the time of the famous *Challenger* Expedition, nearly forty years ago, that any systematic attempts were made to examine the deeper and more remote regions, or to explore the physical and biological conditions of the ocean as a whole.

In the opinion of astronomers the earth is the only planet of our solar system which has oceans on its surface. If Mars and the moon once had oceans, these have apparently disappeared within their rocky crusts. Our earth is in what is called the terraqueous stage of a planet's development. The ocean is less than the hydrosphere, which is regarded as including all lakes and rivers, the water-vapour in the atmosphere, and the water which has penetrated deep into the lithosphere.

If the whole globe were covered with an ocean of uniform depth, and if there were no differences of density in the shells of the rocky crust, the surface of the ocean would be a perfect spheroid of revolution. But, as every one knows, the surface of the earth is made up of land and water, and at all events the superficial layers of the lithosphere are heterogeneous. The figure of the earth departs from a true spheroid of revolution, and is

* From THE DEPTHS OF THE OCEAN by John Murray and Johan Hjort. Macmillan and Company, Ltd. London, 1912. By permission of the publisher. (Reissued by Wheldon and Wesley, New York, 1964.)

British oceanographer and marine naturalist Sir John Murray, 1841–1914, took an active role in explorations of the North Atlantic Ocean and was influential in causing Great Britain to annex Christmas Island (1889) for scientific investigations.

Johan Hjort, 1869–1948, was director of fisheries in Norway from 1900–1917. An oceanographer and biologist, Dr. Hjort was a professor at the University of Oslo from 1929–1939.

called a geoid. The surface of the ocean is, therefore, farther removed from the centre of the earth at some points than at others; the gravitational attraction of emerged land causes a heaping-up of the sea around continental and other coasts. The extent of this heaping-up near elevated continents, and consequent lowering of the sea-surface far from land, appear to have been much exaggerated. The difference of level due to this cause has sometimes been estimated at thousands of feet. Recent researches indicate that the differences of level at different points of the sea-surface do not depart more than 300 to 400 feet from a true spheroid of revolution.

The other causes which, in addition to the tides, may affect the level of the ocean are meteorologic, such as barometric pressure, temperature, the action of wind, evaporation, precipitation, the inflow of rivers, but in no cases do these affect the level of the ocean more than a few inches or a few feet.

All depths recorded by the sounding-line in the open sea are referred to the surface of the ocean, and near coasts to mean sea-level. The first method of ascertaining the depth of the ocean was by means of the hand line and lead, armed with tallow, used by ordinary sailors.

From time immemorial soundings were taken by hand with a plummet, always in shallow water near land, but attempts have not been wanting to sound the ocean without the aid of a line. Thus about the middle of the fifteenth century Cardinal Nicolaus Cusanus invented a bathometer, consisting of a hollow sphere with a heavy weight attached by means of a hook; on touching the bottom the weight was detached, and the sphere returned to the surface, the interval of time from the launching of the apparatus to the re-appearance of the sphere at the surface indicating the depth. A century later Puehler improved on Cusanus' bathometer by adding a piece of apparatus (clepsydra) to measure the time from the disappearance to the re-appearance of the float, using for this purpose a clay vase with a small orifice at the bottom, through which water was made to enter during the period of the experiment, the amount of water in the vase indicating the depth. Alberti subsequently replaced the sphere by a light, bent metal tube. In 1667 Robert Hooke described in the *Philosophical Transactions* a similar apparatus, shown in the tailpiece to Chapter IV., with which experiments were made in the Indian Ocean, but there was always doubt as to the moment when the float returned to the surface, and to remedy this Hooke introduced first a clockwork odometer to register the descent, and then two odometers—one for the descent and the other for the ascent. These various forms of bathometers, though interesting historically, proved of little practical value.

Soundings in shallow water first appeared on a map by Juan de la Cosa in 1504, and soundings were laid down on maps by Gerard Mercator in 1585 and by Lucas Janszon Waghenaer in 1586.

Probably the first attempt at oceanographical research to which the term "scientific" may be applied is Magellan's unsuccessful effort to determine the depth of the Pacific Ocean during the first circumnavigation of the globe. In 1521, we are told, Magellan tried to sound the ocean between the two coral islands, St. Paul and Los Tiburones in the Low Archipelago, making use of the sounding lines carried by explorers at that period, which were only 100 to 200 fathoms in length. He failed to touch bottom, and therefore concluded that he had reached the deepest part of the ocean. This first authentic attempt at deep-sea sounding ever made in the open sea is historically extremely interesting, though scientifically the result was negative.

The expedition of Edmund Halley, Astronomer-Royal, in 1699, to improve our knowledge concerning longitude and the variation of the compass, was a purely scientific voyage, though it may be said that scientific voyages were really initiated at the time of James Cook in the second half of the eighteenth century.

Cruquius introduced bathymetrical contours on a chart of the River Merwede published in 1728. Thus contour lines were first used on maps to show the depths of the sea and not the heights of the land.

In a map published by Philippe Buache in 1737 we find the bottom of the sea again represented by isobathic curves, intended to show that certain elevations of the sea-floor correspond to the orography of the neighbouring land. He develops these ideas in his Essay on Physical Geography, published in 1752, maintaining that the globe is sustained by chains of mountains crossing the sea as well as the land, forming as it were the framework of the globe—a view previously expressed by Father Athanasius Kircher. His conception of submarine mountains was a first step towards founding geography on the real form and relief of each region.

The dredge seems to have been first used by two Italians, Marsigli and Donati, about the year 1750, for obtaining marine organisms from shallow water, and a modification of this form was introduced by O. F. Müller in 1799, which was known as the naturalist's dredge.

In the middle of the eighteenth century Dalrymple and Davy

made observations on the temperature of the equatorial currents during a voyage to the East Indies.

In 1770 Benjamin Franklin published the first map of the Gulf Stream, and in 1776 Charles Blagden was engaged in the study of temperature distribution on the North American coasts, reporting on his results to the Royal Society of London in 1781.

During Cook's voyages (1772–73), temperature observations beneath the surface were taken by the Forsters, father and son, but the first use of self-registering thermometers for determining the temperature beneath the surface of the sea was during Lord Mulgrave's expedition to the Arctic in 1773 by Dr. Irvine, who seems also to have constructed a water-bottle for bringing up water-samples from various depths, one sample giving a reading of 40° Fahr., while the surface temperature was 55° Fahr. During this expedition also some of the earliest attempts at deep-sea sounding were made by Captain Phipps, the deepest sounding being 683 fathoms, from which depth he brought up a sample of Blue mud.

In 1780 Saussure determined the temperature of the Mediterranean at depths of 300 and 600 fathoms by protected thermometers, and in 1782 Six's maximum and minimum thermometer was invented, and subsequently made use of by Krusenstern in 1803, by Kotzebue in 1815, by Sir John Ross accompanied by Sir Edward Sabine in 1818, by Parry in 1819, and by Dumont d'Urville in 1826. Slow-conducting water-bottles were used by Péron in 1800, by Scoresby in 1811, who recorded warmer water beneath the colder surface layers in the Arctic regions, and by Kotzebue accompanied by Lenz in 1823. Protected thermometers were used for deep-sea temperatures by Thouars in 1832, by Martins and Bravais in 1839, and by Sir James Clark Ross during his Antarctic expedition from 1839 to 1843, the last-mentioned making also many observations on the density of the water at various depths. In 1843 Aimé introduced reversible outflow thermometers, and about 1851 Maury used cylinders of non-conducting material for taking temperatures in deep water. But it was only when thermometers with bulbs properly protected from pressure came into use that oceanic temperatures could be recorded with precision. The first themometer of this kind seems to have been used in 1857 by Captain Pullen of H.M.S. *Cyclops,* and shortly thereafter improved forms of the Six pattern (Miller-Casella) and of Negretti and Zambra's reversing pattern were introduced, and have been largely used ever since, improvements and modifications being incorporated from time to time.

Scoresby in 1811 recorded some soundings off the coast of Greenland, and Sir John Ross during his voyage to Baffin's Bay in 1817–18 took some deep soundings by means of an apparatus, designed by him and made on board, called "deep-sea clamms," in depths of 450, 650, 1000, and 1050 fathoms, bringing up from the last-mentioned depth several pounds of greenish mud. With the deposit-samples worms and other animals were brought up, and when sounding in 1000 fathoms a star-fish was found entangled in the line a little distance above the mud, thus proving that animal life was present in deep water.

In 1817 Romme published in Paris a work on winds, tides, and currents, and Risso in 1826, Lowe from 1843 to 1860, Johnson from 1862 to 1866, and Günther from 1860 to 1870, published important papers dealing with deep-sea and pelagic fishes. In 1832 James Rennell published an investigation of the currents of the Atlantic Ocean, based upon the observations recorded by sailors up to that time.

During the United States Exploring Expedition in 1839–1842 under Captain Wilkes, accompanied by Dana, several deep soundings were taken with the aid of a copper wire, and a few dredgings in shallow water were also made.

Important sounding and dredging work was carried out by Sir James Clark Ross, accompanied by Hooker, during the British Antarctic Expedition in 1839 to 1843, the first truly oceanic soundings in depths exceeding 2000 fathoms being taken. After many unsuccessful attempts to sound in deep water, due to the want of a proper line, Ross had a line 3600 fathoms in length specially constructed on board. It was fitted with swivels here and there, strong enough to carry a weight of 76 lbs., and was allowed to run out from an enormous reel in one of the ship's boats. With this line the first abysmal sounding on record was taken in 2425 fathoms on the 3rd January 1840, in lat. 27° 26′ S., long. 17° 29′ W., and frequently during the cruise similar and greater depths were sounded. Such deep soundings could only be attempted in calm weather, and a note was kept of the time each 100-fathoms mark left the reel, a lengthening of the time-interval indicating when the weight had reached the bottom. The dredge also was successfully used during this expedition in depths down to 400 fathoms, abundant evidence of animal life being forthcoming, though unfortunately the deep-sea zoological collections were subsequently lost to science. In April 1840 the dredge came up full of coral from a depth of 95 fathoms, and in the following January dredgings in 270 and 300 fathoms gave abundance of marine invertebrates in great variety, the deepest dredging in 400 fathoms in August 1841 bringing up some beautiful specimens of coral, corallines, flustræ, and a few crustaceous animals. Hooker made known some of Ross's results, and drew attention to the great rôle played by diatoms in the seas of the far south.

In 1839 the British Association appointed a Committee to investigate the marine zoology of Great Britain by means of the dredge, the ruling spirit of this Committee being Edward Forbes, who made many observations on the bathymetrical distribution of life in various seas. Before this time, it is true, Audouin and Milne-Edwards in 1830, and Michael Sars in 1835, had published the results of dredgings in comparatively shallow waters within limited areas along the coasts of Europe.

In 1840–41 Forbes studied the fauna of the Ægean Sea, taking a great many dredgings at different depths, and came to the conclusion that marine animals were distributed in zones of depth, each characterised by a special assemblage of species. He divided the area occupied by marine animals into eight zones, in which animal life gradually diminished with increase of depth, until a zero was reached at about 300 fathoms. He supposed that plants, like animals, disappeared at a certain depth, the zero of vegetable life being at less depth than that of animal life. In his Report on the Investigation of British Marine Zoology by means of the Dredge (1850), Forbes suggested that dredgings off the Hebrides and the Shetlands, and between the Shetland and Faroe islands, would throw much light on marine zoology, thus pointing to the scene of the subsequent important work carried on by Carpenter and Wyville Thomson, and Murray and Tizard.

In 1844 Lovén carried on researches on the distribution of marine organisms along the Scandinavian coasts, confirming and extending the observations recorded by Forbes, and in 1845 Johannes Müller commenced to study the pelagic life of the sea by examining samples of sea-water and by means of the tow-net, thus giving a great impetus to the study of marine biology.

In 1845 Sir John Franklin set sail on his ill-fated North Polar Expedition, accompanied by Harry Goodsir, who recorded the results of dredging in depths of 300 fathoms.

In 1846 Spratt took dredgings in the Mediterranean down to a depth of 310 fathoms; he afterwards brought up shell-fragments from a depth of 1620 fathoms in the Mediterranean.

In 1850 Michael Sars published the results of his dredgings off the coast of Norway, giving a list of 19 species living at depths greater than 300 fathoms. He was afterwards assisted by his son, G. O. Sars, in carrying on this work, and in 1864 they gave a list of 92 species living in depths between 200 and 300 fathoms, and showed a few years later that marine life was abundant down to depths of 450 fathoms.

In 1856 MacAndrew published the results of his observations on the marine Mollusca of the Atlantic coasts of Europe and northern Africa, giving a list of 750 species obtained in his dredgings, which covered 43 degrees of latitude.

The oceanographical researches of the United States Coast Survey may be said to date back to 1844, when the Director, Bache, issued instructions to his officers to preserve the deposit-samples brought up by the sounding-machine. J. W. Bailey studied these deposit-samples, and published the result of his examination in 1851, followed in 1856 by other papers on deposits and on the formation of greensand in modern seas.

The name of M. F. Maury, of the United States Navy, was for a long period associated with the hydrographical work of the United States. He issued several editions of his Sailing Directions to accompany the wind and current charts published by the U.S. Hydrographic Office, the last edition appearing in 1859. About this time the need was felt for an improved and more trustworthy method of sounding in deep water, and various attempts were made to devise forms of apparatus to replace the heavy weight attached to a line which had to be let down and then drawn up to the surface again, the difficulty being to know when the weight touched the bottom. This problem was finally solved by Midshipman Brooke, who conceived the idea of detaching the weight used to carry down the sounding lead upon striking the bottom, the sounding tube, enclosing its deposit-sample, being alone drawn to the surface. He used a spherical weight (a bullet), with a hole passing through the centre to receive the sounding tube, suspended by a cord to the upper part of the sounding tube; on touching the bottom the cord was thrown off its support and remained at the bottom along with the weight. With the aid of Brooke's sounding apparatus, the records of deep-sea soundings rapidly accumulated, and enabled Maury to prepare the first bathymetrical map of the North Atlantic Ocean, with contour-lines drawn in at 1000, 2000, 3000, and 4000 fathoms, which was published in 1854. The deposit-samples procured were examined and described by Bailey and by Pourtalès, the results being of great importance and interest.

Systematic soundings in the North Atlantic were commenced by Lee in the U.S.S. *Dolphin* in 1851–52, and continued in the same vessel by Berryman in 1852–53. In 1856 Berryman on the U.S.S. *Arctic* sounded across the North Atlantic from Newfoundland to Ireland, with the object of verifying the existence of a submarine ridge, along which it was proposed to lay a telegraph cable; his deposit-samples were described by Bailey.

In 1857 Pullen and Dayman in H.M.S. *Cyclops* ran a line of soundings along the great circle from Ireland to Newfoundland, a little to the north of Berryman's line. A modification of Brooke's sounding-machine was used, in which the spherical weight was replaced by a cylindrical one suspended by wire instead of cord, and with a different valve for collecting the deposit. The deposit-samples were examined and described by Huxley, who found in the bottles a viscous substance, described by him as *Bathybius*, which was subsequently shown by the *Challenger* observers to be a chemical precipitate thrown down from the sea-water associated with the deposits by the alcohol used in their preservation.

The reason why the ocean, which plays such an important part in the economy of the earth, has not been investigated until recently is because of the special difficulties which are encountered in making investigations. One great difficulty is, as has been previously mentioned, that it is impossible to observe directly what is going on beneath the surface, and it is necessary to have a special set of apparatus that can be relied upon. The methods have developed with phenomenal rapidity, but the observations are still few in proportion to the extent of the ocean, and consequently it is often difficult to obtain a complete and true image of the actual conditions. Many of the results obtained are therefore merely preliminary, and further study may alter our views on various points; for the solution of many important problems we have not yet sufficiently numerous observations.

~~~~~~~~~~

J. Arthur Thomson:

30.   *JETSAM**

In spite of many disappointments, there is always a mild excitement in a walk along the shore—especially after a storm. One never knows what one may discover among the jetsam—the rubbish, as some people would say. But this is to miscall the jetsam, for although there is sometimes an element of rubbish—the débris of civilisation—the uninviting word is seldom appropriate in reference to the whole. What we mostly find is *the wreckage of life*—creatures that have been torn from their moorings, or that have been forced by currents into the grip of the incoming tide, or that have been battered to death and then swept ashore. The jetsam differs greatly at different seasons and in different localities, but it may be of interest to take a representative sample.

The sand is sometimes mixed with dead or dying Foraminifera (chalk-forming unicellular animals), such as the beautiful *Polystomella*, which is like a microscopic miniature of a Nautilus shell—an instance of that convergence of architecture which we often find among unrelated forms at very different levels in the animal kingdom. This *Polystomella*, which we can sometimes see as a white speck on the freshly dislodged seaweed, is a good illustration of the *relative* nature of simplicity. It is a single cell,—a unit of living matter,—but it is structurally very complex in comparison with a drop of white of egg. It has a spiral chambered shell; it occurs in two different types (like males and females, though that does not seem to be the meaning of the dimorphism), and it has an intricate life-history.

Much higher in the scale of being are the sponges, such as "Mermaids' Gloves," "Elephant Ears," "Crumb of Bread," and the

* From THE BIOLOGY OF THE SEASONS by J. Arthur Thomson, Henry Holt and Company, New York, 1915; Andrew Melrose Ltd. London, 1913.

J. Arthur Thomson, 1861–1933, was a Scotch naturalist and biologist who attempted, both in his writings and lectures, to reconcile science and religion. A prolific writer, he authored over 25 books, including DARWINISM AND HUMAN LIFE, HEREDITY, THE STUDY OF ANIMAL LIFE, and AN INTRODUCTION TO SCIENCE.

like, to give them their quaint but not inappropriate popular names. They have been wrenched away from their anchorage and tossed up on the beach. We cannot look at them with irreverence, for the sponges were the first animals to be successful in having a "body"; and, though they have no organs, they illustrate tissues in the making. We try a piece against our skin, and discover in its rasping effect why even large British forms are of no use for toilet purposes. From a zoological point of view, it is profitable to scrutinise a big sponge carefully, for there are sometimes interesting creatures in its recesses. A sponge is often a living thicket, in which small animals play hide-and-seek.

Even more plantlike than the sponges are the zoophytes, which we find so abundantly among the piled-up seaweed or growing on it—colonies of polyps protected within a firm tubular investment, often aborescent in their mode of growth, and always fascinatingly beautiful. There is something suggestive in the technical names of the great types—Tubularians, Campanularians, Sertularians, and Plumularians, or in the popular names like "sea-fir." Very plant-like, indeed, most of them appear; but that is again only a superficial resemblance of "convergence," as observation of the living creatures makes plain, for they have mouths and food-canals, waving tentacles and stinging lassos, and many of them bud off swimming-bells or medusoids, which swim in the summer seas like miniature jelly-fishes.

Sometimes the whole of the flat beach is thickly strewn with true jelly fishes—a distinctive element in the summer jetsam. They consist in large proportion of "animal sea-water," and it is instructive to watch them in all stages of evaporation till only a thin transparent disc is left on the sand. One remembers the striking fact that quite a number of extinct genera have been described from their exact impress on fine-grained rocks. Jelly fishes are obviously open-sea animals, and their abundant occurrence on the shore illustrates wastage. They have lost their bearings or got into the grip of inshore currents.

Sometimes tossed up together are two creatures which are almost violently contrasted, though, as a matter of fact, they are not very distantly related, namely, Dead Men's Finger (*Alcyonium*), a flabby fleshy colony with no pretence to elegance, and the Sea-Pen (*Pennatula*), a graceful plumose colony with a central axis and the polyps arranged on pinnules up each side, like the barbs of a feather.

There is sometimes a whole bank of the flexible tubes of *Lanice conchilega*, a worm that binds shell fragments and sand particles together, literally "making ropes of sand," and there is never difficulty in finding calcareous worm-tubes, like those of *Spirorbis*, attached to the seaweed, or those of *Serpula* on shells and stones. Now and again among the seaweed we find the sea-mouse, *Aphrodite*, like an entangled fragment of a rainbow, so iridescent is it.

Piled up in great quantities often are the fronds of the sea-mat (*Flustra*), leaf-like or seaweed-like till the eye catches the innumerable small holes tenanted by the animals forming the colony. The biologist handles it with some affection, for was it not the subject of Darwin's first scientific paper? And those who enjoy "beauty-feasts" cannot do better than give some time to the numerous calcareous relatives of the sea-mat which form exquisite growths on shells and stones. In illustration of contrast between two types not very distantly related, we may compare the gelatinous translucent *Alcyonidium gelatinosum* and the lace-like *Membranipora membranacea* spreading like a film on the large fronds of seaweed.

Among the transient components of the jetsam are the delicate shells of the heart-urchin (*Echinocardium*), which we find with all the spines rubbed off and beautifully white. The tread of a black-backed gull's foot is enough to break them, and they soon pass into the common denominator of the sand. The purple heart-urchin (*Spatangus*) is hardly less brittle. It is interesting to find the strong common sea-urchin (*Echinus*), with all its spines worn off and the balls where their sockets fit on to the shell polished smooth. The masticating mill or lantern which Aristotle saw more than two thousand years ago has fallen out and lies by itself on the sand—a puzzling structure to those who do not know what it is, and equally puzzling to those who, knowing what it is, inquire how it came to be. Allied to the sea-urchins are the starfishes, which are often well represented in the jetsam, sometimes occurring in the so-called "comet form"—one arm in process of budding off the missing five. For the regenerative capacity of these creatures is extraordinarily great—a missing arm can be regrown and a surviving arm can regrow all the rest.

As we search among the jetsam, crowds of "sand-hoppers" spring high into the air, light again on the sand, and are gone. Many of them are so like the sand in colour that it is difficult to see them till they move, and then they burrow with great rapidity. Some of them "feign death," as we say in our ignorance, when they are touched, and will lie absolutely motionless for many minutes. Suddenly the machinery begins to move again, they spring into the air, and we see no more of them. These shore-amphipods are interesting in many ways, but we cannot do more than refer to the important part they play in the littoral economy by cleaning things up. They devour everything that is edible in the dead bodies of animals, both large and small, and make beautifully clean skeletons, just as the ants do in the meadow. Along with these genuine inhabitants of the shore there are representatives of the same crustacean class in the jetsam. In the early summer especially we find many moults—from the glassy husks of acorn-shells or barnacles to the substantial cast shell of the edible crab.

On many beaches the most conspicuous component of the jetsam is that furnished by molluscs, whose shells afford an unstinted "beauty-feast." In shape and colour they are singularly attractive, and they are full of unsolved problems. Even to the simplest question, What is the chemistry of their formation? we can give no answer, though there are reasons for suspecting that shell-making is an organised way of using up waste-products.

In the regular lines patent on the surface of the shell, and often accentuated by fine gradations of colour, we have a fine instance of the periodicity of growth, and doubtless also, if we knew enough, of punctuation from without.

To get a good instance of the correlation of habit and structure, we have only to lift a dog-whelk's shell and contrast it with a periwinkle's. The former has a notch at the mouth of the shell, in which, during life, there lies a breathing-tube (or respiratory siphon); the former has no notch and no siphon. And the interesting point is, that those with the notch are almost invariably carnivorous and those without the notch are vegetarian.

Many of the bivalves, such as the very common Venus gallina, show a neatly bored hole up near the hinge, and this explains their presence in the jetsam! The hole was bored by a carnivorous gastropod, which killed the bivalve and devoured its body, leaving the empty shell to be tossed up on the sand.

There are many curious items in the molluscan jetsam. These chaffy balls that the wind blows along the sand are the empty egg-capsules of the giant whelk, or "roaring buckie"—cradles which were the scene of a grim struggle for existence between the first hatched larvæ and those that emerge later. These translucent "sea-pens" of chitin and these "sepiostaires" of spongy lime which are collected for cage-birds to peck at, are both the vestiges of the vanished shells of squid and sepia. Sometimes a whole fleet of cuttle-fishes gets into the grip of the tide and is stranded on the flat beach, where they writhe their arms impotently till the gulls give them their release.

Backboned animals do not contribute much to the jetsam, but here and there we find a stranded fish, a bird that has been killed, or a porpoise that has run aground. Not very uncommon in some places is the body of an angler or fishing-frog. This interesting fish often half buries itself in the sand in relatively shallow water, and the lure that dangles from the end of a long dorsal fin-ray seems to attract little fishes to their destruction. A fresh specimen that has come too near the shore will afford an unforgettable instance of adaptation, for the numerous teeth on the jaws that border the enormous gape are hinged at their base, bending inwards at the least touch, so that entrance to the mouth is as easy as exit is difficult.

A distinctive "common object of the seashore" is the four-cornered "mermaid's purse," with each corner drawn out into a tendril. It is the egg-case of a skate or of a dog-fish; it is made of keratin or horn, just as our finger-nails are; its tendrils twine automatically around seaweed, so that the laid egg is saved from being smothered in the mud, and is rocked by the waves till the embryo is ready to be hatched. Then a chemical change in the white of egg dissolves the horny shell along a line of weakness at one end, and the young fish emerges. Those mermaids' purses thrown up on the shore are usually *emptied* egg-shells, as the opening at one end shows.

The birds among the jetsam are often of great interest—even of biological interest. Thus the large number of young guillemots and razorbills in summer suggests the mortality incident on the first plunge from the rocks. It is the first step that costs, but in some cases the natural mortality is artificially exaggerated by salmon-nets, in which many marine birds get entangled and drowned. It is interesting in another connection to find the stranded bodies of puffins in the winter-time, when there is not a puffin to be seen on any part of the coast for hundreds of miles. These bodies have been washed in from the open sea, where many of our northern puffins seem to spend the winter months. And he must be dull indeed who experiences no thrill in finding among the seaweed on a winter day a rarity like the wedge-tail petrel, a distinctively pelagic bird, killed perhaps by flying against a ship, and probably washed in from a great distance out to sea.

What a variety of biological impressions we gain from this walk among the shore-jetsam. There is sometimes an overmastering impression of the abundance of life. When we see the stranded fleet of jelly-fishes, scores of squids in one small bay, zoophytes to fill a sack with, a litter of sea-mats, hundreds of fragile heart-urchins, and so forth, we return to the old image that life is a stream that is always overflowing its banks.

Nor can we walk along the shore looking at the jetsam without being impressed with the variety of different kinds, as well as with the uncountable number of individuals. Even if we do nothing but gather shells (on a good shore for them) we feel that we are in the presence of an overflowing form-fountain, prodigal multiplicity, endless resources.

"But what an endlesse worke have I on hand
    To count the sea's abundant progeny,
Whose fruitful seede farre passeth those on land,
    And also those which wonne in th' azure sky.
How much more eath to tell the starres on hy,
Albe they endlesse seem in estimation,
    Than to recount the sea's posterity,
So fertile be the floods in generation,
So huge their numbers and so numberlesse their nation."

Another impression is of the wastage of life—in regard to which the physical forces are quite careless. There is absolute insouciance in Nature. The beach is strewn with jetsam as thickly as the woodland with withered leaves, but it is a jetsam largely made up of corpses. There are, indeed, empty shells tossed up, and the moults of crabs and various items of this sort, but the great bulk of the jetsam consists of corpses.

In contemplating the jetsam we see one aspect of the struggle for existence, the non-competitive aspect—the struggle between organisms and their physical environment, between life and fate. What is thrown up on the shore between tide-marks is only a small part of what is continually being dislodged by storms, and there can be no doubt that there is a ceaseless thinning. It may be that this sometimes leaves appreciably more room for those creatures which are not thinned, and it may be that within the members of a species those that vary in the direction of resisting dislodgment survive in appreciably greater numbers. But we have no data. It seems likely, indeed, that in many cases there is no Natural Selection at all, for that is a much narrower category than the Struggle for Existence. From the absence of uniformity in the jetsam in a tract of shore which we have studied for many years we have a general impression that much of the elimination is quite indiscriminate, and therefore without direct importance in evolution. It is very important to understand clearly that the only eliminative processes that can be regarded as counting for much in evolution are those which are *discriminate and consistent*.

Another consideration of some interest is brought home to us

when we watch the jetsam being covered up by the sand either
borne in by the tide or blown by the wind. We see how the first
step towards fossilisation might be taken when some change in currents piles up a heavy sandbank near the high-tide mark, burying a
sample of the jetsam. But even if the sample was a good one,
and if all should be preserved in a future sandstone, the result
would be far from a fit representation of the local fauna of our
times. It would be almost as misleading to judge of the civilisation
of the early twentieth century by the débris washed up on the beach
near a large town. Nor should one fail to notice that even if a
whole stretch of jetsam were quickly buried, many items would
have no chance of being preserved or of being well preserved, for
the Amphipods and Bacteria and other scavengering creatures have
already begun their destructive work. The sea's memoranda are apt
to pass quickly beyond all hope of deciphering.

We cannot watch the jetsam through several consecutive days
without getting vivid illustrations of the circulation of matter. The
squid is scarcely dead before the gulls are pecking at it, and even
land birds like rooks come down to the feast. The Amphipods
already referred to are continually doing with their microscopic
nibbling what birds do when they pick a dead fish clean. We
lift up the substantial shell of an oyster or of a "roaring buckie"
and find it riddled with holes, neatly bored as if with a gimlet,—
the work of a boring sponge Cliona, which thus helps the shell
a long way towards its incorporation with the sand. It is an interesting occupation for a leisure hour to sit with a lens in hand sifting
the sand—distinguishing here a fragment of shell and there a piece
of sea-urchin's spine, here a remnant of an acorn-shell's rampart
and there a Foraminifer. One can arrange a series of grades of fine-
ness, like different samples of sugar; they are stages in the process
of reduction towards that lowest common denominator which we
call the sand of the seashore.

~~~~~~~~~~~

N. A. Transhe:

31.   *ICE COVER OF THE ARCTIC SEA**

TYPES OF ICE RESULTING FROM NATURAL GROWTH
(ACCRETIONAL TYPES)

SLUSH OR SLUDGE

The initial stage in the freezing of sea water and its transformation into ice consists of the development of ice crystals in the
surface water in the form of spicules and plates (the dimensions
of the latter being 2–4 centimeters in length, ½–1 centimeter in
width, and ½–1 millimeter in thickness), which loosely freeze
together and form "ice gruel"; the water at that time is of gruelly
or souplike consistency, and its surface has the appearance of cooling grease, with a peculiar steel-gray or lead tint. Because of this
appearance, this primary stage of the freezing of the sea water has
been called *slush*, or *sludge* (Russian, *salo*, grease).

PANCAKE ICE

"Owing to various disturbing conditions connected with the
slight motion in the upper layers of sea water, the freezing together
of the ice needles and plates does not proceed equally on the whole
surface of the open sea but starts its development as if from a number of centers of freezing, spreading equally in all directions from
these centers. Grouping themselves around these centers the crystals
or plates of ice form small areas having the appearance of rather regular disks, from 1 to 2 or 3 feet in diameter [maximum, 5–6 feet]"
(Kolchak). This phenomenon, called *pancake ice*, is the next stage
of ice formation and, like the previous one, develops when the atmosphere and the sea are calm.

* From "Problems of Polar Research," The American Geographical Society
Special Publication, No. 7, New York, 1928. Reprinted by permission of the
publisher.

YOUNG ICE

"Gradually growing thicker and stronger, the disks of pancake ice begin to congeal together (thanks to the freezing of crystals in the intervals between the disks) and form more or less large, compact ice areas," which, "starting in motion under the influence of the wind, wave movement, and currents, break up into several pieces; these pieces, colliding with each other, have their edges crumpled up to form narrow rims a few centimeters high; under favorable conditions the pieces freeze together again into new, more extensive areas; gradually they grow thicker and more and more solid; and finally they form compact *young ice* consisting of wet ice, saturated with water, which has a coarse crystalline composition of more or less developed ice crystals. The upper surface of this young ice is smooth or more often slightly rough, while the under surface has a coarse, rough appearance, sometimes like a brush of ice crystals. Underneath the under surface of this ice there is a more or less thick layer (about one foot deep) of water saturated with ice crystals, which gradually makes the newly formed ice thicker and thicker. Such young ice is usually 2 or 3 centimeters thick" (Kolchak); it increases continually during the whole winter and in May reaches its full thickness of about 2 meters on the average (maximum thickness of ice observed by Nansen was 3.65 meters).

FAST-ICE

The three preceding paragraphs describe the process of the freezing of sea water and the formation of new ice in general. But near coasts, at the heads of gulfs and bays, in straits, among islands and icebergs, and generally in localities that are comparatively sheltered, the formation of the ice cover takes place sooner than in the open sea and thence spreads outwards.

This new ice that first forms along shore is called *ledyanoi zabereg* in Russian, which means "icy extension off shore." Its development causes the freezing of gulfs and bays, and its constant spreading along the whole coast and into the open sea creates (from the end of November or beginning of December) a more or less wide zone of immovable ice which bears the name of *fast-ice* (Russian, *beregovio pripai*, literally meaning "coastal soldering") and which grows in thickness during the whole winter and spring up to May.

That part of the fast-ice immediately close to shore which is not subjected to the rise and fall of the tide is called *ice foot*.

TYPES OF ICE RESULTING FROM MOTION
(DYNAMIC TYPES)

PACK ICE

In distinction to fast-ice any "sea ice which has drifted from its original position" (under the influence of winds, currents, etc.) is called *pack ice* or pack (Priestley).

Therefore the types of sea ice enumerated in the following are derivatives of the pack ice, resulting from its breaking into pieces as a consequence of its motion, or of the fast-ice itself at the first stage of its breaking up. (The types are taken up in decreasing order of size.)

1. The largest areas of the pack ice are called *ice fields*. They are of such extent that their limits cannot be seen from a ship's mast-head.

They in their turn are broken into:

2. *Ice floes*—areas that range in size from about one-third of a nautical mile in diameter to the dimensions of an ice field.
3. The further breaking up of floes (or the direct breaking up of ice fields or of pack ice or fast-ice into pieces smaller than a floe) forms *glaçons*[1] (Russian, *ldini*), areas ranging in size

---

[1] There is no separate term in the existing terminologies for an individual piece of ice forming a subdivision of an ice floe, and while Scoresby, in defining a floe says "the term (floe), however, is seldom applied to pieces of ice of less diameter than half a mile or a mile," Wordie says "in size a floe may vary from 'pancakes' on the one hand to 'fields' on the other," and he therefore even uses the term "floe" in connection with his definition of "pancake ice" (Priestley also). Such lack of a proper term is inconvenient; meanwhile there is the French term *glaçon* which literally means "an individual piece of ice." This term is suitable to designate an individual piece of ice intermediate in size between a cake about 2 to 3 feet in diameter and a floe one-third of a nautical mile in diameter as well as to define the components of "drift ice" and "brash ice."

The term "drift ice" (included in the terminologies and having the meaning of a collective noun) defines, in the main, the character of the ice but not an individual, definite type of ice. In accordance with: (1) the dimensions assigned to a floe by Scoresby (unfortunately omitted in the subsequent terminologies); (2) his definition of drift ice as "consisting of pieces less than a floe in size"; (3) our definition of the term *glaçon*; (4) our definition of the term "brash ice" —one may say that "drift ice" consists of small and medium-sized glaçons and in character represents loose, very open pack in which water preponderates over ice.

from a cake about 2 to 3 feet in diameter to a floe. In keeping with Russian Arctic practice glaçons may be further subdivided according to size into small, medium-sized, and large.

HUMMOCKING

When the pack ice, or rather its ice fields or floes, moves, the process of *hummocking* takes place. This process consists of the impingement, shock, and pressure of ice masses upon one another; it results in crushing the edges of fields or floes, breaking them up completely, and piling them up one upon another. The magnitude of hummocking depends upon the size of the colliding masses, their speed, strength, solidity, etc.

There are two distinctive phases of hummocking. The first, consists in the marginal crushing of colliding ice masses, the second, in the complete breaking up and piling up of the broken ice.

The chaotic heaps that are the products of the crushing and breaking up of ice masses are called *hummocks* (Russian, *toros*).

Hummocks may be subdivided according to:

a)	Phases of hummocking	hummocks due to marginal crushing (Russian, *vzlom*), which in the pack ice project 2 to 5 meters above the level of the ice hummocks due to complete breaking up (Russian, *razdroblenic*), which in the pack ice project 3 to 7 meters above the level of the ice
b)	Age	hummocks one year old hummocks many years old
c)	Place of formation	sea hummocks coastal hummocks
d)	State	floating hummocks stranded hummocks (Russian, *stamukhi*), whose height is often 18 to 20 meters above sea level in the Siberian and Kara Seas
e)	Season	summer hummock autumn hummock winter hummock spring hummock
f)	Extent	pressure ridges pressure areas

"The formation of the hummocks due to marginal crushing is a primary process at which the hummocking can stop, after the kinetic energy of the colliding ice masses has been spent, or the process may pass into a further form of breaking up and piling up the broken material" (Kolchak).

"Winter and spring hummocks occur in those parts of the sea where the ice is in motion during all the year, and they are not distinguished from the autumn forms except by their greater strength; as for the summer hummock, which forms after the breaking up of the immovable ice of winter, it is distinguished from the autumn hummock not only by its greater strength but also by a difference in its physical properties due to the influence of other temperature conditions, other modes of melting, etc." (Kolchak).

Stranded hummocks (*stamukhi*) are a very important type of hummock, especially in the Russian sector of the Arctic, where the width of the fast-ice depends, among other factors, mainly on the number of *stamukhi* present. In this respect as well as in the initial process of ice formation they play the same rôle as grounded icebergs or groups of small islands.

When the process of hummocking takes place along the outskirts of the pack ice (in the "frontier region of the Arctic Pack," to use Kolchak's expression) the ice masses of the Arctic Pack participate in the formation of pressure areas and pressure ridges. These massive, compact ice masses, or hummocks of the pack ice and Arctic Pack pressed and cemented together, are called *floebergs*.

Small glaçons of hummock origin are called *growlers*.

SUBDIVISIONS OF DERIVATIVES OF THE PACK ICE

As to fields, floes, and glaçons, they may be divided as follows according to:

Age[2]
{ one year old
{ many years old

Strength
{ light—up to 2 feet in thickness
{ heavy—more than 2 feet in thickness
{ rafted[3] (telescoped; Russian, *nabivnoi*)

[2] Strictly speaking, floes and glaçons many years old occur mainly in the pack ice, while, on the contrary, fields occur mainly in the Arctic Pack.

[3] The thickness of rafted floes in the Kara and Siberian Seas is from 3 to 10 meters, and near the limits of the Arctic Pack, with the participation of floes of the latter added, it reaches 20 to 25 and even 30 meters.

Surface $\left\{\begin{array}{l}\text{level (flat)}\\ \text{hummocky}\\ \textit{Moutonnée}^4\\ \text{honeycombed}\end{array}\right.$

Arrangement[5] $\left\{\begin{array}{l}\text{close—when they touch each other for the most part}\\ \text{open—when they do not touch each other for the}\\ \text{most part}\end{array}\right.$

The third class of ice covering the Arctic Sea, the Arctic Pack, consists of the same main types of sea ice which are inherent in the pack ice, i.e. fields, floes, hummocks, but they are of much larger dimensions and power, while the products of the further breaking up and disintegration of the sea ice, namely the types glaçons and growlers, are of insignificant importance in the Arctic Pack, being alternately formed and disintegrated in the temporary polynyas, lanes, or cracks, where also takes place the formation of the primary types of sea ice, slush or sludge, and pancake ice.

SEA ICE DEFINITIONS

We shall now summarize in the form of specific definitions what has gone before.

Slush, or sludge. The initial state in the freezing of sea water when it is of the consistency of gruel or soup and the surface of the water takes on the appearance of cooling grease with a peculiar steel-gray or lead tint.

Pancake ice. Small cakes of new ice approximately circular and with raised rims. Diameter of cakes is from 1 to 2 or 3 feet; their thickness up to 2 to 4 centimeters; rims are 1 to 2 centimeters high.

Young ice. Compact ice sheet formed from the repeated freezing together and breaking up of pieces of pancake ice. Its initial thickness is 2 to 4 centimeters, which increases during the winter to about 2 meters and as a maximum 3 meters.

Ledyanoi zabereg (icy extension off shore). The new ice adhering

---

[4] By analogy with *roche moutonnée*, the weathering of the ice producing rounded surface forms similar to those produced by ice action on rock.

[5] As to navigability these two forms may be characterized as follows:

close pack—when it is not possible to navigate through it.

open pack—when it is possible to navigate through it but changes in the vessel's course are continually necessary.

Certainly, when the pack ice is composed of *glaçons*, the possibility to navigate through it is greater.

to the shore (in bays, gulfs, and among islands) when it begins to grow outward toward the open sea.

Fast-ice. Fully developed *ledyanoi zabereg*. It forms a more or less wide belt of immovable new ice along the coasts—in other words "sea ice while remaining fast in the position of growth" (Priestley). The 12-fathom isobath is approximately the limit of the spread of the fast-ice into the open sea in localities where the configuration of the coast exerts no influence.

Ice foot. The part of the fast-ice immediately close to shore that is not affected by the rise and fall of the tide.

Pack ice. Sea ice which has drifted from its original position.

Ice field. An area of pack ice or Arctic Pack of such extent that its limits cannot be seen from the ship's masthead.

Ice floe. An area of pack ice or Arctic Pack from one-third of a nautical mile in diameter to the size of an ice field.

Glaçon. A piece of pack ice or Arctic Pack ranging in size from a cake about 2 to 3 feet in diameter to a floe.

Hummock. The heaped-up products of the marginal crushing and breaking up of the sea ice as a result of hummocking.

Hummocking. The process of pressure upon sea ice expressed in marginal crushing and breaking up and in the heaping up the products resulting from this pressure.

Floeberg. Massive hummock consisting partly of pack ice, partly of Arctic Pack.

Growler. A small glaçon of hummock origin.

Arctic Pack. Many-years-old rafted ice, mainly in the form of hummocked fields. Its distinctive characteristics are: tremendous power, greater than that of the ice of the marginal seas of the Arctic Sea; solidity, gradually increasing in the course of years; and great size of the fields of rafted ice.

Anchor ice. All submerged ice attached to the bottom irrespective of the nature of its formation.

DESCRIPTIVE TERMS APPLICABLE TO
ALL TYPES OF ICE

Besides the above-mentioned terms defining the types of ice of the Arctic Sea—definitions that are based upon certain stages of the life cycle of sea ice (freezing, melting, marginal crushing, and breaking up)—there are in common use a number of terms relating to sea ice in general and not to any given derivative of pack ice or the Arctic Pack. Most of the adjectives constituting these terms have been applied in the preceding classification to define the character of certain types of pack ice and Arctic Pack.

Grouped According to:	Term	Applied to:
Condition of surface	level	Ice whose surface is flat.
	hummocky	Ice whose surface is hummocked (or jagged).
	rotten	Ice whose surface is honeycombed (or pitted).
Age	young	Ice one year old.
	old	Ice many years old.
Strength	light	One-year-old ice up to 2 feet in thickness.
	heavy	Any ice from 2 feet to 6 feet in thickness.
	rafted (telescoped)	Hummocked, recemented ice with protuberances smoothed by melting (thickness, 6 feet and more).
Arrangement	compact	Continuous, although broken, ice with no signs of water.
	close	Ice with spaces of water, but so close as to hinder navigation.
	open	Ice with spaces of water sufficient for navigation.
	drift ice	An area of small and medium-sized glaçons in which water preponderates over ice.
	brash ice	An area of small glaçons constituting the wreckage of all types of ice.
State	unbroken	Either fast-ice or large ice fields.

TERMS FOR SOME CHARACTERISTIC PHENOMENA OF SEA ICE NOT PART OF THE GENETIC CLASSIFICATION

Crack.[6] Any fracture or rift in sea ice (not navigable).
Lead, or lane. A channel of open water in the pack ice or Arctic Pack; it may be navigable in the former (mostly the antithesis of pressure ridges).

[6] There are three categories of cracks: (1) tidal, (2) temperature, and (3) shock and pressure cracks. The two cracks of the first category are called "active tidal cracks"; one (inshore) marks the ice foot, and the other (offshore) is the line of demarcation between the coastward part of the fast-ice that touches the bottom in low water and that which is constantly in a floating state.

Polynya.[7] Any enclosed water area (other than a crack or a lead) among fields, floes, and glaçons of pack ice or Arctic Pack.

Pool. A depression (or hollow) containing fresh water in the fields, floes, or glaçons of sea ice.

Hole. Opening through the ice (as for instance the holes in the rotten ice, honeycombed in the course of melting).

Frost smoke. The foglike clouds of evaporation over newly formed water areas in sea ice.

Ice blink. The whitish glare on the clouds produced by the reflection of large areas of sea ice (the antithesis of water sky).

Water sky. Dark streaks on the clouds due to the reflection of polynyas or the open sea in the neighborhood of large areas of sea ice.

THE POLYNYA AS A MAJOR REGIONAL FEATURE

The definitions in this list relate to certain features considered as general phenomena. A group of these phenomena, however, namely the polynyas and leads, also occur as large-scale features associated with definite regions, and it is therefore necessary to discuss them briefly in their regional apect.

POLYNYAS AS A GENERAL PHENOMENON

A few words first, however, with reference to the polynya as a general phenomenon.

The polynya occurs both in the pack ice and the Arctic Pack and depends on the mutual motion of parts (field and floes) of the pack. The motion of these parts depends on the winds, currents, tides, resistance met with (islands, stamukhi, shoals, etc.) and on the various dimensions and forms of the parts participating in the motion. Owing to these factors this motion is very complicated in character. Side by side with the progressive motion of the pack as a whole there goes a rotary motion of its parts, as a result of collision, shock, and pressure among them. Owing to this intricate motion, such a grouping of fields and floes may result as to form an area of open water or an area with fragments of ice (glaçons) in it. This area of open water is called in Russian *polynya*. These polynyas are of a temporary character, and, under the influence of the same combination of factors that cause the motion of parts of the pack, they are closed in one place and reopened again elsewhere, and so on. With a relatively large number of polynyas and with channels

[7] For a detailed explanation see the next section.

connecting them, the pack has the appearance of being more or
less favorable for navigation, but it is still tight enough to be called
"close pack."

Now as to the polynya as a major regional feature.

As such it has been observed in two localities, off eastern Siberia
from north of the New Siberian Islands at intervals to about
Kolyuchin Bay and off Grant Land and northern Greenland.

Great Siberian Polynya

The former, which may be termed the Great Siberian Polynya,
is, according to all observations since 1820, permanent in character
and of great dimensions. Its observed positions, when plotted, shows
it clearly to be associated with the outer edge of the fully developed
fast-ice (*beregovio pripai*) as defined in the present paper. The formation, existence, and extension of this Great Siberian Polynya depend
upon those physico-geographical conditions which produce the general motion of the Arctic Pack, or, in other words, they depend in
this region on the northwest and west-northwest direction of the
drift, i.e., a direction obliquely away from the fast-ice. The width of
this polynya depends upon the fluctuations of the outskirts of the
Arctic Pack under the influence of wind, decreasing when it blows
toward and increasing when it blows away from the fast-ice.

Further details about this polynya may here be waived as its existence and the causes therefore are well known; also, it is dealt with
by Kolchak in the chapter from his report that constitutes the next
article. With regard to the other polynya it may not be amiss to
present a more detailed analysis, as the reasons for its existence have
so far been less fully discussed.

Peary's Big Lead

The polynya off Grant Land and northern Greenland might, to
employ the two words used to describe it by him to whom we owe
our sole knowledge of it, be termed Peary's Big Lead. Based on
Peary's repeated observations the following data about this lead are
available: (1) Most of it seems to be situated out beyond the continental shelf where the depth of the sea exceeds 1000 meters; (2) its
location is between latitudes 84° and 84½° N., and it has been met
with on the meridians of 40° and 69° W.; (3) its maximum observed

width is about 2 miles, i.e., much less than that of the Great Siberian Polynya.

Besides that there are the following known physico-geographical factors which are inherent in this locality: (1) the great shock and pressure of ice masses upon the northern shores of Greenland and Grant Land; (2) the eastward direction of the drift of the Arctic Pack approximately along the 84th parallel; (3) the southward discharge through Robeson Channel of part of the ice of Lincoln Sea (the enlargement of the Arctic Sea bounded by the coasts of Grant Land and northern Greenland); (4) a westward surface current along the northern shores of Greenland (observed by Lauge Koch).

Analyzing these facts and data we may come to the following conclusions:

The fact itself of the shock and pressure of the Arctic Pack upon the shores points to the difference between the causes respectively producing the Big Lead and the Great Siberian Polynya. In the case of the latter, the main cause governing the formation of the polynya is the general direction of the Arctic Pack motion away from shore. Hence the Big Lead can develop no such width as that of the Great Siberian Polynya.

The fact itself of the shock and pressure of ice masses upon these shores is due to the circumstance that, from the meridian of 90° W. to Cape Bridgman (26° W.), the Arctic Pack probably maintains a constant drift to the east (with a slight tendency to the southeast). This very direction, in connection with the trend and position of the shores of Grant Land and northern Greenland, must produce this shock and pressure of ice masses on these shores (its maximum should be at Cape Bridgman).

The resistance of these shores to the motion of the Arctic Pack, which, as a body, rushes towards its outlet into Greenland Sea, brings it about that Lincoln Sea (which represents a bay, as it were, in relation to this motion of the Arctic Pack) is filled up with ice masses derived from the Arctic Pack about up to the parallel of 84° N. But as the main body of the Arctic Pack seeks an outlet into Greenland Sea, its outskirts slide along this parallel, so to speak, toward the east and make a line of demarcation between the main body of the Arctic Pack, which is drifting to the east to its outlet into Greenland Sea, and those parts of its outskirts with which Lincoln Sea has been filled and which press on the shores under the pressure of the Arctic Pack itself.

This line of demarcation consequently is a place of possible formation of the Big Lead under the influence of sufficiently strong winds and favorable tidal currents.

Owing to this sliding of the Arctic Pack along the parallel of 84° N., its outskirts feed Lincoln Sea with that many-years-old, hummocked, piled-up, and broken ice (the "paleocrystic ice")[8] that, under the influence of this pressure upon the shore, is partly carried out to the south through Robeson Channel.

The westward surface current along the northern coast of Greenland observed by Lauge Koch we interpret as a result of the same shock and pressure of the ice masses of the Arctic Pack upon the projecting coast of Peary Land, where, under the influence of ice masses pressing upon the shore a deflection of the current seems to take place along and close to the shore in a westward direction. This current, thus turning down Robeson Channel, carries through that channel part of the ice masses of the outskirts of the Arctic Pack which had already been carried past this meridian on their eastward drift.

As the phenomena of the Big Lead and the shoreward shock and pressure of the ice masses are incompatible for the same moment of time, because one phenomenon is the antithesis of the other, although both are due to the same force, namely winds, but of opposite direction, therefore one may suppose that, when the westward current along the northern coast of Greenland is strong, severe hummocking takes place along the edge of the Arctic Pack in about latitude 84° and, vice versa, that, when the current is weak, hummocking is much reduced or even gives way to the formation of the Big Lead.

[8] This, in agreement with Lauge Koch (Ice Cap and Sea Ice in North Greenland, *Geogr. Rev.*, Vol. 16, 1926, pp. 98–107; references pp. 101–104), and not the iceberg derivation theory of the explorers of the seventies and eighties of the last century, whose deductions were necessarily based on a more limited body of observations than is available today, seems the plausible explanation of the origin of the so-called "paleocrystic ice."

~~~~~~~~~~~~~~~~~~~~

J. Harland Paul:

32.   LAST CRUISE OF THE CARNEGIE*

With Portions from the Foreword
by John A. Fleming

FOREWORD

The *Carnegie*—the world's only sea-going non-magnetic observatory
—was constructed by the Carnegie Institution of Washington to
obtain geophysical data over the oceans. This vessel was part of
the equipment of the Institution's Department of Terrestrial Magnetism, founded April 1, 1904, realizing a plan for an international
magnetic bureau submitted by Dr. Louis A. Bauer, the Department's
director from 1904 and its director emeritus from 1930. The purpose
of the Department, set forth in the plan, is "to investigate such
problems of world-wide interest as relate to the magnetic and electric
condition of the Earth and its atmosphere, not specifically the
subject of inquiry of any one country, but of international concern
and benefit." Among the problems proposed was the magnetic
survey of ocean-areas and magnetically unexplored regions, so that
more accurate and comprehensive charts might be constructed. It
was in the realization of this part of the plan that the *Carnegie*
did such useful service during 1909 to 1929. The first six cruises
were made almost exclusively for the surveys of the Earth's magnetism and electricity for which she was designed. The seventh
cruise was to be unique in the vessel's history, as its program
contemplated besides these survey-operations extensive researches in
oceanography, including the exploration of the ocean-depths for the
physical, chemical, and biological conditions found there.

* From J. H. Paul, THE LAST CRUISE OF THE CARNEGIE, portions of the foreword, pp. 1–9 and 325–331, Copyright © 1932, The Williams & Wilkins
Company, Baltimore, Maryland, 21202, U.S.A. By permission of the Publisher.

J. Harland Paul was the surgeon aboard the *Carnegie* at the time of the ill-
fated explosion.

John Adam Fleming, 1877–1956, was an American geophysicist who was
director of the Department of Terrestrial Magnetism, Carnegie Institution of
Washington from 1935 to 1946.

In May 1928 the *Carnegie* left the United States for a three-year cruise of all oceans—the seventh since her launching in 1909 —to further increase the store of geophysical data. Captain James Percy Ault, and the staff under his command, had completed one year and a half of this voyage when disaster struck suddenly. The ship and its unique equipment—evolved in twenty-five years of active endeavor of the Department—were totally destroyed, and the Captain lost his life together with the cabin boy. The tragedy took place November 29, 1929, at Apia, Western Samoa, when a gasoline explosion occurred while supplies of fuel were being stored aboard.

THE EXPLOSION

It was good fortune that our visit to Samoa coincided with the annual swarming period of the famous "palolo." These marine worms live in dead coral throughout the year, but on two days a year, once in October and once in November, they swarm. The posterior half of the worm is set free, to swim to the surface for the "wedding-dance" in which fertilization takes place. These free-swimming portions are really no more than sperm-and-egg cases which discharge their products and disintegrate in a few hours. They are highly prized as food by the natives, who know in advance on which night they will appear and are always on hand to capture them with dip-nets from their canoes.

So on the night of November 23, the first day of the last quarter of the moon, Captain Ault, Graham, and Paul took the dinghy and crossed the harbor to the village of Aua, where the swarm was usually abundant. As the worms would not appear till moonrise, the evening was spent in the native "fales" where excitement reigned, as the torches and dip-nets were prepared. By one o'clock the harbor was aflame for each canoe carried flares and lanterns. The long wait was made an occasion for singing and good-natured horse-play. By two, false alarms were sounded here and there along the line. By two-thirty, although the moon was not yet visible in the harbor, the sea was swarming with jade-green and ivory "palolo"-worms, swimming in every direction a few inches below the surface —elusive creatures which broke into fragments if grasped too roughly. We had brought bottles containing formaldehyde which we proceeded to fill to the disgust of the natives. For was not the "palolo" the year's greatest delicacy—and made to be eaten? With specimens secured, we each turned to and dropped a handful of these wriggling worms into our mouths, while the others bore horri-

fied witness. The experience was disappointing for the fragile creatures melted in the mouth, leaving only the taste of sea-water.

Mysterious as this natural calendar is, some of us were more
impressed by our first meeting with fish that climb rocks and trees!
We had all read stories about the weird habits of certain South Sea
fish, but here before our very eyes we found them scampering about
the blocks of lava, just as much at home on land as they are in the
water.

The day of our departure was drawing near and we had preparations to make. Supplies for the galleys and laboratories had to be
stowed away and long-neglected letters answered. On November 26
we pushed off for Apia, arriving there on Thanksgiving morning.

The day was to be no holiday for us. Parkinson proceeded to
compare his instruments with those at the magnetic observatory;
Captain Ault made his official calls, and ordered gasoline and oil;
Paul arranged for further supplies of distilled water; Graham took
silk-nets ashore for repairs and the others were busy about the
ship at their various tasks.

But on the 29th two excursions were arranged. One, a sunrise
visit to the tomb of Robert Louis Stevenson and his wife, at Vaea,
in which Soule, Forbush, Graham, and Paul took part. The other,
a trip to the eastern end of Upolu, in which Seaton joined Graham
and Paul in collecting specimens for museum use at home.

All morning, Captain Ault and the remaining members of the
staff were at work on board, the crew was engaged in loading the
last of the barrels of gasoline into the ship's tanks. There remained
only one hundred and fifty gallons to stow away when lunch-time
came. After the noon meal, the crew resumed their task; Captain
Ault unfolded a chair and sat on the quarter-deck where he could
watch the men at their work; the engineer and mechanic were
below in the engine-room; and the others were scattered over the
forward half of the ship, at various duties.

With a rumbling roar the ship was shaken from stem to stern
by an explosion—then another. Captain Ault was thrown into the
water. The men at work over the tank-room were hurled to different
parts of the ship. The engineer and mechanic were trapped in
the engine-room and in a moment the whole quarter-deck was enveloped in flame.

The steward and Soule, rushing on deck, dived overboard to
save the Captain. Sturk and Stenstrom fought their way out of
the blazing engine-room by raising themselves through the gaping
hole in the deck. The uninjured men dragged the others free of

the flames. To save the vessel was out of the question and all attention was directed to the saving of lives.

Small boats had been launched at once from the other ships in the harbor. Captain Ault, who had been holding on to a rope as he floated in the water, was helped into one of these and with the other injured men was taken ashore. Apparently he was suffering only minor injuries; but his injuries were serious and on the way to the hospital, our Captain died as the result of them and of shock.

The other men who had been on the quarter-deck suffered fractures and severe burns. They were given immediate surgical attention by the hospital staff, who had been notified by telephone of the accident.

When the survivors were collected ashore, Tony the cabin boy could not be accounted for. He had last been seen in the after galley, immediately next to the tank-room; so it was apparent that he too had lost his life. His remains were not discovered till December 4, when salvage operations on the charred hull of the vessel were commenced.

Seaton, Graham, and Paul returned from their collecting-trip about three hours after the tragedy. The hospital staff and Government officials had done everything in their power for the survivors. There was nothing further to do but to await the arrival of the U.S.S. *Ontario*, the naval vessel from Pago Pago which the Navy had ordered to our aid.

The engineer and mechanic were too severely burned to stand the journey to Pago Pago, so they were left in the hospital at Apia. Parkinson, as second in command, also stayed to take charge of affairs there. On the day following the explosion, all the others were taken to American Samoa to await the steamer from Sydney. The three injured seamen we brought with us were put in the Naval hospital while the members of the staff were taken into the homes of the Naval officers, and the crew was quartered in the barracks.

Everything was done to make us comfortable. We were furnished necessary clothing—for the ship and all its equipment together with our personal effects, had been a total loss. Governor Lincoln, on behalf of the Navy, arranged immigration papers for entry into the United States for those who were not citizens.

On December 6, the survivors accompanied the body of Captain Ault aboard the *Ventura* for the sad journey home.

~~~~~~~~~~~~~~~

John Joly:

33.   *THE AGE OF THE OCEANS* *

Approaching the question of the duration of the geological history of the globe we may proceed on the assumption that denudation has progressed during the past at an average rate not greatly different from that which now prevails. Then, by estimating the quantities of materials which have come into existence as products of denudation, and which exist at the earth's surface in forms capable of estimation, we can arrive at an approximation to the time required for their accumulation. We can apply this method, using the rate of sedimentary deposition and the estimated amounts of the sediments collected over geological time.

More definite in every respect is that method which uses the sodium in solution in the ocean as the modulus. We may calculate the total mass of sodium in the ocean (an easily found and reliable quantity) and then apply to the rivers for information as to the rate at which this element is entering the ocean. The reason for selecting sodium from among the many elements in solution in the ocean is, that this element alone is not withdrawn from it by organisms, or in any appreciable amount otherwise abstracted.

Now all methods founded upon rates of denudation are in approximate agreement in ascribing to the most ancient sediments an age which is about 100 million years. By making certain assumptions the sodium method may be stretched to 175 millions of years.

FINDING THE AGE BY SOLVENT DENUDATION

The method of finding the age of the oceans by the sodium content of the oceans has been the subject of considerable discussion.

---

* From John Joly, THE SURFACE-HISTORY OF THE EARTH, (2nd edition, 1930) by permission of the Clarendon Press, Oxford.

In addition to his research on the crust formation of the earth, British physicist and geologist John Joly also devised a uniform radiation method for use in cancer treatment and was a pioneer in color photography. He died in 1933.

A brief reference to the principal points that have been raised will be given because it will be found that its testimony, after all is said, retains its value.

1. It is suggested that existing conditions tend to minimize the Age, because we live at a period when there are no transgressional seas to cover the lower continental levels; such as prevailed over long ages in the past and must greatly have diminished the activity of surface denudation.

In answer it is contended that the mere extent of the land surface does not, within limits, affect the rate of denudation. The existing rain supply is quite insufficient to denude the whole land surface, about 30 per cent. of which does not drain to the ocean. If the transgressions covered 30 per cent. of the continents, the rainless area may be supposed to diminish and the denuded area remains the same, seeing that no change in the rain supply, save one of increase, is to be expected. There might, even, be increased subaereal denudation under these conditions. Existing rainless areas show every sign of having been exposed to active denudation in past times.

Further, as some guide to the average continental area in the past, Schuchert's estimate that the average area of North America throughout geological time has been about eight-tenths of its existing area may be adduced.[1]

Again, it has been found by comparing the solvent denudation as estimated for the different continents, that there is no connexion between continental elevation and subaereal denudation. Europe, the lowest of the continents, delivers the most matter in solution into the ocean; and North America and Asia, although their average heights are very different, deliver nearly the same amounts of dissolved matter into the seas.[2]

2. It has been said that the chloride of sodium in the ocean may be carried inland by winds, and in this manner circulate from sea to land and back again, and so falsify the true denudative supply of the rivers. The answer is that an allowance can be made for the *limiting* effect of this error by assuming that *all* the chlorine in the rivers is derived from the ocean and carries with it its due proportion of sodium. This would raise the geological age to 141×10^6 years.[3]

3. Salts derived from the ocean might be retained in the sedimentary rocks and unduly increase the river supply. The answer

[1] *Bull. Geol. Soc. Am.*, vol. xx, 1910.
[2] Sollas, *The Age of the Earth*, Fisher Unwin, 1905; Joly, *The Birth-Time of the World*, Fisher Unwin, p. 1 et seq.
[3] *Radioactivity and Geology*, Constable, p. 245.

is very simple. We must suppose these assumed supplies to enter the rivers according as the rocks are denuded. The rate of denudation therefore controls this supply. Calculations based on this rate and on estimates of chlorine in such rocks show that the Age would be affected at most by 0·9 per cent.[4]

4. A possible primitive acid denudation by condensing gases might have introduced into the ocean an initial amount of sodium. It can be shown that this effect is probably small. As it would reduce the numerator in the fraction

$$\frac{\text{quantity of sodium in the ocean}}{\text{quantity supplied by rivers}} = \text{Geological Time,}$$

the effect is, of course, a negative one; unduly diminishing the derived age.

Sollas, as the result of a careful examination of all the data, arrived at extreme limits of 80 and 175 millions of years.[5] Some geologists accept the great ages derived from the uranium-lead ratio; but no explanation has been forthcoming as to how the solvent denudation now progressing on the earth can be eight or nine times greater than the average over the past.

The biological evidence as it bears on this question has been discussed by Sollas and should be read.[6]

Since the discovery of the radioactive elements an entirely different mode of estimating the Age has been evolved. It is based on the assumption that the final products of radioactive change in the case of the parent substances, uranium and thorium, are known. Both are, as it happens, metallic lead. The lead derived from uranium has a lower atomic weight than that derived from thorium. The former has an atomic weight of 206 nearly: the latter of closely 208. These atomic weights can be calculated on our knowledge of the atomic weights of the parent substances, and of the losses of mass which attend the several successive changes in the series of transformations resulting in the final stable element—lead.

Suppose we find a rock rich in uranium. We measure the quantity of uranium present and the quantity of lead which is found associated with the uranium. Next we infer from certain measurements the *rate* at which uranium is now changing into

---

[4] *Geol. Mag.*, vol. vii, May 1900, p. 220, and August 1901, p. 344; also *Report Brit. Assoc.*, 1900.
[5] Presidential Address to the Geol. Soc., vol. lxv, May 1909, p. cxii.
[6] *The Age of the Earth*, Unwin, 1905.

lead. Obviously, from the weight of uranium present and from the weight of the derived lead, we may calculate the Age. A similar procedure can be applied to thorium.

Of course, this method would not be reliable (*a*) if the lead was in either case unstable—i.e. ultimately changed radioactively into something else; or (*b*) were added to by such ordinary lead having the atomic weight of 207·2, as may be found in rocks; or (*c*) if the rate of change of uranium or thorium has not been constant over geological time, so that the resulting lead was produced at a faster or slower rate in the remote past.

We can best realize what that trace of radioactivity means to the life upon the earth by looking forward to a day when it will at length be worn out. Mountains, unrejuvenated, must then sink down into the plains. Continents worn away age after age by sea and sky must be washed irrecoverably into the ocean. Air-breathing life upon the land and land vegetation must finally perish. For the earth itself will have ceased to breathe. And the mind of Man, which alone comprehends it all, will have become part of the forgotten past.

Henry B. Bigelow:

34.   UNITY IN THE SEA*

In the preceding pages (of my book) we have, for the sake of clarity, discussed certain of the underlying problems of oceanography as though the sea, in its physical and chemical nature, were a stable thing, controlling the activities of life within it, though hardly affected by the latter; and as though these problems could profitably be attacked independently one of another. But oceanographers, as a group, have come to realize, during the past quarter-

* From Henry B. Bigelow, OCEANOGRAPHY: *Its Scope, Problems and Economic Importance.* Houghton Mifflin Co., Boston, 1931.

Henry Bryant Bigelow, 1879–1967, was affiliated with the Museum of Comparative Zoology in Cambridge. He made expeditions to the Maldive Islands, Labrador, the East Pacific and the West Indies. He was director of the Woods Hole Oceanographic Institution from 1940 to 1950, and was the author of many scientific papers and books.

century, that this is far from the truth; and with this realization the science of the sea has entered a new intellectual phase.

The foundation for this alteration in viewpoint, from the descriptive to the explanatory, was a growing realization (this could have come only after multitudes of facts had been accumulated) that in the further development of sea science the keynote must be physical, chemical, and biological unity, not diversity, for everything that takes place in the sea within the realm of any one of these artificially divorced sciences impinges upon all the rest of them. In a word, until new vistas develop, our ventures in oceanography will be the most profitable if we regard the sea as dynamic, not as something static, and if we focus our attention on the cycle of life and energy there as a whole, instead of confining our individual outlook to one or another restricted phase, whether it be biologic, physical, chemical, or geologic. Examples of this fundamental unity face the oceanographer at every turn, for while the nature of the sea water governs the lives of the animals and plants that inhabit it, at the same time the functions of the latter are as constantly altering the nature of their environment in a way to which we see nothing comparable on land.

Perhaps the most obvious example of this (one already mentioned) is the constant draft that so many animals and plants make on the water for the materials with which they build their skeletons, as a result of which vast quantities of lime and of silica are constantly being withdrawn. And while some of this goes back into solution when the organisms die, other vast quantities accumulate on the sea floor, in deposits of lime compounds, and of silicates.

On the whole, by this process, lime is accumulating toward the equator, and around the coastlines, silica toward the poles and in the ocean deeps. Why is it that lime accumulates more rapidly on the bottom in shoal water than in deep? Is the solvent power of deep water the greater, as has often been supposed, or have we to do with some bacterial action?

The mass production of plants in the sea withdraws temporarily from circulation the nutrients they need, and there is a certain permanent loss after their death, as of nitrates decomposing to the gaseous state, and of phosphates going into chemical union with bottom sediments. Just how are these losses made up so that the balance is on the whole maintained? How far is the pulse in the available supply of these nutrient substances in the sea responsible for the sudden outbursts of unicellular plants in such unbelievable numbers that they are the most spectacular events in marine economy, and is it their exhaustion of the water that destroys them, or are they self limited in some other mysterious way? In like manner, while the degree of alkalinity of the sea, like that of our own blood serum, is constant within narrow limits and any wide variation means death, the great drafts of carbon that plants make in their photosynthetic activities, added to various other biologic and chemical happenings, are as constantly tending to alter the ionic concentration of the various electrolytes in the solution, and thereby to raise or to lower the alkalinity. But while alterations so caused may actually progress to the fatal limit in enclosed pools, this never happens in the open sea. What role in maintaining this fundamental balance, against their own tendency to upset it, is played by living creatures, and how do they affect the cognate matter of the CO_2 tension of the sea water relative to that of the air?

These illustrations, with those given in the preceding pages, are perhaps enough to show that, at bottom, the composition of the sea water is as much a biologic as a chemical problem, even though in many cases its solution can come only *via* the discipline of chemistry. On the other hand, as is stated repeatedly in the preceding pages, most of the basic problems of oceanic biology equally focus around the fact that the oceans are filled, not merely with water, but with water that is 'salt.'

We can quote no better example of the intimacy with which the disciplines of the biologist, of the geochemist, and of the geophysicist unite in concrete cases, than is afforded by the broad problem of the means by which the uniformity of sea water is maintained, for it is obvious that some of the processes that are constantly tending to disturb the balance fall in one, some in another scientific subdivision.

Thus the problems that center around the fact that the solutes contributed with river water are very different in their composition from sea salts; the withdrawals by animals and plants in the formation of their shells; around the withdrawals of foodstuffs by plants, balanced against the contributions to the water of other stuffs as carcasses decay; or around the alterations in ionic dissociation that result from additions and withdrawals, are biochemical. But, the diluting effect of the rain that falls upon the surface of the sea or of the fresh water that is poured in by rivers, and the concentrating effect of evaporation, all offer problems in physics. Only in conjunction, therefore, can chemist, geologist, and biologist hope to learn how the sea water remains so constant that we must analyze to parts per million, even to parts per thousand million, before we can express the existing variations in the relative proportions of its different salts; or how it is that the alkalinity of the sea never varies outside the narrow range in which protoplasm can live—is in fact as delicately balanced as the alkalinity of our own blood serum.

Another obvious line of connection between the biological and the physical-chemical realms in the sea is *via* temperature; no creature can live, much less thrive, if the water be too hot or too cold. But even as seemingly simple a constant as temperature cannot be considered *per se*, or as an adjunct, in the sea, because water has no inherent temperature of its own, but is given the latter by a complex of constantly changing factors such as solar radiation, back-radiation to the air, evaporation, and the melting of ice. Consequently, in our examination of temperature, we are led without a break into the fields of astrophysics, of meteorology, and of polar geography. We are also led, and very abruptly, to a consideration of the circulation of the sea, because the temperature there at any given time and locality is largely controlled by the currents, as the latter transfer cool or warm water masses from place to place. There is, too, a direct mechanical connection between ocean circulation and the lives of the marine inhabitants quite as important as that *via* temperature, for currents also carry plants and animals about, likewise other materials of all sorts. Currents, in fact, play much the same role in marine economy as do railroads, or any other transportation system on land.

We must realize that, wonderful medium though sea water be for the support of life, any animal or plant would soon exhaust the vital possibilities of the water in its immediate vicinity unless some transportation system were in operation, either to carry the creature elsewhere (whether voluntarily by its own activity, or involuntarily) or to bring to it new water holding in solution or in suspension the substances that the organism in question needs. For the latter sort of transport, the currents and drifts of the sea are wholly responsible; largely so also for the former, by effecting the involuntary migrations of creatures young and old, a kind of dispersal that is constantly going on, and on a scale much broader than is generally appreciated. If the life of the eel is perhaps the most spectacular instance of this type of migration that has yet been followed through to its conclusion, thousands of other kinds of sea animals and plants equally owe their geographic distribution (presence here and absence there), and their dispersal from the regions where they were produced to other regions where they pass the greater part of their lives, directly and solely to mechanical transport by ocean currents. This category of travelers includes the majority of our important food fishes, for most of these, when young, drift at the mercy of tide and current for considerable periods.

Circulation is also solely responsible, for example, for the aeration of the deeps, without which all but the uppermost stratum would be a waste more desert than the Sahara. Currents, too, largely control the distribution of salinity over the oceans; they wear down some coastlines and build up others; they distribute sediments over the bottom of the sea; and they so largely determine the climates of the continents and the system of winds that there is no possible way to disentangle oceanography from climatology.

Reasons as cogent as these make even the biologist admit, no matter how strictly he may confine himself to his own narrow niche, that the currents of the sea offer today one of the most intriguing fields of study in sea science. And, as let us repeat, this is true not only from the descriptive side (for we still have much to learn even about the characteristics of the larger and more impressive ocean currents as described above—Gulf Stream, for instance—let alone the obscure) but from the standpoint of the physical forces that keep the circulation of the sea in its closed and continuous operation. So the unfortunate biologist, even if mathematics are to him a closed book, as is the case with too many of us, must perforce take as keen an interest as do his physical confrères, in the modern applications of mathematics to oceanic dynamics, and hold as high an appreciation of them.

Studies in whatever division of oceanography also lead inevitably into the province of the geologist, if they proceed far enough, for in last analysis the shapes, often the structures of the basins that hold the oceans, must always be taken into account.

The contours of the coastlines and of the submarine slopes confront the student at every turn, no matter what his chosen field of research, because these are the factors that control the whole system of submarine circulation, however the latter be kept in motion. And as every oceanographer realizes but too well, circulation is, in the end, the lifeblood of all events that take place in the sea.

The problems of sedimentation in the ocean also bridge the gap between chemist, biologist, and geologist, because the oozes that accumulate on the floors of the deep basins so largely consist of the skeletons of animals and plants that sift down after death from the upper layers. Where, and in what numbers these skeletons commence to sink, is a problem as strictly biologic as any, for it depends in part on the geographic distribution of the species concerned, equally on their birth- and death-rate. But whether and in what quantities these skeletons do actually reach the bottom, also their effect upon the ocean water as they go back into solution (for given time enough, anything will dissolve in sea water) is a physical-chemical question. The ultimate fate of such of these skeletons as actually reach and accumulate on the bottom is a geologic question of the first rank. And the problems that center around the contributions that are made to the sea floor by reef-builders, and by other bottom-living animals, bridge the gap, no less directly, between the disciplines of biology and chemistry on the one hand, or geology on the other.

There is, we think, no need of further argument to prove that these several disciplines do inevitably interlock, or to point the intellectual necessity not only of recognizing, but of acting upon this unity, if we hope ever to gain any sound understanding of the sea, or of the lives of its inhabitants.

William Beebe:

35.   *IN THE BATHYSPHERE**

At 11:12 A.M. we came to rest gently at 3000 feet, and I knew that this was my ultimate floor; the cable on the winch was very near its end. A few days ago the water had appeared blacker at 2500 feet than could be imagined, yet now to this same imagination it seemed to show as blacker than black. It seemed as if all future nights in the upper world must be considered only relative degrees of twilight. I could never again use the word BLACK with any conviction.

I looked out and watched an occasional passing light and for the first time I realized how completely lacking was the so-called phosphorescence with which we are familiar at the surface. There, whenever an ordinary fish passes, it becomes luminous by reflection

* From HALF-MILE DOWN by William Beebe, by permission of Duell, Sloan and Pearce (affiliate of Meredith Press) New York. Copyright, 1934, 1951, by William Beebe.

William Beebe, 1877–1962, was an American ornithologist and explorer. He was the director of the department of tropical research at the New York Zoological Society from 1919 to 1952 and made expeditions to Central and South America, the Orient and the West Indies. In addition, he was the author of numerous books.

from the lights of the myriads of the minute animals and plants floating in the water. Here each light is an individual thing, often under direct control of the owner. A gigantic fish could tear past the window, and if unillumined might never be seen.

My eyes became so dark adapted at these depths that there was no possibility of error; the jet blackness of the water was broken only by sparks and flashes and steadily glowing lamps of appreciable diameter, varied in color and of infinite variety as regards size and juxtaposition. But they were never dimmed or seen beyond or through any lesser mist or milky-way of organisms. The occasional, evanescent, defense clouds of shrimps hence stand out all the more strongly as unusual phenomena, and are quite apart from the present theme. If the surface light is emitted chiefly by *Noctiluca* and single-celled plants, the explanation of its abyssal absence is easy, for all surface forms of these groups have died out hundreds of feet overhead.

A second thing which occurred to me as I sat coiled in the bathysphere, *more* than half a mile down, was the failure of our powerful beam of light to attract organisms of any kind. Some fled at its appearance, others seemed wholly unconcerned, but not a single copepod or worm or fish gathered along its length or collected against the starboard window from which it poured. We sometimes kept the lesser beam on for three minutes at a time, so there was abundance of time for the plankton, which abounded in all parts of the path of light, to feel and react to its influence. The reason for this demands far more study than I have been able to give it. One factor is doubtless not only lack of the rhythm of day and night, but the eternal absence of all except animal light.

Even in this extremity of blackness I sensed the purity of the water, its freedom from sediment and roiling; six miles from shore and a full mile from the bottom insured this. So there was no diffusion of light, no trails, no refraction. When sparks or larger lights moved they were as distinct as when they were motionless. But reflection was noticeable, as upon the eye or skin from a subocular or a lateral photophore, or upon my face when a shrimp exploded close in front.

Now and then I felt a slight vibration and an apparent slacking off of the cable. Word came that a cross swell had arisen, and when the full weight of bathysphere and cable came upon the winch, Captain Sylvester let out a few inches to ease the strain. There were only about a dozen turns of cable left upon the reel, and a full half of the drum showed its naked, wooden core. We were swinging at 3028 feet, and, Would we come up? We would.

Whatever I thought about the relative value of intensive observation as compared with record-breaking, I had to admit that this ultimate depth which we had attained showed a decided increase in the number of large fish—more than a dozen from three to twenty feet having been seen—and a corresponding greater number of lights, though not in actual size of their diameters.

Now and then, when lights were thickest, and the watery space before me seemed teeming with life, my eyes peered into the distance beyond them, and I thought of the lightless creatures forever invisible to me, those with eyes which depended for guidance through life upon the glow from the lamps of other organisms, and, strangest of all the inhabitants of the deeper parts of the ocean, those blind from birth to death, whose sole assistants, to food, to mates and from enemies, were cunning sense organs in the skin, or long, tendril-like rays of their fins.

Before we began to ascend, I had to stop making notes of my own, so numb were my fingers from the cold steel of the window sill, and to change from my cushion to the metal floor, was like shifting to a cake of ice. Of the blackness of the outside water I have already written too much. As to pressure, there seemed no reason why we should not be outside in a diving helmet as well as in. I thought of a gondola 60,000 feet up in the stratosphere with a pressure of one pound to the square inch. And then through the telephone we learned that at this moment we were under a pressure of 1360 pounds to each square inch, or well over half a ton. Each window held back over nineteen tons of water, while a total of 7016 tons were piled up in all directions upon the bathysphere itself. Yes, we had heard clearly, we were ready to be pulled up at once!

At 2929 feet I heard a metallic twang through the phone, asked what it was, and got some noncommittal answer. I found out later that one of the guy ropes used in spooling the incoming cable on the drum had suddenly given way with a terrific report—a ghastly shock to everyone on deck until they realized it was a rope and not the cable. Truly we in the bathysphere had the best of it at all times.

Whenever I sink below the last rays of light, similes pour in upon me. Throughout all this account I have consciously rejected the scores of "as ifs" which sprang to mind. The stranger the situation the more does it seem imperative to use comparisons. The eternal one, the one most worthy and which will not pass from mind, the only other place comparable to these marvelous nether regions, must surely be naked space itself, out far beyond atmosphere, between the stars, where sunlight has no grip upon the dust and rubbish of planetary air, where the blackness of space, the shining planets, comets, suns, and stars must really be closely akin to the world of life as it appears to the eyes of an awed human being, in the open ocean, one half mile down.

~~~~~~~~~~~~~~~~~

C. *O'Donnell Iselin, II:*

36.   OCEANOGRAPHY*

Until recent years physical oceanography was too frequently considered a branch of science having little importance except to those interested in the ocean itself. This feeling perhaps resulted from the fact that on the earlier expeditions the main emphasis was placed on marine biology, and physical observations were first made mainly with the purpose of exploring the environment of marine plants and animals. Later there developed the necessity of studying the ocean currents and their influence in the transportation of sea life. As a result the physical oceanographer came to be thought of as one who charted the various physical characteristics of the ocean and who had as his ultimate goal the understanding of oceanic circulation.

At the present time, however, it is becoming increasingly evident that several other branches of science must turn to the sea, and therefore to the oceanographers, for help, for only in oceanography can be found the men and equipment for the investigation of the ocean and the problems related to it. Let us briefly consider some examples in which the oceanographer can do important work outside the original conception of his field.

In the first place, geology is naturally much concerned with the ocean basins. Have they been permanent features on the earth's surface, or in the past has there been dry land where now the chart shows one or more thousand fathoms of water? Convincing proof that will settle this problem one way or another can perhaps be

* From the Annual Report of the Smithsonian Institution, 1932, Contribution No. 14, of the Woods Hole Oceanographic Institution.

C. O'Donnell Iselin, 1904–1971, was an assistant curator of Oceanography at the Museum of Comparative Zoology, Cambridge. He taught at MIT and Harvard, and from 1940–1950 was director of the Woods Hole Oceanographic Institution.

brought to light by the oceanographer. A careful study of marine deposits might point to former land bridges between the continents in such a way that they could be accurately located and even dated, much to the satisfaction of all students of the geographic distribution of modern plants and animals, as well as to geologists. Perhaps a less spectacular problem is that of the formation of continental shelves. Again there is reason to believe that the question can best be settled by a careful study of bottom deposits. Thus oceanographic institutions, having developed a technique for bringing up deep-sea mud in the course of exploring the oceans, are now realizing more fully the wide geologic importance of this type of work. With proper equipment much can be learned from the ocean bottom which will extend geologic knowledge out beyond the beach line and perhaps open up a sounder theory for the formation of the earth's surface.

In the same way, but perhaps not to the same extent, meteorological investigations have been largely confined to the air above the continents. Not only is there much meteorological research work to be done at sea, but this science is closely bound up with oceanography. For example, how much influence have fluctuations in the ocean currents on variations in climate and vice versa? From a more technical standpoint, students in dynamic meteorology and dynamic oceanography now see more clearly how similar is the principle of the circulation of the atmosphere to that of the ocean. Thus we can expect in the future a closer relationship between the physical oceanographer and other geophysical students, for many of their problems are interrelated.

On the other hand, the scope and importance of marine biological work has been more generally recognized and in certain lines, for example, fisheries investigations, has developed relatively fast. The many marine laboratories of the world are good evidence that physiologists have realized the importance of studying life in its most natural environment. Hand in hand with the development of marine biology has gone the study of the chemistry of sea water and such questions as the penetration of light below the sea surface and its influence on the life in the upper water layers.

Thus at the present time, oceanography has passed the stage of a science in which the collection and tabulation of facts is considered the main aim, and it is now evident that much productive research of wide interest can be carried out at sea. The reader perhaps now realizes that an oceanographic institution must have on its staff men of wide training and experience in science as well as the specialists in the more restricted phases of oceanography.

The investigation of the ocean naturally divides itself into deep-water problems and shallow-water problems. The well-known fact that most continental land masses are surrounded by a broad, relatively shallow shelf of water less than 100 fathoms deep and that the ocean basins are uniformly twenty or thirty times as deep, serves to emphasize this distinction. Investigations along the coast and even out as far as the edge of the continental shelf can be carried out from almost any boat and with quite inexpensive equipment. Deep-sea oceanography, on the other hand, is an expensive undertaking requiring a strong, able vessel and elaborate winches and instruments. For these reasons there are a number of scientific institutions actively engaged in studies of the shallow-water areas of the ocean, but relatively few can conduct researches outside the hundred-fathom curve. In several ways this state of affairs has been unfortunate in the development of some phases of oceanography, because the shallow waters over the continental shelves are usually much affected by the circulation of the waters of the ocean basins, while tidal and other influences often obscure the picture to such an extent that isolated problems cannot be easily settled.

On the other hand, the shallow-water areas are, of course, the seat of the world's fisheries and for that reason merit governmental study. But even in the case of fisheries investigations, the oceanic waters can not be ignored, because it has been shown that the sudden failures of a fishing ground are sometimes caused by movements of the oceanic waters which periodically flood in over the banks, changing the temperature of the bottom water and driving off the fish. In other words, the investigation of the sea has progressed largely from the shore outward, while it is now evident that there would have been some advantage to oceanography as a whole if it had been possible to put more effort into deep-sea investigations during the early stages of the science. It is perhaps not an exaggeration to say that the heart of most oceanographic problems is to be found in the deep ocean beyond the limits of the continental shelves.

The fact that there has recently been established in the United States an institution largely devoted to deep-sea oceanography is therefore of considerable interest. The Woods Hole Oceanographic Institution, with its headquarters on Cape Cod, is ideally situated for the investigation of the North Atlantic Ocean. The institution is now a going concern with adequate money to support a well-equipped laboratory at Woods Hole, Mass., and a specially designed research ship. If, in the succeeding pages, the reader finds that we have stressed the equipment and methods of this institution unduly, it is because it was founded to counteract the situation in oceanography outlined above and in many ways, we believe, holds a unique position in the world to-day.

The main distinction between an oceanographer and other men of science is that the oceanographer goes to sea. His ship is the all-important part of his scientific equipment for he must be able to make observations in all kinds of weather and at great depths. Not only must he often remain far out at sea for months at a time, but also he must be ready to take an active part in securing his observations. The scientist must thoroughly understand the difficulties and limitations of the work, or he will not be able to evaluate the results properly or suggest practical programs for scientific cruises.

Many types of vessels can be used for oceanography with good results. Fishing craft of various types have proved very satisfactory. The main points are that the vessel should be entirely seaworthy and able to remain at sea longer than ordinary commercial usage requires. For the investigator of the chemistry of sea water especially, the steadier the ship, the more accurate will be his work. But to gain steadiness by using a large ship is often a disadvantage. If the boat is too large, besides being expensive to operate, the scientists are not close enough to the water to handle easily much of their equipment. One solution is to use a sailing vessel, because the sails tend to prevent the boat from rolling excessively in a rough sea. In oceanography, then, we find one instance, at least, where the sailing ship can hold out successfully against the inroads of steam.

One of the most modern examples of a scientific research ship is the *Atlantis* operated by the Woods Hole Oceanographic Institution. She was built especially for the work, after considerable thought, and embodies the experience of many men familiar with carrying out scientific work at sea. The result is a boat that is very satisfactory and at least represents one solution to the problem. She is an auxiliary, steel ketch of about 460 tons displacement, and carries 7,200 square feet of canvas. Her general dimensions are: Length on deck, 142 feet; beam, 29 feet; and draft, 17 feet. She is powered with a 280-horsepower Diesel engine, which besides propelling the ship at a speed of 9 knots in calm weather, supplies through a dynamo the power for the heavy trawl winch. A much smaller Diesel engine generates the power for light, ventilation, and refrigeration, as well as for the hydrographic winch. Perhaps the most specialized piece of equipment is the trawl winch, located, because of its great weight, in the lower hold. It carries 5,000 fathoms of special steel cable of ½-inch diameter, with a breaking strain of about 12 tons. The hydrographic winch, used mainly for lighter work such as securing deep-sea temperatures and water samples, carries a similar length of much lighter wire and is located on deck. Both winches are electrically driven and fitted with automatic devices for guiding the wire smoothly on the drums.

The *Atlantis* accommodations include cabins aft for a scientific staff of five, and amidships two laboratories, one opening out to the deck where the rough work is done and another directly below it where the chemical analyses are carried out and where the microbiologist can examine the catch of his silk net without being disturbed. The permanent crew, exclusive of the scientific staff, numbers 17 men. They have comfortable quarters, and there is ample storage space below decks. The vessel is a smart sailer and an excellent sea boat. Her rig, though small for the size of the hull, is efficient and ideally adapted for heaving to, which is most important for this type of work.

The primary instrument of the physical oceanographer is the deep-sea reversing thermometer. These are now sent down in pairs, one open to the pressure of the water and the other inclosed in a heavy glass case. The significance of this we will see presently. Both the protected and the unprotected thermometers are of the same construction. On being turned over the column of mercury breaks off at a constriction in the capillary and the temperature is read as the length of this detached thread of mercury. Thus the reading cannot be changed on the long haul to the surface by passing through the much warmer surface layers. The deep-sea thermometers are now very accurate and can record the temperature to a hundredth part of a degree centigrade. The pairs of thermometers are sent down in frames which are mounted on the side of instruments known as water bottles. These are fastened to the wire cable at suitable intervals and lowered over the ship's side. A small weight or messenger, is then slid down the wire, which, on striking the uppermost instrument, closes the openings of the water bottle, reverses the thermometers, and releases another messenger which slides on down the wire and repeats the operation with the next instrument. Thus a series of 10 or more water samples and pairs of thermometer readings can be secured at one lowering. In deep water it may take several such lowerings, each successively deeper, to constitute a station.

Although the thermometers and water bottles have been in use for many years and have gradually become much improved in design, there was still one grave inaccuracy which has only recently been eliminated. The depth of each observation was formerly recorded as the length of wire, measured on a wheel of known circumference, from the sea surface to each water bottle. However, in general the wire did not remain vertical in the water. The angle the wire took depended on the relative motions of the ship, the surface layers, and the deep, nearly motionless water masses. In other words, the wire would not only enter the water at an angle, but probably formed an S-shaped curve of unknown extent, so that the depths of all observations was problematical. Since one of the purposes of temperature and salinity observations is to assist in the study of ocean currents—and in regions of currents the trouble of large wire angles (often as much as 40° from the vertical) is at a maximum—it was a great advance when the use of unprotected thermometers became general a few years ago. This method really measures the pressure existing at each instrument of a given series and from these the depths are calculated. The pressure of the water compresses the glass of the unprotected thermometer and makes it read higher than the protected thermometer with which it is paired. The difference in reading between the two instruments can then be translated into depth and with a surprising degree of accuracy. Not only are reliable depths now secured for the temperature observations taken from a modern research ship, but of course these same depths are good for the samples brought up by the water bottles. The water samples are of sufficient volume so that besides salinity, several other chemical factors can be determined. In fact, all physical observations made with this apparatus are now on a comparatively accurate basis.

The primary collecting instrument of the marine biologist is, of course, a net of one sort or another. Many different types are employed, depending on what type of animals or plants are sought and on whether the collections are obtained from the bottom, the surface, or intermediate depths. Of late years, attention (formerly directed chiefly to the bottom fauna) has been largely centered on the drifting community of animals and plants—the so-called "plankton"—which are captured as a rule with some form of tow net. Tows made deep down in the water have, until recently, been confused by the same inaccuracy as have the routine physical observations, namely, the uncertainty as to the precise depths from which the captured specimens came. Not only was the maximum depth reached by the net uncertain but also the animals might have gotten in on the way down or on the way up. This last source of error is especially serious in the case of deep-sea tows, for with these the time involved in lowering and raising the net may be several times as long as the horizontal tow itself. Even for plankton work near the surface, it has been difficult to know at just what depth the net had been fishing or to do accurate quantitative work with more than one net at a time. Improvement in the technique of tow-net work has come gradually and is perhaps not yet at a satisfactory stage of development.

One of the first steps was the perfecting of nets which can be sent down closed, opened during the tow, and closed again before being hauled to the surface. Another improvement has been the use of a kind of bucket at the back end of the net which protects the catch from being rubbed too much against the netting during the long haul to the surface. As many deep-sea animals are ruined as specimens through this cause as through the release in pressure on nearing the surface. This destructive release in pressure, which at first destroyed nearly all specimens of deep-sea fish by causing gas bubbles to form in the tissue, can now be fairly well prevented by using much the same methods as employed in raising a diver.

Recently on the *Atlantis* it has been found possible to make as many as five simultaneous tows with closing nets and know the exact depth of each catch. In this method the wire is so heavily weighted that it remains practically vertical during the tow and the nets are fastened to it one below the other at known intervals. A system of messengers sent down the wire operate the opening and closing devices of the nets. Not only are the opening and closing devices extremely satisfactory but also a further refinement has resulted. Since the frames of the nets are fastened to the wire rigidly, there is no bridle in front of the opening to scare away the animals in the net's path. With large deep-sea nets designed for catching more active animals such refinements are not yet in practice. In fact, even though the net used may be of the closing type, the depth at which the catch is made usually becomes somewhat problematical if the towing wire is at any considerable angle from the vertical. There has been some experiment with pressure instruments which should record the depth of the net at all times during the tow, but there are still many difficulties which must be met. The technique of deep-sea tow-net work is further complicated by the fact that the nets used to-day do not stand much hard usage and soon develop holes and tears which always try the patience of the oceanographer. It is a matter of time and money before biological work at sea can be conducted with satisfactory accuracy.

The study of bottom samples taken from the floor of the ocean has always been productive and has aroused considerable interest among geologists as well as oceanographers. The recent developments in this field have also much improved the accuracy and use of the observations. The old-fashioned piano-wire sounding machine can now be replaced by the accurate and almost automatic sonic method, so that the exact depth of the water can be found at all times. Formerly it took several hours to make each sounding and by the time the wire was hauled back aboard, the vessel could have drifted into water having a different depth. For all bottom sample work, the operation is made much easier by knowing the depth in advance. Otherwise several hundred fathoms extra wire may be run out before the observer is sure his sampling device has reached bottom. With any sampler more complicated than the ordinary sounding tube this may be a great disadvantage. The extra cable coiled on the bottom may kink and the instrument will probably be lost when strain is again put on the wire.

It is a great advantage to investigators to have the bottom sample come up in a water-tight condition so that none of the fine washings are lost on the long haul to the surface. To meet these requirements much attention has been devoted, of late, to devising improvements on the simple "snapper" and other devices which have long been used. For example, various types of valves have been tried that will prevent the mud from washing out of the sounding tube. Other more modern samplers are designed to secure long cores of the bottom material. With the present equipment, samples up to 3 or 4 feet in length have been brought up, and these have shown that the deposits on the ocean floor are often stratified. It is through the study of such material that eventually the problem of whether or not the bottom of the present deep ocean has ever been above sea-level will probably be settled. Still another type of sampler has been gradually evolved that will take either sand or mud from the region over the continental shelf. Another type, mainly used in shallow water, brings up a given area of the bottom which can then be studied for the plant and animal life and their relations as a feeding ground of commercial fish.

We have perhaps described enough of the modern oceanographic equipment to show the reader that not only is the design of all gear being gradually improved, but that the technique of securing good observations from a small ship cannot be easy even in favorable weather. It is this mechanical or engineering side of oceanography that has attracted a good many men to the field. It often seems to the harassed investigator that the sea hides some monster which is most antagonistic to having his realm explored. Unforeseen things are constantly hampering the work of each oceanographic expedition. For example, there are several kinds of marine animals which become wound around the hydrographic wire and stop the messengers. Often a piece of apparatus comes up which has not worked because the messenger never reached it, and this after hours of waiting while miles of cable were unwound and rewound on the winch. If the submarine "devils" are not interfering with the work, the "devils" of stormy weather are very apt to seize the opportunity to persecute the sleepy oceanographer who has perhaps been struggling for hours to complete a series of observations. In wintertime it is a real fight to go to sea and to return home with any of the secrets of the sea safely recorded in the scientific log book. Thus storms and salt water must be combated continually; and although most sensible people very wisely stay ashore, the work at sea holds a real fascination through its difficulties and discomforts, to a small but enthusiastic group of men working in the various oceanographic fields.

~~~~~~~~~~

R. P. *Whitemarsh:*

37.   *GREAT SEA WAVES**

This article was written at sea while I was executive officer of the U.S.S. *Ramapo* employed on transpacific runs. The weather played such an important part in our routes, ballasting, and potential speed that it was always subject to critical analysis. The height of waves during the storm of 1933 was so extreme that it was a subject for comment and discussion for weeks. The solution presented, however, has disclosed no flaws after a year of examination.

The fascinating study of sea conditions, in great vogue over fifty years ago, has, with the advent of steam and its detracting activities, come into a measure of neglect. It is significant that authorities of today in their treatment of the sea find it necessary to refer to theories developed in 1888, 1890, 1900, and 1904 for their latest data. Some of the best work was accomplished by the German scientists Von Helmholts, Borgen, and Zimmermann many years ago in studies of the North Sea.

The extreme height of storm waves is one phase of the subject

* From *U.S. Naval Institute Proceedings*, Vol. 60, No. 8, August, 1934. Reprinted by permission. Copyright © 1934 U.S. Naval Institute.

Lieutenant Commander R. P. Whitemarsh, USN, graduated from the Army Industrial College in June 1934 and served in the Office of Naval Operations, Navy Department.

on which there is no evident agreement. Waves of seismical origin are not considered in this discussion, except that one may serve as an example of a wave of extreme height. In August, 1883, there was an earthquake central near the Island of Krakatoa, Sunda Strait. One of the resulting seismical waves measured 135 feet in height, which figure is generally accepted because of the thorough investigation which followed.

It is a problem to know what to believe when the height of storm waves is under discussion. Starting modestly we learn that waves of 90 meters length and 3 meters height are not uncommon with strong winds in the open sea. One source of information states that 50 feet may be taken as the highest waves found in the open sea. This authority goes on to explain that a hurricane with an 80-knot wind would seem to produce a 40-foot wave, so that the greatest height of waves as found in the open sea and verified by observations is approximately 40 feet.

Riesenberg gives the observed height of seas as approximately 40 feet where there is plenty of "fetch" for the seas to make up in, but concedes that waves of from 50 to 60 feet in height are possible but rare. In a table of about 100 observations, seas 46 feet in height have been noted and in one case there was a height of sea in excess of 50 feet.

The more the experience with the sea, the greater the acceptable height becomes. The greatest waves, according to a noted British authority, are believed to occur in the North Atlantic Ocean and in the great Southern Ocean, where waves 560 feet in length and 50 to 60 feet in height have been experienced. In February, 1841, French marine officers acting under instructions of Arago, observed sea waves of from 42 to 50 feet in height in the vicinity of the Azores. The *National Encyclopedia* shows that during very severe and lasting storms, heights of as much as 75 feet have been observed.

Having established a presumption against waves of extraordinary height, we make bold to announce the observation of a great sea wave. On February 7, 1933, a great sea wave 112 feet high was observed by personnel of the U.S.S. *Ramapo*. This observation was made without prior knowledge of the theory of wave development or other studies of the sea. However, this is one of the largest sea waves found in an aggregate of over 1,021 man-years of seagoing experience.

The length of sea waves is of interest inasmuch as this affords one means of checking the height graphically and by formula.

It is natural that the greatest waves should be observed in the larger oceans where there are no land obstructions for thousands of miles. Many of the longest waves have been found in the South Pacific Ocean where lengths of from 500 to 1,000 feet and periods of from 11 to 14 seconds have been observed.

The longest wave observed was one 2,600 feet long which had a period of 23 seconds. It was measured by the French Admiral Mottez in the Atlantic Ocean near the equator in longitude 28° W. This wave was traveling at a speed of 77 miles per hour. Waves varying for 500 to 600 feet in length are sometimes encountered in the Atlantic Ocean, but the usual length of waves is from 160 to 320 feet with periods of from 6 to 8 seconds.

Another observation of value in determining the characteristics of waves is the speed at which waves travel. There is as wide a divergence in opinion regarding the speed of translation of waves as there is on the subject of wave heights. There is a definite relation between the period of waves, their length, their height, and force of wind, which authorities have attempted to express in precise formulas. However, all seas in the same storm will differ with each other while each wave is being constantly increased or decreased in size.

As a matter of fact, observations have shown that sea waves tend to travel at approximately the same speed as the winds which cause them. For example, from March 19, 1933 to April 3, 1933, the *Ramapo* accompanied a constant trade wind of 14 knots on a great circle course for 3,600 miles. It was observed that the following seas traveled at a speed remarkably close to that of the trade wind, since they slowly overtook the ship traveling at 10 knots' speed.

Krümmel states that while wind velocity is increasing, the wave velocity is less than that of the wind, but that as soon as the wave has reached its maximum height, further wind force is expended in increasing its length, and therefore its speed, until eventually the wave travels faster than the wind.

This information substantiates, or is substantiated by, observations of 55-knot wave velocity during a wind velocity of 60 knots, and applying to the particular sea wave under discussion.

The weather condition in the mid-Pacific in February was unique in that it contained every element favorable to the development of extraordinarily high waves. The *Ramapo* was proceeding from Manila to San Diego in latitude 34°–30′ N. On February 3, the barometer, which had stood at 30.20, began to fall. During the 7-day period of stormy weather which followed, the ship traveled from longitude 169° E. to longitude 155° W. on an easterly course.

From the meteorological plotting chart prepared in the *Ramapo*'s aërological office, it was noted that a well-defined low (29.00), central near Dutch Harbor, Alaska, extended from the Arctic Circle to a secondary low immediately to the northward of the Hawaiian Islands. On February 4 this secondary low developed and deepened to a minimum pressure below 29.10, and apparently drew much of its strength from the northern low whose minimum pressure rose to 29.60.

This system of lows displaced the normal high-pressure area to the eastward of the Hawaiian Islands, whose center usually shows a pressure of 30.20. This resulted in a striking system of high pressure areas extending along the entire coast of North America from the Arctic Ocean to the tip of Lower California.

Incidentally, such a development is characteristic of winter cold snaps in the West and Middle West, since its normal clockwise air circulation draws down the polar air mass from the arctic regions. In this case, extreme low temperatures ($-40°$ F.) were registered in the Middle West with blizzards and snow as far east as New York. These facts are mentioned to indicate the far-reaching influence of an extreme weather condition. The disturbance was not localized as is the case with a typhoon, but reached all the way from Kamchatka on the Asiatic continent to New York. This permitted an unobstructed "fetch" of thousands of miles, with winds from a constant direction, all contributing to extremely high seas.

On Sunday, February 5, we crossed the 180th meridian practically in the middle of the vast Pacific Ocean. Sunday was repeated. The third low whose presence we suspected immediately to the westward became a reality.

The barometer dropped to 29.58 to the accompaniment of winds from astern force 8 and 9. These winds lasted for four hours and resulted in a rather rough sea. This short blow is considered our entry into the real low-pressure area with which we traveled for the next four days.

By the end of the second Sunday, February 5, the barometer had slowly settled to 29.51 and winds of force 3, 4, and 5 were experienced. The wind held to the west. The system of three lows showed marked intensity with minimum pressures below 29.00, 29.30, and 29.20, and occupied much of the North Pacific Ocean.

On February 6, the barometer dropped from 29.51 to 29.24 without any material difference in wind or sea. The wind was a strong breeze of 30 knots' velocity and caused a moderate sea.

The barometer remained at 29.24 for five hours, during which time the elements began to give evidence that something out of the ordinary was about to happen. After two hours the wind became a moderate gale, force 7 or 35 knots, and the sea at once increased to a heavy swell. These conditions were maintained for three hours without change when, for the first time, the barometer rose one hundredth to 29.25.

The result was immediately apparent. At this time the wind increased to a fresh gale of 42 knots while the sea effect was slightly increased. The following hour disclosed a whole gale of 58 knots' force and mountainous seas. This occurred at 2200 on February 6, as we began to leave the vicinity of the low center near which we had been cruising for over two days. We maintained our easterly course with the wind almost directly astern. It would have been disastrous to have steamed on any other course.

Although the ship's draft aft was 21 feet 10 inches, the propeller raced to such an extent upon the passing of the crest of a wave that it became necessary to reduce speed at 2300.

The storm reached its height between 0300 and 0900 when winds up to 68 knots in velocity were clocked with the anemometer. We occupied the bridge from 0400 to 0800 and personally verified all data. The winds came in gusts and squalls during which the greatest velocities were obtained and the highest seas were observed. This fact gives additional evidence that sea waves travel at approximately the same speed as the wind which accompanies them. It is significant that when, at 1000 on February 7, the wind dropped to force 8, the seas were simultaneously reduced from "mountainous" to "very rough."

The great system of three low centers was consolidated during the height of the storm experienced by the *Ramapo* with extreme activity as the result. An extraordinary depth of 28.40 inches of barometric pressure was noted on February 8, 1933. The ship emerged from the low pressure area on February 9, just one week after entering it.

The weather condition may be briefly summarized. February is notoriously the most stormy month in the North Pacific Ocean. And from all reports, this was the most extensive and severe storm of the year. The *Ramapo* was in a position to experience the full force of the storm. The height of waves was materially greater than that noted when the vessel was forced to take reduced speed for three days in a typhoon near the Mariana Islands in October, 1929.

The conditions for observing the seas from the ship were ideal. We were running directly down wind and with the sea. There were no cross seas and therefore no peaks along wave crests. There was practically no rolling, and the pitching motion was easy because of the fact that the sides of the waves were materially longer than the ship. The moon was out astern and facilitated observations during the night. The sky was partly cloudy.

Probably no two seas were identical in length and height. They varied from 500 to 750 feet in length of sides, or total wave length of 1,000–1,500 feet, as measured by the ship itself and the seaman's eye. This is verified by motion picture film taken during the morning watch. The *Ramapo* is 477 feet 10 inches in length. For purposes of illustration, a conservative wave length of 1,180 feet is assumed. It was noted that the ship's entire length glided down the lee slope of waves an appreciable time before the crest overtook the stern. The vessel was dwarfed in comparison with the seas.

The period of the largest sea wave was 14.8 seconds as determined by stop watch. Similarly, a wind velocity of 66 knots was taken and verified, although the average velocity for several hours was 60 knots.

Due to the extreme simplicity of the determination of the height of sea waves in this particular case, none of the factors, including wave length, period, and wind velocity, is required in the solution. These factors are of interest in checking observations and proving formulas. The height determination is by construction wherein the ship itself measured the seas.

Among a number of separately determined observations, that of Lieutenant (J.G.) Frederick C. Marggraff, U. S. Navy, is employed, although one other observation similarly taken by another observer gave greater heights of sea waves. The selected observation gives a height of wave of 112 feet compared with other observations of 82, 86, 107, and 119 feet, all covered by construction based on sworn affidavits of different observers.

Mr. Marggraff declares that while standing watch on the bridge between the hours of 0000 and 0400 on Tuesday, February 7, 1933, he saw seas astern at a level above the iron strap on the boom located against the mainmast crow's nest, and that at the moment of observation the horizon was hidden from view by the waves approaching from astern. Mr. Marggraff is 5 feet 11¾ inches tall. The ship was not listed and the stern was in the trough of the sea.

This gives an exact line of sight from the bridge to the crest of the wave. This also determines the attitude of the ship with the angle of pitch. While the observer was obviously below the line of crests, the amount is indeterminate. It would reduce the observed height of the wave astern if this line were considered truly horizontal. Such an assumption is made in arriving at a height of 112 feet.

The stern of the ship had been sinking into the trough of the oncoming sea, up to the instant of observation, due in part to lack of water support aft. Water rolled aboard aft when the stern was near the crest. Nearly normal conditions of draft obtained when the stern was almost at the trough. For all practical purposes, the trough was at the water line at the stern, 21 feet 10 inches above the keel.

The accompanying figure illustrates the attitude of the ship at the instant the height was determined. Considering the line of sight in the plane of the horizon, we measure vertically downward to the trough to obtain the wave height. The construction was from ship's plans. The height is shown to be 112 feet from this construction. The height determination depends solely upon the observed line of sight and the accuracy of these plans.

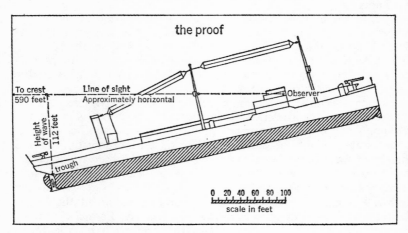

Fig. 37–1.

The form which a sea wave tends to take is best represented by the swell, but is correct with some modifications for the storm waves. This form is a trochoid curve or prolate cycloid. It may be graphically represented by tracing a point on the plane of a circle as it rolls along a straight line. It may vary from a straight line to the limiting form of the trochoid, depending upon the strength of the elements causing wave formation. A modified trochoid curve was used to verify the wave measurement and gave an angle of pitch for the ship similar to the observed angle.

From the motion pictures taken during the storm, it is known that the ship's stern was inclined downward at an angle of 5 degrees when the horizon astern disappeared from view in one case. Further descent of the ship into the trough may be termed a descent below the plane of the horizon. The ship was inclined downward at an angle of 11°–50′ at the instant the observation of the great wave was made. Angles were measured using the ship's normal water line according to draft. Also, the ship pitched through an angle of 24°–12′ according to sextant and other lines of sight to the horizon.

Motion pictures also indicate the extremely small degree of rolling during the storm.

These data make available an approximate check of the wave height. At the instant of observation, the vessel was lying up the windward slope of the wave. Whatever distortion of the trochoid wave form occurs in a storm tends to increase the angle of slope of the lee side above that of the windward side, since the crests break forward in whitecaps. By construction, we note, as previously stated, that the ship's water line intersects the line of sight at an angle of 11°–50′. Taking this angle as the average slope of the lee side of the wave, and the distance 600 feet up the slope of a wave 1,180 feet long, a right triangle is available with a hypotenuse of 600 feet. The calculated height of the wave becomes 600 sin 11°–50′, or 123 feet.

This compares with the reported height of 112 feet. An error is introduced in considering that the slope is a straight line, but a moment's reflection will show that this is on the side of conservatism. The steepest slope of the wave curve occurs at or near the crest.

This check is in turn subject to verification by various accepted formulas which apply to wave lengths. Quantities used in these formulas include gravity as 32.17 feet per second, one meter as 39.37 inches, period of the wave as 14.8 seconds, wave velocity observed at 55 knots, height of sea as 112 feet, and wind velocity as 60 knots. The length of this wave, according to formula, is as follows:

Length	By Formula	Based Upon
1180.0 feet	Observed	Ship length
1121.5 "	A	Period
1685.0 "	B	Wave velocity
1819.0 "	C	Wave velocity
3859.0 "	D	Height
1128.0 "	E	Wind velocity
1798.7 "	None	Average

Although in some cases the calculations agree very closely with observations, certain results are irreconcilable. If a greater length of wave than that selected were taken, it would only operate to increase the height of the wave, the angle of slope remaining as observed.

It is principally because the two observations of heights of 82 and 86 feet were taken from positions two decks below the bridge deck, and therefore deeper in the trough, that they vary to such an extent from the greater values of 107, 112, and 119 feet determined from the bridge. Observations from the flying bridge deck or the foremast crow's nest would possibly have determined even more accurate measurements and therefore greater heights of waves.

A further check is available to any individual who may desire to make the test. Comprehension of the significance of 100 feet height, for instance, may vary with the individual, but in reality, this is a rather short distance. The individual may test his theory of wave height on the illustrative diagram, by measuring vertically downward towards the trough from point C on the line of sight to the crest, a distance which he considers a maximum wave height. A scale is provided for this purpose. The wave form should then be sketched in through this point as the trough. It should be of considerable interest to note what has happened to the ship.

Since time immemorial, seafaring men have been telling the world in their inarticulate way that storm waves attain heights which seem incredible to the rest of mankind. In the absence of satisfactory proof in specific cases, it has been easy to doubt the accuracy of the observations.

Possibly the controversy began in 1837 when Dumont D'Urville estimated and reported a wave 100 feet high off the Cape of Good Hope. It is significant that an authority of today should consider this statement of such a dubious character that probably only seafarers would agree with it.

The privilege of viewing great storm waves of extreme height is a rare one indeed. Furthermore, we have no assurance that the highest waves of the ocean have been observed or measured. If such a wave should ever be encountered, it is probable that all hands would be chiefly concerned with the safety of the ship to the exclusion of any scientific measurement of the phenomenon.

Today the apologetic method of mariners in reporting seas in violation of the 60-foot law of science is as quoted from a *Hydrographic Bulletin:* "A measurement of one sea showed an apparent height of about 70 feet."

This particular observation was made in the North Pacific Ocean on December 31, 1932, during a typhoon in which winds of force 12, hail squalls, and a tremendous sea were experienced.

In view of the undisputable experience at lighthouses throughout the world, it is difficult to understand the apparent low limit placed by science on the maximum height of great sea waves. Lighthouse observations support the conclusion that waves reach heights in excess of 100 feet.

In the winter of 1861, a fog bell 100 feet high on the Bishop Lighthouse, Isles of Scilly, was struck by a sea wave. The breaking crest was formed well above this height and the wave struck with such force that the metal bracket 4 inches thick by which it was supported was broken. The bell crashed to pieces on the rocks below. The sea left sand heavily deposited on the lighthouse gallery.

Occasionally, waves go over the top of the tower of the lighthouse on Minots Ledge, Massachusetts, 75 feet above the water.

In severe storms, rocks have been thrown through the lantern glass of Tillamook Rock Lighthouse, 133 feet above the ocean. This lighthouse is situated on a rock one mile from the Oregon coast between the 10- and 21-fathom lines and 30 miles from the 100-fathom line. This topographical condition serves to modify the extreme height of seas before they reach Tillamook. The height of 133 feet does not, therefore, represent the maximum height of offshore sea waves.

For instance, in certain localities, such as off the Malabar coast, the seas are entirely ironed out by shoal water prior to reaching land and safe anchorage is provided along an otherwise unprotected coast.

The intriguing subject of sea wave study is in the process of development and enjoys no great solidarity of opinion. It is necessary that the scientists receive the co-operation and aid of men who go to sea in ships if improvement is to continue. Perhaps authorities in the past have been radically conservative in the treatment of sea waves. A 60-foot wave as the highest of all time lacks conviction.

There should be no intimation that the modern sea wave exceeds that of the past in size. The theory and law of waves are excellent guides, but, in accordance with the present custom, if the laws cannot be enforced, they should be repealed.

~~~~~~~~~~~~~~

Reginald Aldworth Daly:
38.   ICE AND SEA LEVEL*

The melting of the existing Antarctic and Greenland ice would
add about 50 meters of water to the ocean. Assuming both ice-caps
to have been considerably smaller in Interglacial time than at present,
one can understand corresponding general emergence of continents
and islands during the Pleistocene. This chapter has to do with
the other side of the picture. The older glaciations thinned the ocean
still more than it was thinned by the formation of the existing
ice. The last glaciation, involving a vast amount of evaporation of
sea water, reduced general sea level about 75 meters below its
present position; the maximum glaciation, about 90 meters. The
geographical consequences were legion. Rivers and even inland seas
were drastically affected. Shorelines, a million kilometers in length,
were shifted seaward, quite altering the program of wave and current
action by the sea on continents and islands. Organisms, including
man, reacted to the emergence of new land.

First, the response of rivers to those swings will be exemplified.
Uplift or seaward tilting of a river basin accelerates a river's flow
and the downcutting of its channel. The same results come from
a eustatic drop of ocean level. A eustatic rise of ocean level,
like subsidence or landward tilting of the earth's crust, lessens the
velocity of a river, which, therefore, begins to fill its valley with
sediment. With deglaciation of the lands and consequent rise of
sealevel, the river, now more sluggish, was forced to deposit its
load of sediment.

And what of man's reactions to the rhythmical changes of
sea level in the Ice Age? Archeologists now generally agree that
Homo sapiens or his cousins lived throughout the whole of the
Pleistocene Period. Man-like creatures were making tools at least
as early as the first Interglacial stage. Fishermen of the last Glacial

* From THE CHANGING WORLD OF THE ICE AGE by R. A. Daly. Copyright ©
1934 by Yale University Press. Reprinted by permission of the Publisher.

Canadian born Reginald Aldworth Daly, 1871–1957, was Sturgis-Hooper
professor of geology at Harvard University from 1912 to 1942. He was the author
of numerous books and was editor of the *American Journal of Science*.

stage left their shell-heaps on the shores of lands now drowned. Other men—Neolithic men—fished along the shores of the Littorina Sea, which, we remember, transgressed Scandinavian lands now dry, and later withdrew, as the earth's crust continued its slow

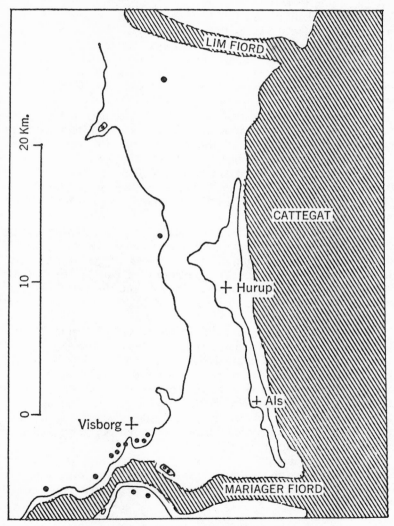

Fig. 38–1. Neolithic sites and the Littorina shoreline.

recoil from the old Glacial basining. The shading on the map of Figure 38–1 represents the sea now washing the shore of eastern Denmark. The continuous lines show the position of the Littorina shore some six thousand years ago, and the dots mark the sites of Neolithic shell-heaps along the Littorina Strand.

A half million years before those Nordics harvested the Littorina Sea, Early Paleolithic man left stone artifacts on the Milazzian marine terrace of Algeria, 55 to 60 meters above the Mediterranean. Anderson is inclined to date the tools, varying in type from Chellean to Mousterian, in the longest of the Interglacial stages— the Mindel-Riss stage of the Alps. The oldest of all Paleolithic relics, the Early Chellean, are dated in the first, Günz-Mindel, Interglacial stage.[1]

One of the outstanding problems of the archeologist is the proper matching of the high eustatic strandlines and river terraces. This Passemard has attempted in the case of the Euphrates Valley.

Civilization developed most rapidly on the great deltas. It is natural to inquire about human sites on deltas that were built out at times of low general sea level. Was primitive agriculture already pursued at the mouths of the Nile, Euphrates, and Huangho Rivers in those old days?

Outside the delta regions, the signs of man's activities during the low-water stages, though now drowned, may have escaped deep burial under sand and mud. Daneš has even suggested that, with submarine and electric light, the bottom of a part of the Adriatic Sea, where sediment accumulates with extreme slowness, might be searched for relics of men who lived while northern Europe was capped with ice.[2]

The last Glacial stage was the Reindeer Age of French history. Men then lived in the famous caves overlooking the channels of the French rivers, and hunted the reindeer which throve on the cool plains of France south of the ice border. The Late-Glacial rise of general sealevel was necessarily accompanied by a rise of the river waters downstream. Hence the lowest caves are likely to have been partly or wholly drowned under river water, or river mud, Post-Glacial alluvium. There the search for more relics of Paleolithic man should be pursued.

In any case geologists and archeologists will do well to join forces in the effort to correlate terraces, visible and submarine, with the records of human activities. Success in this undertaking would

[1] R. V. Anderson, *Bull. Geol. Soc. America,* vol. 43, 1932, p. 847.
[2] J. V. Daneš, *Scot. Geog. Mag.,* vol. 41, 1925, p. 289.

mean a superlative improvement of archeological technique; for human remains belonging to any of the eustatic terraces must be of essentially contemporaneous origin, whether along the seashores of Europe, Asia, Africa, Australia, or the Americas, or along the corresponding river terraces in these same continents. How great the gain if such relative, but rigorous dating of the ancient cultures, all over the world, shall become possible! The geologist has begun the long job of matching terraces, and he can supply useful estimates of the lengths of the Glacial stages in years. The archeologist has begun to relate the old hunters and fishers to the different eustatic terraces. Geological sequence should aid in the more exact writing of archeological history, and the archeologist will furnish valuable checks on the conclusions of the geologists. Is it too much to hope for many vital discoveries by such coöperation through the decades to come? Was it the multiplied climatic stress of the Ice Age that started the civilization of man? With such a goal and such a question before him, the geologist is not likely to lose hope for the great prize, in spite of the complex behavior of the earth when lands or oceans are disturbed.

Once more is illustrated in the field of geology the principle of the ancient proverb: No man "liveth unto himself." Each lowering of general sealevel by glaciation in limited parts of the continents gave new activity to rivers that reached the ocean, rivers on every continent and island. Along every coast new, albeit temporary, lands were made from strips of the former, shallow sea bottom. Across these new lands many rivers were extended, there to cut new channels. Out of the multitude of examples we have noted a few. The area of the continental and island shelves so dried off for the time totaled millions of square kilometers. Straits became land plains, temporary land-bridges, which were of manifest importance in problems of distribution of animals and plants. The winds took sand and mud from the wide flats and built dunes on an extraordinary scale. Probably, too, some of the peculiar and widespread deposits of dust, called loess, were then increased. We have watched the waves changing the pre-Glacial banks and shelves, when the surface of the ocean slowly sank and rose, as if Neptune were breathing with the august dignity of a god.

~~~~~~~~~~~~~~

Selman A. Waksman:

39.   THE ROLE OF BACTERIA IN THE CYCLE
OF LIFE IN THE SEA*

The sea harbors an extensive population of bacteria, varying greatly
in numbers and in the variety of their activities. This variation
depends, in the case of the sea-water, on the distance from shore,
depth of water, season of year, abundance of plankton and uniformity of mixing of the water, and in the case of the sea bottom,
upon the nature of the bottom material, depth from the surface of
the sediment, etc. These bacteria take part in a number of processes
which are of considerable importance in the life of the plant and
animal populations of the sea, namely, in the decomposition of
plant and animal residues, in the transformation of their nitrogen
to such an available form as ammonia and of their carbon to carbon dioxide, in the formation of nitrate as well as the reduction of
nitrate, in the oxidation of sulfur and the reduction of sulfate, in
the fixation of nitrogen, in the direct and indirect precipitation of
calcium and iron, in the formation of organic matter or humus in
the sea bottom and in the decomposition of this humus. To what
extent these processes are absolutely essential in the growth of plant
and animal life in the sea still remains to be determined.

The study of bacteria in the sea includes a series of problems in
bacteriology and in biochemistry which are to be coordinated with
other branches of oceanography, in order to establish the role of
the bacteria in the marine processes. In most instances information
on marine bacteriology has been gathered by individual investigators

* From *Scientific Monthly*, 1934, Volume 38, pps. 35–49. "The Role of
Bacteria in the Cycle of Life in the Sea" by Selman A. Waksman. Contribution
No. 23 of the Woods Hole Oceanographic Institution and Journal Series paper
of the New Jersey Agricultural Experiment Station, Department of Soil Microbiology. Reprinted by permission of the author.

For his work in the discovery of streptomycin, Selman Abraham Waksman
was awarded the 1952 Nobel Prize in Physiology and Medicine. The recipient
of numerous other awards, Dr. Waksman has had a distinguished career as
researcher, teacher and author. He is professor of Soil Microbiology at Rutgers
University and is involved in research at Rutgers' Institute of Microbiology.

during short periods, using material obtained from few localities; less often the work is the result of an expedition, where limited facilities were offered for a detailed study of bacterial life and of bacterial processes under the natural conditions prevailing in the sea. Most of these investigations had a specific purpose of demonstrating either the presence or absence of certain bacteria in the sea, or of organisms capable of bringing about processes which are known to be of importance to marine life. Attempts to correlate the occurrence of a certain organism with an important marine process frequently led to generalizations which were later found to be totally unjustified.

If any phase of biology needs continuous study, it is that of bacteriology, because one deals here with living organisms, rather than with dead specimens, and one must study physiological processes rather than morphological structure. One can not bottle up some sea-water for 6 weeks or even days, then bring it to the laboratory and expect that the numbers and types of bacteria will have remained the same as under the natural conditions of the sea. One can not preserve bacteria, as one does animals or plants, then identify them, as an opportunity arises, since in most cases the bacteria are identified not by their appearance but by their activities.

The fact that a certain bacterium is active in a specific transformation in the laboratory is no proof as yet that it will be responsible for the same reaction in the sea. Samples of sea-water or of bottom material removed from their environment and brought into the laboratory may give, within a very short period of time, frequently within a few hours, a bacterial population which is quite different quantitatively from the corresponding population in the sea itself; a number of factors may be responsible for this change.

In the case of the bacterial population of the sea, as in the case of soil bacteria or bacteria in inland waters and in sewage, one deals with mixed populations and not with pure cultures. It is not merely sufficient to isolate an organism, cultivate it and determine what it does in pure culture; it is far more important to determine what it does in its natural substrate and how these activities dovetail with the activities of other bacteria, as well as with the whole complex mass of higher plants and animals.

In order to illustrate the possible confusion that may arise from the investigation of a single bacterial process in the sea, it is sufficient to call attention to the study of the role of bacteria capable of reducing nitrate in certain important marine processes. The hypothesis of Drew concerning the precipitation of $CaCO_3$ in the tropics and that of Brandt concerning the insufficient plankton development in tropical seas, as compared with that of temperate and arctic regions, were based largely upon this one specific bacterial process. Not only was considerable importance attached to it, disregarding thereby numerous other chemical and bacteriological processes involved, but an attempt was even made to set up highly generalized theories concerning the whole system of metabolism in the sea on the basis of this process.

Drew has shown in 1913 that, in a sea-water medium containing nitrates and calcium salts of organic acids, precipitation of calcium carbonate takes place. This reaction was found to be a result of the reduction of nitrate by certain bacteria, which use the organic acid radicle as a source of energy. On the basis of this experiment, the theory was proposed that the precipitation of $CaCO_3$ in the chalk muds in the Bahama region, off the coast of Florida, and probably in other places is due to action of bacteria. Even granting that Drew was right in his conclusions, namely, that his experiments proved that precipitation of $CaCO_3$ in the sea may be due to the action of bacteria, he made two purely hypothetical assumptions not based upon any experimental evidence, which would tend to nullify these conclusions, as applied to large regions. These assumptions are that nitrates are produced in the sea in sufficiently large amounts and that sufficient quantities of organic acids are present in sea-water to bring about the dissolution of the calcium and to serve as an energy source to the nitrate-reducing bacteria. The mere fact that an organism can reduce nitrate in an artificial culture medium is no proof that this process forms an important phase of the activities of the organism under natural conditions. A great many pathogenic bacteria are able to reduce nitrate, although this substance does not occur in appreciable quantities in the blood or in other tissues where these bacteria are active.

In criticizing this hypothesis, C. B. Lipman suggested that the sea does not contain a sufficient number of bacteria to bring about such an extensive process. However, the activities of the bacteria are not limited by their numbers but by the amount of available energy, the abundance of nutrients and favorable environmental conditions. Lipman concluded that calcium precipitation in large quantities in the sea can be more readily explained by purely physicochemical processes, although he did not deny the possibility that microorganisms may bring about, directly or indirectly, the precipitation of some calcium carbonate. Kellerman and Smith, who upheld Drew's hypothesis, believed that the identifying bacteria are specific "calcium bacteria," indicating thereby that the process of calcium precipitation plays the predominant function in the life activities of these organisms. Molish went even a step further and described various new species of bacteria on the basis of their ability to cause the precipitation of calcium. These conceptions are hardly justified, since the reaction of calcium precipitation, even under Drew's experimental conditions, is only secondary in nature and does not form an important phase of the physiology of the bacteria. Further, in addition to various denitrifying bacteria, other organisms, such as urea and sulfate-reducing bacteria, are also able to bring about the precipitation of calcium. Unfortunately, neither Drew nor those following him seemed to have been familiar with the fundamental work of Nadson on "Bacteria as Geological Agents" published nearly 30 years ago, which tended to illuminate this process.

The second hypothesis based upon the activities of nitrate-reducing bacteria was even more far-reaching in its application. Brandt was among the first to emphasize the important part played by bacteria in the cycle of life in the sea. He suggested the following explanation for the relative abundance of plankton in the arctic and temperate regions and its comparative poverty in the tropics. In warm regions, the denitrifying bacteria are very active and destroy the nitrates, thus bringing about a nitrogen minimum; in cold regions, where the denitrifying bacteria are not so active, the abundance of nitrate permits considerable plankton development. This hypothesis has had a considerable influence upon the subsequent development of research on the bacteria of the ocean. Assuming that the observations concerning the relative abundance of the plankton in the sea, under different climatic conditions, are correct, the explanation suggested is very much open to criticism, since one would have to establish first that nitrates are formed in the tropical regions as abundantly as in the temperate regions, that bacteria are more active in the tropics and that more energy, in the form of plant excreta or residues, is available in the tropical seas to enable those bacteria to reduce the nitrate. Possibly the more rapid disappearance of the organic residues in the tropical waters, due to the greater activity of the bacteria decomposing the organic matter, may have more to do with this phenomenon than the activities of the denitrifying bacteria. Recent studies by Butkewitsch established the fact that nitrate-reducing bacteria are also found in cold regions as in the Barents Sea, while investigations carried out at the Woods Hole Oceanographic Institution brought out the fact that the activities of most of the nitrate-reducing bacteria in the sea are limited to the reduction of nitrate to nitrite and not to atmospheric nitrogen.

These two illustrations are sufficient to emphasize how certain limited observations on the activities of one group of bacteria isolated from the sea, namely, the denitrifying organisms, can be so magnified as to make them appear as among the most important members of the bacterial population of the sea. One should add here that Brandt's hypothesis was not accepted by Gran and other prominent oceanographers, who demonstrated that the available evidence is either insufficient or even contrary to it.

THE CYCLE OF LIFE IN THE SEA AND
BACTERIAL ACTIVITIES

A graphic representation of the role of bacteria in the cycle of life in the sea is given in Figures 39–1 and 39–2. Figure 39–1 shows

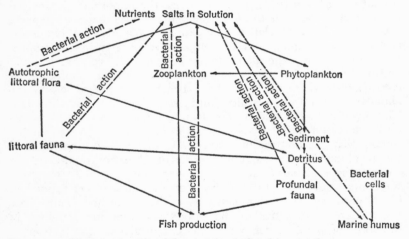

Fig. 39–1. Plant, animal and bacterial relationships in the sea.

the general relation of the bacterial activities to the interrelationships of plants and animals in the sea and to the various degradation products, while a more detailed analysis of the specific marine processes in which bacteria are chiefly concerned is shown in Figure 39–2.

According to Thienemann, the plankton consists of three groups of organisms: (1) "producers," comprising largely the chlorophyll-bearing diatoms and algae which build up organic substances from the inorganic nutrients dissolved in the water; (2) "consumers," or the animal representatives of the plankton which feed upon the

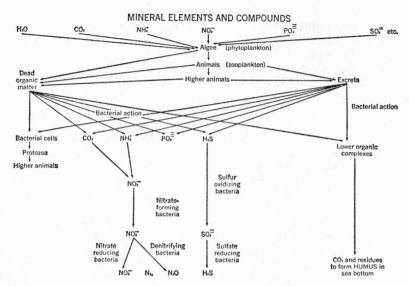

Fig. 39-2. Role of bacteria in the cycle of life in the sea.

living or dead members of the phytoplankton or their metabolic products; (3) "reducers," comprising the bacteria, which decompose and mineralize the high-molecular compounds formed by the producers and consumers. The last two groups are in definite nutritional relations to one another. One can easily enlarge upon this idea and include among the consumers also the higher animals, which feed both upon producers and consumers of a lower order; among the reducers one can include not only the bacteria of the plankton but also the bacteria of the sea bottom which take an active part in the destruction of plant and animal residues in the sea, as well as the animal population of the sea. Certain groups of bacteria will also be found among the producers, such as the nitrogen-fixing bacteria; bacteria may also be considered as consumers, since they synthesize bacterial cell substance. One can add a fourth group, namely, "transformers," which comprise those bacteria, like the nitrifying, sulfur-oxidizing, nitrate-reducing and others, which play a most important role in the transformation of various elements and compounds, aside from the above three general processes.

The plant population of the sea synthesizes, under proper light conditions, organic substances out of the simple nutrients, namely, the water, CO_2, available nitrogen compounds, soluble phosphates and other inorgánic salts. The animals of the sea which are unable to utilize the photosynthetic energy of the sun must obtain their energy and materials necessary for the construction of their body substance from the plants, either directly or indirectly. Some lower animals, such as certain foraminifera, radiolaria, coelenterata and others, actually carry living algae which synthesize organic matter and thus serve for the nutrition of their host. After the death of the numerous plants and animals which inhabit the sea, their bodies as well as their excretion products are decomposed by bacteria living in the water, on the plankton or in the bottom sediments.

Among the most important activities of the bacteria in the sea are the decomposition of plant and animal residues and the transformations of nitrogen. By decomposing the residues of marine plants and animals as well as their waste products, the bacteria return, in a mineralized form, to circulation in the sea, and in the atmosphere those elements from which the diatoms and algae inhabiting the sea synthesize their cell substance, namely, the carbon as carbon dioxide, and nitrogen as ammonia, the phosphorous as phosphate, etc. Without these actions of the bacteria, the sea bottom would soon become covered with a mass of dead plant and animal débris, and the limited supplies of available carbon (CO_2), of available combined nitrogen and of phosphate would soon become transformed into organic forms which are unavailable for growth of marine plants; this would result in cessation of plant life in the sea. In the process of decomposition of the residues, the bacteria themselves synthesize considerable cell substance, which may actually serve as food for various invertebrate animals and thus form a constituent part of the plankton of the sea.

Bacteria may also live symbiotically with various marine plants and animals. Among these symbiotic relationships, that of the green algae and the nitrogen-fixing bacteria has been suggested. In recent investigations carried out at the Woods Hole Oceanographic Institution, a close parallelism was found in the water and in the plankton between the abundance of diatoms and other plant and animal constituents and the numbers of bacteria. When the diatoms die, as shown by the rapid diminution in numbers, as shown in Figure 39–3 the bacteria still continue to develop at the expense of the diatom cells. This suggests the probability that the bacteria live in the free water only to a limited extent, but that they are largely associated with the plant and animal forms of the plankton, attacking their excretion products, as well as the dead bodies.

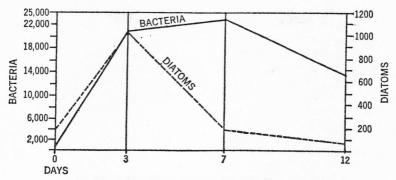

Changes in numbers of bacteria and diatoms in sea water cultures; numbers in 1 cc of culture.

Fig. 39–3. Changes in numbers of bacteria and diatoms in sea water cultures; numbers in 1 cc of culture.

METHODS OF STUDY OF MARINE BACTERIA

Studies of marine bacteria have four distinct ends in view: (1) determination of the relative abundance of bacteria in the sea-water and in the sea-bottom material; (2) detection of the specific nature of the bacterial population, namely, the types or organisms that make up this population under the various conditions; (3) determination of the physiological activities of the bacteria isolated from the sea; (4) interpretation of the role of these bacteria in the cycle of life in the sea itself.

In the study of the occurrence, abundance and activities of bacteria in such a medium as the sea, in which they occur not in pure culture but as mixed populations, the methods employed are of considerable importance. These methods are both direct and indirect. In view of the small size of the bacterial cell, the relatively extreme dispersion of the bacteria and their comparatively low numbers in the ocean, any direct examination of the sea-water can tell very little concerning the occurrence and abundance of the bacteria; these cells should be concentrated, by removing much of the water, either by centrifugation, by filtration or by evaporation, before a microscopic examination is attempted. Most of the methods commonly employed in the past for the study of the abundance of marine bacteria were cultural in nature; here belong the gelatin and agar plate methods, the dilution method and the enrichment culture methods. Since no single medium will allow the development of all the bacteria present, even in a small quantity of sea-water or sea-bottom material, various media have to be employed. The early investigators limited themselves to counting bacteria by means of the plate method. At first the gelatin media were employed, soon followed by agar media, such as sea-water gelatin or sea-water fish extract gelatin and sea-water agar, with various modifications. It was recognized, however, at an early date that the sea contains many bacteria which are unable to develop on the culture plate. This led to the adoption of various dilution methods and specific enrichment culture methods. More recently there has been a tendency to use direct microscopic methods for the enumeration of bacteria both in the sea-water and in the sea bottom.

The plate method presents certain advantages but also various distinct limitations. The fact that one can determine the numbers of bacteria which are actually present in the sea in a living state, after they are allowed to develop on the plate, and the fact that one can isolate these bacteria from the plate for further study of their morphological and physiological characteristics are distinct advantages of the method. However, not all the bacteria present in the sea are able to develop on the common plate, some of the most important organisms, such as the nitrifying, sulfur-oxidizing, nitrogen-fixing, not developing at all; but even those bacteria that are able to grow on the plate will not all develop and form colonies. The plate method may thus give an unbalanced picture of the bacterial population of the sea. To meet these objections, Cholodny and others suggested the use of a direct microscopic method. This method has certain advantages, since it gives a more correct picture of the abundance of bacteria in the sea; however, it does not enable one to distinguish the living from the dead bacteria or to separate the various types of organisms for further study of their physiological characteristics.

To determine the specific nature of the bacteria, the enrichment or elective culture method is usually employed; the sea-water or bottom material is added to a medium of specific chemical composition and the nature of the transformation brought about in the medium is determined. This method is very convenient for the purpose of demonstrating the occurrence of specific bacteria in the sea. By combining the dilution method with that of elective culture, the relative abundance of the specific bacteria can be estimated. This method was used for the purpose of demonstrating and isolating some of the most important bacteria now known to be found in the sea. The solution medium can be replaced by the silica-gel medium, which has found application in various investigations recently carried out at the Woods Hole Institution.[1]

No single method can be used for the study of the bacterial population of the sea as a whole. Various methods have to be combined in order to obtain an insight into the nature and abundance of this population. For the study of the abundance of proteolytic bacteria, the gelatin plate may be used, for agar-liquefying bacteria—the agar plate, for cellulose-decomposing bacteria—the silica gel cellulose plate, for demonstrating the presence of various other specific bacteria—various special methods have to be adapted.

For study of the biochemical activities of marine bacteria, methods are employed which are based both on the nature of the organism and upon the specificity of the process under consideration. These methods are in most instances adaptations of methods employed in general bacteriology. The most important phase of the subject, however, namely the study of the role of the bacteria in marine transformations under natural conditions, has scarcely been considered at all.

NATURE OF THE BACTERIAL POPULATION OF THE SEA

Fungi are either entirely absent in the sea or are found at infrequent intervals. Whenever reference is made to their occurrence in the sea, a closer examination of the data will reveal the fact that this was due either to contamination in the process of the preparation of the plates or to their chance infiltration from land and from dust (wind), especially at places close to shore. The fact that the genera Aspergillus and Penicillium occupy a prominent place among the fungi which were thus commonly reported adds further weight to the above conclusion, since these genera comprise the common dust and wind-borne fungi. One need not exclude, however, the possibility that fungi play a part in the decomposition of algal material and Zostera, when exposed to the atmosphere, as shown in the figures. Actinomyces are also either entirely absent or infrequently observed. Yeasts have frequently been found, especially certain Torulae, but their role in marine processes has been studied but little.

The bacterial population of the sea is quite characteristic. It is distinct in nature from the population usually found on land, as shown by the more limited number of bacterial types found in the sea. Spore-forming bacteria, which comprise an important part of

[1] S. A. Waksman, C. Carey, and H. W. Reuszer, *Biol. Bull.*, August, 1933.

the bacterial population in soil, are practically absent in sea-water, although they may be present in considerable abundance in the sea bottom. Cocci are also of limited occurrence in the sea. Motile rods and various types of vibrios, or comma-shaped organisms, usually make up the major part of the bacterial population thus far studied. The poverty of bacterial species in the sea depends largely upon the specific nature of sea-water as a medium for the growth of these organisms.

Certes oberved in 1884 that only aerobic bacteria are present in the ocean; no anaerobic forms were noted. Bacteria were found to occur in the water to very considerable depths, namely 5,100 meters. Fischer determined that, on an average, 1 cc of sea-water contains 1,083 bacteria, with a maximum of 29,400 and a minimum of o. More bacteria were found in the winter than in the summer months. The marine bacteria were shown to be morphologically and physiologically distinct from the land forms, most of them being curved or spirilloid in shape.

In 1892, Russell demonstrated that sea mud contains greater numbers of bacteria than the above lying water: at a depth of 50 meters, there were only 121 bacteria in 1 cc of water, while 1 cc of mud contained 245,000 bacteria. Russell believed that the bacteria settle upon the mud in the form of spores or vegetative cells from the upper layers of water. The nature of the mud and its depth were found to influence the number of bacteria considerably. Most of these bacteria were proteolytic and were able to reduce nitrate to nitrite. According to Bertel, away from the coast in the open sea, the bacteria increase in numbers with depth. A marked difference in the numbers of bacteria in sea-water and in sea mud was also reported by Smith, Bavendamm and others. As many as 16,000,000 bacterial cells were found in 1 gram of mud from the mangrove swamps of the Bahamas. Many of these bacteria were strongly agar-liquefying, pointing to their capacity of decomposing the organic complexes which are synthesized so abundantly by the algae in the sea.

In a recent study carried out at the Woods Hole Institution,[2] it was found that in ocean waters close to land and at sufficient depth to preclude agitation of the bottom by currents and wave motions, the numbers of bacteria are very small, usually not more than a few cells per 1 cc of water. The depth of the water and the nature of the sea bottom are of importance in this connection. Along shores receiving considerable land drainage, the numbers are much greater.

[2] H. W. Reuszer, *Biol. Bull.*, 1933.

The bottom deposits, especially the mud bottoms, are much richer in bacteria than the waters. A marked parallelism was found between the plankton organisms and the abundance of bacteria in the water, as well as a definite relation between the organic matter or humus content of the mud and the abundance of bacteria.

Among the specific bacteria commonly found in the sea, the nitrifying and denitrifying organisms have attracted particular attention. The formation of nitrates in the sea and their disappearance have aroused considerable interest. It was at first believed that the nitrates are brought into the sea from land or by atmospheric agencies. However, more recent evidence seems to point to the fact that nitrate formation is largely a result of bacterial activities in the sea itself. Thomsen and later Issatchenko, Lipman and others established the fact that, although nitrifying bacteria are not found in the surface waters of the sea, they can be readily demonstrated in the sea bottom. The investigations carried out at the Woods Hole Institution seem to point in the same direction.

As to the bacteria capable of reducing nitrate in the sea, one must avoid confusing nitrate-reducing bacteria with denitrifying bacteria: the first may reduce the nitrate only to nitrite and possibly to ammonia, while the latter break down the nitrate to atmospheric nitrogen or to gaseous forms of nitrogen. Although nitrate-reducing bacteria are present abundantly in the sea, denitrifying bacteria are found there but seldom, except possibly near shore or in the sea bottom. The results of Issatchenko, Butkewitch and those obtained recently at Woods Hole point in that direction. The mere fact that nitrite can be formed from nitrate by bacteria in the sea is no proof as yet that it leads to losses of nitrogen, since the nitrite can be assimilated by the phytoplankton organisms in their nutrition.

The presence in the sea of bacteria capable of bringing about the fixation of nitrogen has also attracted considerable attention. Benecke and Keutner were the first to isolate from the sea the aerobic *Azotobacter* and the anaerobic *Clostridium pastorianum*, the first organism occurring largely in the plankton and the second in the lower layers of water. Keutner, Keding and Issatchenko later demonstrated that Azotobacter cells are found on various algae growing in the sea; the same was frequently true of Clostridium and of accompanying bacterial forms. Reinke believed that a certain form of symbiosis exists between the algae and the Azotobacter, similar to that of the nodule bacteria and the leguminous plants. Unfortunately, the importance of these organisms in ocean life has not yet been definitely established. Their occurrence in sea-water and in the sea bottom under different conditions, at different depths and at different temperatures, as well as the conditions influencing their activities, still remain to be determined.

Among the bacteria capable of bringing about the decomposition of marine residues, the agar-liquefying organisms, which are particularly abundant in the phytoplankton, have attracted considerable attention. These bacteria are capable of producing an enzyme which liberates soluble sugars from the complex carbohydrates which form the important constituents of the marine plants. The occurrence in the sea of cellulose-decomposing, of fat-splitting, of proteolytic and of various other bacteria has also been established.

DECOMPOSITION OF PLANT AND ANIMAL RESIDUES
AND TRANSFORMATION OF NITROGEN

In order to understand the mechanism of the decomposition of the organic residues, it is important to know their chemical nature. Among the members of the phytoplankton in the sea, the diatoms are most abundant in the colder regions, while the Peridineae and the Schizophyceae are present largely in the warmer regions. The chemical composition of several members of the phyto- and zooplankton has been reported by Brandt as follows:

Chemical constituents, per cent. of dry material	Nature of organism		
	Chaeto-ceras	Cera-tium	Cope-pods
Protein	10.0	13.0	59.0
Chitin	—	—	4.8
Fat	2.8	1.3	7.3
Soluble carbohydrate	22.0	39.0	22.5
Cellulose	0	41.5	0
SiO_2	54.5	—	—
Salt and other ash materials	10.7	5.2	9.2

In general, the organic carbon of the plankton is found to range from 14 to 48 per cent., the nitrogen from 1.5 to 10.6 per cent., and the ash from 13 to 65 per cent. The diatoms are richest in ash and lowest in nitrogen, while the zooplankton is low in ash and high in protein. Only the Peridineae contain cellulose, while the hemicelluloses form the most abundant group of carbohydrates among the diatoms and the various lower and higher algae. Fats are present abundantly, while the nature of the proteins still remains to be studied. It is of interest to note that 1 gram of dry matter in the plankton corresponds to 500,000 copepods, to 65,000,000 peridinia and to 675,000,000 diatoms.

It is of interest to compare the above analyses with that of a typical marine alga, namely, *Fucus vesiculosus* (see table below).

When the dead plants and the animals, their excreta, the various residues and degradation products undergo decomposition in the sea by the action of the bacteria, a number of organic and mineralized complexes are formed. A part of the organic substances may become soluble in the sea-water, while some of the residual substances as

Chemical constituents	Per cent.
Protein	5.4
Fat	2.3
Alcohol-soluble material	6.7
Cold water-soluble organic matter	13.6
Hot water-soluble organic matter	7.8
Pentosan*	28.7
Uronic acid anhydride*	27.5
Cellulose	3.9
Ash	13.9

* These two fractions represent largely the same chemical complex determined by two different procedures.

well as the synthesized bacterial cells may drop to the bottom and contribute to the formation of the marine humus.

The most important compounds formed in the process of decomposition of the marine plant and animal residues are ammonia, carbon dioxide and phosphates; the ammonia is oxidized by certain specific bacteria to nitrite, and then to nitrate. These compounds are thus made available for the nutrition of the marine plant population, namely, the phytoplankton and the algae. Raben and a number of other investigators demonstrated the fact that the deep water in the open ocean contains more nitrate and phosphate than the upper layers in which phytoplankton organisms are active; the North Sea waters contain more nitrate and phosphate in the summer than in the winter months. According to Brandt, the nitrate of the sea is continually renewed by rain and by rivers; he suggested that the denitrifying bacteria reduce the concentration of nitrates in warm regions, which thus accounts for the reduced phytoplankton production. Harvey concluded, however, that the introduction of nutrients from land into sea plays only a minor part, when compared with the quantity of nutrients formed yearly from the dead organic residues in the ocean itself. After death, the algae and the animal members of the plankton sink to the bottom and are decomposed there by bacteria, with the result that the phosphate and nitrogen are liberated in an available form. These mineralized nutrients are then brought to the upper layers by vertical circulation. The bacteria are thus recognized as playing a most essential function in the cycle of elements in the sea.

ORGANIC MATTER IN SEA-WATER
AND IN THE MARINE BOTTOM

The question of the abundance, chemical nature and function of the organic matter found in the sea in an unorganized form, either in solution in the water or in a solid state on and in the sea bottom, presents a number of highly important problems in which the activities of the bacteria play a prominent part. The function of the dissolved organic matter in the nutrition of the marine animals has been emphasized by Pütter. This theory was submitted to considerable criticism by Krogh and others. Pütter's figures for the dissolved organic matter in the sea were shown to be too high, and some of this organic matter was shown to be due to the suspended bacteria, protozoa and unicellular plants present in the water. Although a part of the organic matter in solution may be liberated by the algae, there is no doubt that another part is produced by the bacteria in the process of decomposition of the plant and animal residues in the ocean.

Another source of organic matter in the sea is the marine bottom. This organic matter can be designated as "marine humus," because of its similarity in chemical nature, and probably in origin, to the humus found in soils. The concentration of this humus in the marine bottom varies considerably, namely, from 0.5 per cent. in the case of sand bottoms to nearly 10 per cent. in the case of certain mud bottoms. In some localities, such as protected harbors or fjords, the mud bottom may contain as much as 20 per cent. humus. This humus is best calculated from the organic carbon content, by the use of a certain factor. Boysen-Jensen suggested the use of a factor of 2, assuming that the carbon content of the humus is 50 per cent. However, a study of the chemical composition of the humus brought out the fact that this factor should be lower than 2, namely, 1.923, due to the presence in the humus of lignin-like complexes with a high carbon content.

One of the most important characteristics of this marine humus is its carbon-nitrogen ratio. Boysen-Jensen found this ratio to vary from 8:1 to 12:1, with an average of about 10:1. These results were fully confirmed by other investigators. When one recalls the fact that a similar ratio of carbon to nitrogen holds also for soils, the similarity of the marine humus to soil humus becomes even more apparent. Organic complexes similar to those found in soil humus can also be isolated from the marine humus. There are several reasons for the similarity: (1) a part of the marine humus is of terrestrial origin, being brought into the sea by streams and rivers; (2) the marine humus, just as the soil humus, is formed by similar microorganisms in a very similar manner. Certain differences observed in the chemical nature of the humus can easily be accounted for by the fact that marine residues, from which all or part of the humus is formed, are different in chemical composition from the land residues from which all the soil humus is formed.

The organic matter in solution in the sea-water as well as the humus in the mud are only slowly acted upon by bacteria; otherwise neither form of organic matter could be present in great abundance in the sea. However, even their slow decomposition is sufficient to provide a certain amount of available energy and nutrients for various bacteria living in the water and especially in the sea bottom.

Truly, the life of the plant and animal world in the ocean is variously dependent upon the manifold activities of the oceanic microscopic population composed principally of bacteria.

The author is indebted to Mr. C. E. Renn for the preparation of the sections of the marine plant material.

CONDENSED BIBLIOGRAPHY

W. Bavendamm, *Arch. Mikrob.*, 3: 205–276, 1932. W. Benecke and J. Keutner, *Ber, deut. bot. Gesell.*, 21: 333, 1903. R. Bertel, *Bull. Inst. Oceanogr. Monaco*, No. 224, 1912. P. Boysen-Jensen, *Rept. Danish Biol. Sta.*, 22: 5–39, 1914. K. Brandt, *Wiss. Meeresunters. Kiel*, N. F. 4: 213–230, 1899; 6: 23–79 1902; 18: 185–429, 1916–1920; 19: 251–252, 1919. W. C. Butkewitch, *Trans. Russian Oceanogr. Inst.*, 2: No. 2, 1932. A. Certes, *Compt. Rend. Acad. Sci.*, 98: 690–695, 1884. N. Cholodny, *Centrbl. Bakt. Abt.*, II. 77: 179–193, 1929. G. H. Drew, Papers from Tortugas Laboratory, Carnegie Inst. Washington, 5: 15–191; *Jour. Mar. Biol. Ass.*, 9: 479–524, 1913. B. Fischer, *Centrbl. Bakt.*, 15: 657–666, 1894; Ergebnisse der Plankton-Expedition der Humboltstiftung, Lipsius & Tischer., Kiel and Leipzig, 4: 1894. H. W. Harvey, "Biological Chemistry and Physics of Sea Water," Cambridge Univ. Press, 1928. B. L. Issatchenko, "Récherches sur les microbes de l'ocean Glacial Arctique, Petrograd, 1914. M. Kednig, *Wiss. Meeresunters. Kiel*, N. F. 9: 273–309, 1906. K. Kellerman and N. R. Smith, *Jour. Wash. Acad. Sci.*, 4: 400–402, 1914. J. Keutner, *Wiss.*

Meeresunters. Kiel, N. F. 8: 27–55, 1905. A. Krogh, *Rapp. Proces-Verbaux. Cons. Intern. Expl. Mer.*, 75: 1–36, 1931. C. B. Lipman, Carnegie Inst. Washington, Dpt. Marine Biol., 19: 179–191, 1924. H. Molish, *Centrbl. Bakt.*, II. 65: 130–139, 1925. G. Nadson, "Microorganisms as Geological Agents" (Russian), St. Petersburg, 1903. A. Pütter, *Pflüger's Arch. Physiol.*, 204: 94–126, 1924. E. Raben, *Wiss. Meeresunters. Kiel*, 11: 119–132, 1910. J. Reinke, *Ber. deut. bot. Gesell.*, 21: 481, 1903. H. W. Reuszer, *Biol. Bull.*, to be published, 1933. H. L. Russell, *Bot. Gaz.*, 17: 312–321, 1892. N. R. Smith, Carnegie Inst. Wash., No. 344: 67–72, 1926. A. Thienemann, *Die Naturwiss.*, 13: 589–600, 1925. P. Thomsen, *Ber. deut. bot. Gesell.*, 25: 16–22, 1907; *Wiss. Meeresunters. Kiel*, N. F. 11: 1–27, 1910. S. A. Waksman, *Soil Science*, August, 1933.

~~~~~~~~~~~~~~~~~~~~~

Harald U. Sverdrup:

40.   PHYSICAL PROPERTIES OF
SEA WATER*

Since the absorption of long-wave radiation from the earth's surface and the condensation of water vapor that is supplied to the atmosphere from the earth's surface are factors of dominant importance to the heat budget of the atmosphere, it is evident that the thermal characteristics of the surface must be examined when studying the atmospheric circulation. Over the land areas, an interaction between the surface and the circulation of the atmosphere evidently takes place. Thus, a covering of snow greatly increases the reflection of incoming short-wave radiation, dense clouds alter the radiation phenomena, heavy rainfalls that moisten the ground change the possibilities for evaporation, and so on, and every change must be reflected in a change in the pattern of atmospheric circulation.

The character of the ocean surface is very different from that of the land, mainly because the ocean water can be set in motion. The heat absorbed near the surface is distributed over a relatively deep water layer through the stirring by waves and wind currents and it is transported over long distances by ocean currents that are more or less directly produced by the prevailing winds. Heat which

* From H. U. Sverdrup, OCEANOGRAPHY FOR METEOROLOGISTS, copyright 1942. By permission of Prentice-Hall, Inc., Englewood Cliffs, New Jersey.

Norwegian meteorologist and oceanographer Harald Ulrik Sverdrup, 1888–1957, was director of the Scripps Institution of Oceanography from 1936 to 1948. He returned to Oslo in 1948 to become director there of the North Polar Institute. In addition to the book above, he co-authored THE OCEANS.

in one season is absorbed in one part of the sea may therefore in another season be used for evaporation in a different part of the sea, depending upon the types of currents that the general circulation of the atmosphere induces. The oceans, as far as their interaction with the atmosphere is concerned, are a flexible medium that responds to changes in the circulation of the atmosphere. Inasmuch as the greater part of the water vapor in the atmosphere is supplied by evaporation from the oceans, the relation between the atmosphere and the circulation of the oceans becomes important, because this relation will determine the seasons and the regions from which excessive evaporation takes place. Thus the heat budget of the oceans and of the ocean currents is of the greatest importance to the atmosphere. In order to discuss this heat budget and the currents it is necessary first to deal with some of the physical properties of sea water.

The physical properties of pure water depend upon two variables, temperature and pressure (Dorsey, 1940; International Critical Tables), whereas for sea water a third variable has to be considered—namely, the salinity of the water, which will be defined and discussed below. Some of the properties, such as compressibility, thermal expansion, and refractive index, are only slightly altered by the presence of dissolved salts, but other properties that are constant in the case of pure water, such as freezing point and temperature of maximum density, are dependent, in the case of sea water, on salinity. Furthermore, the dissolved salts add new properties, such as osmotic pressure and electrical conductivity.

When dealing with sea water as it occurs in nature, it must also be taken into account that important characteristics are greatly modified by the presence of minute suspended particles or by the state of motion. Thus, the absorption of radiation in the sea is different from the absorption of radiation in pure water or in "pure" sea water because the waters encountered in nature always contain suspended matter that causes increased scattering of the radiation and, consequently, an increased absorption in layers of similar thickness. The processes of heat conduction, chemical diffusion, and transfer of momentum from one layer to another are completely altered in moving water, for which reason the coefficients that have been determined under laboratory conditions must be replaced by corresponding eddy coefficients. Some of the physical properties of sea water, therefore, depend only upon the three variables, temperature, salinity, and pressure, which can all be determined with great accuracy, whereas others depend upon such variables as amount of suspended matter or character of motion, which at present cannot be accurately determined.

SALINITY, TEMPERATURE, AND PRESSURE

Salinity. Salinity is commonly defined as the ratio between the weight of the dissolved material and the weight of the sample of sea water, the ratio being stated in parts per thousand or per mille. In oceanography another definition is used because, owing to the complexity of sea water, it is impossible by direct chemical analysis to determine the total quantity of dissolved solids in a given sample. Furthermore, it is impossible to obtain reproducible results by evaporating sea water to dryness and weighing the residue, because certain of the material present, chiefly chloride, is lost in the last stages of drying. These difficulties can be avoided by following a technique yielding reproducible results which, although they do not represent the total quantity of dissolved solids, do represent a quantity of slightly smaller numerical value that is closely related and by definition is called the *salinity* of the water. This technique was established in 1902 by an International Commission, according to which the *salinity* is defined as *the total amount of solid material in grams contained in one kilogram of sea water when all the carbonate has been converted to oxide, the bromine and iodine replaced by chlorine, and all organic matter completely oxidized.*

The determination of salinity by the method of the International Commission is rarely if ever carried out at the present time because it is too difficult and slow, but, inasmuch as it has been established that the dissolved solids are present in constant ratios, the determination of any of the elements occurring in relatively large quantities can be used as a measure of the other elements and of the salinity. Chloride ions make up approximately 55 per cent of the dissolved solids and can be determined with ease and accuracy by titration with silver nitrate, using potassium chromate as indicator. The empirical relationship between salinity and chlorinity, as established by the International Commission, is

$$\text{Salinity}=0.03+1.805\times\text{Chlorinity}.$$

The chlorinity that appears in this equation is also a *defined* quantity and does not represent the actual amount of chlorine in a sample of sea water. Both salinity and chlorinity are always expressed in grams per kilogram of sea water—that is, in parts per thousand, or per mille, for which the symbol $^0/_{00}$ is used. In practice, salinity is determined with an accuracy of $\pm 0.2^0/_{00}$.

The salinity of a water sample can also be found by determining the density of the sample at a known temperature, because empirical relationships have been established by which the density can be represented as a function of salinity (or chlorinity) and temperature. Other indirect methods for determining salinity are based on measurements of the electrical conductivity or the refractive index at a known temperature. In order to obtain the needed accuracy, the difference is measured in electrical conductivity or refractive index between the sample and a sample of known salinity that lies fairly close to that of the unknown sample.

The salinity in the oceans is generally between $33^0/_{00}$ and $37^0/_{00}$. In regions of high rainfall or dilution by rivers the surface salinity may be considerably less, and in certain semi-enclosed areas, such as the Gulf of Bothnia, it may be below $5^0/_{00}$. On the other hand, in isolated seas in intermediate latitudes where evaporation is excessive, such as the Red Sea, salinities may reach $40^0/_{00}$ or more. As the range in the open oceans is rather small, it is sometimes convenient to use a salinity of $35.00^0/_{00}$ as an average for all oceans.

Temperature. In oceanography the temperature of the water is stated in degrees centigrade. In the oceans the temperature ranges from about -2° to $+30^{\circ}$C. The lower limit is determined by the formation of ice, and the upper limit is determined by processes of radiation and exchange of heat with the atmosphere. In landlocked areas the surface temperature may be higher, but in the open ocean it rarely exceeds 30°C.

Pressure. Pressure is measured in units of the c.g.s. system, in which the pressure unit is 1 dyne/cm². One million dynes/cm² was designated as 1 bar by V. Bjerknes. The corresponding practical unit used in physical oceanography is 1 decibar, which equals $\frac{1}{10}$ bar. The pressure exerted by 1 m of sea water very nearly equals 1 decibar; that is, the hydrostatic pressure in the sea increases by 1 decibar for approximately every meter of depth. *Therefore the depth in meters and the pressure in decibars are expressed by nearly the same numerical value.* This rule is sufficiently accurate when considering the effect of pressure on the physical properties of the water, but details of the pressure distribution must be computed from the density distribution.

Owing to the character of the distribution of temperature and salinity in the oceans, some relationships exist between these quantities and the pressure. The temperature of the deep and bottom water of the oceans is always low, varying between 4° and -1°C, and high pressures are therefore associated with low temperatures. Similarly, the salinity of deep and bottom water varies within narrow limits, $34.5^0/_{00}-35.0^0/_{00}$, and high pressures are therefore associated with salinities between these limits. Exceptions are found in isolated seas in intermediate latitudes such as the Mediterranean and Red Seas, where water of high temperature and high salinity is found at great depths—that is, under great pressures.

DENSITY OF SEA WATER

The density of any substance is defined as the mass per unit volume. Thus, in the c.g.s. system, density is stated in grams per cubic centimeter. The specific gravity is defined as the ratio of the density to that of distilled water at a given temperature and under atmospheric pressure. In the c.g.s. system the density of distilled water at 4°C is equal to unity. In oceanography specific gravities are now always referred to distilled water at 4°C and are therefore numerically identical with densities. The term *density* is generally used, although, strictly speaking, specific gravity is always considered.

~~~~~~~~~~~~~~

Roger Revelle and Milner B. Schaefer:

41.   *THE OCEAN AS A RECEPTACLE FOR ARTIFICIALLY RADIOACTIVE MATERIALS**

I. INTRODUCTION

In this report, we have attempted to summarize both the present knowledge and the areas of ignorance concerning the oceans that must be taken into account in considering the biological effects of radiation.

The oceans of the world furnish essential sources of food and

---

* From Publication No. 551, National Academy of Sciences—National Research Council, Washington, D.C. 1957. Contribution from the Scripps Institution of Oceanography, New Series, No. 901. Reprinted by permission of the authors.

Roger Revelle is Richard Saltonstall Professor of Population Policy at Harvard University. Dr. Revelle was formerly Director of the Scripps Institution of Oceanography.

Milner B. Schaefer was professor of oceanography and director of Marine Resources at the Scripps Institution of Oceanography. He died July 26, 1970.

other raw materials, vital routes of transportation, recreation, and a convenient place in which to dispose of waste materials from our industrial civilization. These different ways in which men use the sea, however, are not always compatible. The use of the sea for waste disposal, in particular, can jeopardize the other resources, and hence should be done cautiously, with due regard to the possible effects. Waste products from nuclear reactions require special care: they constitute hazards in extremely low concentrations and their deleterious properties cannot be eliminated by any chemical transformations; they can be dispersed or isolated, but they cannot be destroyed. Once they are created, we must live with them until they become inactive by natural decay, which for some isotopes requires a very long time.

Waste products from nuclear reactions arise in two ways: (1) from the slow controlled reactions involved in laboratory experimentation, in the production of materials for nuclear weapons, the production of reactor fuels, and the "burning" of fuels in power reactors; (2) from the rapid, uncontrolled reactions involved in testing of weapons or in warfare. Up to the present time, the largest quantities of fission products introduced into the aquatic environment have been from weapons tests; most of the products from controlled reactions have been isolated on the land, and only relatively small quantities have been introduced into the sea or fresh water. In the future, however, industrial nuclear wastes will present difficult disposal problems and the sea is a possible disposal site, particularly for small, densely populated nations with long sea coasts. We have, therefore, given particular attention to the long-range problems that may arise from the large-scale disposal of both high-level and low-level industrial wastes, as well as to the effects of weapons tests.

Among the variety of questions generated by the introduction of radioactive materials into the sea, there are few to which we can give precise answers. We can, however, provide conservative answers to many of them, which can serve as a basis of action pending the results of detailed experimental studies. The large areas of uncertainty respecting the physical, chemical, and biological processes in the sea lead to restrictions on what can now be regarded as safe practices. These will probably prove too severe when we have obtained greater knowledge. It is urgent that the research required to formulate more precise answers should be vigorously pursued. Fortunately, the use of radioactive isotopes is one excellent means of acquiring the needed information, and the quantities of these isotopes required for pertinent experiments are well within limits of safety. Moderate quantities of the very waste products we are concerned with can, therefore, provide one means of attacking the unsolved scientific problems.

II. THE NATURE OF THE OCEAN AND ITS
CONTAINED ORGANISMS

The ocean basins cover 361×10^6 square kilometers and have an average depth of 3,800 meters, giving a total volume of 1.37×10^9 cubic kilometers. They are characteristically bordered by a continental shelf, which slopes gently out to a depth of about 200 meters. Inside it is a steeper slope extending down to the deep sea floor with depths of 4,000 meters or more. The average width of the continental shelf is about 30 miles, varying from almost nothing off mountainous coasts, such as the West Coast of South America, to several hundred miles in the China Sea. The shelf is not everywhere smooth, but is often intersected by submarine valleys and canyons. In the deep ocean basins there are high mountains and long, deep trenches, features larger than any on land. Some of the deeper parts are isolated by submarine ridges which restrict the exchange of water between adjacent areas.

The waters of the oceans are stratified. Within a relatively thin layer at the surface, varying in thickness in different places but averaging about 75 meters, vertical mixing caused by winds is fairly rapid and complete. In consequence, the temperature, salinity and density are nearly uniform from top to bottom. Relatively fast wind-driven currents exist in this upper mixed layer; these are the "surface" currents of the oceans depicted on many charts. Here also the horizontal mixing is relatively rapid. The mixed layer is the region of the sea in which most of man's activity takes place.

Below the mixed layer is a zone within which the temperature decreases and the density increases rapidly with depth. This thermocline, or pycnocline, separates the surface mixed layer from the layers of intermediate and deep water, the latter extending to the bottom, within which there are gentle gradients of decreasing temperature and increasing salinity and density with depth. Vertical movement in the intermediate and deep layers is much slower than in the mixed layer, and horizontal currents are more sluggish. The strong density gradient across the pycnocline tends to inhibit physical transport across it, because work is required to move water vertically in either direction, and thus the pycnocline acts as a partial barrier between the mixed layer and the lower layers. There is, however, some interchange of both living and non-living elements;

indeed the continued existence of some marine resources depends on such interchange.

Living resources

The most important extractive industry based on the resources of the sea is the harvesting of its living resources.

On land the cycle of life is relatively simple; we may describe it in four figurative stages. First is the grass, which by a subtle and complex chemistry captures the energy of sunlight and builds organic matter. Sheep and cows live on the grass; tigers and men eat them. The cycle is closed by bacteria, which decompose the dead bodies and the excreta of all living creatures, making their constituent substances again available as building materials for the plants. In the sea, the cycle is longer. Instead of grass there are the tiny floating plants called phytoplankton; in place of cows, the zooplankton animals that eat the plants are small crustaceans, no bigger than the head of a pin. Many kinds of tigers eat the cows, but they are mostly also zooplankton, only a fraction of an inch in length. Other intermediate flesh-eaters exist between them and the fishes of our ocean harvest. Because every link in this long food chain is inefficient, we reap from the sea only a small fraction of its organic production.

Other characteristics of the ocean also tend to limit the harvest as compared to that from the land. One is its giant size; more than 70 per cent of all the sunlight that penetrates the atmosphere falls on the sea; moreover, this sunlight can act throughout the top 20 to 100 meters, thus the living space for plants and animals is far greater than on land. This great areal extent and volume, combined with the fluidity of the oceans, results in a low concentration of organisms per unit volume and therefore inefficiency in harvesting.

On land, the standing crop of plants and animals is of the same order of magnitude as the amount of organic production per year, while in the ocean the crop is very small, compared to the production, because of rapid turnover. The average rate of organic production per unit area is probably about the same on land and in the sea, but the efficiency of harvesting depends more on the size of the crop than on the total amount of organic matter produced.

The plants of the sea, on which all other living things depend, grow only in the waters near the surface where bright sunlight penetrates. These waters differ widely in fertility. Like the land, the ocean has its green pastures where life flourishes in abundance, and its deserts where a few poor plants and animals barely survive.

The fertility of the land depends on four things: water, temperature, intensity of sunlight, and available plant nutrients—substances that usually occur in very small amounts but are essential for plant growth. In the sea, water is, of course, always abundant; the plants are well adapted to the narrow range of temperature; the intensity of sunlight determines the length of the growing season and the depth of growth, but usually not the differences in fertility. These depend only on the plant nutrients in the waters near the surface. As in any well-worked soil on land, the nutrients in the waters must be replenished each year. They are continually depleted by the slow sinking of plant and animal remains from the brightly lighted near-surface layers into the dark waters of the depths.

Men plow the soil to restore its fertility; the fertility of the sea is restored when nutrient-rich deeper waters are brought up near the surface. The "plowing" of the sea is accomplished in three ways. In some regions winds drive the surface waters away from the coast or away from an internal boundary, and nutrient-rich waters well up from mid-depths. In other areas, the surface waters are cooled near to freezing in the winter, become heavy and sink, and mix with the deep waters. Elsewhere, violent mixing occurs along the boundaries between ocean currents, and deeper waters are thereby brought into the brightly lighted zone.

The influx of nutrients to the upper layer, and the corresponding loss from this layer by sinking of plant and animal remains, do not directly involve the deep waters. Upwelling and vertical mixing take place only in the upper few hundred meters. The exchange between these mid-depths and the abyssal deep is a very much slower process, of the scale of hundreds of years.

Most of the commercially important marine organisms are harvested in coastal waters or in offshore waters not very far from land. Several factors are involved: (1) Profitable fisheries can be conducted more easily near ports and harbors; (2) the coastal waters are of high fertility, because of greater upwelling and turbulent mixing and the ease of replenishment of plant nutrients from the shallow sea floor, and perhaps also because of the supply of nutrients and organic detritus from land; (3) the standing crop of plants and animals attached to or living on the bottom in coastal areas is large, relative to the total organic production.

None of the animals of the great depths are the objects of a commercial fishery. Even the truly pelagic, high seas fisheries, such as the great offshore fisheries for tuna, herring, redfish and whales, harvest animals that live primarily in the surface layer. Some of these animals, however, do much of their feeding in the deeper layers. The sperm whales, for example, feed on deep-sea cephalopods at great depths. Moreover, much of the food for commercially harvested organisms consists of small animals, including crustaceans, squids, and fishes, that perform vertical diurnal migrations from several hundred meters depth to the surface.

The sea fisheries produce about 25 million metric tons per year of fishes and marine invertebrates, in addition to about 4 million tons of whales. The great bulk of the harvest is taken, at present, from the waters of the northern hemisphere, despite the fact that the southern oceans constitute 57 per cent of the world's sea area. The following table indicates the production in 1954 by latitude zones:

TABLE 1 HARVEST OF FISHES AND MARINE
INVERTEBRATES IN 1954, BY LATITUDE ZONES
(FROM FAO, 1957)

Zone	Millions of metric tons	%
Arctic region	1.2	5
Northern hemisphere-temperate zone	17.5	72
Tropical zone	4.1	17
Southern hemisphere-temperate zone	1.4	6
Antarctic regions	0*	0*

* About 4 million tons of whales were taken in the Antarctic, but few fish or marine invertebrates.

The disproportionately large yield in the northern hemisphere is related to three factors: (1) Human populations are heavily concentrated there; (2) the major fishing nations are the industrialized maritime nations, which are mostly located in the north; (3) except for some of the fisheries for tuna, salmon, herring, and whales, the important fisheries are located in the relatively shallow areas along the continents, and the extent of these areas is much greater in the northern than in the southern hemisphere.

The sessile algae of shallow coasts are also the object of important industries in Japan, the United States, the United Kingdom, Norway, and some other countries. Some of these plants are used directly for human consumption, while others are employed indirectly in pharmaceutical and food products.

Petroleum and natural gas

It is estimated that about 30 million cubic meters of possible oil-bearing sediments underlie the 11.8 million square miles of the submerged continental shelves. These sediments contain some 400 billion barrels of recoverable crude oil.

Exploitation of these deposits of petroleum and the associated natural gas has commenced in the waters of the Gulf of Mexico; intensive geophysical prospecting has been conducted offshore from California and in the Persian Gulf. It may be expected that this source of fossil fuels will be extensively utilized in the near future. The resource is confined to the subsoil of the marginal seas, since only there do we find oil-bearing sediments.

Minerals

Extraction of sea salt for sodium chloride is an ancient industry, and is now highly developed also for production of sodium sulfate, potassium chloride, and magnesium chloride. Bromine is extracted directly from sea water for the manufacture of ethylene dibromide. Magnesium metal has been produced commercially from sea water by chemical and electrolytical procedures for nearly two decades.

All of these industries use sea water taken from near the surface at the shore but the quantity of water utilized is insignificant. For example, a single cubic kilometer of sea water contains over a million tons of magnesium, about five times the peak world annual production of this metal.

The floor of the deep sea is known to contain low-grade deposits of cobalt, nickel and copper (0.1 to 0.7 per cent by weight of the metals) associated with deposits of iron and manganese. The problems of mining these materials, in the face of the great depths and pressure, have not been solved, and they certainly will not soon be economically useable.

Ocean transportation

Long-distance transportation of large cargos by sea is the indispensable basis of international commerce. The economy of the United States and of other industrial nations is in large part dependent on the sea-borne commerce that flows through the seaports.

Contamination of the sea by nuclear wastes will certainly not present a hazard to shipping, since acceptable levels of such materials in the surface layer of the sea will be limited by other considerations (such as the effects on the fisheries) to much lower levels than would constitute a hazard to ships' personnel. On the other hand, it is almost certain that nuclear power plants will be extensively used in merchant vessels; they are already in use in naval craft.

Serious hazards may arise in confined waters from collisions in which the reactor is damaged and the fuel elements with their contained fission products are lost in the water. Suppose for example that a 50,000 kilowatt reactor (probably fairly typical for a large fast freighter) has been in service without refueling for one year on a ship that has spent half its time under way. Approximately 10 kilograms of fissionable material will have been used up and the total amount of fission products will be approximately 10^7 curies. If, owing to a collision, the reactor is lost in a harbor, say 8 miles long by 3 miles wide by 50 feet deep, and the fission products become uniformly distributed, the water in the harbor would contain 10^2 curies per cubic meter giving an almost constant radiation dose of about 0.5 r per day on the surface. Dock pilings, ship bottoms and other structures covered with fouling organisms would accumulate a much higher level of radioactivity, and local concentration in the water might be extremely high.

Recreation

For coastal populations in the temperate, subtropical, and tropical regions, the sea and its contents provide healthful sports and satisfaction of men's curiosity and their desire for beauty. Boating, swimming, sport fishing, and other recreations are engaged in by millions of people, and are the basis of tourist and service industries of very considerable monetary value.

Waste disposal

Disposal of domestic sewage and industrial wastes is often conveniently accomplished near coastal population centers by running them into the sea. The large volume and rapid mixing of the ocean waters dilute the wastes, and the bacteria in the sea break down the organic constituents. Unless care is exercised, however, this discharge into inshore sea areas may be deleterious to other resources. Dumping of excess volumes of sewage and industrial wastes, without proper regard to the local characteristics of the sea bottom, currents, and other factors, has already resulted in ruining some harbors and beaches for recreation, damage to the living resources of adjacent areas, and even serious problems of corrosion to ships.

The use of the sea for the disposal of atomic wastes has, fortunately, been so far approached with great caution and with due regard to the possible hazards. The problems, because of the dangerous character of small amounts of atomic wastes, are of a different order of magnitude than those of the disposal of other kinds of wastes.

III. POTENTIAL HAZARDS FROM RADIOACTIVE
MATERIALS

Direct hazards

A direct hazard to human beings from radiation may exist if the levels of radiation in the environment are sufficiently high.

The natural radioactivity of the sea is very much lower than that of the land. According to Folsom and Harley, a man in a boat or ship receives only about half a millirad per year from the radio isotopes in the sea, compared with about 23 millirads per year from sedimentary rock or 90 millirads per year from granite. Thus, it would be necessary to increase the radioactivity of the sea many fold to equal the radiation that man normally receives from the land on which he lives. Due to the rather rapid mixing in the upper layers of the sea, and to its very large volume, even large quantities of activity introduced at the surface in the open sea become sufficiently dispersed to constitute no direct hazard after a relatively short time, as has been shown by the dispersion of the activity resulting from weapons tests in the Pacific. If the direct hazard were the only consideration, sea disposal of radioactive wastes would give rise to difficulties only in small areas near the disposal sites.

Some radioactive wastes have been disposed of in the sea by placing them in containers designed to sink to the sea bottom. In this way, the wastes are isolated and not dispersed by the ocean currents. Direct hazards could arise if the containers in some manner were to come into contact with humans, such as through accidental recovery during fishing or salvage operations or if, through improper design, the containers were to float to the surface and come ashore.

Indirect hazards

The most serious potential hazards to human beings from the introduction of radioactive products into the marine environment are those that may arise through the uptake of radio isotopes by organisms used for human food. There are several reasons why these indirect hazards are more critical than the direct hazards: (1)

The radiation received from a given quantity of an isotope ingested as food is much greater than the dose from the same quantity in the external environment; (2) many elements, including some of those having radioactive isotopes resulting from nuclear reactions, are concentrated by factors up to several thousand by the organisms in the sea; (3) the vertical and horizontal migrations of organisms can result in transport of radioactive elements and thereby cause distributions different from those that would exist under the influence of physical factors alone; for example, certain elements may be carried from the depths of the sea into the upper mixed layer in greater amounts than could be transported by the physical circulation.

It is quite certain that the indirect hazard to man through danger of contamination of food from the sea will require limiting the permissible concentration of radioactive elements in the oceans to levels below those at which there is any direct hazard. Any part of the sea in which the contamination does not cause dangerous concentrations of radioactive elements in man's food organisms will be safe for man to live over or in.

A reduction of the harvestable living resources of the sea could conceivably occur through the effects of atomic radiations on the organisms that are the objects of fisheries, or on their food. This might result from mortality induced by somatic effects, or from genetic changes. There is no conclusive evidence that any of the living marine resources have yet suffered from either of these, and they are not likely to be undesirably influenced at radiation levels safe from other standpoints. The knowledge of radiation effects on marine organisms is, however, inadequate for firm conclusions.

Pollution in general

The introduction of atomic wastes into the aquatic environment is but one aspect of the general problem of pollution.

Man's record with respect to pollution of lakes, streams, and parts of the sea by sewage and industrial wastes has not been good. In many places, the waters have been ruined for recreation and useful living resources have been destroyed or made unfit for human consumption. This unhappy record results from two factors: (1) the insidious nature of pollution of the aquatic environment, and (2) the fact that the waters and most of their resources are not private property, but are the common property of a large community (in the case of the high seas, the whole world); what is everyone's business often becomes no one's business.

The ruin of an aquatic resource by pollution seldom has been rapid. Quantities of waste products, at first very small, increase year by year until finally the concentrations become so large as to have obvious deleterious effects. For example, in the depletion of oxygen by organic wastes, sharp critical levels of tolerance of low oxygen content exist for some of the living resources, so that there is little adverse effect until a critical concentration of pollutant is reached, whereupon catastrophic mortality occurs. In other cases, the effects are more or less proportional to the concentrations. The destruction of a resource may then proceed gradually and it may not even be clear whether the pollutant has, indeed, been the cause rather than some other environmental change. For these reasons, it is necessary that the introduction of waste materials of any kind into the aquatic environment be carefully monitored, so that the effects may be detected before they become serious. Unfortunately, such monitoring is seldom the concern of those who produce the pollutants.

The record of the control and monitoring of the disposal of atomic pollutants has, so far, been excellent. We are, however, at the threshold of a tremendous growth of the atomic energy industry, and it behooves mankind to make sure that as much caution is exercised in the future as in the past.

Ordinary pollutants in sewage and industrial wastes are rapidly neutralized by the chemical and biological processes in the sea, and when effects of pollution are detected they can be rather quickly reversed by the cessation of introduction of the waste. A number of the radio isotopes, on the other hand, are very long-lived. Having reached harmful concentrations in the sea, they will diminish only by very slow decay, so that the effect of any serious pollution is not reversible. For this reason, the *prevention* of atomic pollution is of paramount importance.

REFERENCES

Anon. 1956. Report of a meeting of United Kingdom and United States scientists on biological effects of radiation in oceanography and fisheries. Nat. Acad. Sci.—Nat. Research Council, Oct. 31, 1956, 8 pp. (mimeographed).

Bowden, K. F. 1954. The direct measurement of subsurface currents in the oceans. *Deep Sea Research*, Vol. 2, pp. 33–47.

Culler, F. L. 1954. Notes on fission product wastes from proposed power reactors. ORNL Central File No. 55-4-25.

Dietrich, G. 1957. Selection of suitable ocean disposal areas for radioactive waste. (A preliminary report with 6 charts.) M.S., 10 pp.

Food and Agriculture Organization of UNESCO. 1957. Yearbook of fishery statistics. FAO, Rome, Vol. 5 (1954–55).

Goldberg, E. and Arrhenius, G. O. S. 1957. Chemistry of Pacific pelagic sediments. In press.

Greendale, A. E., and N. E. Ballou. 1954. Physical state of fission product elements following their vaporization in distilled water and sea water. USNRDL Document 436, pp. 1–28.

Harley, John E. (Editor). 1956. Operation Troll. U.S., A.E.C., N.Y. Operations office 1956. 37 pp.

Hyama, Y. 1956. Maximum permissible concentration of Sr 90 in food and its environment. Records of Oceanographic Work in Japan, Vol. 3, No. 1, March 1957, pp. 70–77.

Hyama, Y., and R. Ichikawa. 1956. Movement of fishing grounds where contaminated tuna were caught. Japan Society for the Promotion of Science; Research in the Effects and Influences of the Nuclear Bomb Test Explosions, pp. 1079.

Japanese Fishery Agency. 1955. Report on the investigations of the effects of radiation in the Bikini region. Res. Dept., Jap. Fish. Agency, Tokyo, 191 pp.

Kawabata, T. 1956. Movement of fishing grounds where contaminated tuna were caught. Japan Society for the Promotion of Science; Research in the Effects and Influences of the Nuclear Bomb Test Explosions, pp. 1085.

Krauskopf, K. B. 1956. Factors controlling the concentration of thirteen rare metals in sea water. Geochim. et Cosmochim. Acta 9, pp. 1–32.

Kulp, J. L., Eckelmann, W. R., and A. R. Schulert. 1957. Strontium 90 in man. Science, Vol. 125, No. 3241, pp. 219–225.

Laevastu, T., and T. G. Thompson. 1956. The determination and occurrence of nickel in sea water, marine organisms, and sediments. Jour. du Cons., Vol. 21, pp. 125–143.

Lapp, Ralph E. 1956. Strontium limits in peace and war. Bull. Atomic Scientists, Vol. 12, No. 8, pp. 287–289, 320.

Libby, W. F. 1956a. Radioactive fallout and radioactive strontium. Science, Vol. 123, pp. 657–660.

1956b. Radioactive strontium fallout. Proc. Nat. Acad. Sci., Vol. 42, No. 6, pp. 365–390.

Miyake, J., Sugiura, Y., and K. Kameda. 1955. On the distribution of radioactivity in the sea around Bikini Atoll in June 1954. Pap. Meteorol. Geophys., Tokyo, Vol. 5, No. 3–4, pp. 253–262.

Munk, W. H. 1950. On the wind-driven ocean circulation. Jour. Meteorol., Vol. 7, No. 2, pp. 79–93.

Munk, W. H., Ewing, G. C., and R. R. Revelle. 1949. Diffusion in Bikini lagoon. Trans. Am. Geophys. Union, Vol. 30, No. 1, pp. 59–66.

National Bureau of Standards. 1953. Maximum permissible amounts of radio isotopes in the human body and maximum permissible concentrations in air and water. U.S. Dept. of Commerce, Nat. Bureau Standards. Handbook 52, 45 pp.

1954. Radioactive waste disposal in the ocean. Nat. Bureau of Standards. Handbook 58, 31 pp.

Nucleonics. 1956. Calder Hall, over-all description. Nucleonics, Vol. 14, No. 12, pp. S10–S11.

1957. Roundup of key developments in atomic energy. Nucleonics, Vol. 15, No. 6, pp. 17–28.

Rankama, K., and T. C. Sahama. 1950. Geochemistry. Univ. of Chicago Press, 1950.

Revelle, R. R. 1957. Statement by Professor Roger Revelle before the joint Committee on atomic energy, 28 May 1957. The Nature of Radioactive Fallout and its Effects on Man; Hearings before the Special Subcommittee on *Radiation of the Joint Committee on Atomic Energy.* Congress of the United States, 1957.

Revelle, R. R., Folsom, T. R., Goldberg, E. D., and J. D. Isaacs. 1955. Nuclear Science and Oceanography. Int. Conf. on the Peaceful Uses of Atomic Energy. A/Conf. 8/P/277, 22 pp. (mimeographed).

Seligman, N. 1955. The discharge of radioactive waste products into the Irish Sea. Part I: First experiment for the study of movement and dilution of released dye in the sea. Proc. Int. Conf. on Peaceful Uses of Atomic Energy, United Kingdom paper number 418, 25 pp.

Sverdrup, H. U., Johnson, M. W., and R. H. Fleming. 1942. The Oceans. Prentice Hall, New York, 1942, 1060 pp.

Swallow, J. C. 1955. A neutral-buoyancy float for measuring deep currents. *Deep Sea Research,* Vol. 3, pp. 74–81.

Vinogradov, A. P. 1953. The elementary composition of marine organisms. Sears Foundation for Marine Research, Memoir No. 2, 647 pp.

Wüst, G. 1957. Report on the current velocities, volume transports and mixing effects in the Atlantic deep sea as physical processes important to the transport and dispersal of radioactive wastes. M.S. (mimeographed), 19 pp.

~~~~~~~~~~~~~~~~~~~~~~~

Adopted by United Nations Conference at Geneva, 1958:

42.   CONVENTIONS ON THE LAW OF THE SEA*

(*All conventions contain similar procedural articles for signing, ratification, and revision. They come into force on the thirtieth day following the deposit of the twenty-second instrument of ratification or accession with the United Nations. In the following reprint of the conventions these procedural articles are omitted.*)

* Reprinted from Publication 10–1 of the United States Department of Commerce, Coast and Geodetic Survey, U.S. G.P.O., Washington, D.C. 1962. pp. 371–377.

A. CONVENTION ON THE TERRITORIAL SEA AND THE CONTIGUOUS ZONE[1]

The States Parties to this Convention, Have agreed as follows:

PART I: TERRITORIAL SEA

Section I. General

Article 1

1. The sovereignty of a State extends, beyond its land territory and its internal waters, to a belt of sea adjacent to its coast, described as the territorial sea.

2. This sovereignty is exercised subject to the provisions of these articles and to other rules of international law.

Article 2

The sovereignty of a coastal State extends to the air space over the territorial sea as well as to its bed and subsoil.

Section II. Limits of the Territorial Sea

Article 3

Except where otherwise provided in these articles, the normal baseline for measuring the breadth of the territorial sea is the low-water line along the coast as marked on large-scale charts officially recognized by the coastal State.

Article 4

1. In localities where the coastline is deeply indented and cut into, or if there is a fringe of islands along the coast in its immediate vicinity, the method of straight baselines joining appropriate points may be employed in drawing the baseline from which the breadth of the territorial sea is measured.

2. The drawing of such baselines must not depart to any appreciable extent from the general direction of the coast, and the sea areas lying within the lines must be sufficiently closely linked to the land domain to be subject to the régime of internal waters.

3. Baselines shall not be drawn to and from low-tide elevations, unless lighthouses or similar installations which are permanently above sea level have been built on them.

4. Where the method of straight baselines is applicable under the

[1] Adopted Apr. 27, 1958 (U.N. Doc. A/Conf. 13/L.52).

provisions of paragraph 1, account may be taken, in determining particular baselines, of economic interests peculiar to the region concerned, the reality and the importance of which are clearly evidenced by a long usage.

5. The system of straight baselines may not be applied by a State in such a manner as to cut off from the high seas the territorial sea of another State.

6. The coastal State must clearly indicate straight baselines on charts, to which due publicity must be given.

Article 5

1. Waters on the landward side of the baseline of the territorial sea form part of the internal waters of the State.

2. Where the establishment of a straight baseline in accordance with article 4 has the effect of enclosing as internal waters areas which previously had been considered as part of the territorial sea or of the high seas, a right of innocent passage, as provided in articles 14 to 23, shall exist in those waters.

Article 6

The outer limit of the territorial sea is the line every point of which is at a distance from the nearest point of the baseline equal to the breadth of the territorial sea.

Article 7

1. This article relates only to bays the coasts of which belong to a single State.

2. For the purposes of these articles, a bay is a well-marked indentation whose penetration is in such proportion to the width of its mouth as to contain landlocked waters and constitute more than a mere curvature of the coast. An indentation shall not, however, be regarded as a bay unless its area is as large as, or larger than, that of the semi-circle whose diameter is a line drawn across the mouth of that indentation.

3. For the purpose of measurement, the area of an indentation is that lying between the low-water mark around the shore of the indentation and a line joining the low-water marks of its natural entrance points. Where, because of the presence of islands, an indentation has more than one mouth, the semi-circle shall be drawn on a line as long as the sum total of the lengths of the lines across the different mouths. Islands within an indentation shall be included as if they were part of the water area of the indentation.

4. If the distance between the low-water marks of the natural en-

trance points of a bay does not exceed twenty-four miles, a closing line may be drawn between these two low-water marks, and the waters enclosed thereby shall be considered as internal waters.

5. Where the distance between the low-water marks of the natural entrance points of a bay exceeds twenty-four miles, a straight baseline of twenty-four miles shall be drawn within the bay in such a manner as to enclose the maximum area of water that is possible with a line of that length.

6. The foregoing provisions shall not apply to so-called "historic" bays, or in any case where the straight baseline system provided for in article 4 is applied.

Article 8

For the purpose of delimiting the territorial sea, the outermost permanent harbour works which form an integral part of the harbour system shall be regarded as forming part of the coast.

Article 9

Roadsteads which are normally used for the loading, unloading and anchoring of ships, and which would otherwise be situated wholly or partly outside the outer limit of the territorial sea, are included in the territorial sea. The coastal State must clearly demarcate such roadsteads and indicate them on charts together with their boundaries, to which due publicity must be given.

Article 10

1. An island is a naturally formed area of land, surrounded by water, which is above water at high tide.

2. The territorial sea of an island is measured in accordance with the provisions of these articles.

Article 11

1. A low-tide elevation is a naturally formed area of land which is surrounded by and above water at low-tide but submerged at high tide. Where a low-tide elevation is situated wholly or partly at a distance not exceeding the breadth of the territorial sea from the mainland or an island, the low-water line on that elevation may be used as the baseline for measuring the breadth of the territorial sea.

2. Where a low-tide elevation is wholly situated at a distance exceeding the breadth of the territorial sea from the mainland or an island, it has no territorial sea of its own.

Article 12

1. Where the coasts of two States are opposite or adjacent to each other, neither of the two States is entitled, failing agreement between them to the contrary, to extend its territorial sea beyond the median line every point of which is equidistant from the nearest points on the baselines from which the breadth of the territorial seas of each of the two States is measured. The provisions of this paragraph shall not apply, however, where it is necessary by reason of historic title or other special circumstances to delimit the territorial seas of the two States in a way which is at variance with this provision.

2. The line of delimitation between the territorial seas of two States lying opposite to each other or adjacent to each other shall be marked on large-scale charts officially recognized by the coastal States.

Article 13

If a river flows directly into the sea, the baseline shall be a straight line across the mouth of the river between points on the low-tide line of its banks.

SECTION III. RIGHT OF INNOCENT PASSAGE

SUB-SECTION A. RULES APPLICABLE TO ALL SHIPS

Article 14

1. Subject to the provisions of these articles, ships of all States, whether coastal or not, shall enjoy the right of innocent passage through the territorial sea.

2. Passage means navigation through the territorial sea for the purpose either of traversing that sea without entering internal waters, or of proceeding to internal waters, or of making for the high seas from internal waters.

3. Passage includes stopping and anchoring, but only in so far as the same are incidental to ordinary navigation or are rendered necessary by *force majeure* or by distress.

4. Passage is innocent so long as it is not prejudicial to the peace, good order or security of the coastal State. Such passage shall take place in conformity with these articles and with other rules of international law.

5. Passage of foreign fishing vessels shall not be considered innocent if they do not observe such laws and regulations as the coastal

State may make and publish in order to prevent these vessels from fishing in the territorial sea.

6. Submarines are required to navigate on the surface and to show their flag.

Article 15

1. The coastal State must not hamper innocent passage through the territorial sea.

2. The coastal State is required to give appropriate publicity to any dangers to navigation, of which it has knowledge, within its territorial sea.

Article 16

1. The coastal State may take the necessary steps in its territorial sea to prevent passage which is not innocent.

2. In the case of ships proceeding to internal waters, the coastal State shall also have the right to take the necessary steps to prevent any breach of the conditions to which admission of those ships to those waters is subject.

3. Subject to the provisions of paragraph 4, the coastal State may, without discrimination amongst foreign ships, suspend temporarily in specified areas of its territorial sea the innocent passage of foreign ships if such suspension is essential for the protection of its security. Such suspension shall take effect only after having been duly published.

4. There shall be no suspension of the innocent passage of foreign ships through straits which are used for international navigation between one part of the high seas and another part of the high seas or the territorial sea of a foreign State.

Article 17

Foreign ships exercising the right of innocent passage shall comply with the laws and regulations enacted by the coastal State in conformity with these articles and other rules of international law and, in particular, with such laws and regulations relating to transport and navigation.

SUB-SECTION B. RULES APPLICABLE TO MERCHANT SHIPS

Article 18

1. No charge may be levied upon foreign ships by reason only of their passage through the territorial sea.

2. Charges may be levied upon a foreign ship passing through

the territorial sea as payment only for specific services rendered to the ship. These charges shall be levied without discrimination.

Article 19

1. The criminal jurisdiction of the coastal State should not be exercised on board a foreign ship passing through the territorial sea to arrest any person or to conduct any investigation in connexion with any crime committed on board the ship during its passage, save only in the following cases:

(*a*) If the consequences of the crime extend to the coastal State; or

(*b*) If the crime is of a kind to disturb the peace of the country or the good order of the territorial sea; or

(*c*) If the assistance of the local authorities has been requested by the captain of the ship or by the consul of the country whose flag the ship flies; or

(*d*) If it is necessary for the suppression of illicit traffic in narcotic drugs.

2. The above provisions do not affect the right of the coastal State to take any steps authorized by its laws for the purpose of an arrest or investigation on board a foreign ship passing through the territorial sea after leaving internal waters.

3. In the cases provided for in paragraphs 1 and 2 of this article, the coastal State shall, if the captain so requests, advise the consular authority of the flag State before taking any steps, and shall facilitate contact between such authority and the ship's crew. In cases of emergency this notification may be communicated while the measures are being taken.

4. In considering whether or how an arrest should be made, the local authorities shall pay due regard to the interests of navigation.

5. The coastal State may not take any steps on board a foreign ship passing through the territorial sea to arrest any person or to conduct any investigation in connexion with any crime committed before the ship entered the territorial sea, if the ship, proceeding from a foreign port, is only passing through the territorial sea without entering internal waters.

Article 20

1. The coastal State should not stop or divert a foreign ship passing through the territorial sea for the purpose of exercising civil jurisdiction in relation to a person on board the ship.

2. The coastal State may not levy execution against or arrest the ship for the purpose of any civil proceedings, save only in respect

of obligations or liabilities assumed or incurred by the ship itself in the course or for the purpose of its voyage through the waters of the coastal State.

3. The provisions of the previous paragraph are without prejudice to the right of the coastal State, in accordance with its laws, to levy execution against or to arrest, for the purpose of any civil proceedings, a foreign ship lying in the territorial sea, or passing through the territorial sea after leaving internal waters.

SUB-SECTION C. RULES APPLICABLE TO GOVERNMENT
SHIPS OTHER THAN WARSHIPS

Article 21

The rules contained in sub-sections A and B shall also apply to government ships operated for commercial purposes.

Article 22

1. The rules contained in sub-section A and in article 19 shall apply to government ships operated for non-commercial purposes.

2. With such exceptions as are contained in the provisions referred to in the preceding paragraph, nothing in these articles affects the immunities which such ships enjoy under these articles or other rules of international law.

SUB-SECTION D. RULE APPLICABLE TO WARSHIPS

Article 23

If any warship does not comply with the regulations of the coastal State concerning passage through the territorial sea and disregards any request for compliance which is made to it, the coastal State may require the warship to leave the territorial sea.

PART II: CONTIGUOUS ZONE

Article 24

1. In a zone of the high seas contiguous to its territorial sea, the coastal State may exercise the control necessary to:

(*a*) Prevent infringement of its customs, fiscal, immigration or sanitary regulations within its territory or territorial sea;

(*b*) Punish infringement of the above regulations committed within its territory or territorial sea.

2. The contiguous zone may not extend beyond twelve miles from the baseline from which the breadth of the territorial sea is measured.

3. Where the coasts of two States are opposite or adjacent to each other, neither of the two States is entitled, failing agreement between them to the contrary, to extend its contiguous zone beyond the median line every point of which is equidistant from the nearest points on the baselines from which the breadth of the territorial seas of the two States is measured.

PART III: FINAL ARTICLES

Article 25

The provisions of this Convention shall not affect conventions or other international agreements already in force, as between States Parties to them.

[Articles 26 to 32 inclusive are procedural in nature and have been omitted.]

B. CONVENTION ON THE CONTINENTAL SHELF[2]

The States Parties to this Convention, Have agreed as follows:

Article 1

For the purpose of these articles, the term "continental shelf" is used as referring (*a*) to the seabed and subsoil of the submarine areas adjacent to the coast but outside the area of the territorial sea, to a depth of 200 metres, or, beyond that limit, to where the depth of the superjacent waters admits of the exploitation of the natural resources of the said areas; (*b*) to the seabed and subsoil of similar submarine areas adjacent to the coasts of islands.

Article 2

1. The coastal State exercises over the continental shelf sovereign rights for the purpose of exploring it and exploiting its natural resources.

2. The rights referred to in paragraph 1 of this article are exclusive in the sense that if the coastal State does not explore the continental shelf or exploit its natural resources, no one may undertake these activities, or make a claim to the continental shelf, without the express consent of the coastal State.

3. The rights of the coastal State over the continental shelf

[2] Adopted Apr. 26, 1958 (U.N. Doc. A/Conf. 13/L.55).

do not depend on occupation, effective or notional, or on any express proclamation.

4. The natural resources referred to in these articles consist of the mineral and other non-living resources of the seabed and subsoil together with living organisms belonging to sedentary species, that is to say, organisms which, at the harvestable stage, either are immobile on or under the seabed or are unable to move except in constant physical contact with the seabed or the subsoil.

Article 3

The rights of the coastal State over the continental shelf do not affect the legal status of the superjacent waters as high seas, or that of the airspace above those waters.

Article 4

Subject to its right to take reasonable measures for the exploration of the continental shelf and the exploitation of its natural resources, the coastal State may not impede the laying or maintenance of submarine cables or pipelines on the continental shelf.

Article 5

1. The exploration of the continental shelf and the exploitation of its natural resources must not result in any unjustifiable interference with navigation, fishing or the conservation of the living resources of the sea, nor result in any interference with fundamental oceanographic or other scientific research carried out with the intention of open publication.

2. Subject to the provisions of paragraphs 1 and 6 of this article, the coastal State is entitled to construct and maintain or operate on the continental shelf installations and other devices necessary for its exploration and the exploitation of its natural resources, and to establish safety zones around such installations and devices and to take in those zones measures necessary for their protection.

3. The safety zones referred to in paragraph 2 of this article may extend to a distance of 500 metres around the installations and other devices which have been erected, measured from each point of their outer edge. Ships of all nationalities must respect these safety zones.

4. Such installations and devices, though under the jurisdiction of the coastal State, do not possess the status of islands. They have no territorial sea of their own, and their presence does not affect the delimitation of the territorial sea of the coastal State.

5. Due notice must be given of the construction of any such installations, and permanent means for giving warning of their presence must be maintained. Any installations which are abandoned or disused must be entirely removed.

6. Neither the installations or devices, nor the safety zones around them, may be established where interference may be caused to the use of recognized sea lanes essential to international navigation.

7. The coastal State is obliged to undertake, in the safety zones, all appropriate measures for the protection of the living resources of the sea from harmful agents.

8. The consent of the coastal State shall be obtained in respect of any research concerning the continental shelf and undertaken there. Nevertheless, the coastal State shall not normally withhold its consent if the request is submitted by a qualified institution with a view to purely scientific research into the physical or biological characteristics of the continental shelf, subject to the proviso that the coastal State shall have the right, if it so desires, to participate or to be represented in the research, and that in any event the results shall be published.

Article 6

1. Where the same continental shelf is adjacent to the territories of two or more States whose coasts are opposite each other, the boundary of the continental shelf appertaining to such States shall be determined by agreement between them. In the absence of agreement, and unless another boundary line is justified by special circumstances, the boundary is the median line, every point of which is equidistant from the nearest points of the baselines from which the breadth of the territorial sea of each State is measured.

2. Where the same continental shelf is adjacent to the territories of two adjacent States, the boundary of the continental shelf shall be determined by agreement between them. In the absence of agreement, and unless another boundary line is justified by special circumstances, the boundary shall be determined by application of the principle of equidistance from the nearest points of the baselines from which the breadth of the territorial sea of each State is measured.

3. In delimiting the boundaries of the continental shelf, any lines which are drawn in accordance with the principles set out in paragraphs 1 and 2 of this article should be defined with reference to charts and geographical features as they exist at a

particular date, and reference should be made to fixed permanent identifiable points on the land.

Article 7

The provisions of these articles shall not prejudice the right of the coastal State to exploit the subsoil by means of tunnelling irrespective of the depth of water above the subsoil.

[Articles 8 to 15 inclusive are procedural in nature and have been omitted.]

William R. Anderson:

43.   NAUTILUS AT 90° N*

When we crossed the Pole, of course, no bells would ring, nor would we feel a bump. Only our instruments could tell us how close we had come. Since we had made the decision to cross the Pole, we were determined to hit it precisely on the nose. Along with Navigator Shep Jenks and his assistant, Chief Petty Officer Lyle B. Rayl, I had stationed myself in the Attack Center, and although we were almost as far north as man can go on this planet, we were literally sweating over the charts and electronic position-indicators, making minute, half-degree adjustments at the helm.

The hour by *Nautilus* clocks, which were still set on Seattle time, was 1900, or seven o'clock in the evening. Our nuclear engine, which up to then had pushed *Nautilus* more than 124,000 miles, was purring smoothly. Our electronic log, or speedometer needle, was hovering above twenty knots, the depth-gauge needle about four hundred feet. Our sensitive sonar indicated that the endless polar ice pack was running between eight and eighty feet thick. Above the ice, we imagined, the polar wind was howling

---

* Reprinted by permission of World Publishing Company from NAUTILUS 90 NORTH by Captain William R. Anderson and Clay Blair, Jr. Copyright © 1959 by William R. Anderson & Clay Blair, Jr.

William R. Anderson was captain of the nuclear submarine *Nautilus* at the time of its history making underwater polar expedition.

across its trackless, barren stamping ground, grinding massive floes one upon the other.

By then we had been under ice for sixty-two hours. Obviously, it was not possible to take the usual fix on heavenly bodies to determine our position, so we were navigating primarily by dead reckoning. This means that we were spacing our speed and course on the chart and plotting our position every half-hour or so, accordingly. Our bottom soundings, sometimes useful in submerged navigating, did not help, of course, in this uncharted, unsounded area. Our precision fathometer had indicated differences of as much as eight thousand feet at those rare points where soundings were made, so we could not rely on it. Our only check on our navigating was the inertial navigator. At the exact moment we crossed the Pole, we knew, the instrument would give a positive indication. Tom Curtis moved closer to his dials and scopes as we drew near.

A mile south of the Pole, I told Jenks to inform me when we were four tenths of a mile from the Pole as indicated by the electronic log. The mileage indicator was moving rapidly. It was only a matter of seconds. *Nautilus* crewmen had gathered in the Attack Center and the Crew's Mess.

On Jenks' mark, I stepped up to the mike of the ship's public-address system:

"All hands—this is the Captain speaking . . . In a few moments *Nautilus* will realize a goal long a dream of mankind—the attainment by ship of the North Geographic Pole. With continued Godspeed, in less than two days we will record an even more significant historic first: the completion of a rapid transpolar voyage from the Pacific to the Atlantic Ocean.

"The distance to the Pole is now precisely four tenths of a mile. As we approach, let us pause in silence dedicated with our thanks for the blessings that have been ours during this remarkable voyage—our prayers for lasting world peace, and in solemn tribute to those who have preceded us, whether in victory or defeat."

The juke box was shut off, and at that moment a hush literally fell over the ship. The only sound to be heard was the steady staccato of pinging from our sonars steadily watching the bottom, the ice, and the dark waters ahead.

I glanced again at the distance indicator, and gave a brief countdown to the crew. "Stand by. 10 . . . 8 . . . 6 . . . 4 . . . 3 . . . 2 . . . 1. MARK! August 3, 1958. Time, 2315 (11:15 P.M. Eastern Daylight Saving Time). For the United States and the

United States Navy, the North Pole." I could hear cheers in the Crew's Mess.

I looked anxiously at Tom Curtis. He was smiling. The inertial navigator had switched precisely as expected, positively confirming that we had crossed the exact North Pole. Curtis sang out: "As a matter of fact, Captain, you might say we came so close we pierced the Pole."

I stood for a moment in silence, awe-struck at what *Nautilus* had achieved. She had blazed a new submerged northwest passage, vastly decreasing the sea-travel time for nuclear submarines from the Pacific to the Atlantic, one that could be used even if the Panama Canal were closed. When and if nuclear-powered cargo submarines are built, the new route would cut 4,900 miles and thirteen days off the route from Japan to Europe. *Nautilus* had opened a new era, completely conquered the vast, inhospitable Arctic. Our instruments were, for the first time, compiling an accurate and broad picture of the Arctic Basin and its approaches. *Nautilus'* achievement was dramatic proof of United States leadership in at least one important branch of science; and it would soon rank alongside or above the Russian sputnik in the minds of millions. Lastly, for the first time in history a ship had actually reached the North Pole. And never had so many men—116—been gathered at the Pole at one time.

I was proud of what *Nautilus* had done, yet I felt no sense of personal triumph or achievement. That we had reached the Pole was the work and support of many people. My reaction, frankly, was an overwhelming feeling of relief that after months and months of preparation and two unsuccessful probes we had finally made it.

Precisely at the Pole, for the record, I made note of some statistics which may or may not prove useful. The water temperature was 32.4 degrees Fahrenheit. The depth of the sea was 13,410 feet, exactly 1,927 feet deeper than reported by Ivan Papanin, a Russian who landed there, he claims, in an airplane in 1937. (In 1909 Admiral Peary had found the depth "greater than 9,000 feet.") At the exact Pole our ice detectors noted a pressure ridge extending twenty-five feet down.

After crossing the Pole, I made my way forward to join in the "North Pole Party" in the Crew's Mess. My first act was to pay modest tribute to the man who, more than any other, had made our historic voyage possible: the President of the United States. A few minutes before, I had written him a message. It concluded: "I hope, sir, that you will accept this letter as a memento of a voyage of importance to the United States." In the Mess, before seventy crew members of *Nautilus*, I signed this letter, and one to Mrs. Eisenhower, who had christened the ship.

Other events followed. A "North Pole" cake, prepared especially by leading Commissaryman Jack L. Baird, was cut, distributed, and wolfed down. Electrician's Mate First Class James Sordelet raised his right hand and became the first man in history to re-enlist at the North Pole.

An "extra" edition of the ship's newspaper was published that day, entitled "*Nautilus* Express—North Pole Edition." It was un-usually mild in tone and contained nothing libelous, which is an indication, I believe, that all hands were deeply moved by *Nautilus'* triumph. The feeling of the crew was summed up in an article by the paper's editor, John H. Michaud.

He wrote:

At NAUTILUS' Greatest Moment

The crew of the USS *Nautilus* (SS(N)571) have at this time accomplished one of the greatest feats that is possible for a peaceful nation composed of average citizens. We have reached a point that has never been attained before this time. Many courageous men have tried, few succeeded. Of all those men that have tried we humbly ask their forgiveness. They had courage and fortitude that many of us never had, never will have in our lifetime. To those men this is dedicated. We have arrived at the North Pole. The very last region of the earth that has never been explored. True we came to this region in a habitat that is not normal for man. We came with the best equipment, the best men, and a relative new form of power. Without this power we would have never attained the goal we set out for, now that we have reached that goal this same power will take us home to our loved ones, who have endured many hardships that will never be told to us.

~~~~~~~~~~~~~~~~~~~

Edward D. Goldberg:

44.   CHEMISTRY IN THE OCEANS*

Studies in marine chemistry have gone through several phases since its birth with the first quantitative assays of sea water by Torbern Bergman, the famed Swedish scientist, and Antoine Lavoisier, the father of modern chemistry, at the turn of the eighteenth century. The seas were depicted as arising from the washings of the surface of the earth by natural waters, and investigations on both its chemistry and that of the organisms had a significant role in the development of chemistry. As you are well aware, the elements bromine and iodine were discovered in sea salt and marine algal ash, respectively.

When the rather dramatic effects of primary plant production on the distribution of some chemical species in the oceans were established during the first several decades of the twentieth century, impetus was given to work on the fertility of surface waters and the results of the combustion of the organic material in the deeper waters.

In the mid-twentieth century some attention again has been focused on the inorganic chemistries in the oceans, work paralleling and reflecting advances made in the mother science, chemistry. The geochemical behavior of elements during their residence in the sea, subsequent to their introduction from the continents and atmosphere, has provided the background for many recent investigations.

Although the discovery of new elements is apparently limited to a small group of people working in the foothills of Berkeley, California, two naturally produced radioisotopes have been initially found in the marine domain. Both of these isotopes, Be^{10} and

* From a paper presented at the first International Oceanographic Congress (New York), August 31–September 12, 1959, as it appears in Publication No. 67 of the AAAS. © 1961 by the American Association for the Advancement of Science. By permission of the publisher and the author.

Edward D. Goldberg is a professor of chemistry at the Scripps Institution of Oceanography. He was the co-discoverer of silicon-32 in nature.

Si^{32} are produced in the upper atmosphere by the cosmic ray fragmentation of the earth's enveloping gases, Be^{10} from nitrogen and Si^{32} from argon. The beryllium isotope with a half-life of 2.7 million years was simultaneously found by groups led by Dr. James Arnold (1956) of Princeton and Dr. B. Peters (Goel *et al.*, 1957) of Bombay in the deep-sea sediments of the Pacific Ocean. Dr. Lal of Bombay and I (1959) have sought and observed Si^{32} in siliceous sponges taken from waters of the mixed layers.

In both cases the marine realm provides the unique sites for the accumulation of these radioactive species in amounts that are readily extractable for quantitative assay. These cosmic ray-produced isotopes come down to the land and sea surfaces in atmospheric precipitation but are heavily diluted in the relatively large amounts of stable silicon and beryllium contained in the continental surfaces, whereas in the oceans, the quantities of stable beryllium and silicon, at least in surface waters, are small and allow the specific activity, the disintegrations of the isotope per weight of its stable form per unit time, to attain reasonably high values.

The beryllium concentration in sea water (Merrill *et al.*, 1960) is of the order of 6×10^{-4} of a part per billion by weight. Hence, a 4000-m water column, representing the average oceanic depth, contains per square centimeter about the same amount of beryllium as a millimeter depth of average earth's crust which has for all practical purposes a uniform beryllium content of a few parts per million. Thus, two effects tend to reduce continental specific activities of Be^{10} to values lower than those of the marine environment: (*a*) mixing of the radioisotope with stable beryllium to levels on land greater than a millimeter; and (*b*) the runoff into the oceans of any of the isotopes taken up by the rivers. Hence, the authigenic minerals on the sea floor, solid phases that derive their components from the chemical species in sea water, readily revealed measurable quantities of Be^{10}.

Similarly, the low concentrations of silicon in surface sea waters, resulting from the assimilation of monomeric silicic acid and/or its ions by the photosynthesizing diatoms, suggest a promising medium for the attainment of high specific activities of Si^{32}. If we assume the depth of the mixed layer to be 100 m and to contain 15 micromoles of silicon per liter, a 1-cm^2 column of such waters contains about the same amount of inert silicon as 0.01 cm of earth's surface. We have found that a disintegration rate of one per minute, readily measurable, necessitates the extraction of roughly 100 g of opal or silicon dioxide. Such quantities are available from siliceous sponges living in environments of the mixed layer waters. For every 100 g of sponge-produced opal, the equivalent of 100 tons of sea water must have had its silicon depleted to zero by the activity of these animals. Deep-sea sponges require the equivalent of 10 tons of sea water to obtain a corresponding amount of silicon inasmuch as these waters contain on the average 10 times more silicon.

Let us now turn to the more general problem of chemical processes in the oceans. Chemical reactions take place at phase discontinuities, i.e., the atmosphere-hydrosphere, biosphere-hydrosphere, and sediment-hydrosphere interfaces. We shall focus our attention mainly on the reactions of sea water with the solid components of the sea floor.

We can reasonably expect that most inorganic species correspond closely to those predicted from complete equilibration between all reacting substances. Such thermodynamically unstable species as iodide and manganous ions probably exist because the waters that contain them have been inaccessible to surfaces at which reactions to stable substances might occur. We shall return to this concept in considerations of the formation of ferromanganese minerals on the sea floor.

Insight into the *relative reactivities* of elements in the marine hydrosphere has been obtained from considerations of the average time an element spends in the oceans. An extremely simple model of the ocean is used in which it is assumed that the presently observed chemical composition represents a steady state system in which the amount of material introduced per unit time is compensated by an equal amount deposited as sediments. A further assumption is that there is a complete mixing of materials introduced into the oceans in times that are short with respect to the residence times. We can then define the residence time of an element as the total amount of the element in sea water divided by the amount of the given element introduced by the rivers or precipitated to the sediments per unit time.

About seven years ago Barth (1952), on the basis of river influxes of the elements, initiated such calculations, and his data are shown in Table I. An alternate approach has been made upon the basis of the total amount of sedimentation in the marine environment (Goldberg and Arrhenius, 1958), and the residence times so derived also are shown in Table I. A remarkable agreement is observed between these sets of data. The only striking discrepancy is found for the case of calcium. The many difficulties in trying to obtain a geochemical balance for this element are well known, and we certainly have not been able to resolve this difficulty, at least within a factor of 8.

Although many independent assumptions are involved in the calculations, both the absolute and relative values for most of the residence times appear reasonable. Sodium has a residence time within an order of magnitude of the age of the oceans, several billion years. This lack of reactivity is in accord with its aqueous chemistry. The alkali and alkaline earth metals have residence times in the range of 10^6 to 10^8 years. Manganese shows a remarkably low value, 7000 years, especially in comparison with the metals nickel and zinc, which probably have similar chemistries

TABLE I. RESIDENCE TIMES OF ELEMENTS IN THE OCEANS

		Residence Time, Years	
Element	Amount in Oceans, g	Goldberg and Arrhenius (1958)	Barth (1952)
Na	1.47×10^{22}	2.6×10^8	2.1×10^8
Mg	1.8×10^{21}	4.5×10^7	2.2×10^7
Li	2.8×10^{17}	2.2×10^7	
Sr	9.8×10^{18}	1.6×10^7	
K	5.3×10^{20}	1.1×10^7	1.0×10^7
Ca	5.6×10^{20}	8.0×10^6	1.0×10^6
U	5.2×10^{15}	6.5×10^5	
Zn	1.4×10^{16}	1.8×10^5	
Cu	5.2×10^{15}	6.5×10^4	
Co	7.0×10^{14}	1.8×10^4	
Si	5.2×10^{18}	1.0×10^4	3.5×10^4
Pb	$<4.0 \times 10^{14}$	$<1.0 \times 10^4$	
Mn	1.4×10^{15}	7.0×10^3	
Th	$<2.8 \times 10^{13}$	$<1.4 \times 10^3$	
Fe	1.4×10^{16}	1.4×10^2	
Ti	1.4×10^{15}	1.6×10^2	
Al	1.4×10^{16}	1.0×10^2	

in the divalent state and are associated with manganese in marine deposits. The residence times of these latter elements are about 500 times higher. This reactivity of manganese is apparently related to the removal of this element from solution by oxidation to the tetravalent state to form the ferromanganese deposits, a subject we shall discuss subsequently. The sorption of the associated metals like zinc and nickel to the precipitated manganese requires a relatively larger amount of manganese. This results in longer residence times, compared to manganese, for these metals.

Silicon and aluminum are among the elements with the shortest calculated residence times. Both elements enter the oceans in both solid and dissolved phases; the solid phases, such as quartz, feldspars, and clay minerals, rapidly settle to the bottom. Iron and titanium which also quickly pass through the hydrosphere, prevail as solid phases during the major part of their residence. The absolute values for the residence times of these elements are somewhat tenuous as the assumption that such times are small in comparison with the mixing times of oceanic water masses, say of the order of hundreds to thousands of years, is invalid. It may be worthwhile in the future, when values exist for the contribution of solid and dissolved phases of these elements to the total concentrations, to calculate more accurately the residence times of the components.

The utility of such computations, the derivation of residence times, arose recently in our laboratory in the study of thorium isotopes as a dating tool for marine sediments. We were concerned primarily with two isotopes, normally occurring thorium, Th^{232}, and ionium, Th^{230}, which is one of the daughter products of the most abundant isotope of uranium, U^{238}. The residence of thorium can only be given in terms of an upper limit inasmuch as the thorium concentration in sea water has never been determined. A value of a life in sea water of less than one thousand years, probably closer to one hundred years, is derived for thorium on the basis of a maximum concentration in sea water of 10^{-8} g/liter.

The extremely short residence time of thorium suggests the possibility of ocean to ocean variations in its concentration. Those bodies of water exposed to the introduction of large amounts of continental runoff may very well be enriched in normally occurring thorium compared to sea waters which are isolated from land drainage for times comparable to the residence time of thorium.

The uranium-derived isotope of thorium, Th^{230}, provides a convenient normalization for intraocean comparisons of thorium contents. Uranium has a residence time of the order of a million years, a time that is long with respect to oceanic mixing processes. Hence, one would expect and one does find a uniform content of uranium in sea water, a value around 3.5 μg/liter. Thus, the rate of production of its daughter ionium per unit volume of sea water is constant in all oceans. The ionium input from land is less than one-fourth of this oceanic production value and is unimportant in our considerations. Since the aqueous chemistry of thorium involves only one valence state, we can make the initial assumption that both thorium and ionium will be present in the oceans in similar chemical forms. Thus, we shall seek out the ratio of ionium to thorium as a measure of possible thorium variations in the ocean.

Although the thorium content of sea water is so low that its actual value so far has escaped detection by modern analytical techniques, some surface minerals on the sea floor, which accumulate thorium in measurable amounts from the over-lying sea waters, should provide a convenient index of the sea water concentrations. The thorium isotopic ratios given in Table II were obtained from the authigenic minerals in the upper 2 or upper 4 cm of deep-sea sediments. The lowest values of thorium compared to ionium are found in the South Pacific Ocean whereas the highest numbers occur in the Atlantic Ocean. Intermediate values are found in the North Pacific.

These values are reasonable when one looks at the relative

TABLE II. VALUES OF IONIUM/THORIUM RATIO IN HYDROGENOUS MINERALS FROM SURFACE SEDIMENT SAMPLES

Area	Io/Th, Units of Disintegrations of Ionium/ Disintegration of Thorium/Unit Time
Atlantic	12
North Pacific	25
South Pacific	150

contribution of land runoff waters to these oceanic areas. Table III gives the areas of the oceans and the respective areas of land that are drained into the oceans. The Pacific receives but one-sixth of the amount of drainage waters that enter the Atlantic on an areal basis, which apparently accounts for the higher values of thorium, normalized to ionium, in the Pacific sediments. Similarly, the well-known observation that more and larger rivers drain into northern hemispheric marine areas is reflected in the higher ionium/thorium ratios in southern Pacific deposits as compared to their northern counterparts. Thus, the concentration of thorium in the deeper parts of the ocean is seen to have an ocean to ocean variation, explainable, on the basis of our simple thesis of the residence time of thorium being small with respect to the times of oceanic mixing, coupled with the yearly contributions of thorium draining into the world's oceans.

TABLE III. OCEANIC AREAS AND COMPLIMENTARY LAND AREAS DRAINING
INTO THEM (THOUSANDS OF SQUARE KILOMETERS) (LYMAN, 1958)

Ocean	Area	Land Area Drained	Percentage
Atlantic	98,000	67,000	68.5
Indian	65,500	17,000	26.0
Antarctic	32,000	14,000	44.0
Pacific	165,000	18,000	11.0

Let us now turn to a rather dramatic example of chemistry occurring on the sea floor, the formation of the ferromanganese minerals, the major components of the manganese nodules. These minerals represent the most nearly unique and possibly the most abundant, and for these reasons, the most studied of the marine authigenic minerals. They exist in the form of nodular concretions which range in size from millimeters to about a meter, coatings about rocks and shells, and as components of the unconsolidated sediments. The two principal metals, iron and manganese, which occur as oxides or hydroxides, are normally present in similar amounts, although, less generally, either of these two elements can be dominant. They are found on all oceanic floors and normally occur in localities where the total rate of accumulation of sediments is low. Menard and Shipek (1958) estimate that between 20% and 50% of the deep-sea floor in the southwestern Pacific is covered with nodules on the basis of the photographs of the bottom and the occurrence of nodules in cores. Phillipsite, barite, and fish debris, phases which are strongly diluted in rapidly amassing deposits, are found in high concentrations in areas associated with ferromanganese minerals.

The ferromanganese minerals act as hosts for a suite of elements which include copper, nickel, cobalt, zinc, lead, thorium, and the rare earths. These guest metals, which are enriched in the ferromanganese minerals, as well as the manganese, exist in sea water in states of undersaturation (Goldberg, 1958), and their assimilation by these minerals has been postulated to account at least in part for this situation.

Their unique chemical composition, unlike that of any terrestrial mineral has strongly indicated the authigenic character of the ferromanganese accumulations (Table IV). Further support comes from the lead isotopic analyses of Chow and Patterson (1959), who point out that the distinctive values of the radiogenic lead isotopes suggest a derivation of the lead from sea water.

TABLE IV. AVERAGE COMPOSITION OF MANGANESE NODULES FROM THE
PACIFIC OCEAN

Element	Weight %
Fe	14
Mn	19
Ni	0.4
Co	0.3
Cu	0.5
Ti	0.8
Zn	0.04
Pb	0.1
P	0.5
Al	0.7
Zr	0.006

Structural investigations by Buser and Grütter (1956) by x-ray
and electron microscopic techniques indicate the minerals are composed of the crystalline iron and manganese compounds, δ-MnO_2,
manganites and goethite, as well as some amorphous fractions.
δ-MnO_2 is composed of disordered sheets of manganese dioxide,
whereas the manganite crystals possess a double layer-lattice structure
in which ordered layers of manganese dioxide alternate with disordered layers of manganous or ferric hydroxides or basic salts.
The disordered layer is the site for the accumulation of the
metal ions whose enrichment in these materials has been pointed
out previously. In nodules with amounts of iron, greater than can
be accommodated in the disordered layer, the mineral goethite
appears. Buser (personal communication) points out that the appearance of goethite in the minerals suggests that particles of
fresh iron hydroxide, or oxides of lower molecular weight, are
initially deposited, which possess the potentiality of transformation
to goethite.

The rates of accretion of these minerals on surfaces or during
formation of the nodules is extremely slow. The "Horizon" nodule,
a large concretion dredged from the North Pacific with a longest
dimension of about 1 m, was analyzed by the ionium-thorium
method and was found to amass its solid phases at a rate of
somewhat less than 0.01 mm per thousand years or a rate of
about one atomic layer per day. This is probably one of the
slowest reactions occurring in nature in which a measure of the
rate of the reaction can be ascertained. It should be emphasized
that such rates are not necessarily continuous, as often layers of

clay or detrital materials are found between the slowly accreting ferromanganese lamina.

The rather exotic nature of these minerals has inspired a number of hypotheses as to their mode of formation. The early workers were more concerned with the immediate origin of the manganese and associated elements, rather than any physicochemical considerations. Such sources of manganese as Foraminifera, volcanic debris, and subsurface springs were postulated. Further, both biochemical and inorganic mechanisms to deposit the manganese and iron oxides were invoked. Of special interest today is the thesis of biological oxidation, first proposed by Dieulafait (1883), taken up again by Dorff (1935), and recently revived by Graham (1959). I shall return to this problem somewhat later.

A satisfactory hypothesis must account not only for the chemical and physical characteristics of the materials, but also for the geological observations concerning their occurrences. Thus, whereas manganese is in a reduced, dissolved state in sea water, in the ferromanganese minerals it is in both the divalent and tetravalent forms, although mainly the latter. The only nonbiological species in the ocean in sufficient amounts capable of oxidizing manganese is dissolved gaseous oxygen and the reaction

$$2OH^- + Mn^{++} + \tfrac{1}{2}O_2 = MnO_2 + H_2O$$

has a free energy of -9 kcal at a pH of 8, a manganous ion concentration of $10^{-9}M$, and a partial pressure of oxygen of 0.25 atmosphere. All these concentrations are similar to those in near-bottom sea waters.

Since tetravalent manganese is not found in sea water, although from the above data it is the thermodynamically stable form, a reaction site or surface is probably necessary for the reaction to proceed. The well-known catalytic properties of iron oxide surfaces suggest the association of such material in the formation of the nodules. Iron exists in sea water dominantly in particulate phases, partly collodial. The accumulation of iron oxides on surfaces, where either the bottom topography or the lack of sediment source material does not allow any appreciable accumulation of solid phases, would initiate formation of the ferromanganese minerals. In areas of rapid deposition, where nodules or accretions are not found, the burial of any iron oxide surface by other sediment components minimizes any mineral formation.

The catalytic oxidation of manganese on the oxide surfaces leads directly to the formation of the ferromanganese minerals. Where an excess of iron is accommodated, the mineral goethite appears. The scavenging of the reactive, high charge density ions from sea water, those previously described as having relatively short residence times, and their incorporation into the disordered layer follow. The formation of the new mineral surface, allowing sites for further oxidation of manganese, i.e., the reaction becomes autocatalytic, completes the picture.

The recent and significant observation by Graham (1959) that these nodular materials contain appreciable amounts of organic matter has resulted in the revival of the hypothesis of biological origin. Although bacteria and other organisms have been sought on the nodules by previous investigators, possibly with not enough elegance, and not found, the enthusiasm of the adherents of bio-chemical theories has not been dampened.

The alternate hypothesis that the organic matter in the nodules was adsorbed from sea water appears plausible. The ferroman-ganese minerals possess rather high specific surface areas, ranging from 6 to 190 m^2/g (Buser and Grütter, 1956), reactive sites capable of the uptake and retention of organic phases. Further, it is conceivable that bacterial activity does take place at such sur-faces and that benthic organisms might not be attracted to such material. But an extension of such thought to a direct biological deposition at the present time seems unwarranted.

On a biochemical basis, it is very difficult to account for the relative proportions of certain metals in these minerals, two in particular, cobalt and cerium. Cobalt exists in sea water at a concentration of about one-seventh that of nickel (Taivo Laevestu, personal communication) on the basis of recent, refined analyses. Although cobalt and nickel show a strong geochemical coherence in behavior during the major sedimentary cycle, the ferroman-ganese phases contain nearly as much cobalt as nickel on the average (Table IV). Cobalt shows a wider spectrum of concen-trations in nodules than does nickel.

An explanation for these abundances may well be found in the greater ease of oxidation of cobalt from the divalent to the tri-valent state. The oxidation potential of cobalt for such a reaction is slightly higher than that for manganese and the free energy of the reaction, using typical marine concentrations, appear to be positive, i.e., the reaction should not proceed. However, a com-bination of the cobalt and manganese oxidation reactions to form a solid solution of the cobalt oxides in the manganese dioxides gives a thermodynamically possible reaction, which could result in a fractionation of cobalt over nickel. Where the redox potential of the environment is relatively low, the cobalt/nickel ratios of sea water would be expected in the nodules, as only the divalent ions are involved. Thus, the cobalt/nickel ratios may well be a sensitive indicator of the oxidation environment in the vicinity of ferromanganese mineral formation.

Cerium, one of the rare earths susceptible to oxidation to a higher state than the normal plus three, is enriched in these minerals relative to its periodic table neighbor lanthanum, which exists solely in the trivalent state. In ferromanganese minerals, in which cerium is apparently oxidized in part to the plus four valence state, the cerium/lanthanum ratio normally is of the order of six, although this value was over an order of magnitude higher in the case of a Triassic nodule from Timor. Whereas in crustal rocks on the earth's surface, the cerium/lanthanum ratio is about three. Hence, it is proposed that the oxidation of cerium, which like that of cobalt is not evident from thermodynamic considerations, proceeds through the incorporation of ceric oxides into the manganese dioxide lattice with a coupling of the manganous and cerous oxidation reactions. The high concentrations of metals susceptible to oxidation offer a dilemma to any biological hypotheses. Are we to have not only manganese oxidizing capabilities in the organisms but also cerium and cobalt oxidizing capacities?

I do not wish to leave a picture of chemical reactions on the sea floor not influenced by the large biomass of the oceans. The plants and animals of the seas are responsible for the most dramatic compositional changes in the oceans. In the surface waters where plant production occurs, carbon dioxide and oxygen, the intake and release gases of photosynthesis, respond to this biological activity. Depletion of the former and supersaturation of the latter are often observed in waters near the surface. Also, the plant nutrients, chemical species of phosphorus, nitrogen, and silicon vary over wide ranges of concentrations both in time and space.

Barium is one non-nutrient element which shows very positive correlations between concentrations in sediments and biological activity. Concentrations of this element are markedly higher in pelagic sediments below productive oceanic areas than in bottom samples below the more barren seas (Goldberg and Arrhenius, 1958; Goldberg, 1958). The high barium contents are associated with both siliceous and calcareous deposits, although the concentration of this element is not markedly high in the siliceous or calcareous hard parts of organisms. The barium is probably accumulated in the sediments through chemical reactions involving the organic debris.

A clue to the marine geochemical behavior of barium may be found in its distribution in sea water. Dr. T. Chow and I have recently found barium existing in sea water in a state of under-saturation with respect to precipitation of the sulfate and with concentrations ranging between 10 and 70 μg/liter. The lower values are found in surface waters, and there is a consistent increase in barium content with depth. The depth profiles are somewhat similar to those previously reported for radium.

Possibly, the release of high concentrations of sulfate ion, resulting from the oxidation of organically bound sulfur in biological debris in the oceans, can result in a consequential precipitation of barium sulfate in the microenvironment of this organic material. As simultaneous sinking and combustion of this organic matter occurs in the oceans, part of the incorporated barium may be returned to the sea water through dissolution of the barium sulfate. Part of the barium may end up in the sediments. Further, one can conceive that any oxidation of organic matter in the sediment may result in the uptake of barium by the mechanism illustrated above. Such processes would result in an increase in barium with depth and its accumulation on the sea floor.

Early German and Russian workers pointed out the striking accumulation of heavy metals over sea water by a whole spectrum of marine organisms. Iron, vanadium, zinc, and nickel were amassed by the biosphere to average enrichments over sea water by factors of tens of thousands. Recently, a wealth of values on the heavy metal contents of members of the marine biosphere has resulted from problems involving the disposal of radioactive wastes and bomb fallout. Such work has strengthened the observation of the concentration of heavy metals in organisms of the sea. These metals are retained by strong chemical bonds and cannot be eluted (washed out) by repeated rinsings with fresh or sea waters.

The relative concentration factors of metals in the marine biosphere as compared with those of sea water closely parallel the order of stability of metal ions with a variety of organic complexing agents (Goldberg, 1957). If one takes the stability constants of metals forming organic complexes with a large suite of organic complexing agents, independent of the functional group, the increasing order of stability for the metals shows a covariance with the relative enrichment of the metals in marine organisms. The animals and plants of the sea provide a huge reaction area for the uptake of dissolved metallic ions. One governing factor for the uptake of specific ions in competition with other ions is the equilibrium constants of the chelating reactions.

Concepts in modern chemistry should provide an entry into the resolution of the host of problems confronting the marine chemist. Why, for example, do manganese nodules close to coastal areas contain extremely high amounts of manganese compared to iron? A nodule recently dredged from the Gulf of California contained essentially pure MnO_2 and was devoid of the normally associated metals such as nickel, cobalt, zinc, and copper.

What is the intimate chemistry involved in the formation of phosphorites and glauconites on the sea floor? What redox conditions are required for their buildup and what associations with the biochemistry of the seas, if any, are involved?

The distinction between detrital and authigenic clay minerals is not clear-cut, if it can ever be. It has been known since the early thirties, after the work of Goldschmidt, that boron is enriched in marine, compared to continental, clays. Marine sediments contain hundreds of parts per million of boron whereas continental clays contain but one-tenth to one-twentieth of this amount. The boron is strongly held in the clay lattice, not removed by various washing or chelating elements. Where does it sit in the clay lattice? Boron, much more abundant in the oceans than in terrestrial waters, may well enter the clay structure or additions to the already existing minerals resulting in higher contents of this element in marine clays. Any continental clays introduced into the oceans would obtain their boron on the sea floor rather than during their passage to the sea floor because of the much longer time periods. The problem of detrital versus authigenic marine clays in the extreme reverts to the classical conundrum of the sock which is repeatedly darned until none of the original material is left. Is this a new sock or not? A continental clay rearranges on the sea floor. Is this a new clay or not?

These are but a few of the problems that may be found in the chemistries at the sea floor-sea water interface. Solutions will be found not solely in the bases provided by modern chemistry, but only in the coupling of such knowledge with the physical, biochemical, and geological processes in the oceans.

REFERENCES

Arnold, J. R. 1956. Beryllium-10 produced by cosmic rays. *Science, 124,* 584–585.
Barth, T. W. F. 1952. *Theoretical Petrology.* John Wiley and Sons, New York.
Buser, W., and A. Grütter. 1956. Über die Natur der Mangen Knollen. *Schweiz. mineral. petrog. Mitt., 36,* 49–62.

Chow, T. J., and C. C. Patterson. 1959. Lead isotopes in manganese nodules, 1959. *Geochim. Cosmochim. Acta*, 17, 21–31.

Dieulafait, L. 1883. Le manganese dans les eaux de mers actuelles et dans certains de leur depots. *Compt. rend.*, 96, 718–721.

Dorff, F. 1935. *Biologie des Eisens und Mangan Kreislaufes*. Berlin.

Goel, P. S., D. P. Kharkar, D. Lal, N. Narsappaya, B. Peters, and V. Yatirajam. 1957. The beryllium-10 concentration in deep-sea sediments. *Deep-Sea Research*, 4, 202–210.

Goldberg, Edward D. 1957. Biogeochemistry of trace elements. *Geol. Soc. Am., Mem.*, 67 (1), 345–358.

————. 1958. The processes regulating the composition of sea water. *J. Chem. Education*, 35, 116–119.

————. 1958. Determination of opal in marine sediments. *J. Marine Research*, 17, 178–182.

Goldberg, Edward D., and G. O. S. Arrhenius. 1958. Chemistry of Pacific pelagic sediments. *Geochim. Cosmochim. Acta*, 13, 153–212.

Graham, John. 1959. Metabolically induced precipitation of elements from sea water. *Science*, 129, 1428–1429.

Lal, Devendra, Edward D. Goldberg, and Min Koide. 1959. Cosmic-ray produced Si^{32} in nature. *Phys. Rev. Letters*, 3, 380.

Lyman, John. 1958. Chemical considerations. In "Physical and chemical properties of sea water." *Natl. Acad. Sci.-Natl. Research Council, Publ. No. 600*, 89.

Menard, H. W., and C. J. Shipek. 1958. Surface concentrations of manganese nodules. *Nature*, 182, 1156–1158.

Merrill, John R., Edward F. X. Lyden, Masatake Honda, and James R. Arnold. 1960. The sedimentary geochemistry of the beryllium isotopes. *Geochim. Cosmochim. Acta*, 18, 108–129.

~~~~~~~~~~~~~~~~

Don Walsh:

45.   TRIESTE I AND THE DEEPEST DIVE*

In January of 1960 the U. S. Navy Bathyscaph *Trieste* dove 35,800 feet to the deepest spot on the ocean floor known to man.

On the 23rd of January, 1960, the United States Navy Bathyscaph *Trieste* dove almost seven miles down into the deepest known

* From "New Eyes for the Scientist" by Lt. Don Walsh, U.S.N., *Frontiers*, October, 1960, Volume 25, No. 1. Reprinted by permission of the author.

Lieutenant Commander Don Walsh graduated from the United States Naval Academy in 1954. He received his Ph.D. in physical oceanography in 1968 and is currently on active duty in the United States Navy as a commander of a submarine.

place on the ocean's floor. This dive into the Challenger Deep, 200 miles southwest of Guam, took nearly nine hours for the 14-mile round trip. Its completion was the final goal of the Navy's Project Nekton.

The strange-looking vehicle that performed the feat certainly does not look like something that could withstand the 16,000 pounds per square inch pressure that was found at the bottom of the Challenger Deep. Rather, it resembles, as one farm boy described it, "a giant striped cow with a centralized udder." To be sure it is not a conventional submarine, and yet it can go with ease almost 90 times deeper.

Actually, the craft is built along very simple lines utilizing the principle of the free balloon. The sausage-shaped upper structure is the balloon, and instead of using helium or hydrogen for buoyancy it is filled with aviation gasoline. By using a buoyant fluid the problem of gas compression is avoided. The shape of the balloon is dictated by the fact that the craft is towed through the seas and has to have some sort of hydrodynamic form so that it will be strong and yet easily towed.

Even "solid" gasoline compresses when subjected to the great pressures in the depths, and it is therefore necessary to be able to drop some weight to compensate for the loss of buoyancy. If weight were not dropped, the craft would go faster and faster towards the bottom as the sea pressure squeezed the buoyant substance into a smaller mass. Of course, in coming up the reverse will be true, and it will go faster and faster as it gets nearer to the surface; however, no control is needed then, as a rapid arrival at the surface can do no harm.

The weight dropped to control the descent is in the form of iron shot ballast. The shot is held by electro magnetism in two tubs under the float. By keeping the shot magnetized it cannot fall, and when the current is turned off the shot is demagnetized and it falls. In this way very fine control of the craft's buoyancy can be maintained. Simple, yes, but very safe and very efficient.

In actual use it was found that one ton of shot would have to be dropped for every 3000 feet of depth to maintain equilibrium. Each of the tubs has an eight-ton capacity, giving a generous safety factor even in the greatest depths.

The ballast tubs themselves are so constructed that they can be dropped in case of emergency. Either the operator can throw a switch to release them or they will drop automatically if the electrical power should fail.

The final important item on our "underwater balloon" is the

sphere. The sphere is suspended below the float (or balloon) and serves the same purpose as the gondola on the free balloon. Housed inside the 15-ton steel ball are the bathyscaph's pilot and observer, their instruments and controls, plus all of the batteries needed to run the various equipment. The sphere is the only pressure proof part of the *Trieste* and as such has to be very strong to withstand the crushing pressures of the depths. The walls are from 4½″ to 6″ thick depending on the section. On one side is the small entrance hatch, on the opposite, the main observation window or port. The cone-shaped windows (the other one is in the hatch) are made of plastic and are 6½″ thick. Despite their thickness visibility through them is excellent.

The *Trieste*'s crew enters the sphere via an entrance tube which runs from topside down through the float to the rear of the sphere near the hatch. This tube is flooded once the crew is inside and the hatch is closed. In this way the tube does not have to be of heavy construction to withstand pressure.

Powerful mercury vapor floodlights are installed on the bottom of the float to enable the craft's crew to see and photograph the bottom of the ocean at any depth. This is necessary in that all daylight has faded by the time you have passed 1000 feet.

From the foregoing brief description of the craft's design and operation, it can be seen that the bathyscaph is indeed very safe and practical for the manned exploration of Earth's last geographic frontier. In fact, we might even call the *Trieste* our first "inner spaceship."

Why does our Navy own and maintain a craft of this sort? It can never fire a shot in anger, and it will never evolve into a weapon. The answer to this question is science. Science is a vital factor in our defense effort, and it is only by staying ahead in all areas of the sciences that we can maintain the technical superiority needed for national security. It is this fact along with man's need for more knowledge about the oceans which cover 72% of the surface of his planet, Earth, that prompted the Navy to buy the *Trieste* from the craft's inventor, Auguste Piccard. It was this same Professor Piccard who was the first man into the stratosphere with his famous balloon ascensions in the early 30's.

Active Navy interest started in 1957 when the Navy through its Office of Naval Research contracted for a series of dives with the *Trieste* in the Mediterranean. The object of this program was to evaluate the craft from the point of view of as many different scientific disciplines as possible. The participating scientists would then be able to report to the Navy on the advisability of purchasing the craft.

At the completion of the diving program the scientists recommended that the Navy purchase the *Trieste*, in that they felt that it would be an important tool for the manned exploration of the oceans, both for military and for scientific objectives. Accordingly, the Navy began the necessary arrangements to obtain it and to bring it to the United States.

Along with the *Trieste* came the services of the inventor's son, Jacques Piccard, and Mr. Buono, Jacques' assistant. These two would teach the Navy the operation and upkeep of the bathyscaph.

The U.S. Navy Electronics Laboratory at San Diego, California was selected as home port for the little craft, and in August of 1958 the *Trieste* arrived, in pieces, aboard a cargo ship. It was, at first, like having a new baby in the house! Tools, material, and equipment had to be purchased; a building for office space had to be found, and finally a place to berth the craft had to be located at N.E.L.'s busy piers.

By early December 1958 the *Trieste* had been assembled and tested and was ready for its first ocean dive with the U.S. Navy. The diving point was selected, about two miles outside of Point Loma where we could find 800–900 feet of water. The "maiden" dive went very well, and upon completion of this first test dive the craft was towed back to the Electronics Laboratory for inspection.

The beginning of 1959 found the *Trieste* out of water again for more modifications and repairs. Nothing had been damaged by the dive, but there was a continuous need for proper maintenance. For almost all of 1959 the *Trieste* underwent an intensive program of continuous testing and evaluation. The craft had to be evaluated in terms of what specific function it could perform. When these functions were determined, then the proper instrumentation had to be built. There was no such thing as buying instrumentation off the shelf. Each piece had to be designed and built specifically for the *Trieste*. The major item of the modification program was the installation of a new sphere which would give the craft the capability of reaching any spot on the ocean's floor. Also, the float was lengthened to give greater buoyancy at the great depths. We all found that it was a slow and meticulous process getting acquainted with the strange submersible.

October 1959 saw the *Trieste* loaded aboard a cargo ship at San Diego. Destination: Guam and Project Nekton. This project would have as its objective the conquest of the Challenger Deep, which is situated in the Marianas Trench near Guam. The Navy base at Guam would be our temporary home base for the duration of the project. The real objective of this program would not be merely to see how deep we could go but to make valuable measurements in the deepest known water column and to observe with the human eye the bottom of this vast trench. We would go where no man had ever gone before, and this alone was reason enough to make the dives. To see what had been unseen, and to measure that which had not been measured.

By the end of October the *Trieste* was on Guam and ready for preliminary testing. We would not make the deep dive our first target, but rather we would work our way down to that depth by a series of progressively deeper test dives. As each deeper stage was checked off as satisfactory, we could then go on to the next with confidence.

On the 15th of November Jacques Piccard and Dr. Andreas B. Rechnitzer, the Scientist-in-Charge of Project Nekton, made a record-breaking dive to 18,600 feet, giving the United States the world's depth record—a record that we would soon best.

The former holder of this record was the French Navy. Their bathyscaph, the FNRS-3, plunged to 13,400 feet off Dakar, French West Africa. Their bathyscaph actually is the *Trieste*'s older brother, as it too was designed by Auguste Piccard. He started work on this craft just prior to World War II and did not leave it until he started work on the *Trieste* in 1952.

Between dives the *Trieste* received minor alterations and much new instrumentation. (The instrumentation in many cases had been ordered earlier in the year but had not caught up with the project until we had arrived in Guam.) As the matériel arrived it was put aboard the *Trieste*, and with each piece she became more valuable to science.

The test dives continued successfully, and early in January 1960 the *Trieste* broke her own record by diving to 24,000 feet. Jacques Piccard and I were aboard this time—and though we could not land on the bottom due to a minor malfunction—we did count the dive as a success. The 24,000-foot dive was the last hurdle to clear before we went after the "big one" in the Challenger Deep. Up to this point the little submersible had performed as expected, and we had gathered much valuable information and experience.

By the middle of January the bathyscaph was ready for the last dive in Project Nekton. As we left Apra Harbor under tow we noticed that the seas appeared to be a little rougher than before, but we continued hoping that they would calm by the time we reached the diving point. The tow went quite slowly as the *Trieste* wallowed through the high seas. Our speed averaged two miles an hour over the 200-mile trip to the deep.

Early in the morning of the 23rd, just after sunrise, Jacques and I slid down the entrance tube and squeezed into the steel sphere. After a few rapid tests and checks we bolted the heavy door and commenced the dive.

Time went by very quickly, even though nine hours is a long time to sit in a 17-cubic foot space. We were kept very busy controlling the descent, taking measurements and observations, and communicating with the surface on our underwater telephone.

The bottom, seven miles down, was distinctly different from the bottom seen on previous dives. It appeared to be made up of very fine white particles. Our landing stirred up the sediment, and we were engulfed in a white cloud. I found out later that this type of bottom is made up of "diatomaceous ooze" and that this material had been found before in the deepest trenches.

Just before landing we saw a flatfish lying on the bottom. He was white and about one foot long. After we had landed we saw him swim off into the cloud. The only other living thing of note was a small shrimp that Jacques saw as he glanced out of the window near the bottom.

The trip to the surface was fast, and we arrived in the late afternoon light. Shortly after we got up we committed an American Flag to the depths to commemorate the conquest of the last frontier on Earth. We could not plant the flag on the bottom, in the classical way of the explorer, due to the formidable technical problems involved; but we felt that this would be the next best thing.

Thus Project Nekton came to a successful finish. We had shown that our Navy is capable of investigating the ocean's floor, no matter what the depth; and we had discovered a great deal of useful scientific information to add to man's knowledge of the sea.

Manned vehicle exploration may prove to be the key to the solution of many of the mysteries of the sea. Newer vehicles are being planned and built, both in the United States and in Europe. These submersibles will be designed to perform different functions in accordance with the needs of the oceanographers, in that one type of craft such as the *Trieste* cannot satisfy all of their requirements. A family of vehicles will be needed to best perform the various missions. We know that the *Trieste* is a "Model T," but she is the best in the world at this time and will continue to be very useful for many years to come.

~~~~~~~~~~~~~~~

Jacques-Yves Cousteau:

46.   *DIVING SAUCER TAKES TO THE DEEP**

Soon we feel the chill and put on sweaters. And the saucer starts down once more.

Suddenly at the depth of 360 feet we become aware of something wrong. The saucer hits the bottom and stays there, sluggish. Then in the silence we hear bubbles! First a few. Then more, like water boiling in a kettle.

"The batteries again," we say, and look at each other. "Back to the surface," I order. "Drop the 50-pound navigation weight."

The saucer slowly rises above the bottom, while the sound of bubbles keeps increasing. The voltmeter swings often to zero, confirming a bad short circuit in the batteries. Inside them gas has developed, and the pressure has exploded the battery cases.

Falco turns to me with an alarming quietness. "Look, Commandant," he says. "We sink again."

Through the porthole I see that particles suspended in midwater move up, proving we go down. The bottom gets nearer.

I prefer to keep to myself the little ugly pinch I feel in my heart for a fraction of a second. Then reason and confidence come back. I cut the safety tape and turn the lever that releases the 330-pound emergency weight. There is not a noise, but immediately the saucer tilts its tail up about 30 degrees and rises swiftly, irresistibly to the surface.

"Falco," I say, "they don't expect us up so early. We might as well have a snack."

The chicken sandwiches and red wine, now that our emergency is over, taste superb.

* From *The National Geographic Magazine*, April, 1960, Volume 117, No. 4, Copyright © 1960 by National Geographic Society, Washington, D.C. Reprinted by permission of the publisher and the author.

The underwater exploits of French oceanographer Jacques-Yves Cousteau are manifold. In addition to designing the famed "saucer," he invented a process to use TV underwater, co-invented the aqualung, and was the first man to take color pictures underwater. He is the author of several books, including THE SILENT WORLD and THE LIVING SEA.

DENISE DIVES FOR 1,000-FOOT GOAL

We move into the Mediterranean off Corsica while *Denise's* batteries are being repaired. Then Falco and I go down again. "This time we shall try for 1,000 feet," I say.

Divers wave goodbye at 200 feet as we move down the steplike bottom. At 400 feet we settle on the edge of a steep incline for a careful check of our little craft.

The Falco pumps mercury forward, and the sub tilts 35 degrees. *Denise* motors off down the slope. Steadily our instruments mark the depth . . . 600 feet . . . 800 . . . 950. At 1,001 feet, there is a gentle bump; *Denise* touches bottom. At last she is where we want her!

The trip upward is breath-taking. We glide around huge rocks and cliff faces, their colors shining under our lamps. Four hours after setting out, we surface. Our trip is over. But it is only the beginning of explorations we know our jet sub will make.

〰〰〰〰〰〰〰〰

Willard Bascom:

47.   *PROJECT MOHOLE**

The National Science Foundation is responsible for managing the federal government's basic-research program. As a part of this it contributes to the financial support of scientific projects in universities and laboratories by means of grants and research contracts. In order to make sure that this money is utilized most effectively, panels of experts review the proposed research projects and recommend which ones should be supported.

In the spring of 1957 after two days of sitting around a table in Washington discussing requests for grants, the Earth Sciences review

* From Willard Bascom, A HOLE IN THE BOTTOM OF THE SEA, pp. 47–55. Copyright © 1961 by Willard Bascom. Reprinted by permission of Doubleday & Company, Inc. New York.

Willard Bascom is the president of Ocean Science and Engineering, Inc. From 1959 to 1962 he was director of the Mohole Project of the AMSOC Committee of the National Academy of Sciences.

panel adjourned with an air of mild discouragement. They had reviewed some sixty-five proposals, most of which were for small, desirable pieces of research. The projects were worthwhile and well thought out; each was proposed by a scientist of some stature in the field of geology-geophysics.

Why the discouragement? None of these attempted to courageously break through to a new ground on any of the most important problems of the earth sciences. While the proposals were by no means trivia, it did not appear likely that any major advance would be produced even if each were carried out to the complete satisfaction of its proponent. Two of the panel members, whom we met before while they were exploring the Pacific, were especially bothered by this. They were geologist Harry Hess and geophysicist Walter Munk and they asked themselves, "How could the earth sciences take a great stride forward?" Munk suggested that they should consider what project, regardless of cost, would do the most to open up new avenues of thought and research. He thought that the taking of a sample of the earth's mantle would be most significant.

They talked it over: "How do you sample the mantle? You drill a hole where it's closest to the surface. Like a deep oil-well hole. Perhaps on an island. Or under the ocean, if that is possible. This would be the perfect antianalogue of a space prove. Think of the attention it would attract to the earth sciences. Maybe we would get some support from the big oil companies."

These were brave bold words. The scope could not then be imagined but obviously such a project would be a heroic undertaking costing a large sum of money and requiring new techniques and monumental equipment. Their own grand ideas, so far from realization, made them a little self-conscious. Hess suggested that it be referred to the American Miscellaneous Society for action.

The following month, April of 1957, on a sunny Saturday morning in La Jolla, California, there was an informal breakfast meeting of the Society at Walter Munk's house. The agenda was, as always, diverse, but in time the talk turned to the suggestion for drilling to obtain a sample of the mantle. Curiously enough, none of those present were aware of the previous proposals by Jaggar, Ewing, or Estabrook, but oceanic drilling seemed like a fine idea. They talked of drilling to the Moho from an island—essentially a deepening of the old Eniwetok holes—and of the possibility of using a new technique, drilling from a floating vessel. They were not certain about the minimum depths to the Moho, or of the maximum depths that had been reached in the search for oil, so they could not even make a good guess whether or not such a hole was possible.

What they could do was talk about past experiences and who should be consulted and what such a hole might find.

Then they reviewed the history of scientific drilling on atolls and they thought about the men who had been involved in getting those holes drilled. The idea of a major effort to directly explore the deep rocks was appealing; maybe it would reach the mantle and revolutionize geological thinking about the nature of the deep rocks. The thing to do was to form a committee of the experienced scientists to look into the matter and see if such a hole were possible.

Gordon Lill, founder of AMSOC and head of the Geophysics Branch of ONR, was acclaimed chairman on the spot. In the best tradition of AMSOC Lill is able to see the lighter side of heavier problems but he took this assignment seriously. The rest of the group helped him pick the other members. They nominated those whose names have already been mentioned: Dr. Roger Revelle, Director of the Scripps Institution of Oceanography, who had worked to get the first holes drilled at Bikini; Drs. Joshua Tracey and Harry Ladd, geologist and paleontologist, respectively, with the U. S. Geological Survey who had supervised the Marshall Islands drilling. Dr. Walter Munk, Professor of Geophysics at the University of California, and Dr. Harry Hess, Professor of Geology at Princeton, originators of this version of Moho-drilling were of course included.

This was the special deep-drilling committee of AMSOC. In a way the formation of such a group was a meaningless gesture since there was no means of support in sight. Nevertheless the enthusiasm was great and the thought never occurred to those present that the proposed committee members might not want to participate—they were all personal friends; as soon as they heard the idea they would become enthusiasts. The question of where the money would come from to bring them together and make preliminary studies never arose; somehow it would be provided. The project sounded so simple and logical at a breakfast meeting on a sunny patio. The members lazily looked down a desert canyon at the sparkling Pacific below and felt pleased with the morning's work. The American Miscellaneous Society had its first "formal" committee: the Committee on Deep Drilling. That afternoon a delegation called on Roger Revelle to inform him about the grand new idea that had blossomed on his campus.

On April 27, back in Washington, the first meeting of the new committee was held at the Cosmos Club. By this time Dr. William Rubey of the U. S. Geological Survey, an expert on the history of the oceans, had been added; Dr. Maurice Ewing, who chanced to be passing by, was invited to join in the discussion and thus became a member. At a later meeting in 1957 Dr. Arthur Maxwell, Chief of Oceanography for the Office of Naval Research and expert on heat flow through the floor of the ocean, was added to the committee.

It was decided to ask the National Science Foundation for funds to make a feasibility study. With genteel horror that august organization declined, politely suggesting that such a distinguished group of scientists might be able to attach themselves to a more reliable group than the American Miscellaneous Society.

While this exchange was going on, the IUGG (International Union of Geodesy and Geophysics) met at Toronto, Canada. There, in several of the discussion groups, the subject of deep drilling arose again, prodded by AMSOC members and by Dr. Tom Gaskell, a British geophysicist. Finally on September 14, 1957, resolution number eleven was adopted:

The I.U.G.G.

Considering that the composition of the earth's mantle below the Mohorovičić discontinuity is one of the most important unsolved problems of geophysics.

And that, although seismic, gravity and magnetic observations have given significant indications of the nature of this material, actual samples that could be examined petrographically, physically and chemically are essential,

And that modern techniques of drilling deep wells are rapidly developing to the point where drilling a hole ten to fifteen kilometers deep on an oceanic island may well be feasible,

And that the crustal material above the Mohorovičić discontinuity is also of prime interest

Urges the nations of the world and especially those experienced in deep drilling to study the feasibility and cost of an attempt to drill to the Mohorovičić discontinuity at a place where it approaches the surface.

During the discussion from the floor of the Toronto resolution, a Soviet scientist arose and said, "We already have the equipment to drill such a hole, we are now looking for the place." By the following September the Soviet Academy of Sciences was rumored to have appointed its equivalent of a deep-drilling committee.

The IUGG resolution made everybody feel better because once the idea had received the stamp of international approval there were fewer snickers when the subject of drilling to the Moho was mentioned. It was also useful because the Russian's remark had pricked the pride of the U.S. oil industry. "Anything they can do we can do better" was the instant reply and before long a group of Texas oilmen held a meeting to ask themselves critically, "What are the limits on deep drilling?"

On December 6, 1957, the next meeting of the AMSOC Committee was held at Dr. William Rubey's house in Washington. One government agency, jittery in the uproar over the recent Russian success in launching the first satellite and sensitive to the remarks at Toronto about their deep-drilling abilities, actually stationed a security guard around the house, presumably to protect whatever advantage the United States might have in a drilling race. However, since that time no AMSOC meeting has been so honored and no part of the project has ever had a security classification.

At this meeting there were some new faces present, including Texas oil operator John Mecom, who was then co-holder of the world's record for deep drilling, with a hole called the LL & E which had reached 22,570 feet in a Louisiana bayou. Those present decided that the problem of drilling to the mantle should be broken down into three parts: (1) a "practice" hole on the continent to 35,000 feet (an idea that was soon discarded), (2) a "sedimentary-section" hole in the deep ocean basin, (3) a mantle hole beneath the ocean.

No one was sure whether or not some form of the floating platforms that were used for offshore oil drilling could be used in deep water but all felt that if they could the Moho was within reach— somehow, somewhere. For by then the geophysicists had located sites where the Moho was only 30 percent deeper than the LL & E. Two days later Harry Hess, chairman of the Earth Sciences Division of the National Academy of Sciences, appeared before the Academy's governing board to ask that the Academy take the deep-drilling committee under its wing. As he put it:

"The American Miscellaneous Society has no officers, no constitution, no bylaws and consequently can act expeditiously when action is appropriate. It is an organization which warrants respect; note that five of its nine-man committee are members of the Academy [Ewing, Rubey, Revelle, Munk, Hess]. Its present organization is not such that it can accept funds from the National Science Foundation and therefore it comes to the Academy-Research Council for sponsorship. Our division strongly recommends that the academy take over the entire committee as is and accept up to $50,000 in funds to study the feasibility of the project."

Professor I. I. Rabi, Nobel laureate on the board, remarked dryly,

"Thank God we're finally talking about something besides space." And with that the American Miscellaneous Society's deep-drilling committee became the AMSOC Committee of the National Academy of Sciences, the letters no longer representing anything but a memory as far as the Academy is concerned.

The National Academy of Sciences is a private organization of distinguished scientists dedicated to the furtherance of science for human welfare. Election to membership in the Academy is considered to be one of the highest honors that can be visited on a scientist, for it is awarded solely on the basis of distinguished achievement in original research. The Academy was established in 1863 under a Congressional charter signed by President Lincoln and is required by that charter to act as an advisor to the federal government on scientific matters. It receives funds from both public and private sources to stimulate and promote the interests of science. In order to enable scientists generally to associate themselves with the work of the Academy, a working organization known as the National Research Council was set up by means of which thousands of scientists and engineers can participate in the Academy's work by serving on its various boards and committees. The AMSOC committee is one such committee in the NAS-NRC division of Earth Sciences. It was a big step upward for AMSOC's committee to be taken into the Academy-Research Council organization for it gave formal recognition to the idea of drilling deep into the earth for scientific purposes.

The year 1957 was the International Geophysical year and I had spent most of it in Tahiti and the South Seas installing ocean-wave measuring instruments. But luckily, I had returned to the Academy the week before it accepted the AMSOC Committee and, on hearing what had happened while I was away, became an enthusiastic advocate of oceanic drilling. I vowed to become associated with the project somehow and before long was invited to become its part-time executive secretary.

In April of 1958 a form letter was sent out by Dr. William R. Thurston, executive secretary of the Earth Sciences Division of the National Academy of Sciences to nearly two hundred scientists who were planning to be in Washington for the annual meeting of the American Geophysical Union. It invited "knowledgeable friends of the division—to a meeting in the Academy's Great Hall—preparatory to conducting a study to determine the feasibility of drilling to the Mohorovičić discontinuity." The meeting was intended to lay the idea before the men who would be most interested in the scientific results and to develop a broad base of support.

So it was that on the afternoon of April 26, 1958, many of the leaders of geophysics in the United States were arrayed around a square of tables that had been set up in the Great Hall. Presiding was Harry Hess, sponsor, AMSOC founder, and chairman of the Earth Sciences Division. AMSOC chairman Gordon Lill began by describing the plan as it was then conceived, but he barely was able to enumerate the main advantages of the Mohole project to geophysics before unexpected opposition developed and a three-point salvo was fired. The objectors said, in effect: You won't prove anything! You shouldn't do it! You can't do it! But the proponents were ready and a scientific battle began which went something like this:

"What good will it do to get a single sample of the mantle? The material beneath the Moho is probably not homogeneous and one sample cannot be expected to be representative. It might throw us off the track for years; ten or even a hundred holes may be needed before we will know what the mantle is made of."

To which Harry Hess answered, "Perhaps it is true that we won't find out as much about the earth's interior from one hole as we hope. To those who raise that objection I say, if there is not a first hole, there cannot be a second or a tenth of a hundredth hole. We must make a beginning."

The second objection dealt with money: "This project will cost many millions of dollars—you cannot even estimate how much. If it is paid for out of geophysical research money it will strip all other projects of funds for years. If that amount of money were divided up among the existing institutions, we would all be able to do more and better geophysics."

Now the fact is that most large new scientific projects are carried on essentially independently of previously existing efforts. They do not strip established laboratories of funds; on the contrary they attract students and money to the particular field of endeavor so that in the end all the scientists in it are benefited. But Roger Revelle gave a much better answer when he said, "I imagine that an argument like that was used against Columbus when he asked Queen Isabella for funds for his adventurous project. One of the Queen's advisors probably stepped forward and said, 'Your Majesty, it won't be important even if this crazy Italian does reach India by sailing west. Why not put the same amount of money into new sails and better rigging on all the other ships? Then the whole fleet will be able to sail half a knot faster!'" This devastating analogy silenced that part of the opposition.

The third objection was: "It's impossible to drill a hole in the bottom of the ocean in the foreseeable future. Nobody has any idea how it can be done. Why doesn't AMSOC forget about oceanic drilling until it has done some research on deep-drilling techniques on land? Perhaps after a few years work on metallurgical and mechanical developments, better machines and materials will be available that will be capable of drilling to the Moho on land through miles of hot rocks."

The answer to this was given by A. J. Field, an engineer from the Union Oil Company, who showed movies of the ship *Cuss I* (a name compounded from the initials of the oil companies who owned it—Continental, Union, Shell, Superior) drilling an oil well at sea off the California coast in two hundred feet of water with a full-sized oil-drilling rig. Admittedly the ship was a long way from being capable of drilling to the Moho, but it demonstrated new possibilities to every man present. Almost until that moment the capabilities of floating drilling platforms had been kept closely guarded commercial secrets and virtually no one present had seen or even heard of such equipment before. But now they could see a new sort of tool which looked as though it could be developed into the first deep-sea drilling rig. A wave of enthusiasm went through the audience and they saw the project in a new light. If American technology could go this far it could drill to the Moho. Why not? In fact the *Cuss* itself looked as if it could be used without major changes to drill shallow holes and sample the upper part of the sedimentary layers of the sea floor.

By the time most of those who had been on the fence were persuaded that the deep-drilling project was a better idea than it had at first seemed and a vote was taken on the resolution "The project as outlined by Gordon Lill is approved." It carried unanimously.

Under the aegis of the Academy and with the support of geophysicists generally it was not long before a grant of $15,000 was received from the National Science Foundation as a down payment on a feasibility study. Thus it was that the idea, the scientists, the Academy, and the money all came together.

The feasibility study began at once. We looked into various possible sites in both Atlantic and Pacific; we persuaded the office of Naval Research to sponsor site surveys; we examined nearly all the floating drilling vessels in the world. Behind the scenes things were proceeding nicely, but by October the committee was becoming disturbed about the misinformation reaching the public. Rumors were flying which made it sound more like science fiction than science: The hole would have to be at least ten miles deep; the rock at the bottom would be too hot to permit any ordinary kind of drilling; the project would cost hundreds of millions of dollars, and so on.

It was decided to scotch these wild rumors with a complete public statement, for by then possibilities had narrowed and thoughts on how the work should proceed were more orderly. At least the committee could say with reasonable certainty what the scientific objectives were, which drilling sites seemed the most promising, and what kind of equipment might be used. The result was an article in the *Scientific American* (April 1959) entitled "The Mohole," which summarized our thinking.

The Mohole story—which first used that word—was treated as news and the material in it was widely reprinted. It triggered an outburst of comment and reaction.

Industrial interest was immediate and widespread. Oil companies became worried that we might find oil beneath the sea and upset the economics of that business. Drilling companies wanted contracts. Tool and machinery companies called to explain how their equipment would solve our problems. But for each company who wanted something from us there were two others who wanted to give us something just so they could become involved in the project.

The fame of the Mohole spread abroad and before long a letter was received from Stjepan Mohorovičić, a retired professor of geophysics at the University of Zagreb and son of the discoverer of the seismic discontinuity. He had heard about the project on the Voice of America and sent us some photos and personal data on his father.

At this time the implications of the undertaking just began to be understood by the remainder of the scientific community outside the geological sciences. The workers in these other fields had adjusted to satellites—and gladly accepted the boost the Russian Sputnik gave to public interest in all forms of American science. The Mohole project might achieve a similar result.

Most scientists hoped that AMSOC was right and that it would be able to sample the earth's history and interior with a hole in the sea floor—yet they retained their normal skepticism. Few could refrain from making jokes—both erudite and crude—about what would happen when the crust was penetrated. Our friends were sarcastic but fascinated, snide but envious. The 1960 Pick and Hammer show —an annual musical mockery of the Washington Geological Society —was entitled "Mo-Ho-Ho and a Barrel of Funds." Its hero, Glib Bunkum, uses a posthole digger in the bottom of the ocean while the chorus sings about drilling to the Moho.

~~~~~~~~~~

Edward L. Beach:

48.   THE VOYAGE OF THE TRITON*

The sealed-ship test, by design, had been scheduled to terminate on Sunday, the twenty-fourth of April. It would be a good way to finish off the circumnavigation, Will Adams had suggested, to give us something to think about during the last few days.

But on Sunday, as we resumed normal daily ventilation, I, for one, found it hard to keep from feeling a tingling excitement. Tomorrow, Monday, the twenty-fifth of April, we would have completed the first of our missions. With the return to St. Peter and St. Paul's Rocks, carefully passing on the *western* side this time, *Triton* would become the first ship to accomplish the submariner's dream of traveling, entirely submerged, completely around the world.

It would be on the sixtieth day of the circumnavigation, by our reckoning, but a man perched on the Rocks would have counted the sunrise sixty-one times; for we had lost a day by making the circuit in a westerly direction, following the sun.

On the other hand, we had been forced to set our ship's clocks back one hour twenty-three times. Twenty-three of our days had thus been twenty-five hours in length (the shift to daylight saving time had also occurred, and the twenty-fourth extra hour would be returned to us in October).

The last several weeks of our trip had been singularly free from malfunction of any parts of the ship. It seemed as though we had finally shaken most of the bugs out. As events were shortly to prove, however, our travail might have been almost over—but it was not yet, quite.

* From AROUND THE WORLD SUBMERGED by Captain Edward L. Beach, U.S.N. Copyright © 1962 by Edward L. Beach. Reprinted by permission of Holt, Rinehart and Winston, Inc.

Edward L. Beach was the commanding officer of the U.S.S. *Triton* when it completed the first submerged circumnavigation of the world. For his distinguished service as a U.S. naval officer, he has received numerous medals and awards.

From the Log:

24 April 1960, Sunday 2001 Serious casualty in the after torpedo room. The manner in which this develops is illustrative of a point many naval officers are fond of making—there is no sudden alarm, no quick scurry of many people carrying out an expected drill. By the time anyone in authority even knew what had happened, the need for alarm was past. There was left only the correction of the trouble and clean up of the mess, which took some time. What took place is instructive:

The torpedoman on "Room Watch" in the after torpedo room, Allen W. Steele, TM3 (who had only last night been notified of his prospective advancement to Second Class), heard a loud report, nearly like an explosion as he later described it, followed by a heavy spraying noise. Turning, he saw clouds of oil vapor issuing from beneath the deck plates forward on the starboard side. Instantly realizing that this was serious trouble, Steele called the control room on the 7MC announcing system and reported a heavy hydraulic oil leak in the stern plane mechanism; then he plunged into the hydrant stream of oil hoping to find the leak and isolate it.

In the control room, Lt. Rubb was starting to make the necessary preparations to bring the ship to periscope depth. His first indication of trouble came when Raymond J. Comeau, Electrician's Mate Second Class, at the stern plane controls, noticed failure to respond to a small movement of his control arm, and called out in a voice edged with concern, "The stern planes are not working right, sir!" At nearly the same moment, the report of a large hydraulic leak in the after torpedo room was received from Steele.

"Whitey" Rubb's action was the one for which we have trained many times: "Shift to Emergency!" Comeau threw a single toggle switch, tested controls and reported them satisfactory. This restored control of the ship, but it did not solve the basic difficulty [the quickness with which this action was taken is demonstrated by the fact that planes and rudder automatically switch to emergency power if the pressure in the main system falls to 1000 lbs; this had not yet occurred].

In the after torpedo room, Steele determined the leak to be in the stern planes' normal power-hydraulic system, and correctly diagnosed it as a massive hydraulic failure. His third immediate decision was also a correct one. Diving into the midst of the high-pressure spray, he reached the two quick-closing valves to the supply and return pipes and shut them. One came shut easily but the other, in the center of the 3000 lbs-per-square-inch oil spray, was very difficult to move because of the pressure unbalance across its seat and an extremely slippery handle. Desperately struggling with the valve, and aided by Arlan F. Martin, Engineman Third Class, who ran to his aid, Steele finally got it also shut. By this time, fifteen to thirty seconds after the onset of the leak, the entire after part of the compartment was filled with oil vapor and visibility was reduced to only a few feet. The fumes were choking; an explosive mixture undoubtedly existed.

With the closing of the isolation valves, the oil flow stopped immediately. Estimates later were that approximately 30 gallons of hydraulic oil had been lost into the after torpedo room bilges out of a 120-gallon system pressurized to 3000 lbs per square inch. Had Steele's action not been so instantaneous and so precisely correct, complete loss of the ship's main hydraulic system must inevitably have happened within a few seconds more. This would have caused a momentary loss of all diving plane control and steering as well. Even with automatic shift to "emergency control," the ship's high speed at the time does not permit this possibility to be viewed other than with deepest concern.

Personnel who behaved with credit were Arlan F. Martin, Engineman Third Class, who ran to Steele's assistance and participated with him in shutting the last and most difficult of the two hydraulic cutoff valves, and Ronald Dale Kettlehake, who had just entered the compartment in process of tracing some system required for submarine qualification. Realizing the possible danger to personnel from the oil spray which was rapidly fogging the atmosphere, he showed presence of mind by waking the dozen or more sleepers and routing them forward into the after engine room.

2002 Things had been happening so swiftly that the first anyone other than those dealing with it knew of the casualty was when Rubb ordered "Smoking lamp out!" "Rig after torpedo room for emergency ventilation." There had been no confusion, no warning, not even any raised voices. Tom Thamm, our Damage Control Officer, quickly got to his feet and strode purposefully aft, followed by Jim Hay, his assistant.

2030 This is far from a pleasant casualty to think about. It should never happen. Our preliminary investigation disclosed that the stern plane control valve, located just underneath the floor plates in the after torpedo room, had broken right through its body at one of the flanged joints. There had been no warning of any kind. The cause may possibly stem from excessive flexing and metal fatigue or from a faulty forging. It will undoubtedly be carefully investigated by qualified metallurgists and design personnel. In *Triton,* this control valve handles hydraulic oil at 3000 lbs pressure in lines 2½ inches in diameter. Steele's swift and decisive action is living proof that if you train for every possible type of casualty, there is a good chance that you can also control the few impossible ones that happen anyway.

Steele has been recommended to receive the Secretary of the Navy Letter of Commendation with Commendation Ribbon for meritorious service. We are preparing the papers now.

2130 Everything is pretty much back to normal so far as the after torpedo room and the hydraulic system is concerned, except that we are still in "emergency" on the planes and shall have to remain so until a replacement is found for the fractured control valve. It turns out there are no spares in stock, and it will be necessary to steal a valve from another system. After due consideration, even this presents no choice; the only hydraulic system in the ship which has an adequately large control valve is the steering system. Steering from now on will have to be in emergency; but after the exchange has been made, we shall have normal stern plane control.

Monday, 25 April 1960 0432 Normal power is restored to the stern planes. The main hydraulic system is back in full commission with a control valve stolen from the steering system. Steering is permanently in "emergency."

0754 Crossed equator for the fourth and final time this cruise at longitude 28°—03′ West.

1200 Position 00°–53′ North, 29°–01′ West. We are within a few miles of St. Peter and St. Paul's Rocks, at which point we will have completed the first submerged circumnavigation of the world.

1330 St. Peter and St. Paul's Rocks in sight, bearing due west.

1500 First submerged circumnavigation of the world is now complete.

We are circling and photographing the islet again, as we did just two months ago. The weather is nice and the sun is shining brightly. Our mileage [Rock to Rock] is 26,723 nautical miles and it has taken us 60 days and 21 hours [days calculated at twenty-four hours each]. Dividing gives an average overall speed of just over 18 knots. No other ship—and no other crew—could have done better. We are proud to have been selected to accomplish this undertaking for our nation.

Our total mileage for the trip will be a little more than 36,000 nautical miles [including the two thousand-mile mercy mission for Poole], and it now looks as though our overall time since departure from New London will be 85 days [New London computation].

We have been instructed to proceed to a rendezvous point off Cadiz, Spain, where the destroyer *Weeks* is to meet us. *Weeks* will send aboard the completed bronze plaque we designed in tribute to Magellan, but it is our understanding it is to be presented at a later date, possibly by the US ambassador. For the time being we are to avoid detection, making our rendezvous off Cadiz beyond sight of curious onlookers.

John B. Hersey:

49. THRESHER SEARCH*

At two o'clock in the morning on April 11, 1963, I was awakened from a sound sleep by the jangling ring of the telephone. It was A. C. Vine who told me that the Navy had decided that the nuclear submarine U.S.S. *Thresher* (SSN 593) had been lost during a post-repair test dive in the deep water east of Georges Bank. Later that morning we learned of strenuous operations near the last known position of *Thresher*, which were proceeding in hope of finding a disabled submarine. As such hopes disappeared a determination built up to find the *Thresher* so as to learn the cause of the disaster. The seagoing laboratories engaged in research for the Navy quickly offered their services through a meeting of laboratory directors which happened to be convened that day at the Naval Research Laboratory in Anacostia, D. C. We also happened to have a ship at sea nearest the search area. *Atlantis II* was just starting her second cruise. N. Corwin was in charge and the program was to collect a series of water samples and biological collections south from Halifax, N. S. Dr. Fye requested Captain Hiller of *Atlantis II* to break off the program and proceed at once to render all possible assistance in the search.

There followed several days of intensive planning and organizing. Mr. Corwin's group was well able to cope with analyzing water samples for telltale traces of radioactive materials, but they are

* From *Oceanus*, Vol. X, No. 1, September, 1963. Reprinted by permission of the publisher.

John Brackett Hersey is a geophysicist with the Office of Naval Research, Washington, D.C. The above article was written when Dr. Hersey was Head of the Department of Geophysics at the Woods Hole Oceanographic Institution.

somewhat allergic to electronic devices such as our special echo sounder, the Precision Graphic Recorder (or PGR), which was an obvious, available search tool. However, they did get a rudimentary system working. Consequently, S. T. Knott, one of the PGR's chief co-designers, with a supporting team from the Geophysics Department were taken aboard the U.S.S. *Hazelwood* (DD 531) from Newport to join *Atlantis II*.

In early April the weather east of Georges is not apt to be calm, but when Knott and his team arrived a proper gale was in progress. After two days they were able to board the *Atlantis II* by high line. Before the *Hazelwood* sailed a plan had been advanced to bring the bathyscaphe *Trieste* from the Naval Electronics Laboratory, San Diego to help in the search. The *Trieste*, which descended to the bottom of the Marianas Trench, east of Guam, seemed a logical means of observing directly the hulk of *Thresher*, and the most sanguine hope of determining the cause of the disaster. But the *Trieste* has little speed (maximum of 1.5 knots) to compete with strong currents. Hence it was immediately important to know the deep currents in this area: were they small, say one or two tenths of a knot, or a knot or more? We didn't know. J. Bruce went out on the *Hazelwood*, staying aboard her long enough to get a reference buoy close to the last known position of *Thresher*— thereby also judging the strength and direction of the surface currents.

The biologists on *Atlantis II* took water samples for radioactive determinations, measured temperature and salinity of the water to determine the current pattern and even improvised a coring tool to sample the bottom sediments. With the PGR team on board, *Atlantis II* participated with three Naval ships in the first systematic bathymetric (echo-sounding) survey of the ten mile square centered about the last known position of *Thresher*.[1] After this work, it seemed wise for *Atlantis II* to return to Woods Hole to be more properly fitted out for the search.

Meanwhile in Washington, the Chief of Naval Operations had requested an ad-hoc group of scientists to serve as the Technical Advisory Committee for the *Thresher* search (the author is the Institution representative on this committee). A few days later the Secretary of the Navy requested Admiral Stephan, USN (Ret.) until recently the Navy's Oceanographer, to serve as the chairman of a study group to look into the broader problems of search and salvage operations in the deep ocean. Mr. A. C. Vine was requested by Admiral Stephan to serve as a member of this group. The first of

[1] See "Thresher Search", *Oceanus*, Vol. IX, No. 4.

these committees had an immediate operational problem: find the *Thresher*. Despite the hard fact that there was left no hope of rescue still almost the same sense of urgency pervaded planning and preparing for the search operations. What could Woods Hole contribute? Our ship schedules are always tight and this spring seemed tighter than usual. *Chain* was thousands of miles away in tropical Atlantic waters. *Atlantis II* was closely scheduled for geophysical research north of Puerto Rico. There was the biological cruise that had been broken off when *Thresher* sank, and, finally, the completion of *Atlantis II* had been timed to get her to the Indian Ocean in time to observe the after effects of the shift from the dry monsoons to the wet monsoons; a weather phenomenon unique to the Indian Ocean. This shift occurs in mid-June. The ship had to be there as early as possible in July—early August at the latest.

During intense sessions we decided that the biologists would have to wait and complete their work after *Chain* returned home. This gave us a week when the *Atlantis II* could search for *Thresher*. Possibly this might be all the time necessary. We would wait and see, but we doubted *Atlantis II* could be made available for more time. In any event we prepared by assembling all the experienced seagoing talent that was available at Woods Hole. We also invited assistance from both the Schlumberger Oil Well Surveying Company and Knowles Electric Laboratories, both to assist in radioactive detection measurements. Schlumberger proposed using an electrical self potential measuring detector (SP) which their parent company, a French concern, had used with great success to find sunken metallic objects, including a French submarine. At Woods Hole the PGR's were refurbished, W. Dow prepared a self-contained suspended echo sounder for use as a deep echo-ranging device. A. Johnston prepared our underwater cameras. R. M. Snyder and G. L. Erlanger prepared current meters and buoys for continuing study of the deep currents.

The previous cruise had shown the need for good navigational data. We attempted to make this possible by installing both Loran C and a Decca Navigator, the Sperry Rand Corporation and the Decca Company furnished a specialist each to tend these two instruments and assure their successful operation. Their help proved invaluable.

Knott had found one indication in his previous survey that could be the hulk of *Thresher* resting on the bottom. All were agreed that *Atlantis II* should concentrate on evaluating this target. We departed on April 21st and arrived in the search area to find another gale. We did some echo sounding, but otherwise, hanging on was all we could do for the next three days. During the echo sounding we re-discovered the "bump" that Knott had found (by then it was known officially as contact "Delta"). We pushed our navigation systems to the limit and managed to show that Delta was small enough to qualify as a possible *Thresher*. We planted the current buoys. Between that work and the gale and the time required to learn how to use navigational tools, the week was nearly spent. We had time for a few inspections by the underwater camera in the "Delta" area. These revealed animal tracks in a muddy bottom, sea urchins, starfish, brittle stars, and an occasional fish as the only evidence of life, but did show that good photographs could be made in the area. Hence it seemed worthwhile to develop the photographic or visual search. After returning to Woods Hole the decision was made to extend the participation of *Atlantis II* in the search, since by rescheduling *Chain* after her return from the equator she could assume part of the work previously scheduled for our new ship. Preparations were based on the lessons learned during the previous week of operations. S. L. Stillman built a huge framework for mounting not only the lights and cameras but also an echo ranging set converted from Dow's inverted echo sounder. The Schlumberger radioactive detector and the SP gear were added as well. In about five days *Atlantis II* returned to sea. E. E. Hays led the group for a week, then Dow, and finally Knott. The echo ranging set worked well and it seemed to form an effective partnership with the SP gear. Unfortunately we had no magnetometer, but other groups were preparing at least two; thus, this means of searching was not to be neglected.

At the end of this two-week cruise Knott made two long drifting runs with the whole set of detectors mounted on Stillman's framework (the frame and its instruments were soon dubbed the "Beast"). At this time L. Baxter and Knott put into use a means of locating the lowered equipment relative to the ship's position. They then returned to Woods Hole, tidying up the ship as they went.

A. Johnston was developing the last set of negatives. He had developed literally thousands of bottom photographs during the two weeks. Although ordinarily an optimist, he was no longer expecting much from those films—"say, what was *that?*" It looked exactly like a crumpled piece of stationery,—and this; surely this has the look of a crumpled sheet of metal. And there are more of the same. "Maybe some of these had better be enlarged before we reach Woods Hole!" The enlargements confirmed Johnston's suspicions, and the whole roll of 500 negatives showed an area nearly one tenth of a mile across strewn with paper, crumpled sheet metal, torn lengths of electrical cable, and many artifacts impossible to identify. Clearly this could be debris dropped by *Thresher* as she

sank—but it could also be refuse thrown over by a passing ship.
Knott radioed Woods Hole to make sure that I would meet his
ship on her return. Something about the way he asked the question
made me call Dr. Fye and E. E. Hays, suggesting that we meet the
Atlantis II in Nantucket Sound. With those on board we inspected photographs, shared doubts, and tried to check quick conclusions. In this we were fortunate because, although public interest
was high, we were by ourselves and able to think, to doubt, to
question, and to examine the logical consequences of the most
optimistic guesses without our thoughts going farther than the group
on board. Later during the *Thresher* search such freedom frequently was not to be had. Following an intensive study of the
photographs with the Thresher Technical Analysis Group, then
stationed at Woods Hole, we concluded that the paper, metal, and
other debris were very likely from the *Thresher*. Now, although
we felt the pressure of *Atlantis II*'s schedule, we also were compelled to follow this lead in the hope of bringing the search to a
successful conclusion. So yet another week of work was scheduled
and again Knott led a group on *Atlantis II*. They made many
camera, echo ranging, and SP sweeps over the search area near the
debris (which was found due north and near the Delta contact).
They photographed more debris, and developed possible echo-ranging and SP contact. Although the time was short, other laboratories were now assisting. R. S. Gerard of Lamont Geological
Observatory dredged some O-ring gaskets which might well have
come from *Thresher*. Not to be outdone, F. R. Hess on *Atlantis
II* improvised a dredge which recovered large quantities of rock—
and a piece from a lead acid battery plate of a type used only on
nuclear submarines. At the end of the fifth week of search, (May
21–27), the trail looked hot. But the achievements were by accumulation, not in any one quick, clever thrust. This was our last
week of direct participation at sea since the *Atlantis II* simply
had to be released for other commitments. She had played her
part well.

Shortly thereafter the Thresher Analysis Group, which had been
our guests since early April, departed for Hudson Laboratories, to
continue the analysis of all evidence bearing on the *Thresher*
search. We had defined the area strewn with small debris. The
Lamont group and NRL photographed large objects which probably came from *Thresher*. The bathyscaphe *Trieste* completed
several dives on the scene adding significantly to the mounting
evidence. Magnetometer surveys have been made by three laboratories.

Throughout all of this work no need has been more obvious than that for reliable, precise navigational control, both for ships and for instruments or submarine searching near the ocean floor. As this is being written *Chain* is returning from a ten-day cruise spent testing a navigational aid for the *Thresher* search. This is an anchored sonobuoy having the hydrophone near the bottom and feeding into a radio sender at the surface over a long cable. Such a system should provide precise positioning. The first test was successful, but improvements need to be made. In addition we extended our previous camera and SP surveys. From our studies we now conclude Contact "Delta" is not *Thresher* nor any other large metallic object, but we still don't know what it is. Probably a large boulder. We have learned a great deal about how to locate instruments suspended near the bottom by long cables. We have even made schemes operational that give us the position of our camera so quickly (by means of a digital computer on board *Chain*) that we can maneuver the ship to guide the camera where we want it to go and know almost immediately whether it so went. We did photograph some more debris, but not necessarily from *Thresher*.

We have learned much about deliberate search in the deep sea, about precise navigating and even controlling the position of suspended instruments. These advances will be most useful in our scientific research, and they will also be particularly useful in advancing deep-sea engineering.

~~~~~~~~~~~~~~~~

Bernard D. Zetler:

50.   *TSUNAMIS AND THE SEISMIC SEA WAVE WARNING SYSTEM**

Mariners, perhaps more than men of any other profession, distinguish themselves by their ability to utilize the elements. However, while sailing through favorable currents and fair winds, the mariner has learned to keep a weather eye cocked for the caprices of nature.

* From *Mariners Weather Log*, Vol. 9, No. 5, September, 1965, pp. 149–152. "The Seismic Sea Wave Warning System, An Aid to Mariners" by Bernard D. Zetler. Reprinted by permission of the author.

Bernard D. Zetler is Acting Director of the Physical Oceanography Laboratory of the Environmental Science Services Administration.

Nature does indeed like to play tricks on occasion and two of her favorite "Sunday punches" are the hurricane and the seismic sea wave. The latter is popularly known as a "tidal wave," a term scientists dislike because the wave results from an underwater earthquake and is completely unrelated to the tide. The mariner frequently seeks the shelter of a port during a hurricane whereas he heads for safety on the high seas when warned that a seismic sea wave is coming. The Japanese word for the seismic sea wave, tsunami, is very descriptive. "Tsu" means port and "nami" wave, the combination describing a wave that is dangerous only in port.

Long before meteorologists learned to track hurricanes, seasoned mariners developed a technique for anticipating their coming. Ground swells, increasing seas, falling barometer, and shifting winds telegraphed a stream of evidence, sometimes days in advance of the most destructive portion of the hurricane. When a port was inaccessible or threatened directly by a hurricane, they maneuvered for a favorable position relative to the "eye" and for additional sea room.

The seismic sea wave, however, does not telegraph its punch nor is there ordinarily a cushion of time for deliberation. Indeed, although seismic sea waves have been with us as long as recorded history, only within the past 18 yr. has a method of warning been developed. When there is a warning of an impending tsunami, ships leave port to go out to sea and those about to enter a port are instructed to wait outside the harbor. On the open sea the waves are very long, possibly 100 mi. or more, and are only about 1 ft. high. Consequently, not only are they no menace to ships, they are not even noticeable.

During a seismic sea wave alert, ships do not have to move far out to sea to avoid the destructive part of a tsunami. The master of a ship lying off Hilo during the destructive wave of April 1, 1946 reported he could see heavy waves breaking on shore while experiencing no extraordinary waves on the ship. The log of the S.S. *Lurline* on March 9, 1957 shows that she put to sea from Honolulu on receiving a warning of an impending tsunami. Despite the fact that the *Lurline* waited at a distance of only 2 mi. off the entrance to the harbor, she apparently experienced no difficulty. At the same time a submarine, the U.S.S. *Wahoo*, expecting small waves, left dockside to ride them out in the harbor of Nawiliwili, Kauai. Rapid water-level changes of 10 ft. and more caused the small funnel-shaped harbor to be alternately drained and refilled. A giant whirlpool action (about 300 yd. in diameter) was set up in the basin. The turbulence was so strong that in spite of a maximum twisting combination (by using right full rudder with the starboard engine at Back Emergency and the port engine at Ahead Flank), the ship's head changed at least 50 degrees in the opposite direction. With flank speed of 15 kt., the *Wahoo* at times had sternway (moved backwards). The commanding officer of the submarine, reporting on the maneuvering, said that in his opinion the worst possible place would have been alongside a dock as it was unlikely that mooring lines could be tended during a 10- to 12-ft. change in depth of water.

Ancient history contains numerous references to destructive waves that appear to have been seismic sea waves. Eyewitness accounts usually describe the seas receding suddenly, leaving vessels stranded on the newly exposed sea bottom. Then there follows a mighty wave roaring in from the sea, smashing upset ships before it and carrying surviving vessels thousands of feet onto the shore, and leaving them high and dry. Frequently there are a series of waves lasting over a period of hours. Particularly frustrating to the medieval seaman must have been the complete absence of advance notice, for this could occur in fair weather with the sea as calm as the proverbial millpond immediately before the first wave.

On April 1, 1946 the seas suddenly receded in Hilo Harbor in Hawaii and then returned, smashing the waterfront, claiming many lives, and causing millions of dollars of damage. Man had learned to identify this as a seismic sea wave and knew it was caused by an underwater earthquake somewhere in the Pacific. As photographic seismograph records were developed many hours or days later, it became clear that the epicenter was located about 2,000 mi. to the north in the Aleutian Trench, a deep canyon running east and west immediately south of the Aleutian Islands.

Oceanographers had also learned by then that these waves move across the ocean at speeds up to 500 m.p.h. and that the speed increases with depth. As reports came in, it became clear that the wave had reached the Pacific coast of South America and had inflicted damage in various areas throughout the Pacific.

Shortly after the 1946 seismic sea wave, seismologists and oceanographers in the U. S. Coast and Geodetic Survey joined in an effort to formulate a warning system. There were many problems. A seismograph with a visible record and a warning signal to announce large earthquakes was invented. A technique for calculating wave speed was developed so that accurate arrival times of the tsunami could be computed. Although earthquakes occur frequently, destructive seismic sea waves are not always generated by them. A system of reporting tide stations was set up to establish the existence of a seismic sea wave. These are necessary as the seismological records are not sufficient to determine this condition. There are many earthquakes, few tsunamis. Therefore at least one report based on visual evidence from a tide station is necessary before a warning is disseminated. This required an umbrella of tide stations in all possible directions from the Hawaiian Islands to insure that one or more tide stations would lie in the path of a wave en route to the Islands. With seismic sea waves moving at such terrific speeds (the travel time of a wave from the Aleutian Trench to Hawaii requires only 4-½hr.), high speed communication facilities between the Coast and Geodetic Survey's Honolulu Observatory (the center of the system during an alert) and the seismological and tide stations were an absolute necessity. The Defense Department and the Civil Aeronautics Administration (now FAA) cooperated to the fullest extent, assigning high priorities to the transmission of warning messages during an alert.

The available communication centers near some of our tide stations are manned only during certain scheduled hours, making these tide stations undependable sources of information as messages are not received at all hours. Oceanographers in the Coast Survey developed a seismic sea wave detector, (Figure 50–1) a mechanical device using pressure chambers in tide wells at these stations to filter out both short period wind waves and the gradual rise and fall of the tide. The detector sounds an alarm when sea level rises or falls rapidly during an intermediate period of from a few minutes to an hour, roughly the period of a seismic sea wave. When the alarm sounds, the tide observer can contact the communication facility and initiate a message even though he has not heard from the Honolulu Observatory.

By 1948 the Coast and Geodetic Survey had an operating warning system designed to protect the Hawaiian Islands. Those who worked on it had their fingers crossed, for they knew that in announcing the service, they were accepting a fearful responsibility. Yet this warning system was built on a negligible budget with instrumentation developed internally and dependent on the devotion to service and good-will of men in various portions of the Pacific over whom they had little or no control.

The warning system has expanded greatly from its original design to protect the Hawaiian Islands. Many countries bordering the Pacific and various islands in the Pacific are now receiving the warning services. In April of this year, 12 countries (Canada, Chile, Republic of China, France, Japan, Mexico, New Zealand, Peru, Republic of the Philippines, United States of America, USSR, and

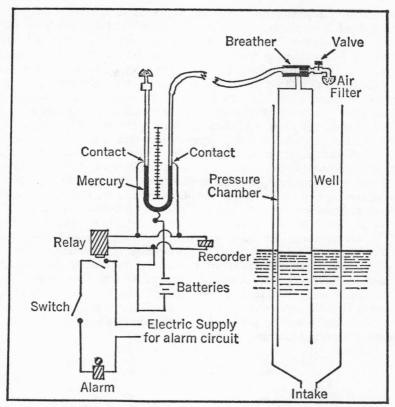

Fig. 50–1. Seismic sea wave detector.

Western Samoa) sent official delegations to a meeting in Honolulu on the international aspects of the tsunami warning system in the Pacific. Improved international cooperation stemming from this meeting is expected to considerably expand and strengthen the warning system.

There have been four destructive seismic waves since 1948, one in 1952 from Kamchatka, one in 1957 from the Aleutians, one on May 22, 1960 from Chile and one recently from Alaska on March 28, 1964. The warning system worked well in all four instances, giving a 6-hr. advance notice to the Hawaiian Islands in 1960.

However, the warning system did not protect the Alaskan area nearest the earthquake in 1964, nor did it protect Adak in 1957. The mechanisms for providing warnings were not designed to warn areas immediately adjacent to the tsunami source. In fact, to minimize the number of false alarms and thereby maintain public confidence in the warning system, it ordinarily relies on positive reports of observed tsunami before issuing warnings to places farther away from the epicenter. Although plans are underway for a tsunami warning system in Alaska based on seismological evidence only, even such a system requires some time to interpret the available data and to disseminate warnings. Consequently, the prudent person on shore heads for higher elevation when he feels a severe earthquake and the prudent captain of a ship immediately puts out to sea.

The Weather Bureau has assisted the Coast and Geodetic Survey in its operation of the warning system by maintaining tide gauges in isolated areas and furnishing communications, etc. On July 13, 1965 these two agencies were merged into the new Environmental Science Service Administration (ESSA). President Johnson's message of May 13, 1965 proposing the consolidation of these agencies said "The organizational improvements made possible by the reorganization plan will enhance our ability to develop an adequate warning system for the severe hazards of nature—for hurricanes, tornadoes, floods, earthquakes, and seismic sea waves, which have proved so disastrous to the Nation in recent years." The mariner is thereby assured that the government of the United States is determined to utilize its full scientific potential in maintaining and improving the seismic sea wave warning system.

Mendel Peterson:

51.   *HISTORY UNDER THE SEA**

For most of his life on this planet man has been a traveler. In the earliest period he often was forced by unkind nature or human enemies to migrate. Later, as simple commerce developed, he traveled land trails and ventured timorously along rivers or coast-

* From *History Under the Sea: A Handbook for Underwater Exploration* by Mendel Peterson, The Smithsonian Institution, 1965. Reprinted by permission of the author and Smithsonian Institution Press.

Mendel Peterson is Curator of the division of Historic Archaeology and Director of the Underwater Exploration Project of the Smithsonian Institution.

lines in search of trade. With the beginning of the ancient civilizations in the Mediterranean basin, he began to put to sea in ships and to venture to far-off lands to conduct war or to search for exotic products with which to make his life more comfortable or more interesting.

Man is not only a traveler but is also a changer, user, and destroyer. He converts the products of nature to forms which make them of utility; he uses these objects and in so doing frequently breaks them, wears them out, or loses them. He attacks his enemies, looting them of their goods and destroying what he cannot carry. And because man is a changer of nature, he is the untidiest of God's creatures. The course of his migrations across the world's land masses may be traced in a line of broken buildings, broken tools and dishes, and the refuse of his kitchens.

It is indeed fortunate for the archeologist and historian that man is such a slovenly being. Had he been neat and orderly, had he swept up his trash and burned it, and carefully ground up his broken pots to use the material for other purposes, we would be in almost complete ignorance of him. One can only speculate on the unfortunate archeologist of 500 years hence who will be investigating a civilization which knew the use of the great incinerator that reduced all matter to a shapeless mass.

As man scattered his untidy remains across the continents, so did he scatter them in the shallow waters fringing those continents. When he ventured along the coasts in pursuit of trade, he exposed himself to sudden disaster by stranding or storm. From the earliest days of maritime navigation the wrecks of ships began to pile up in coastal waters and more rarely in the deep waters of the open sea when traders began to venture there. The very suddenness of such disasters has made these underwater shipwreck sites, in effect, accidental time capsules. Thus there is deposited in the waters of the world a mass of material—dating from the earliest historical times to the present—capable of being located, recovered, identified, and preserved. Such a mass of material will give historians and archeologists a priceless collection of objects that can be identified accurately as to period and that will in turn furnish an index to the material remains of Western man from the beginnings of his culture.

Until the 20th century even the shallow waters fringing the land masses of the world remained largely "lost" to archeologists and historians. These waters now are easily accessible to divers using equipment perfected within the past 25 years. This diving gear represents the culmination of several hundred years of human thought. Designers of the 15th and early 17th centuries simply did not understand that air must be fed to a diver at the same pressure as the water surrounding his body; consequently, the designs of diving gear which they suggested were not successful. By the middle of the 17th century the relationship of air to water pressure was better understood and the diving bell was perfected. With this first workable apparatus many notable feats of salvage were performed, including recovery of some of the bronze guns from the *Vasa* in the 1650's and '60's and the recovery of the great Hispaniola treasure from Silver Shoals by William Phipps in 1686. In the 18th century diving suits were designed, but efficient pumps to supply them with air at the proper pressure were not developed and these suits were not really successful. The beginning of the 19th century saw the invention in England of the first successful diving suit, and by the middle of that century the suit had assumed practically its modern form. Apart from subtle refinements of valves, air and gas mixtures, and scientific progress in the study of physiology of diving, the diver of that period resembled the full-suited diver of today. During World War II the self-contained diving apparatus was perfected in France incorporating the principles of an apparatus used in the French Navy a hundred years earlier. This new equipment gave men the freedom of fish under water. In the United States a light hose-type gear with a rubber mask in place of the helmet was perfected in the war years. Such gear makes possible long periods of submersion in shallow water and supplies the diver a flood of air sufficient for hard labor under water.

The invention of this gear makes accessible those coastal areas which are littered with the remains of ships and sunken landsites. Students now may go beneath the sea to recover remains which promise to be of the utmost importance in the study of historic archeology and naval and commercial history.

Another and darker side to the picture exists. The very accessibility of these underwater sites has made them vulnerable to destruction by divers who are not informed on the techniques by which a site may be systematically explored and by which objects from it may be recovered, preserved, and identified. In the past 10 years many sites have been destroyed or poorly and improperly explored. Thousands of artifacts from them have been allowed to disintegrate. This has not, in general, been the fault of the diver but rather is owing to a lack of information which could have prevented this loss. There is no single volume to which a serious underwater explorer may turn for instruction on exploration, recovery, and preservation techniques, and for the identification of artifacts. A few professional museum historians and archeologists have given attention to the new field but their efforts have of necessity been limited and their knowledge has not been communicated to the diver in the field to any appreciable extent.

THE SUBMERGED CITY OF PORT ROYAL

Around the edges of the world's seas or on islands, ruins of cities may be found beneath the water. Generally such ruins have sunk beneath the sea through a gradual subsidence of the earth's surface, but in the case of Port Royal, Jamaica, a great earthquake dumped much of the city into the sea in a few moments. This disaster, one of the greatest natural disasters of the Western Hemisphere, occurred June 7, 1692, betwen 11:30 A.M. and 12 noon.

In 1655 the Lord Protector of England, Oliver Cromwell, sent an expedition under the command of Admiral Penn (father of the proprietor of Pennsylvania) and General Venables to capture a base in the West Indies from which to threaten the treasure route from the Indies to Spain. The troops attacked Santo Domingo but were poorly organized and an inferior Spanish force repulsed them. Rather than return home as failures the commanders decided to attack the island of Jamaica which they knew to be only lightly defended. In this they were successful, capturing the capitol St. Iago de la Vega (now called Spanish Town), and routing the few Spanish troops which attempted to defend it. Realizing that their intrusion would arouse the enemy to reprisals, the English selected the tip of the peninsula which forms the southern shore of the present harbor of Kingston as the site of their settlement. Using the natural defenses of the place to an advantage, they planted three forts around the end to cover attack by sea, Forts Charles, James, and Carlysle, and cut off the land approaches with a palisade across the peninsula. Later the seaward approaches were reinforced with a water battery stretching down the beach from Fort Charles and commanding the channel leading into the harbor. This became known as Morgan's line after Governor Henry Morgan, the reformed buccaneer. It is a tribute to the efficiency of these works that they were never attacked by an enemy, the highest accolade that can be bestowed upon a fortification.

Port Royal thrived and became the center of operations against the Spanish in the West Indies and along the Spanish Main. The town became the capital of the buccaneers at the height of their power, and the treasures of the Indies flowed over the docks. This great wealth attracted merchants, tavern keepers, and prostitutes to the town and the place became known as the "wickedest city on earth." Any merchant who could get a place on the waterfront was virtually assured of a fortune from trade with the buccaneers, and property values rose to equal those of London. Because of the high price of land and the limited area of the town, merchants built houses of three stories along the docks. Unknown to them they were built on a shelving beach of sand, gravel, and rotten mangrove trees. When the great earthquake struck, the tremendous weight of the brick houses and the unstable nature of the ground caused two-thirds of the town to slide into the harbor. In two or three minutes the city was submerged or shaken down and 2,000 of the 5,000 population were destroyed. Only parts of Fort Charles remained standing. Forts James and Carlysle were tumbled into the harbor.

Today the old city of Port Royal is only a layer of rubble under the harbor or the beach on the harbor side of the peninsula which has been built up since the time of the earthquake. The layer of rubble is covered with sand, broken coral, mud, and debris which has settled over it. Some writers, with more imagination than accuracy, have pictured the city as standing under the water permitting a diver to enter the buildings and even to find a church steeple standing with the bell in it! Actually, only the foundations of some buildings and parts of Fort James and Carlysle still stand, and these are covered by silt.

In 1956 the site was explored by Mr. and Mrs. Edwin A. Link, with Mr. Peterson participating, to determine its condition and to make plans for a future expedition to the area. The conditions described above were found and Mr. Link set about to design special equipment to move the tremendous quantities of silt which shrouded the remains. At the same time he designed a new salvage vessel equipped to handle any problem which might present itself at this or other underwater sites. The result is the new *Sea Diver*, the finest vessel of its type engaging in exploring historic underwater sites. The ship can support six to eight divers at once, has all types of electronic gear for searching under water, can lift loads weighing up to 6 tons, and offers comfortable air-conditioned rooms to the divers after an exhausting day under water. The ship has special gear to assure ease of maneuvering and anchoring over sites to be explored. Special water jets in the bow, invented by Mr. Link, add to the ease of handling the 164-ton vessel.

Soon after the *Sea Diver*'s shakedown cruise, early in the summer of 1959 an expedition sponsored by Mr. Link, the National Geographic Society, and the Smithsonian Institution assembled at Port Royal for an assault on the mud and coral which shrouded the remains of the historic town. After a survey of the site it was decided to begin the digging behind Fort James where old charts indicated the presence of several brick buildings and one end of the King's warehouse. The few days were spent in cutting exploratory trenches in the overburden of 4 to 5 feet of mud, sand, coral, and debris. After several days during which several test trenches were dug, the airlift began to uncover clay pipes, broken pottery, bricks, roof tiles, and other evidence of a building. The site proved to be a brick building which had contained a fireplace. The homes of Port Royal normally did not have fireplaces since heat in that tropic climate was not required. Cooking was done in small cookhouses separate from the dwelling. The location of the fireplace led us to believe that we were in a cookhouse, and the uncovering of cooking utensils, pewter spoons, plates, and platters confirmed this. The site has been identified as a cookhouse located in back of Ft. James and perhaps belonging to the dwelling of a Mr. Littleton identified by a pre-earthquake chart of the lots of the town.

During the operations on this site, Mr. Link suggested that a team of divers go over the area with his underwater detector. This device, which indicates an electrical conductor, can in effect see through several feet of mud or sand and has led to the discovery of much material which would otherwise have been overlooked. The team took it down and a few minutes later came up to get the airlift moved to a spot where they had detected the presence of metal under the mud. After a very short period of pumping mud the divers uncovered a bent and battered brass pot and brought it to the surface. When Mr. Link cleaned the sand and mud from the interior he found in it animal bones which later were identified as those of a cow and a turtle and he observed dark red brick from the interior of a fireplace. We know that the earthquake struck just before noon and the evidence here indicates that a beef and turtle stew was cooking in the fireplace when the chimney collapsed crushing the pot with its contents still in it.

The quantities of building materials which were recovered, including flat clay roof tile, bricks, plaster fragments, pieces of wattle and plaster showing impressions of it, confirmed pre-earthquake descriptions of the buildings of the old town. Exploration in two other sites near that of Littleton's house produced a collection of iron artifacts, including a steel yard with weights, tools such as axes, and fittings for ship's rigging. Perhaps the most unusual object from this site was an unused yard for a small ship some 20 feet long. This was found lying along the side of a foundation of the building.

These finds indicated the site of a supply house, perhaps that of a ship's chandler.

The site of Fort James, which we had investigated in 1956, was not neglected on this expedition. We had reason to believe that the interior of the fort might yield some interesting weapons. A team from the Navy contingent, which was cooperating with us, was sent to look over the area and after several hours of diving and digging came up with two interesting shot. One of these was half a bar shot with hemispherical ball, the other a solid lead shot for a swivel. Since authentic projectiles of the 17th century are quite scarce, these specimens were most welcome.

The navy team consisting of six expert underwater demolition men and a submarine surgeon did yeoman service under water. Their knowledge of search techniques was most valuable since the water over Port Royal is in reality liquid mud when the silt on the bottom is stirred up by the salvage operations.[1]

The largest object recovered was a 24-pounder iron tube which was found at Fort James in 1956 and now lifted from the water near the shipyard dock where it had been placed to preserve it. This was the largest gun in the defenses of Port Royal and served to defend the harbor against attack by large enemy warships carrying guns of similar size. The tube weighed 5,000 pounds. It was probably cast between 1660 and 1690. It bore the crowned rose normally appearing on English tubes until the reign of the Hanoverians and the weight mark according to the English system.

While working on the site of the "chandler's" house, there was turned up a wrought iron, breech-loading swivel gun. This piece proved to be a type made in the last of the 15th century and during the 16th century. This type of piece was not being made when Port Royal thrived and it was probably at least a century and a half old when the earthquake struck the town. It may have been held as a curio from the old Spanish fortifications but could have been in the stores as a usable weapon since several of its breech blocks were found with it. It is known that similar pieces were used for very long periods. These swivels were stone throwers. They were simply loaded with a handful of gravel which formed scatter shot when the piece was fired. They were usually carried on the poop

[1] The team in charge of Lt. C. D. Grundy consisted of A. J. Banawsky, W. L. Collins, W. T. Farrell, C. E. Nowell, and D. E. Peck. LCR. Charles Aguadro, USN., submarine surgeon and expert diver, was on hand to administer any emergency care the divers might require; fortunately, no injuries occurred during the entire operation.

and forecastles of ships and used to resist boarders although they were used also in land fortifications against attack by foot troops.

In the last month of the operations an object of utmost importance turned up. This was a watch with a brass case and silver dial. Inside it was signed "Paul Blondel." The face of the watch was covered with the normal coral sand crust stained with iron oxide. Mr. Link had an X-ray plate made which revealed distinct lines where the steel hands had been. These showed the time when the watch stopped to have been 17 minutes to twelve. Later in the Victoria and Albert Museum Mr. Link learned that the watch had been made before 1686 by a French watchmaker working in the Netherlands. He was told that the case was originally covered with fine leather held in place with silver studs, some of which remained. Thus the time of the earthquake was recorded on the timepiece of one of the victims!

The expedition recovered hundreds of objects; however, only a very small portion of the submerged city could be explored in the time available. There remain today beneath the water and mud of Port Royal the most important remnants of 17th century English America to be found anywhere. Here is a cross section of the material culture of an important city of the New World which has furnished and will continue to furnish historians with a graphic picture of life in late 17th-century America.[2]

THE TUCKER TREASURE

A young diver named Teddy Tucker was exploring a reef off the western end of Bermuda in 1950, when he discovered six encrusted cannon in a coral pocket. Tucker lifted the guns from the water and sold them to the Government of Bermuda. His work kept him from revisting the site for 5 years, but late in the summer of 1955 he returned to the spot and began a careful search of the sand in the bottom of the pocket. He discovered portions of the ribs and keel of a moderate-size vessel preserved beneath the sand in the hold. After a few days search he turned up a gold bar weighing 32 ounces. During the next week or so Tucker discovered a magnificent emerald-studded cross, two cakes of gold, two sections of gold bar, and pearl-studded gold buttons. This treasure is the most important to be discovered in the Western Hemisphere in modern times. Not only did the site yield treasure of gold and gems

[2] See: "Exploring the Drowned City of Port Royal," by Marion Clayton Link. In *National Geographic Magazine*, vol. 117, No. 2, pp. 151–183, February 1960.

but, more importantly for the historian, it produced a collection of artifacts which has been called the most significant Tudor period find of this century, for the wreck is now known to have occurred about the year 1595. The collection from it included navigating instruments, fittings from the ship's rigging, pewter, tools, and silver and ceramic utensils. The wreck also yielded weapons and other artifacts of the Carib Indians which are of the utmost rarity and interest. Today, this priceless collection is exhibited in The Aquarium Museum in Flatts, Bermuda. This find is spectacular, and there is every reason to believe that other and perhaps more fantastic finds will be made in the wreck-studded waters of Bermuda.

~~~~~~~~~~~~~~~~~

Kenneth O. Emery:

52.   MINERAL DEPOSITS ON THE OCEAN
       FLOOR*

ABSTRACT

Geological considerations of the potential mineral resources on the ocean floor indicate that primary igneous mineral deposits are unimportant as compared with sedimentary mineral deposits. This difference is due to the thick cover of Tertiary sedimentary strata on most continental shelves and the general lack of deep weathering and erosion of igneous and metamorphic rocks in the few places where they are exposed on the continental shelves.

The chief sedimentary mineral resource of the ocean floor at present and probably in the future is oil and gas, which are almost restricted to thick marine sedimentary sequences. The only other minerals that have been recovered commercially are the heavy concentrates of placers (tin, diamonds, iron, gold) and cheap supplies of shell and other sediments in shallow nearshore areas.

Much interest has been focused on ocean-floor deposits of phos-

* From EXPLOITING THE OCEAN, Trans. of the 2nd Marine Technology Society Conference, June 27–29, 1966, pp. 24–43. Contribution No. 1791 of the Woods Hole Oceanographic Institution. Reprinted by permission of the author and the M.T.S.

Kenneth Orris Emery is a Senior Scientist at the Woods Hole Oceanographic Institution and author of numerous geological papers and books.

phorite and manganese oxide, but the low quality of the deposits and the uncertainties in the costs of mining delay their possible exploitation.

INTRODUCTION

This Marine Technology Society contains many members who are great optimists about the potential of the oceans to supply mineral resources in quantity at costs that are competitive with resources from the land areas of the world. Perhaps the optimism is an occupational hazard of those whose livelihood is the selling of devices or services for marine exploration or exploitation. The truth probably lies between the beliefs of these optimists and the beliefs of the less well represented pessimists who have found neither gold nor diamonds in their thousands of ocean-floor samples. Let us attempt to set some general limits on our expectations of the ocean's bounty by using geological methods. Other limits are set by political and legal restrictions (Shalowitz, 1962) and by mechanical and economical factors that will change in time.

Tangible resources of the ocean can be grouped into biological, chemical, and geological ones. Practically impossible to evaluate are other aspects such as transportation, recreation, military, and supply of water for desalination. Biological resources are presently the most exploited ones; during 1964 the United States harvested only about six per cent of the value of the world's crop of fish, mammals, and algae from the ocean. It also recovered less than one-third of the salt (NaCl) but nearly all of the magnesium and bromine that was chemically extracted from sea water. This report, however, is supposed to be concerned with the geological resources that are on the sea floor or far beneath it. In this field the United States recovered 20 per cent of the total world value, with United States' capital responsible for much of the remaining 80 per cent—such as products of the submarine oil fields of Lake Maracaibo and the Persian Gulf.

The most important of the geological products obtained from the ocean floor adjacent to the United States is oil and gas ($700 million for 1964) and the closely associated sulfur from offshore salt domes ($15 million). Shell deposits dredged from shallow bays yielded $30 million in 1964. In proportion to recoveries from land, the offshore products are relatively small, but they are rapidly increasing in quantity and value. Ocean-floor recoveries from other areas of the world include besides oil and gas the more exotic tin, diamonds, iron, and gold—but altogether their value was only $10 million during 1964. Why have the resources from off the United States not included diamonds and gold? Why does oil and gas dominate on most continental shelves? How does the type of resource control the method of geological exploration? In order to answer these questions we should consider the geology of mineral deposits.

ORIGIN OF MINERAL DEPOSITS

Mineral deposits are classified here in a way slightly different than the usual geological way, as an adaption to the marine environment. Most fundamental of all are the primary igneous mineral deposits, because some can be mined directly as ores and others have served as original sources for other kinds of ore deposits. These primary igneous deposits include magmatic segregation, pegmatites, deep-moderate-and-shallow veins, and contact metamorphism. All are virtually restricted to intrusive igneous and associated metamorphic rocks. Outcrops of these kinds of rocks are known at only three places on the continental shelf of the United States: the Gulf of Maine, Monterey Bay, and off the Golden Gate in California. At none of these places have samples exhibited valuable mineralization.

Many primary mineral deposits on land are too low grade to be mined as ores until after they have been enriched by weathering and erosion. Enrichment may take two forms: (1) solution and concentrated redeposition of the valuable mineral (copper, silver) accompanied by erosion of some of the worthless residue left at the surface, or (2) solution and removal of the worthless material leaving at the surface a residual concentrate of the valuable mineral (iron, bauxite, diamonds). Both enrichment processes require many million years of exposure to weathering and erosion; thus, they are much less likely to be important on the ocean floor (even on the continental shelf) than on the long-exposed land areas. In fact, most igneous rocks that have been dredged from outcrops on the ocean floor are so fresh that any incipient weathering is a curiosity.

A mineral deposit somewhat related to secondary concentration by solution and redeposition is produced by long-distance transportation and redeposition within sedimentary strata by ground water (lead, uranium). Although fresh ground-water has been found in drilled samples of sedimentary strata 100 km at sea (Bunce and others, 1965), its probably low hydrostatic pressure head must cause especially slow circulation that greatly reduces the likelihood of the development of such mineral deposits on the ocean floor.

Three kinds of direct sedimentary origin for mineral deposits are common. One is the placer deposit (gold, tin, diamonds) that is formed where streams or waves and currents cause heavy minerals to be selectively deposited in isolation from relatively worthless lighter minerals that are carried away. The minerals must previously have undergone extensive weathering and erosion from their original position within igneous and metamorphic rocks. Because the ocean floor lacked sufficient weathering and erosion, few if any placer deposits should have originated on it. Instead, placers on the ocean floor should be extensions of well-known ones on land—such as the gold of Alaska, the tin of Malaya and Cornwall, and the diamonds of Southwest Africa. Placers are unrelated to the composition of their substrate, but they occur only near their primary igneous or metamorphic source rocks.

A second kind of sedimentary mineral deposit is a chemical or biochemical precipitate. The best example is manganese oxide in the form of nodules and crusts on the ocean floor. The manganese is independent of the type of substrate, being found on or in deep-sea sediments and on volcanic rock and limestone of seamounts. An essential condition for its formation is a slow rate of deposition of detrital or biogenic sediments because of their diluting effect. Two other sedimentary mineral deposits are phosphorite and glauconite, but the origin of each is complicated in some ocean-floor deposits by the inclusion of some material from reworked older deposits. Nevertheless, all three materials (manganese oxide, phosphorite, and glauconite) can be primary sedimentary deposits formed by precipitation from sea water. Their depth ranges overlap, but manganese nodules and crusts are best known from the deep-sea floor, and phosphorite and glauconite are mainly from the outer part of the continental shelf and the top of isolated banks.

The last and most important sedimentary deposits to be considered here is oil and gas, which begin as organic matter grown largely by phytoplankton near the ocean surface. The organic matter is partly transformed through ingestion by small and large marine animals and by bacteria. Eventually it is buried deep beneath detrital and biogenic sediments where further modification to oil and gas is followed by migration into structural or stratigraphic traps from which it may be released to the earth's surface through seeps or drilled wells. Alteration of the organic matter also causes most of the sulfate in the associated brines to be converted into elemental sulfur; deposits of this sulfur associated with salt domes can be melted by injected steam and pumped to the surface.

In summary, the ocean floor is primarily a depositional region in which weathering has been insignificant and erosion minor in comparison with the possibly several kilometers of total weathering and erosion on land (Gilluly, 1964). Supergene enrichment or residual enrichment of primary igneous mineral deposits should therefore be far less important on the ocean floor, even on the continental shelves, than on the continents. Even the unenriched primary igneous mineral deposits are likely to be deeply buried under a blanket of Late Cretaceous to Recent sediments that covers most of the shelves off the United States and probably the shelves of most of the rest of the world except where it was removed by Pleistocene glaciers. Accordingly, let us turn our attention more to the sedimentary mineral deposits than to the igneous ones.

SAND AND GRAVEL

Probably the simplest sedimentary deposits are those of sand, gravel, and shells. In areas of high population concentration these materials are needed for construction, earth fill, road material, and some minor miscellaneous purposes. About $890 million worth was mined in the United States during 1964 according to D'Amico (1965, Table 1). Only a small percentage came from the ocean floor, because of easier availability from stream valleys and older strata; however, Gaber and Reynolds (1965a, 1965b) reported the recovery of $30 million of shell from offshore—probably almost entirely from shallow bays of Florida, the Gulf of Mexico, and California. In addition, many new building sites are made by filling parts of salt marshes with dredged sediment, but the value of the sediment is difficult to compute owing to the concomitant intent to deepen channels for navigation through other parts of the marshes. In some countries (Israel and Jordan, for example) sand for making concrete blocks has been mined so extensively that some beaches have virtually disappeared. In order to avoid similar losses of United States' beaches, the Coastal Engineering Research Center (U. S. Army) contracted for surveys of suitable construction sand and gravel farther offshore during 1964–1965.

Extensive sampling of the surface of the continental shelf off the Atlantic coast by a joint undertaking of the U. S. Geological Survey and the Woods Hole Oceanographic Institution revealed a blanket of relict sand covering almost the entire width of the shelf (Emery, 1965). Relict gravels also are present locally (Schlee, 1964). The sand and gravel were deposited during times of glacially lowered sea level when large quantities of sediment were contributed to the ocean and when waves and currents were able to winnow out most of the clay and silt, leaving the coarser material as a sort of crude placer. Similar relict sands have been found on the continental shelves off the Gulf and Pacific coasts of the United States and off Brazil, China, Israel, and other countries (Emery, 1961). Surface samples and bottom photographs provide the best data for locating the sands and gravels, but vibrocoring or drilling, supplemented by seismic reflection profiles are needed for determination of thicknesses. Mining and transportation should be cheap, commensurate with mining costs on land that permit the sand and gravel to be sold at about $1/ton. As the population along the coast increases (such as for the coming megalopolis between Washington, D.C. and Boston) demand for offshore supplies of sand and gravel probably will increase markedly.

Concentrations of heavy minerals such as gold, tin, diamonds, and platinum are more classical types of placer deposits than are ordinary sand and gravel. They require much more wave and current energy to be transported than do the quartz and feldspar that comprise the bulk of sand deposits. Thus, most valuable heavy mineral deposits form in high-energy shore zones. Changes in sea level during deposition caused the heavy minerals to be distributed in a thin and discontinuous blanket deposit interbedded with sand and gravel or lying just above bedrock. The main contribution that geology can make to the discovery of heavy-mineral placers is through knowledge of source areas and inferences about direction

TABLE 1

VALUE OF GEOLOGICAL RESOURCES MINED FROM THE OCEAN FLOOR DURING 1964 IN COMPARISON WITH THE VALUE OF THE SAME RESOURCES MINED ON LAND[1]

| Resource | 10^6 | | | |
| | From Ocean Floor | | From Land | |
	United States	Rest of World	United States	Rest of World
Sand, Gravel, Shells	30	?	860	?
Iron	0	0.7	800	4500
Gold	0	?	50	1500
Tin	0	5	0.02	600
Diamonds	0	4	0	?
Phosphorite	0	0	160	215
Manganese Oxide	0	0	3	420
Oil and Gas	700	2900	10,500	17,000
Sulfur	15	0	100	140

[1] Gaber and Reynolds (1965b), Weeks (1965a), and D'Amico (1965)

of movement in the shore zone. Evaluation must depend upon coring or drilling, coupled with seismic measurements of thickness of overlying sands and gravels.

PHOSPHORITE

Phosphorite, a complex calcium phosphate containing some fluorine, has long been used as a source of phosphate for fertilizer and chemicals. During 1964 phosphorite valued at $160 million was mined in Florida, Tennessee, and Idaho (and adjacent Montana, Utah, and Wyoming). At the present rate of mining, more than a thousand years' supply is present on land in the United States. A major part of the cost per ton at the point of use is for freight charges. If phosphorite can be mined from the sea floor near the point of use, the cost of mining can be greater than on land and yet the operation can be profitable. To-date, however, no commercial production from the ocean floor has been reported.

Phosphorite was discovered in samples dredged from Agulhas Bank off Africa by H.M.S. *Challenger* in 1873 (Murray and Renard, 1891, p. 391). In 1937 it was found in samples from the tops of banks and locally from the outer parts of the mainland and island shelves off California by Dietz, Emery, and Shepard (1942). Subsequently, it was found off Florida (Gorsline and Milligan, 1963). In these areas and others it occurs as pellets, nodules, and crusts ranging up to about 60 cm in length and 75 kg in weight. Few analyses show P_2O_5 greater than 30 per cent, whereas the P_2O_5 in most of the phosphorite being mined on land is 31 to 36 per cent (Mero, 1965, p. 58).

Prospecting for phosphorite can be guided by the known control exerted by rate of phosphate deposition and rate of dilution by detrital sediments. Precipitation appears to be fastest in sea waters having a high concentration of dissolved phosphate—generally areas of great upwelling which support high concentrations of phytoplankton. The areas of greatest upwelling corresponding with deposits of phosphorite lie above shelves at mid-latitudes on the eastern sides of oceans (Figure 52–1). Related high-phosphate waters occur in east-west trending belts at both low and high latitudes, but phosphorite deposits are not associated, probably because of the great depth of the ocean floor below these zones. The areas of upwelling are characterized by low rainfall on adjacent lands and absence of large rivers; thus, the rate that detrital sediments are contributed to the ocean is not great. A further decrease in the rate of deposition of detrital sediments is produced by the top-

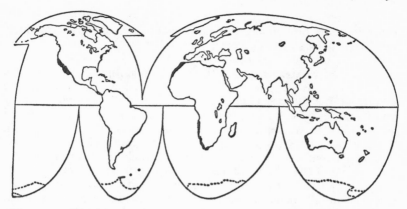

Fig. 52–1. Most favorable areas for ocean-floor deposits of phosphorite on the basis of continental shelves associated with upwelled water rich in dissolved phosphate and absence of diluting sediment from rivers and glaciers.

ographic isolation from the sediment sources by offshore banks. After potentially rich areas of the ocean floor are selected on the basis of upwelling and isolated topography, the next step is field prospecting. Because phosphorite probably is restricted to a thin layer on the ocean floor, surface sampling is adequate. The best tools are large dredges and clear bottom photographs, perhaps supplemented by underwater television. Data provided by these tools are probably adequate to establish the volume of the deposit. At present, however, the question of profit in mining depends upon the costs of ocean-floor mining and of beneficiation, or processing, of the deposits. Estimates of these costs vary so much that opinion is strongly divided about whether the ocean-floor deposits can be competitive with the land ones (Mero, 1965). One commercial test off southern California was aborted by the presence of an associated naval ordnance dump. We await the results of other tests with interest.

MANGANESE OXIDE

Manganese largely for metallurgical purposes is presently in short supply in the United States. Only $3 million worth of manganese was mined in this country during 1964, in comparison with about $420 million from the rest of the world. Imports during 1964 amounted to about $100 million worth of ores averaging more than 35 per cent manganese (DeHuff, 1965). Because of insufficient domestic production, the government offers a subsidy amounting to 50 per cent of approved exploration costs.

Nodules of black manganese oxide have been known for about one hundred years to occur on the ocean floor. In fact, some of the best descriptions and pictures of the nodules were published in the reports of the famous *Challenger* Expedition of 1872–76 (Murray and Renard, 1891). The nodules from the ocean floor are widespread as a surface or near-surface deposit, but they are not very rich in manganese. Mero's (1965) 181 analyses for worldwide samples average 18 per cent manganese; those for the Blake Plateau off the Atlantic coast of the United States average 13 per cent of total weight. Only six of the analyses contained more than 35 per cent of manganese. For all analyses silicon averages 8.1 per cent. The usual method of extraction by chemical reduction allows silicon to withhold about twice its weight of manganese; thus, most or all of the manganese must be considered a waste product of the nodules until a better method of extraction becomes economical (Institute of Marine Resources, University of California, 1965, pp. 13–1 to 13–29). According to Mero (1965), the associated 0.2 to 2.0 per cent of copper, nickel, and cobalt may justify the mining of manganese nodules, but these concentrations correspond to only marginal or low-grade ore deposits.

Manganese nodules and crusts are widespread on the deep-ocean floor, appearing in many photographs and samples by American, Soviet, and British expeditions. They are concentrated at the surface but do occur at depths of at least a few meters (Bender, Ku, and Broecker, 1966). The origin of the deposits is not well known, thus their distribution cannot be inferred from origin but only by empirical methods. These methods fail to predict the patterns of distribution and concentration, and so recourse must be made to dredges, large grab samplers, corers, and cameras. Using such devices, Pratt and McFarlin (1966) outlined in detail an area of manganese oxide on the Blake Plateau that previously was sampled by Mero (1965) and others. The middle of the area has a pavement-like concentration of crusts, and it is surrounded by an annular area in which nodules are concentrated. Phosphorite nodules present at the landward side of the area of manganese oxide may be coincidental —a result of proximity to the known phosphorite deposits on the adjacent continental shelf and the gentle slope between the shelf and the Blake Pateau. Probably detailed mapping of nodules and crusts of manganese oxide in other oceanic regions will reveal distribution patterns that are different but perhaps as complex as that of the Blake Plateau. Whether the nodules can profitably be mined in any region is uncertain, but the author is pessimistic about the matter.

Most of the world's oil and gas comes from Tertiary marine strata. These strata underlie coastal plains of all continents, and where the geology is known, they thicken seaward beneath the adjacent continental shelves. This thickening increases the likelihood of future discoveries of oil and gas resources on the shelf within suitable structures or stratigraphic traps. Most present production is from seaward extensions of structures originally discovered on land (southern California, Lake Maracaibo, Persian Gulf), or from structures having a distribution pattern related to similar structures previously discovered on land (salt domes off Louisiana and Texas). In only a few instances (Australia, Persian Gulf) has production developed from ocean-floor discoveries of structures unrelated to those of the adjacent land.

Wells on the ocean floor cost considerably more than wells on land; thus the prospecting for suitable structures is more rigorous than on land. The chief geophysical method is a form of seismic profiling, commonly supplemented by magnetic or gravimetric surveys. Final tests require actual drilling and examination of the strata. Both geophysical and geological studies must be detailed and closely spaced because of the small percentage of the continental shelf that is occupied by individual structures.

This Society probably has no particular interest in the results of such detailed studies as are necessary to identify and delimit potential oil-bearing structures, but it may like to see the results of a general seismic reflection survey of the entire Atlantic coast of the United States. Forty-four profiles made at right angles to the continental shelf (Uchupi and Emery, 1968) reveal a thickness of 200 to 800 meters of Tertiary strata beneath the continental shelf. The beds continue farther seaward beneath the continental slope and locally beneath the continental rise. Seaward growth of the continental shelf from 5 to 10 km between Nova Scotia and Cape Hatteras to more than 35 km in the area of the Blake Plateau off Florida and Georgia occurred during the Tertiary. The profiles also depict many buried erosional surfaces. Geological testing of the geophysical results was accomplished by a series of six holes drilled during 1965 off northern Florida to maximum depths of 320 meters into the bottom beneath maximum water depths of 1032 meters.

The bulk of the prism of sedimentary strata overlying basement rocks off the Atlantic coast is believed to be Cretaceous limestones and shales. Seismic refraction measurements summarized by Drake, Ewing, and Sutton (1959), Hersey, Bunce, Wyrick, and Dietz (1959), and Antoine and Henry (1965) reveal major variations in the total thickness of these strata. Greatest thicknesses off New England occur in two trenches that may join to form a single trench south of Cape Hatteras. The ridge between the two trenches may contain minor structures and traps whose identification may lead to offshore oil fields along the Atlantic coast. An extension of this ridge off eastern Canada is actively being explored by several oil companies. Other potential oil fields may be associated with large cross structures known off New York (Drake, Heirtzler, and Hirshman, 1963) and southwest of Cape Hatteras (Hersey, Bunce, Wyrick, and Dietz, 1959).

At present, oil companies are producing annually about $700 million worth of oil and gas from the continental shelves off Louisiana, California, and Texas. Bonus payments (leases), rentals, and royalties for this production have found their way into federal, state, and coastal community treasuries. Revenue to the federal treasury alone for the years 1960 to 1964 was $1,234 million, considerably more than the $469 million that was returned to the ocean in the form of support for oceanography during the same period (Figure 52-2). One can confidently predict that future activities by oil companies will produce a steady rise in the recovery of offshore oil above the present 16 per cent of the total number of barrels produced from all of the world's oil fields. Probably offshore production will rise to 25 per cent of the total during the next 25 years.

CONCLUSIONS

Mineral deposits on the ocean floor have been considered by many men as surrounded with a kind of mystery akin to that given all mineral deposits during medieval times. The fact that the deposits are covered by water should not blind us to the need for geological investigations to locate them. Elaborate instrumentation may help, but often it hinders, and it cannot substitute for geological thinking based upon data obtained by conventional techniques. A good example is provided by oil companies that have been highly successful in their use of modifications of the same techniques and the same geological thinking that are used on land to locate oil fields on the ocean floor. Oil, gas, and associated sulfur dominate the inventory of successful recoveries from the ocean floor around

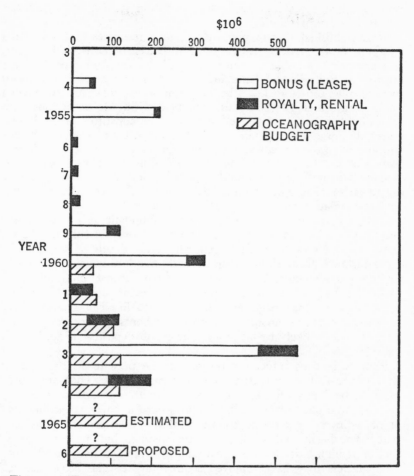

Fig. 52–2. Federal revenue from oil, gas, and sulfur compared with federal support of oceanography. From Conservation Division (1965) and Interagency Committee on Oceanography (1961, 1962, 1963, 1964, 1965).

the United States and off the coasts of other countries as well. The reason for the importance of oil and gas is the typical presence of thick Tertiary sedimentary strata beneath probably most continental shelves. In addition, once the wells have been completed, production of oil and gas requires little supervision unlike, for example, any form of strip mining.

Most published lists of potential mineral resources of the ocean floor are dominated by heavy mineral placer deposits. These are real and some have been mined, but all are extensions of placers known on the adjacent land and derived from nearby igneous or metamorphic source rocks. Where suitable source rocks are unknown on land, a search for heavy mineral placers on the ocean floor is unprofitable. Sand and gravel deposits also constitute a form of placer, because the originally accompanying silt and clay has been winnowed away; moreover, sand and gravel can be derived from many kinds of abundant source rocks. Though cheap per unit weight compared with diamonds and gold, sand and gravel is probably a far more important mineral resource of the ocean floor owing to its abundance and general lack of cover.

Phosphorite and manganese oxide are abundant as nodules and crusts in certain areas of the ocean floor, but only in thin blankets. In the author's opinion, their generally great depth of water and great distance from shore, coupled with the low concentration of the desired elements, are heavily weighted against profitable exploitation. Engineering breakthroughs in efficient recovery from the ocean floor or the assignment of large subsidies can change this forecast, but improvements in methods of beneficiation of the material are more likely to bring vast low-grade deposits on land into competition.

Primary igneous mineral deposits may be present on the ocean floor but probably with little secondary enrichment. They are most likely to be found off coasts having abundant exposures of igneous and metamorphic rocks on land and where a cover of sediments or of sedimentary rocks is absent or thin. No continental shelves that have been well studied to-date qualify, but perhaps some shelves at high latitudes are worth field investigation because Pleistocene glaciers may have removed sedimentary covers. Nevertheless, if the rocks on the adjacent land contain no valuable primary igneous mineral deposits, a good hard look at the general geology of the ocean floor should precede expensive diamond drilling.

REFERENCES

Antoine, J. W., and Henry, V. J., Jr., 1965, Seismic refraction study of shallow part of continental shelf off Georgia coast: Bull. Amer. Assoc. Petroleum Geologists, vol. 49, pp. 601–609.

Beyschlag, Franz, 1929, Geological Map of the Earth, scale 1:15,000,000, 12 sheets: Gebrüder Borntraeger, Berlin.

Bender, M. L., Ku, Teh-Lung, and Broecker, W. S., 1966, Manganese nodules: Their evolution: Science, vol. 151, pp. 325–328.

Bunce, E. T., Emery, K. O., Gerard, R. D., Knott, S. T., Lidz, Louis, Saito, Tsunemasa, Schlee, John (for JOIDES), 1965, Ocean drilling on the continental margin: Science, vol. 150, pp. 709–716.

Conservation Division, 1964, Annual and accrued mineral production, royalty income, and related statistics (oil, gas, and other leasable minerals): U. S. Geol. Survey, 127 pp.

D'Amico, Kathleen J., 1965, Statistical summary: Minerals Yearbook for 1964, U. S. Bureau of Mines, vol. 1, pp. 105–151.

DeHuff, G. L., 1965, Manganese: Minerals Yearbook for 1964, U. S. Bureau of Mines, vol. 1, pp. 735–754.

Dietz, R. S., Emery, K. O., and Shepard, F. P., 1942, Phosphorite deposits on the sea floor off southern California: Bull. Geol. Soc. America, vol. 53, pp. 815–848.

Director of the Geological Survey of India, 1959, Geological Map of Asia and the Far East, scale 1:5,000,000, six sheets, Secretariat of the United Nations Economic Commission for Asia and the Far East, Bangkok, Thailand.

Drake, C. L., Ewing, M., and Sutton, G. H., 1959, Continental margins and geosynclines: The east coast of North America north of Cape Hatteras: Physics and Chemistry of the Earth (Editors—L. H. Ahrens, Frank Press, Kalervo Rankama, and S. K. Runcorn), Pergamon Press, New York, vol. 3, pp. 110–198.

Drake, C. L., Heirtzler, J., and Hirshman, J., 1963, Magnetic anomalies off eastern North America: Jour. Geophys. Research, vol. 68, pp. 5259–5275.

Emery, K. O., 1960, The Sea off Southern California: A Modern Habitat of Petroleum: John Wiley & Sons, Inc., New York, 366 pp.

Emery, K. O., 1961, Submerged marine terraces and their sediments: Zeitschrift für Geomorphologie, Supplement vol. 3, pp. 17–29.

Emery, K. O., 1965, Geology of the continental margin off eastern United States: Submarine Geology and Geophysics (Editors—W. F. Whittard and R. Bradshaw), Proc. 17th Symposium of the Colston Research Soc., Univ. Bristol, April 5–9, Butterworth, London, pp. 1–20.

Gaber, N. H, and Reynolds, D. F., Jr., 1965a. Ocean engineering and oceanography from the businessman's viewpoint: Ocean Science and Ocean Engineering, Marine Tech. Soc. and Amer. Soc. Limn. and Oceanog., Trans. Joint Conf. 14–17 June 1965, Washington, D.C. vol. 1, pp. 128–148.

Gaber, N. H., and Reynolds, D. F., Jr., 1965b, Economic opportunities in the oceans: Battelle Technical Review, vol. 14, no. 12, pp. 5–11.

Gilluly, James, 1964, Atlantic sediments, erosion rates, and the evolution of the continental shelf: Some speculations: Bull. Geol. Soc. America, vol. 75, pp. 483–492.

Goddard, E. N. (Chairman), 1965, Geologic Map of North America, scale 1:5,000,000, 2 sheets: U. S. Geol. Survey.

Gorsline, D. S., and Milligan, D. B., 1963, Phosphatic deposits along the margin of the Pourtales Terrace, Florida: Deep-Sea Research, vol. 10, pp. 259–262.

Hamilton, Warren, 1963, Antarctic tectonics and continental drift: Polar Wandering and Continental Drift: Soc. Econ. Paleontologists and Mineralogists, Sp. Publ. 10, pp. 74–93.

Hersey, J. B., Bunce, E. T., Wyrick, R. F., and Dietz, F. T., 1959, Geophysical investigations of the continental margin between Cape Henry, Virginia, and Jacksonville, Florida: Bull. Geol. Soc. America, vol. 70, pp. 437–466.

Institute of Marine Resources, University of California, 1965, California and use of the ocean: A planning study of marine resources: Prepared for the California State Office of Planning, October 1965: IMR Ref. 65-21.

Interagency Committee on Oceanography, 1961, National Oceanographic Program, Fiscal Year 1962: Federal Council for Science and Technology, 27 pp.

Interagency Committee on Oceanography, 1962, National Oceanographic Program, Fiscal Year 1963: Federal Council for Science and Technology, ICO Pamphlet No. 3, 31 pp.

Interagency Committee on Oceanography, 1963, National Oceanographic Program, Fiscal Year 1964: Federal Council for Science and Technology, ICO Pamphlet No. 11, 67 pp.

Interagency Committee on Oceanography, 1964, National Oceanographic Program, Fiscal Year 1965: Federal Council for Science and Technology, ICO Pamphlet No. 15, 50 pp.

Interagency Committee on Oceanography, 1965, National Oceanographic Program, Fiscal Year 1966: Federal Council for Science and Technology, ICO Pamphlet No. 17, 73 pp.

Isakov, I. S. (Chief), 1953, Morskoi Atlas: Ministry of the Navy of the U.S.S.R., vol. 2, plate 10.

Lobeck, A. K., 1942, Geologic Map of Europe, scale 1:5,000,000, 1 sheet: The Geological Press, Columbia University, New York.

Lombard, Jean (General Coordinator), 1963, Geological Map of Africa, scale 1:5,000,000, 9 sheets, Association of African Geological Surveys, United Nations Educational, Scientific and Cultural Organization, Paris.

Mero, J. L., 1965, The Mineral Resources of the Sea: Elsevier Publ. Co., New York, 312 pp.

Murray, John and Renard, A. F., 1891, Report on Deep-Sea Deposits Based on the Specimens Collected during the Voyage of H.M.S. *Challenger* in the Years 1872 to 1876: Her Majesty's Stationery Office, London, 525 pp.

Nalivkin, D. V., (Editor-in-chief), 1955, The Geological Map of the U.S.S.R., scale 1:5,000,000, 8 sheets: The Ministry of Geology of the U.S.S.R., Moscow.

Pratt, R. M., and McFarlin, P. F., 1966, Manganese pavements on the Blake Plateau: Science, vol. 151, pp. 1080–1082.

Schlee, John, 1964, New Jersey offshore gravel deposit: Pit and Quarry, vol. 57, pp. 80, 81, 95.

Shalowitz, A. L., 1962, Shore and Sea Boundaries: With Special Reference to the Interpretation and Use of Coast and Geodetic Survey Data: U. S. Dept. Commerce, Coast and Geodetic Survey Publ. 10-1, vol. 1, pp. 209–276.

Stose, G. W., 1950, Geologic Map of South America, scale 1:5,000,000, 2 sheets, Geol. Soc. America.

Tectonic Map Committee, Geological Society of Australia, 1960, Tectonic Map of Australia: Scale 1:2,534,400, 4 sheets: Bur. Mineral Resources, Geol. and Geophys., Dept. Natural Development.

Uchupi, Elazar and Emery, K. O., in press, Structure of the continental margin off the Atlantic coast of the United States: Bull. Amer. Assoc. Petroleum Geologists, vol.

Warren, Guyon, 1965, Geology of Antarctica: Antarctica (Editor—Trevor Hatherton): Methuen & Co., Ltd., London, pp. 279–320.

Weeks, L. G., 1965a, Offshore Oil: The Oil and Gas Journal, 21 June 1965, pp. 127–134, 138, 140, 142, 143, 145, 147, 148.

Weeks, L. G., 1965b, World offshore petroleum resources: Bull. Amer. Assoc. Petroleum Geologists, vol. 49, pp. 1680–1693.

~~~~~~~~~~~~~~~~~~~~~

William O. Rainnie, Jr.:

53.   ALVIN . . . AND THE BOMB*

The call came from the Office of Naval Research[1] in Washington on the night of January 22, 1966—the suspenseful beginning of an episode that would bring international recognition to our Institution and the *Alvin*, the small deep diving (2000 meters) research submarine. The mission—to find a hydrogen bomb lost near the Spanish coastal village of Palomares in the unfortunate collision on January 17 of an Air Force bomber and a refuelling airplane.

The *Alvin* was just completing an overhaul mainly devoted to correcting annoying mechanical and electrical problems discovered during the disappointing deep diving test program of the summer and fall of 1965. However, these problems did not prevent the *Alvin* from reaching her design operating depth of 2000 meters.[2] The overhaul as luck would have it, was being done at the Otis Air Force Base near Woods Hole in a borrowed hangar. Plans were made for departure from Woods Hole on or about February 1 aboard the catamaran, the special mother-ship designed to launch, retrieve and support the *Alvin* at sea. After a week of discussions and preparations the decision was made to fly the sub to Rota, Spain, for trans-shipment by LSD (Landing Ship Dock) to the search scene. Although not specifically designed for air transport, by removing the conning tower (also required for truck shipment), the submarine and its necessary battery charging vans, machine shop,

* From *Oceanus*, Vol. Xii, No. 4, August, 1966, pp. 17–21. Reprinted by permission of the publisher and author.

W. O. Rainnie, Jr. is program manager and chief pilot of the Deep Submergence Research Vehicle Program at the Woods Hole Oceanographic Institution.

[1] Sponsor of the *Alvin* Program.

[2] See: "The *Alvin*" Oceanus, Vol. Xii, No. 1, Oct. 1965.

electronic shop, etc. were loaded onto two U.S. Air Force cargo planes on February 1 and arrived in Rota by the 5th. Bad weather delayed our departure and extended the normal routing of the flight through Labrador and the British Isles.

A quick re-assembly and fix of a minor problem, believed to have been caused by the aircraft vibrations, permitted the *Alvin* to make a test dive in Rota harbor on February 9. On the same day she was loaded onto the U.S.S. *Plymouth Rock* which also carried the *Aluminaut* and departed for Palomares, arriving the next morning. To our surprise we found that the submersibles were not to be supported by the *Plymouth Rock* but were to be transferred to another LSD, the U.S.S. *Fort Snelling*. The transfer included plans to moor both the *Alvin* and the *Aluminaut* to buoys. Unfortunately, the infamous Mediterranean "mistral" came up during this period with winds over 70 knots, causing minor damage to the *Alvin*. Therefore, diving operations did not commence until February 14 when the *Alvin*, launched from the *Fort Snelling*, descended to 600 meters on the first of 34 dives made in the Mediterranean.

Prior to this dive we were briefed on what was known about the accident. There still was a strong possibility that the missing weapon had fallen on land. The Air Force personnel ashore were making an "inch by inch" search. The most significant clue seemed to be the report of a Spanish fisherman who had seen a "half man" on the end of a strange looking parachute hit the water and sink immediately about 70 meters from his boat on the day of the accident. At the time his boat was about 9 kilometers offshore. After the Decca network[3] for surface ship navigation had been set up, the fisherman was taken several times to show the spot. The location was marked on the chart along with other positions such as the computed position of impact using all of the known data from the crash. The local terrain sloped gently to seaward to the north and toward the south broke off into a submerged canyon. The *Alvin* was assigned to the highest probability area, south of the fisherman's position toward the deeper rougher canyon walls, while the *Aluminaut* at first was assigned to the northwest area and then to the northeast over the flatter bottom more suited to her capabilities. Quite often the two submersibles were searching as close as one kilometer from each other without difficulty except for some communication interference. The submarines often could talk to each other more readily than to their own surface support units.

On the ninth dive on March 1, the *Alvin* found a peculiar track that had the characteristics we had expected the weapon would make

[3] A radio-navigation system somewhat similar to Loran.

on the bottom. On this dive the track was lost on the steep slope in 788 meters of water.

The tracking of the *Alvin* was crude at this point. Underwater telephone ranges, submarine depth and rough bearings from the surface support ship, generally a minesweeper, gave an approximate position somewhere in a circle with a radius of 300 to 400 meters (as we found out later). Because of the surface tracking errors, attempts to regain the same track were frustrating. It was not until March 12 on the sixteenth dive that the *Alvin* found the bottom track again. As before, the track was found late during the dive and low batteries forced surfacing. Poor surface tracking prevented finding the bottom furrows again until two dives later on March 15. This time the track was found soon after reaching the bottom and instead of going forward down the steep slope Pilots McCamis and Wilson backed down the track and found the parachute covered bomb 758 meters below the sea surface. On this dive the first rendezvous in deep "inner space" was accomplished when the *Aluminaut* moved to within 30 meters of the *Alvin* on the bottom and remained there for about 24 hours after we surfaced to re-charge batteries. The *Aluminaut* was fitted with a pinger[4] which transponded to a signal sent from the surface for the U.S.N.S. *Mizar* tracking system. This permitted the most accurate plotting of the position ($\pm$40 meters compared to the previous $\pm$300 meters). The same tracking system was used with the *Alvin* on subsequent dives and made it possible to return to the bomb at will. Used in conjunction with Decca navigation for the surface ship this tracking system played a key role in the eventual success of the operation. The method was developed as a result of the difficulties experienced in the search for the *Thresher*, lost off Georges Bank in 1963.[5]

The *Mizar* subsequently planted an anchor on the end of a nylon line 15 meters from the lost bomb, a neat trick in 758 meters of water. The *Alvin* took another 8 cm circumference nylon line from the anchor and with the mechanical arm hooked a grapnel into the shrouds of the parachute. The *Mizar* attempted to lift the weapon but the nylon line was cut by the anchor and the bomb was lost for another agonizingly long nine days. This delay was caused chiefly by bottom evidence that the bomb had been dragged upslope during the lifting attempt while it had fallen back down the track into 848 meters of water where the *Alvin* finally found it again.

By this time CURV (Controlled Underwater Recovery Vehicle), an unmanned vehicle designed for the recovery of torpedoes

[4] See: "The Pinger" by G. E. R. Deacon. *Oceanus*, Vol. V, nos. 1 and 2.
[5] See: "*Thresher* Search" by J. B. Hersey, page 296.

by the Naval Ordnance Test Station at Pasadena, had arrived on the scene. The CURV proceeded in a workmanlike manner to attach lines to the parachute so that the bomb could be hoisted to the surface on April 7, to the great relief of the 2000 or so military and civilian personnel involved in this strange operation.

Our *Alvin* played a lesser, but still important role in the final recovery. She attached pingers to the parachute, assisted the crew operating the CURV in finding the bomb, and while submerged watched on sonar as the weapon was hauled to the surface.

The *Alvin* was returned to the United States on the U.S.S. *Lindenwald* the third LSD from which we operated.

From this expedition, away from our primary tasks, we learned some lessons that will make the vehicle and the people who operate and support her much more valuable and efficient to our basic mission. The navigation system, especially the one planned for the near future work of the *Alvin* had not been previously evaluated. We know now that the system is not too accurate but that it is good enough to put the *Alvin* in position as required for most of the suggested scientific investigations. It is even good enough to return us to a given place on the bottom if a marker such as a transponder, a pinger, or even a flashing light is planted on a previous dive. All of these devices were planted by us and used successfully during the bomb hunt. The fairly sophisticated system on the *Mizar* was effective and is available when special circumstances justify the need. We could spend more time with the *Mizar* reducing the errors in the system by calibration. We also are developing a better system for our own use. We have a much better appreciation now of what really is needed and can plan accordingly. One thing is certain, the bottom of the ocean is not flat in our operating depths, and plans for navigation systems must take this into account.

We gained invaluable experience in operating in deep ocean currents and in rugged terrain, an experience that will pay dividends when our scientists want to investigate similar territory. Quite a number desire this capability. We found that the mechanical arm is an effective tool and we gained a lot of experience using it in difficult tasks. To be more dexterous we need a second arm.

The *Alvin* has proven to be reliable and safe in deep water. She can be used more often for longer periods than we had hoped as regards to submerged time, operating hours, battery charging times, etc. It must be realized that the batteries and the people on board run down at about the same rate; i.e. 6–8 hours. For special studies, this time can be expanded. Our longest dive off Spain was 10½ hours.

~~~~~~~~~~~~~~~~~~~~~

James W. Mavor, Jr.:

54.   "ATLANTIS" REVISITED*

The island of Thira, 100 kilometers north of Crete in the Aegean Sea erupted with tremendous violence between 1500 and 1450 B.C. At the end of this period a large part of the island collapsed into the sea creating enormous tidal waves which caused floods and coastal damage as far away as Egypt. The roar of the explosion may have been heard as far away as Scandinavia.

Standing on the edge of the collapsed volcanic cone (caldera) of Thira, a sheer drop 400 meters above the sea, one can see the surrounding islands of Anaphi, Amorgos, Sikonos, Ios, and Pholegandros and in the winter, Crete. The enormity of the cataclysm is brought home with frightening clarity. Around the rim of the caldera, some 10 kilometers in diameter, the 40 meter thick white volcanic ash layer of the Minoan eruption is visible, contrasting with the layers of black and red lava beneath.

Professor A. G. Galanopoulos, who is director of the seismic laboratory at the University of Athens, proposed in 1960 that Thira was the metropolis of Plato's Atlantis, the smaller of two islands making up the royal lands. The other, the royal state, was Crete. Other settlements on the Aegean islands, and along the eastern Mediterranean coasts were ruled from these two islands. Galanopoulos has presented considerable evidence to support his theory. Moreover, Mellis, and Ninkovich and Heezen have reported the analyses of deep sea cores which indicate the widespread effects of the great volcanic explosion.

The Minoan civilization in its palace period from 1900–1000 B.C. is known from excavations of the Cretan palaces. Written letters and artifacts of the surrounding cultures appear to relate to the Minoans and to the collapse of their civilization. The records

* From "Volcanoes and History or 'Atlantis' Revisited" by J. W. Mavor, Jr. Oceanus, Vol. XIII, No. 1, November, 1966. Reprinted by permission of the publisher and the author.

James W. Mavor, Jr. is a research scientist at the Woods Hole Oceanographic Institution. He has done considerable 'on location' research on the history of Atlantis and is the author of a book on the subject.

include Plato's dialogues Timaeus and Kritias, the Tell-el-Amarna letters of Egypt, the excavations at Tell-el-Qedah in Palestine, the tradition of the flood of Deukalion, the Hittite legend of Ullikummi, and the Etruscan excavations in Italy. Also pertinent are the Old Testament books of Judges, Exodus, Amos, Jeremiah, Zephaniah, and Joshua, and the inscriptions of Tel-el-Yahudiya. References in Egypt include the Hermitage papyrus, the Ipiwer papyrus, and the inscription at Speos Artemidos. J. G. Bennett has discussed the Egyptian sources showing that the Thira cataclysm was destructive in Egypt.

PRELIMINARY SURVEY

Late this summer, from August 26 through September 10, we made a preliminary survey to discover further evidence to support Professor Galanopoulos suggestions that Thira is the site of "long lost Atlantis." Two items of Plato's story were considered major areas of interest. 1. A comparison of the physical description of the island. 2. A search for remnants of the Atlantean civilization. Kritias described the metropolis of Atlantis as a circular island 100 or 105 stadia in diameter. Inside this circle were three naturally formed ring-shaped harbors with a connecting channel between and to the sea. White, black and red building blocks were said to be quarried from the raised banks of the harbors. On the center island, five stadia in diameter, was a hot spring and a cold spring. To verify this description, it is necessary to reconstruct the topography of the island prior to the collapse of 1450 B.C.

We were fortunate in that the R.V. 'Chain' was on a geophysical cruise in the eastern Mediterranean with Mr. E. F. K. Zarudski as Chief Scientist on board. Due to his interest in Thira our survey party was transported on the 'Chain' from Athens to the island. The ship then spent one day at Thira to make a seismic sparker profile[1] through the caldera and around the island. Although we have to await complete analysis of the records the seismic profile indicated a radial cross section of the collapsed portion of the island underwater and a deep filled basin within the caldera which could have been a pre-eruption waterway. An examination of the cliff strata and underwater bottom profiles made by the survey party, using Professor Edgerton's short-ping sediment profiler, indicated a complex volcano having many lava plugs or tubes.

---

[1] See: "The seismic profiler", *Oceanus*, Vol. VII, No. 4. June 1961.

It does not appear that the island was a single cone before the eruption but several intersecting cones. It may well have had a caldera of smaller size than the present one. The cyclic behavior of the volcanic activity (building up the collapsing) reported by Ninkovich and Heezen supports this thesis. The Minoan eruption of fine white ash does not appear to have come from a central single vent since it varies in both thickness and size over the island.

The present island group is smaller than the metropolis of Atlantis was reported to be. There is evidence that land slumping took place on the island periphery either during or after the eruption. The survey indicated a 2 to 4 kilometer larger pre-eruption outline which fits Plato's 100 stadia diameter exactly.

Plato described a caldera with volcanic islands inside the collapsed cone. The lava, pumice, and tuff of Thira which are cut from the cliffs and used for building blocks are white, black and red. Hot springs occurs on the central volcanic cone and a single cold spring occurs presently on the limestone mountain, Mt. Elias, a 600 meter sheer outcrop.

SEARCH EVIDENCE

The second major area of interest was the search for evidence that Thira was the religious center of the Minoan of Atlantean civilization and that temples and palaces are to be found. No evidence has yet been found of large Minoan temples. Certainly, any ruins on the central part of the collapsed island have been destroyed beyond recovery. In 1879, Fouque reported three excavations on separate parts of the island. A fourth was found by Galanopoulos in 1956. These ruins were all discovered at the bottom of the top white and rose pumice layers and were well preserved, buried as at Pompeii. Minoan artifacts including pottery, gold jewelry, copper tools, and skeletons were found. The habitations seemed to be farms. Most discoveries were made during mining operations when the pumice was dug from the cliffs and conveyed to ships for use in cement. The modern practice of blasting and bulldozing is constantly destroying Minoan ruins. In spite of this, wood and pottery were observed during the current survey in the red weathered lava earth just under the rose pumice. Wood samples were taken for carbon 14 dating. In one pumice mine, evidence of a fresh water lake or marsh was found. From the thickness and composition of the earthy Minoan surface in two locations, it appears that there were wooded regions on the island. Plato mentions spring fed ponds and excellent soil.

FOSSIL MONKEY

Previous to the present survey, E. Loring found a fossil monkey head on the beach at Kamari. This fossil found in the pumice and lava formed during the eruption of Thira was inspected by Professor Poulianos, a leading anthropologist, who identified it as *Cercophitecus callitrichus* or West African Green Monkey. Such animals are known to have been brought to Crete by ship for the amusement of royalty. This implies the presence of royalty on the island and one might speculate that adequate quarters comparable to the Cretan palaces were available.

At the summit of Messavouno, a 350 meter high spur of Mt. Elias, lie the extensive ruins of ancient Thira, settled since Phoenician times in 1100 B.C. Each succeeding people rebuilt with the stones of the preceding culture, there being no sedimentation to establish the strata upon which archaeologists depend for relative dating. Inscriptions, architecture, and design are the guides here. On the site of this great ruin, all the white pumice layer has weathered away leaving bare limestone. While no Minoan antiquities have been found at this site, an ancient Greek stone inscription reading ΕΥΜΝΛΟΣ exists. According to Plato, Ευμηλος which means "rich in sheep", was the twin brother of Atlas, King of the islands of Atlantis. Ευμηλος was given as his lot an island nearest the pillars of Herackles. Galanopoulos has suggested that the Egyptian manuscript of the story of Atlantis did not mention the pillars of Herackles and that this place known as the present day Strait of Gibraltar was an embellishment added by Plato. Plato was presented with a description of the geographical location of Atlantis which clearly places it in the Aegean Sea. However, he was faced with dimensions far too large to place it in the Mediterranean. Furthermore, he did not know of the eruption of Thira. Faced with this dilemma and being a logical person, he placed Atlantis in the Ocean Stream beyond Gibraltar. The name Atlantis in its Greek meaning, daughter of Atlas, may have been part of the original story or it may have been invented by Plato. The narrow passage identified by Plato as Gibraltar was more likely one of the many straits in the Aegean such as Dhiavlos Elafonison at the southeastern corner of the Peleponnesus. The island of Melos, West of Thira, may be the ancient domain of King Μηλος. The location of Atlantis on the Mid-Atlantic ridge of the Atlantic Ocean, considered by many people as the most likely location, is based solely on a few brief sentences of Plato whereas an Eastern Mediterranean location is clearly indicated by many other parts of the text. Radio-isotope measurements of sediment of the Mid-Atlantic Ridge suggest no major changes for the past 73,000 years. Geophysical studies in the central Atlantic Ocean Basin indicated no major changes over a period of 280,000 years.

FACTOR OF 10

One of the more significant pieces of evidence supporting the Minoan-Atlantis theory concerns the numbers used in Plato's story. Atlantis is clearly said to be a bronze age civilization. The bronze age in Europe and the near East is dated from 2000 to 1000 B.C. Plato dates the destruction of Atlantis at 9000 years before the time of Solon in 590 B.C. Plato certainly did not describe a mesolithic culture, as this date implies, so there must be an error. Let us assume that there is a factor of 10 error in the date, that in translation or recording, 100 was read as 1000. Such an error is easily made. The date of the destruction then comes out 1490 B.C. To make this more believable, there must be a consistent error throughout Plato's story and a substantial number of instances. This is the case. The royal state is described as an oblong region 3000 by 2000 stadia. Reducing this to 300 by 200 is just the size of the Neogene basin of Crete which is described perfectly in other terms. Moreover, a ditch or river is described surrounding the plain, 10,000 stadia long. This would be 1100 miles. The periphery of the plain of Messara in Crete is about 110 miles. The royal state is presented as one of the 10 kingdoms of Atlantis, the others being possibly in Libya, Tyrrhenia, etc. The army of this kingdom is organized in relation to each lot of land, about one square mile, furnishing so many chariots, archers, javelin throwers, etc. The number of lots is given as 60,000 and when reduced to 6,000 results in a more reasonable number of soldiers which probably still is exaggerated. The navy of 1200 ships is said to require 200 sailors per ship. From "frying pan" drawings, seals, and wreck excavation, we know that a typical Minoan vessel did not require a complement of over thirty men.

EXAGGERATIONS

In picturing the cultures of prehistoric times, it is important to scale down one's impression from the inevitable exaggerations that occur in historical reporting. The people of Minoan times may have been less in number than today's population even though the land was more fertile. The geographical extent of Athens proper is given precisely and covers a small portion of Attica. The army was said to be drawn from the surrounding people. The war between Athens and Atlantis, won by Athens, was most likely a land engagement which took place on the shores of Attica. In the opening paragraph of this article it was said, referring to the Athenians, that "all your warlike men in a body sank into the earth". This was likely an earthquake associated with the collapse of Thira. Professor Galanopoulos has shown by studying seismic records that Attica has not been subject to large seismological disturbances in historical times. Only the earthquakes and floods accompanying the collapse of Thira would create such an opening of the earth. Plato also reported that the Acropolis in Athens had a fountain spring which was extinguished by the earthquake. Evidence of such a spring has been found.

ACTIVE DIGS

Active Minoan digs are currently underway on the island of Zea near Attica and at two recently discovered palaces on Crete, Zakros and Arkhanes. It is hoped that Thira can be added to this list in the near future. Needless to say, we are anxious to return.

A word should be said about possible underwater ruins at Thira. Several sites have been reported. They were examined acoustically and where the water depth permitted, by swimmers. No diving equipment was used. On the caldera rim the bottom is very rough, covered with large rocks and deeply faulted. At three locations, formations which appeared man-made from surface, looked natural on close inspection. Off the southern and eastern beaches a stratum 2-6 meters under the sand was found which became irregular near shore. This could be a ruin or a naturally formed concrete geologically known as beachrock, which was found above the bottom in some places. Our conclusion is that the work should be pursued with more powerful equipment and facilities for diving. Both in archaeological and geological points of view, Thira would be a most interesting place for a deep submersible capable of working to a depth of 700 meters.

Edwin A. Link:

55. *UNDERSEA DWELLINGS**

ABSTRACT

The feasibility of flexible materials for the structural portions of manned undersea dwellings has been demonstrated in design studies and proven in at-sea tests. Since the maximum differential pressures encountered are small and are directly proportional to the height of the pressure equalized flexible structure, a wide variety of materials such as rubber, nylon, plastics and other synthetics may be utilized.

The concept of flexible structures permits economical solution to many diverse undersea tasks. Flexible structures offer inherent advantages for operation from small research vessels with a minimum of logistic support requirements and operating personnel.

The problems of life support, atmosphere control, biomedical support and diver safety remain as urgent as those associated with large undersea dwellings. The use of a small bottomed dwelling along with a system of "commuter diving" does offer significant operational and safety advantages for certain missions.

Application of this concept to many tasks is envisioned. Among these are:

Diver Rest and Refuge Stations
Oceanographic Observation Stations
Bottom Sitting Dry Environment Work Areas
Workshops and Storage Areas
Submarine Escape Techniques

In July 1964, the author planned and directed a deep ocean saturation dive utilizing a pressure equalized flexible dwelling to support two divers at 432 feet for 49 hours.

* From "Man's Extension into the Sea", Transactions of the Joint Symposium of the Marine Technology Society, January 11–12, Washington, D.C. Reprinted by permission of the author and the M.T.S.

Edwin A Link is best known for originating the Link Trainer aircraft training device used during World War II. Recently he has been involved with deep diving and marine archaeological projects for the National Geographical Society.

The techniques of saturation living and diving conceived by the U.S. Navy provided a new method for Man's extension into the sea. The medical and physiological proofs that Man could exist for long periods at high ambient pressures gave rise to several different engineering approaches to exploit this capability.

The concept of the pressure equalized flexible dwelling resulted from a desire to provide maximum safety and comfort for deep ocean divers while conforming to the operational capabilities and limitations of a small diving research ship. Earlier Man-In-Sea work, notably a 24 hour, 200 foot dive in 1962 by a single diver, had demonstrated that properly planned saturation diving work could be accomplished from an independent research ship. This experience also showed the need for additional underwater habitation if the depth, duration or length of manned submergence were to be increased. A submersible, portable, inflatable dwelling analogous in many respects with a tent was determined to best offer a solution to this problem.

DESIGN

The prototype dwelling (submersible, portable, inflatable dwelling (SPID) was designed to be constructed of commercially available components. The dwelling portion of the structure is a modification of a rubber storage bag modified externally with an access trunk and two view ports on the longitudinal axis. The usable internal space measured 7 feet in length by 4.5 feet diameter.

The 110 cubic foot internal volume was outfitted with two bunks, gas analyzer equipment, heaters, dehumidifier, CO_2 removal equipment, lighting, provisions and water, and diver personal clothing and equipment. The fabric was internally strengthened to support the loads suspended from it. The dwelling internals were painted with non-toxic high reflectant paint to provide maximum internal illumination.

The inflatable dwelling portion was mounted within a pipe structure frame and restrained by a nylon webbing. Eight compressed gas cylinders, each with a 240 cubic foot capacity were mounted on the external frame and manifolded for control from within the dwelling. A bridle was fabricated to fit the frame and provide a lifting point for the entire dwelling.

Ballast to compensate for the 3.5 tons submerged displacement and to provide firm anchoring on the ocean floor was contained in a structural steel basket beneath the dwelling. The ballast consisted of lead pigs and cast lead shot 1 inch in diameter. Use of the lead shot permitted final ballasting of the SPID while it floated near the surface ship without swimmer or diver manpower. The ballast basket further provided a stowage space for pressure tight containers loaded with life support consumables, provisions and diver clothing.

The SPID as fully outfitted and configured required a deck stowage area of 9 feet by 6 feet on the surface vessel deck. Partially ballasted, it required a dry weight lift of only 2 tons, well within the capability of most research vessel booms and cranes.

Concurrently with the SPID design and manufacture, a second pressure equalized flexible structure was designed and built. This unit was designed to provide a completely dry bottom environment for inspection and work on the ocean floor.

This bottomed work area, nicknamed IGLOO, consists of an 8 foot diameter hemisphere of nylon reinforced rubber attached to an external ballast ring around its lower circumference. The ballast ring provides external stowage space for compressed gas stowage and consumable supplies.

IGLOO was designed for use in two configurations; either negatively ballasted for semi-permanent bottom installation with a sub-bottom entry passage, or, ballasted to be raised and lowered above an anchor by an occupant. In the latter mode, proper ballasting and use of a hauldown device and bottom anchor permits positioning of the anchor prior to placing IGLOO on the bottom. Final positioning of the slightly positively buoyant structure and blowing out the residual water is accomplished by a diver utilizing conventional breathing equipment or breathing the mixture entrapped in the IGLOO itself.

OCEAN OPERATIONS

IGLOO, the inflatable bottom work shop, was operated for 50 days at 40 foot depths to determine its capabilities. Throughout this period, diver teams investigated various techniques for positioning, entry, and use of this dry work area.

SPID, the inflatable dwelling, was integrated into a system for more extensive deep ocean testing. This deep diving system included a submersible decompression chamber (SDC) for diver transport, a deck decompression chamber with which the SDC mated for diver transfer at high pressures, a master control console, and the SPID.

After operational trials in 80 foot depths, the SPID was lowered to the ocean bottom at 432 foot depths in late June 1964. Throughout the descent, internal pressure was measured through a pneumofathometer while a constant water seal was monitored with closed circuit television equipment. Accurate depth positioning of the SPID was accomplished by descent line markings and thorough use of a fathometer which presented a continuous descent profile. A pre-mixed helium-oxygen breathing composition was hose supplied to the dwelling to maintain the desired water level.

The SPID bottomed on an eight degree sloping sandy and coral bottom. Surface supplied gas was secured and the inflated dwelling remained anchored to the bottom for forty eight hours prior to the arrival by SDC of the two men who would live in and work from SPID. Throughout this waiting period, no gas makeup was required.

Concern regarding helium diffusion through the dwelling fabric was ended. This confirmed earlier tests that has shown the small pressure differential across the fabric (3.4 psi maximum at the top of the dwelling) has not caused significant gas leakage. Subsequent to occupancy of the dwelling by the two divers, Robert Stenuit and Jon Lindbergh, all gas analysis and makeup of oxygen and mixed gas for water seal maintenance were controlled by the occupants.

Throughout the 49 hour bottom dwelling period, the SPID provided a warm, dry environment for the deepest ocean dwellers to date. After the ascent of the two divers, the SPID was raised to the surface and reloaded aboard the surface vessel without incident.

FUTURE CAPABILITIES

The missions Man will accomplish in the sea are many, varied and often not yet completely defined. The equipment, living facilities, and work areas he will require are as varied as his missions will be. The use of pressure equalized flexible structures will fill some of these needs just as some will require larger structural components.

Some of the future uses foreseen for flexible structures include:
1) Rest and refuge tents for deep dives using a "commuter" technique where the main support facilities are located on the surface vessel. In this technique, a small bottomed refuge provides a safe haven for deep divers in the event of a SDC cas-

ualty. Proper design of such a haven will permit its recurrent use for rest and minor repairs during prolonged bottom work tasks.

2) Oceanographic observation stations which can be maintained, launched and recovered by existing research vessels for many biological, geological and physical oceanography tasks.

3) Provision of a dry bottom environment for cable repair, pipeline installation and maintenance, extensive bottom construction work, and accurate in-site bottom analysis.

4) Underseas workshops and storage areas which are readily relocated and maintained.

5) Escape from disabled submarines, either military or civilian, by controlled decompression within an ascending flexible structure. Once surfaced, the flexible dwelling may be converted to a life raft for the survivors until aid arrives.

SUMMARY

The economy of manufacture and operation of pressure equalized flexible dwelling systems have been demonstrated. Increased operating experience with flexible dwellings and workshops will provide information for future designs and uses.

The continued use of pressure equalized flexible structures for manned dwelling will permit a multitude of scientists, engineers and explorers to live in the oceans and perform their specific tasks.

~~~~~~~~~~~~~

Robert C. Cowen:

56.   TO DRINK FROM THE SEA*

At the height of the Northeast's water shortage in the summer of 1965, President Lyndon B. Johnson told his science adviser, Donald F. Hornig, to tackle the problem of desalting the sea as though

* From THE WORLD BOOK YEAR BOOK. © 1966 Field Enterprises Educational Corporation. Reprinted by permission of the publisher and the author.

Robert C. Cowen is Science Editor of the *Christian Science Monitor*. He has written on a variety of scientific subjects and is the author of FRONTIERS OF THE SEA: *The Story of Oceanographic Exploration*.

he had run out of water and "his wife was thirsty." This underscored the federal government's continuing interest in desalting, even though it did not accurately reflect the progress made since Congress set up the Office of Saline Water (OSW) under the Department of the Interior in 1952. Funds for OSW were about to be voted to continue the government program through 1972. The President wanted to emphasize the need to carry out the mandate vigorously.

But if Lilli Hornig had really been thirsty, her husband need not have waited on the researchers. He could have bought a desalting plant right then that would deliver several million gallons per day (gpd) at a cost of $1 or less per 1,000 gallons. Now, compared to an average cost of 35 cents for municipal water in the United States, a dollar for a thousand gallons is high. But it is inexpensive for the many people whose need for fresh water is acute.

At St. Thomas, Virgin Islands, for example, a 1,000,000-gpd plant has been desalting seawater (and generating 7,500 kilowatts of electric power) since December, 1965, for 90 cents to $1 per 1,000 gallons. Residents consider this a bargain compared to the $2 per 1,000 gallons it cost to produce water in a 1962 desalting plant and the $3 it costs to transport it by barge from Puerto Rico.

Meanwhile, residents of Key West, Fla., are looking forward to a 2,620,000-gpd plant scheduled to go "on stream" in March, 1967. For a while at least, it will be the largest desalting plant in the United States and the biggest single-unit plant in the world. The new plant is expected to produce water for 88 cents. Residents now pay $1.52 per 1,000 gallons for surplus water piped to Key West from the mainland via a pipeline operated by the U.S. Navy.

Even international politics has had a hand in the progress of desalination. In 1964, when Cuban Premier Fidel Castro threatened to "shut off the water" to the U.S. naval base at Guantánamo Bay, Cuba, the navy took over an experimental desalination plant from Point Loma, San Diego, and moved it to the island. Today, this and two other units provide the naval base with its entire water needs—2,200,000 gpd—and generate 15,000 kilowatts of electric power as well.

CUTTING THE COST

These examples typify the growing use of desalination. In a little more than a decade, determined research has cut the cost of desalted water from more than $4 per 1,000 gallons to a point where many coastal communities find it feasible to manufacture fresh water from the easily accessible seawater.

By the middle of 1966, there were enough desalting plants around the world, operating and under construction, to produce over 100,000,000 gpd. World production is expected to exceed 200,000,000 gpd by 1970. Many experts think the figure will be even higher.

And it will need to be. The demand for water is rising rapidly. The United States, for example, consumed water at the rate of 40,000,000 gallons a day in 1900. By 1965, the rate had risen to 359,000,000,000 gpd. It is expected to reach 494,000,000,000—approaching the national dependable water supply—by 1980. Then, there will be little margin for drought or other emergencies.

Desalinated seawater can be a great help to coastal cities. But no matter how inexpensive the desalting process itself becomes, the cost of transporting water long distances, especially above sea level, will preclude its use for areas far from the seacoasts. These areas must turn to *brackish* water—a term for water with a salinity between 1,000 and 20,000 parts per million (ppm) of salts. Seawater, by comparison, averages 35,000 ppm. (The standard for drinking water recommended by the U.S. Department of Health, Education, and Welfare is 500 ppm.) In the United States, there is a great deal of inland water with a brackishness of a few thousand ppm that can be treated for use by nearby cities.

While desalting holds no immediate promise for making deserts bloom, its use is becoming imperative as an additional supply of municipal water where natural sources are becoming exhausted. Israel, for example, expects to fully develop its natural water sources by 1970. To maintain normal economic growth after that, Israel will have to greatly extend its desalting program, now consisting of desalinating plants at Elath on the Red Sea. In southern California, desalted water from a plant proposed by the Metropolitan Water District conceivably could compete in cost with water from a natural source—the Feather River Project—now being developed near Oroville in the northern part of the state. This dam and aqueduct complex is believed to be the last supply of natural water for southern California. In that area, too, desalting one day may be essential.

USING THE ATOM

Both Israel and southern California are participating in large-scale projects involving atomic-powered generators. These plants will provide electric power and heat for the desalination process in one plant. The one proposed for Israel would produce 100,-000,000 gpd plus 200 megawatts of electric power. The southern California project would provide 150,000,000 gpd plus 1,800 megawatts of power. Detailed engineering studies suggest these plants could be in operation by 1970, producing water for under 30 cents per 1,000 gallons. Bigger plants lead to cheaper power, and atomic power has an advantage over conventional power in large installations. This is pointed out by Alvin Weinberg, director of the Oak Ridge National Laboratory. He notes, moreover, that the lowering of the cost of atomic power through advances in reactor technology is what will make plants, such as those proposed for Israel, feasible.

Atomic-powered desalting plants producing over 100,000,000 gpd would also help New York City and other big, water-short seaboard cities hedge against drought. But there are relatively few areas that can use such massive amounts of supplemental water. Over the next decade, plants in the range of 1,000,000 to 25,000,000 gpd will be more useful.

To speed the growth of desalting projects, OSW has set a pair of target costs it hopes to meet by 1970. For large plants—50,000,000 to 150,000,000 gpd—it aims for water costs of 25 to 30 cents per 1,000 gallons. For plants in the 1,000,000 to 15,000,000 gpd range, it wants to keep costs to 60 to 80 cents per 1,000 gallons. Because desalination costs depend on many factors—basic plant design, price of land, financing, labor, and material—OSW expresses its goals in ranges rather than in definite figures.

The processes by which water can be desalinated vary widely. Distillation, first used by the ancient Greeks, is still by far the most successful technique. Simply stated, the process removes dissolved minerals from water by evaporating it, trapping and condensing the vapor, and collecting the condensate which is salt free. More than 90 per cent of today's plants distill their product. Other methods being seriously considered to meet the growing water needs of the world include freezing, reverse osmosis, and electrodialysis.

Distillation is itself achieved in several different ways, ranging from simple evaporation to "flash" methods. The preferred method is based on what engineers call *multistage flash evaporation*.

In a flash plant, the *brine* (saline water) is led through a series of evaporation chambers to a heater. The pipes carrying this relatively cool water provide a surface for steam to condense on. (The condensing steam, in turn, helps warm the incoming water.)

Heated to a temperature just below the boiling point, the brine travels back through the system. First, it flows into the bottom of the first evaporation chamber, where the pressure is slightly below one *atmosphere* (14.7 pounds per square inch at sea level).

As a result of the reduced pressure in the chamber, some of the hot brine explodes or "flashes" into steam. The brine, its temperature lowered a few degrees by the flashing action, flows into a second chamber where the pressure is lower still. Here, more brine flashes into steam. This continues for two dozen or more stages. The brine may be only 100°F. when it enters the last stage, but it still flashes vigorously under a pressure that then may be only one-tenth of an atmosphere. The fresh water, condensing on the outside of the brine-carrying pipes, is collected in a separate section of each of the evaporation chambers.

The third major distillation process under study is vapor compression. It is based on the fact that compressed steam will condense at temperatures above the normal boiling point. OSW is studying this method in a 1,000,000-gpd plant in Roswell, N. Mex. In this plant, brine is contained in a bundle of tubes heated by compressed steam rising around and condensing on the tubes. Some of the heated brine turns into steam at a lower pressure. This, in turn, is compressed and released to the next stage to heat more brine. The condensed steam is collected as fresh water and piped away. One major advantage of this process is that most of the energy for distillation is supplied by mechanical compressors; relatively little heat has to be added. Noting this, Paul Tomalin, staff engineer of the Distillation Branch of OSW, believes vapor compression has a future, especially where electricity is the cheapest energy available.

Further refinements, even of the successful multiflash process, will be difficult. It now is as hard to cut a nickel from the cost per 1,000 gallons as it once was to cut a dollar. Looking ahead, Tomalin says, "The main problem will be just some grubby hard-nosed engineering to get the costs down by details. There is nothing glamorous in this and there probably will be no sudden breakthrough."

Three technical problems contribute to the inefficiencies of distillation: *scaling, corrosion,* and *heat transfer.* Scale is a deposit that builds up on surfaces that come in contact with hot brine. It is a tightly clinging precipitate of materials commonly known as limestone and plaster of Paris (*calcium carbonate* and *calcium sulfate*), similar to what forms inside a teakettle used to boil hard water. In a desalting plant, scaling reduces efficiency by acting as an insulator of heat.

One way to prevent scaling is to soften the seawater before it enters the plant. For example, the addition of acid neutralizes the salts. To remove scale after it has formed, chemicals such as *sodium hexametaphosphate* or *ferric chloride* can be used.

The least expensive way to deal with scale in present desalting plants is to add about 120 ppm of sulfuric acid to the incoming seawater. This increases the cost as much as four cents per 1,000 gallons. But it keeps scaling under control in systems using temperatures as high as 250°F.

Scaling depends on brine concentration as well as temperature. In 1966, the OSW opened bids for the construction of a 1,200,000-gpd plant at Point Loma, San Diego, in which brine temperatures may run as high as 290°F. The plant will be so built that some of the salts can be removed as the brine becomes more concentrated, or more seawater can be added to dilute it, at many points throughout the succession of flashing chambers.

The Point Loma plant should be running by mid-1967. In its predecessor (the one sent to Guantánamo), OSW tested a number of improvements in the multiflash system, including acid pretreatment of the seawater. Besides running at higher temperatures, the new plant will double the 10-to-1 performance ratio of the former plant. This means it will provide 20 gallons of water (instead of 10) for every 1,000 British Thermal Units (BTU) of heat.

Even without the temperature barrier, cost-conscious engineers face a formidable enemy in the second major barrier to distillation efficiency—corrosion. Few usable materials stand up well to the harsh environment of a desalting plant, and those that do are expensive. For example, corrosion resistant copper-nickel alloys are preferred for heat transfer surfaces. But copper-nickel tubing is not only expensive, it is also difficult to obtain in the amounts needed for big plants. Steel, also expensive, is used extensively in distillation plants, including the flashing chambers, where it may represent as much as 40 per cent of the capital cost of the plant.

One hope for cutting costs is to replace steel with concrete chambers. Tests run for OSW by the U.S. Bureau of Mines indicate that concrete is a practical material for distillation plants, and some concrete structures will be tested in the new Point Loma installation. But it is the British who have the most ambitious plans for using the material. The United Kingdom Atomic Energy Authority (UKAEA), which directs Britain's desalting program, is studying the use of concrete in an imaginative new type of distillation plant called *Clementine*.

In this method, concrete flashing stages are stacked one on top of another, instead of being strung out horizontally. Brine, heated by hot oil bubbled through it, enters the bottom of the plant. It is raised from stage to stage by a stepped reduction in pressure, similar to the multiflash systems. At each stage, steam is sucked into a vertical condensing tower where it mingles with, and condenses on, droplets of relatively cool oil. Fresh water and oil are drawn off from the bottom of the tower and separated. The oil is then reheated and returned to the cycle.

Clementine's use of concrete flashing stages could cut capital costs substantially. Also, heating by the oil would eliminate scaling because there would be no solid surface for scale to accumulate on. Moreover, it would be the first system to attack the third obstacle to efficiency—poor heat transfer. By mingling with the water it heats and the vapor it cools, oil transfers heat more efficiently than do solid surfaces.

The UKAEA admits to uncertainties. Oil may taint the water, and there is no assurance that concrete can support the heavy vertical plant. Nevertheless, the British think they may have a pilot plant going within five years. Similar projects are also under study in the United States. But OSW's Tomalin is "not as optimistic about it as the British are."

SOME OTHER METHODS

Meanwhile, other processes are being studied to determine if the snags of distillation can be by-passed altogether. One of them is simple freezing. When seawater is frozen, the ice is free from salt. Washed clean of clinging salts and melted, the ice becomes fresh water. This has two advantages over distillation: minimum scaling, because of low temperatures; and improved efficiency, because less heat has to be taken out of the seawater to freeze it than is put in to boil it. A process kindred to freezing is based on the fact that many substances combine with water to form water-rich crystals called *hydrates*. For example, propane gas bubbled through seawater forms waxy, insoluble crystals about .1 millimeter in diameter which contain 17 molecules of water for every molecule of propane. Washed free of salt and gently warmed, these crystals decompose to yield fresh water and the original propane.

Perhaps the most promising of the nondistillation processes is *reverse osmosis.* In normal osmosis a more concentrated liquid will flow into a less concentrated one. Where fresh water and seawater are separated by a thin membrane, the membrane will let water molecules pass but hold back dissolved salts. Fresh water will flow through the membrane and dilute the salt solution. The molecular action causes pressure to build up on the fresh water side. Therefore, to reverse the flow (to reverse the osmosis), pressure must be put on the salt water side. (For brackish water, for example, about 600 pounds per square inch is necessary.) Fresh water is literally squeezed out of the salt solution.

A BETTER MEMBRANE

The biggest technical problem in reverse osmosis is the membrane. Cellulose acetate, which is now used, is an inherently weak material. Engineers are seeking something that will stand up better to high pressure and permit a greater flow rate than the 10 gpd per square foot so far attained. Everett D. Howe, director of the University of California's Sea Water Conversion Laboratory at Richmond, notes that as of mid-1966, no one had yet been able to keep a membrane in operation for as long as a year. Yet he believes the membrane problem will be solved. "We think we can design a plant to demineralize seawater," he says. John Heintz, chief of special projects at OSW, agrees. He says, "Reverse osmosis looks good. While we have not yet developed a good seawater membrane, there is no reason to doubt that we will."

In reverse osmosis, water does not have to evaporate and condense, or freeze and melt. This saving of energy is an advantage shared with only one other desalting process now of practical interest—*electrodialysis*—a process that takes the salts out of water instead of taking water out of the salts. In electrodialysis, salt water is contained in compartments formed by semipermeable membranes. The membranes let salts pass but hold back water molecules. Under the influence of an electric current, these salts are drawn into adjacent compartments, leaving the fresh water behind.

Electrodialysis is already a commercial success. More than 150 such plants around the world now desalt brackish water. The largest is in Buckeye, Ariz., where the water supply has a salinity of 2,076 ppm. When operating at full capacity, the Buckeye plant should produce 650,000 gpd for about 32 cents per 1,000 gallons. So far, it has been run at only 50 per cent capacity with a water cost almost twice as high. But in Arizona, where fresh water is precious, even this provides inexpensive drinking water.

Where water has a salinity of 10,000 ppm or lower, electrodialysis generally has the economic edge. Between 10,000 and 20,000 ppm, the cost advantage shifts to distillation. It may be a long time, if ever, before electrodialysis will be useful for freshening seawater. It is handicapped by the fact that the cost goes up with increased salinity. Reverse osmosis, in which efficiency is tied less to salinity, does have potential application to seawater.

Howe says that reverse osmosis is now at the stage electrodialysis was 10 years ago. "What is needed," he says, "are more pilot plants to develop the process." These are now under construction. The biggest plant in daily use supplies 4,000 to 7,000 gpd to Coalinga, Calif. Coalinga gets another 28,000 gpd from an electrodialysis plant. Both plants work with water with a salinity of 2,500 ppm. Soon the Coalinga reverse osmosis plant will be joined by two OSW-sponsored portable pilot units. One, a 10,000-gpd unit, to be built in San Diego, will be designed so that it can later be expanded to 100,000 gpd. The other reverse osmosis plant, which is designed to produce 50,000 gpd, will be erected in Azusa, Calif.

Over the next decade, OSW expects the most widely used plants to be moderate-sized multiflash units that will not differ radically from those being built today. Frank C. Di Luzio, Assistant Secretary of the Interior for Water Pollution Control, says that "in terms of the short-range need, large plants—those of 50,000,000 gpd or larger —are the exception rather than the rule. The present world-wide demand for desalting units is for plants of from 1,000,000 to 10,000,000 gpd, with most emphasis on the lower range of the bracket. We expect plants in the size range of 10,000,000 to 25,000,-000 gpd will soon be receiving greater attention."

The new 1,200,000-gpd Point Loma plant is a "process slice" of a 50,000,000-gpd plant. This means it can provide data for estimating the economics of the bigger installation. OSW also will build full-size experimental stations on the West Coast. One, for example, will be built with a capacity of 17,000,000 gpd. Its design will be based on experience gained from the Point Loma plant and from 15 separate design studies being made by U.S. firms. Data from these installations will be needed, among other things, for the final design of the nuclear plants for Israel and southern California.

A NEEDED VARIETY

As the various desalting methods develop, the growth of desalination will be a matter of matching plants and processes to specific needs. Nuclear units already promise distillation at a cost that is reasonable for supplementary water for the relatively few areas that can consume their massive outputs. At the other extreme are relatively expensive solar stills that are serving small communities overseas—mainly islands off Greece and in the Pacific. Were electrodialysis or reverse osmosis never to be feasible for desalting seawater, they would still be valuable for treating the brackish waters that have been called "the most widely distributed natural resource in the United States."

The need for developing several methods of desalination has been expressed by Secretary of the Interior Stewart L. Udall. He has said that while big plants for desalting seawater are important, "we want the technology by which small, economically feasible plants can be strung across this country wherever brackish water is available. . . . That could mean more than anything else in serving our own people and the people of other lands."

FOR FURTHER READING:

Davis, K. S., and Day, J. A., *Water: The Mirror of Science*, Doubleday, 1961.
Desalination Research Conference, Woods Hole, Mass., 1961, *Proceedings of the Conference*, National Research Council, 1963.
U.S. Department of the Interior, *Saline Water Conversion Report for 1965*, U.S. Government Printing Office, 1966.

~~~~~~~~~~~~~~~~

M. Scott Carpenter:

57.   *SEA LAB II TRAINING**

This paper deals briefly with crew selection criteria for the Sea Lab Project, and with the training activities during the 6-month period preceding the Sea Lab II experiment. In the section on daily activities during submersion the scientific investigations are enumerated, some of the Sea Lab and diving equipment is explained, and a num-

* From "Man's Extension Into the Sea," Transactions of the Joint Symposium of the Marine Technology Society, January 11–12, 1966, Washington, D.C. Reprinted by permission of author and the M.T.S.

Having made history with his 3-orbit space flight in May 1962, NASA astronaut M. Scott Carpenter has been involved in the exploration of the ocean depths as an aide to the U.S. Navy Aquanaut Project.

ber of the problems encountered with design and procedure are discussed.

INTRODUCTION

Any manned operation involving exploration or exploitation of a foreign environment is customarily subdivided into two separate but related endeavors:

1. The design, fabrication, and testing of the machines that will be required.

2. The selection, training, and testing of the men who will participate.

Although this discussion is limited mainly to the activities of the crew, it necessarily includes some of the hardware development endeavor because during the period immediately preceding the dive our training consisted solely of redesigning, modifying, completing, and testing the Sea Lab, personnel transfer capsule, and the deck decompression chamber. Considerable work was done on the surface support vessel as well, in order to make her compatible with our needs.

SELECTION

To treat the problem of Sea Lab crew member selection, it is necessary to go back in time to Sea Lab I or perhaps even project Genesis, which was a 2-week 100-psi chamber test prior to Sea Lab I.

In Genesis, Captain Bond selected from among his diver acquaintances men who he intuitively felt were well-qualified to withstand the rigors of isolation and prolonged exposure to high atmospheric pressure. All did exceedingly well. Although I have not discussed the matter in detail with Dr. Bond, I am sure that he agrees with Captain Cousteau, who feels that elaborate selection criteria and testing procedures are unnecessary for selecting small crews. Further, Captain Cousteau says that given the opportunity to talk to a prospective crew member through a 2-hour luncheon he can know beyond any shadow of doubt whether or not that man would make a good member of his team. There is certain merit to this system, but it has shortcomings. Two notable quotes bear on this subject. Sargent Shriver said in Congressional testimony: "Our psychologists have said, and our experience has borne them out, that a selection process must depend on a conglomeration of considerations. No one test nor any one procedure can be counted upon." Dr. Abraham Carp, psychologist with Peace Corps, backing up

Shriver said: "The selection of people is a young science. No one selection tool even begins to be perfect. That is why Peace Corps selection is deliberately structured to bring to bear many different selection tools. As Mr. Shriver testified, no one element of this process is determinative, but each makes a definite and distinctive contribution to the process."

If there is to be a larger program of manned undersea research undertaken by this nation, then we need not only more crewmen but also they must come from a younger age group than the present one, and therefore, out of reach of the personal acquaintance of the current principals in the program.

For instance—with a few exceptions—the Sea Lab II diving team was composed of the crew and surface divers from Sea Lab I. By and large, these men were senior divers with many years experience. Experience is always needed, but there is also a need to enlist younger men to replace, as time wears on, the seniors. This will require a selection program which takes into account interest, age, education, and motivation as well as physical condition and past experience, but with less emphasis on the last.

TRAINING

Training activities for crew members began April 1, 1965, in Panama City, Florida, nearly 6 months prior to the scheduled beginning of the underwater experiment. Classroom work included diving physiology and physics, detailed study of the Mk VI semiclosed circuit breathing apparatus which was used throughout the operation, underwater photography techniques and equipment, and familiarization with the hookah breathing apparatus or "arawak." In addition, many hours were spent becoming familiar with the Mk I SPU or swimmer propulsion unit and other auxiliary equipment, such as test kits and gas charging pumps for the MK VI tanks.

Underwater audio communication equipment, handheld active and passive sonars were studied and operated, and many hours were spent in the diving locker designing and building equipment to support our operation, mix our gas, store and ship our gear. Divers, in addition to being a very special breed are, by necessity, jacks-of-all-trades.

Classroom familiarization with the Mk VI breathing apparatus took 1 week. This may seem excessive, but the Mk VI is not the simple open-circuit scuba gear that most people associate with diving. The gas bottles and carbon dioxide absorbent canister is worn on the back. The control block or pressure and flow regulator is above the center canister. The Mk VI vest is made up of an inhalation bag on the diver's right side and an exhalation bag on his left. Hoses and a mouthpiece connect the two and on the upper part of the exhalation bag is an exhaust valve which can be adjusted in the water by the diver. Adjustment of this valve regulates the amount of each exhalation that is exhausted, usually about one-third, and this is what qualifies the Mk VI as a semi-closed circuit breathing apparatus. This valve, used in conjunction with a bypass valve on the control block, also controls the degree of inflation of the breathing bags. This gives the diver some control of his buoyancy which is very useful when he works at varying depths.

We began our actual use of the equipment in the swimming pool. After two 1-hour sessions, we took to deep water where we conducted the rest of the diving training. One day was spent diving in 30-foot water, 4 days in 60-foot water, 5 days in 100-foot water on nitrogen-oxygen mix, and another 5 days in 200-foot water on helium-oxygen mix.

We were led to believe by some of the divers with hard hat helium-oxygen diving experience that the use of the helium mix would result in much more rapid loss of body heat and more rapid onset of the shivers because of the substantially higher thermal conductivity of the helium. If this was so, it went unnoticed by us.

A good portion of our time was spent in becoming familiar with the physiological and psychological testing equipment and procedures. This was necessary in its own right, of course, but it also provided good base-line performance data on each man. In addition, a day was spent at the Pensacola Naval Hospital with EEG, ECG, cardio-pulmonary function, long bone X-rays, and other physiological base-line studies.

Unfortunately, the entire Sea Lab team was not available for training at the same time which necessitated conducting all of the training at least twice. This, plus the lack of fast surface transportation to deep water, which was quite a way out, made for a not-too-efficient use of our time during this phase of our training.

Throughout the 3-month training period at Panama City there was little opportunity to learn much about Sea Lab II herself, or the two decompression chambers we would be using. When the crew moved to Long Beach in July, we saw for the first time the nearly completed Sea Lab and became busily engaged in learning her functions, valving procedures, mechanisms, and idiosyncrasies. Under the critical eyes of this crew, and those of Captain Walt Mazzone and Joe Berkich of the Naval Ordnance Test Station (NOTS), many design changes were proposed and incorporated.

Serious, potentially fatal deficiencies, involving the design and fabrication of both decompression chambers were uncovered and corrected. Testing procedures had to be devised, operating instructions drawn up—and all by trial and error—before training in the proper use of the PTC and DDC could be conducted. Throughout this period, much time was spent doing the back labor required to get our home ready for the sea floor. The time might have been better spent in study of procedures, blueprints, system operation, and continued on-site deep water exposure with the Mk VI. This however, would have required more men, more time, and of course, more money than we were allotted.

Each day of the 6-month training period was started with 30 to 40 minutes of compulsory physical training in the form of running and calisthenics. I firmly believe that this was one of the most valuable activities in the entire training syllabus. We all needed the exercise, it always got the day off to a good start, it gave the crew a chance to engage in some idle chatter and horseplay as a unit, and it gave everyone something to complain about. All of these, in proper measure, are important to sailor morale.

DAILY OPERATION

The lowering operation went off with only one hitch—the loss of one lab-load of 100-psi helium through improperly sealing port covers. Once this was overcome, the lab was lowered smartly to the bottom, ballasted, monitored for a day, and the occupation began. It was not really that simple at all but the NOTS lowering scheme worked so well that it appeared to be.

The first two divers of the first team opened and inspected the lab. The second two opened and inspected the PTC. When these two jobs had been accomplished, the surface was advised and the other six crew members joined us. Then the work began.

Our first tasks involved unsecuring all of the equipment that had been lashed down for the tow from Long Beach to La Jolla and restowing it so that there was room enough for the ten men. The water lines, safety anchor line, sewage lines, drain lines, diving light leads, benthic lab lines, "arawak" hoses and guide lines had to be connected. All drain plugs, external and internal port covers, and lowering lines had to be removed and stowed. Logistic support from the surface required tremendous expenditures of time and energy both on the surface and below. And so it went throughout the experiment—housekeeping and supply, through pots—for dry equipment, and baskets—for wet equipment, consumed altogether too much time.

Once the lab was reasonably habitable, all of our spare time in the water was devoted to the scientific programs and equipment evaluations. This included the erection of the strength test platform and associated torque wrenches, the two-hand coordinator, the current meter, underwater weather station and sound range, visual acuity range, stationary target array, water clarity meter, pneumofathometer, fish cages, homing beacons, compass rose, external TV cameras, bioluminescence meter, foam and salvage project equipment, bottom current trailers, underwater stud-gun equipment, photo and diving lights, bathythermograph, wave gage, and anti-torque underwater tool test equipment.

Interesting work was done with electrically heated suits. The power was supplied by a battery pack worn around the diver's waist in lieu of his weight belt, or by an umbilical cord leading back to the lab. These suits need considerable refinement before they are completely satisfactory, but they are indispensable to the efficient use of a saturated diver in cold water. Compression of the standard type of wet suit is another problem that needs solution. The surface divers who visited the lab were easily spotted by their paper-thin wet suits. Ours had been in the lab long enough to absorb the high-pressure helium and expand to their normal size, but when they were sent to the surface they suffered an embolism of a sort and needed a like period to contract to their original size. Needless to say, the thermal barrier a suit provides degrades as the suit is compressed and one answer to the cold water might be a suit filled with an incompressible fluid which would help the suit maintain its original thickness.

Our daily jobs consisted of repairing diving lights, adapting equipment to the list and pitch of the lab, replacing leaky valves, cooking, cleaning up, inspecting all equipment for signs of deterioration, repairing "arawak" pumps and gages, improving drainage, setting up the Mk VI breathing equipment and drying all the Mk VI vests and personal equipment. All this is in addition to the activity associated with getting each man into the water at least once each day.

Before and after each dive, strength and manual dexterity tests were performed in the water with the aid of equipment designed specifically for this purpose. Each evening we did daily activity and mood check lists, and occasionally worked with brain teasers and simple arithmetic tests to get a feel for the effect on the higher thought processes the elevated atmospheric pressure might have.

The outside "arawak" hoses continually fouled and kinked and had to be straightened almost daily. And throughout it all, the constant battle with pots and baskets raged.

During the third teams' tenure on the bottom, the storm of activity centered around resupply abated somewhat because of the installation of a high-pressure helium-oxygen mix line in the lab. This line, supplied by pumps on the surface ship, permitted recharging of the Mk VI bottles in the lab instead of sending them topside for refilling. It not only reduced the workload on the men and saved a great amount of time but also was kinder to the equipment.

Although some of us had spent more than one full week practicing with the swimmer propulsion unit (SPU) Mk I, these units were not used during this experiment. Control of this unit is not good and degrades when two men are riding it. That fact, coupled with the very poor visibility and unreliable homing equipment, made the disorientation of a team of divers a likely event. This would be acceptable for surface divers, but for men saturated at 200 feet it would be fatal.

This type of equipment is very definitely needed for future work of this sort, but it needs considerable refinement also before it can be used with any degree of safety by saturated divers.

A substantial amount of time was devoted to physiological studies which are the subject of other papers. We recorded EEGs both inside the lab and on free swimmers. Blood samples were reluctantly given daily by some, and on a less frequent basis by all. Saliva and urine samples were more freely donated. Pulmonary studies continued on a daily basis as did the recording of blood pressure, pulse rate, body temperature, and weight. Although we all ate much more and used more oxygen than we normally did on the surface, we all lost weight. There were no serious medical problems however. The ear infections were easily controlled by medication and drying. The skin rash was not so easily controlled, but not particularly bothersome.

I think the synergistic effect of pressure, humidity, ventilation, and the helium atmosphere was responsible for the fitful sleeping at first, but we acclimated in a few days and the problem disappeared.

Tuffy, the porpoise and the most popular member of the crew, performed very well. He showed himself to be a very fine and funny fellow and proved that he could not only function as courier, but that he could easily locate two separated divers in dark water. A porpoise with this training provides a very effective method for locating a disoriented diver, and showing him the way home by means of a line trailing from his harness and attached to the lab. When Sea Lab III is on the bottom at 450 feet, she will be beyond the reach of surface scuba divers and the value of an animal with this training is greatly enhanced.

CONCLUDING REMARKS

Sea Lab II was a great step forward in man's attempts to colonize the ocean floor. We found there were a number of things we do not need to worry about that we thought we might. For instance, the submerged crew did not experience any marked psychological breakaway from the surface as they were expected to do. They responded to direction from the surface and from the submerged team leader with even more gusto than they did on the surface. Morale was exceptionally good and, except for rare instances, camaraderie flourished everywhere. Further, there was no evidence that I could see of a general slowing down of movement and thinking, and we did not require more sleep than normal plus an afternoon nap. Subjectively, there was really no way to be aware of the strange environment except by looking out of the port holes or by listening to your own voice. We also discovered many things that must be done before we pursue this course much further. Among them:

1. Develop a reliable diver-diver-surface-sea lab communication system, one that does not compromise the breathing apparatus and does not encumber the diver with wires. It must also incorporate integrally a helium voice unscrambler.

2. Develop a reliable, durable, easily donned and doffed heated suit.

3. Develop a self-contained closed circuit breathing apparatus which carries enough gas to support a diver at 1000 feet for 3 to 4 hours. Cryogenic storage may be required, and new methods for monitoring carbon dioxide and oxygen are definitely needed.

4. Develop small, reliable, light-weight sonar equipment as part of the communication equipment. This is an absolute requirement if we are to have any reasonable diver mobility in dark and dirty water.

Perhaps the most important need that became apparent after the successful completion of Sea Lab II is that of better public recognition of its meaning. The whole endeavor is not yet well understood. Knowledgeable engineers still come to me and say, "Didn't you feel awful cooped up inside that thing?"—or—"Were you ever able to get out of it?" Many people with above average awareness think Sea Lab II was just a submerged pressure chamber test and have no inkling of its essence.

The essence of man-in-the-sea, in my opinion, is twofold. First, it is to make man a free agent to explore and work underwater with mobility, efficiency, endurance, and reliability comparable to that of a man working on dry land. Second, it is to allow him to exploit the ocean floor, and here it is necessary to make people aware of the tremendous potential for exploitation that awaits us on the sea floor. Conservative estimates show that the bottom of the ocean holds riches beyond measure in the form of diamonds, gold, copper, manganese, oil, fresh water, artifacts, and yes, even pirate's treasures. The paradox is that most of this wealth lies within a scant 1000 feet of a luxury liner's dance floor, and yet it is farther from the state-of-the-art to attain than it is to prospect the far side of the moon—240,000 miles away. Great benefits await no matter where we explore, but it is clearly apparent that the most immediately available are waiting for us underwater.

~~~~~~~~~~~~~~

Milner B. Schaefer:

58. OCEANOGRAPHY AND MARINE
     FISHERIES*

Oceanography, for fisheries or any other purposes, is concerned with *describing* the distribution of physical, chemical and biological properties and their changes in space and time, and with *understanding* the forces and processes that bring these things about, and the interrelationships among all of the different factors. The descriptive phase, that is determining *what* happens *when* and *where*, is of considerable use to the development of the commercial fisheries. However, understanding *why* brings the application of the observations to much firmer ground, especially when it comes to reliably forecasting future events.

At the present stage, the descriptive aspects of oceanography are

* From Circular 250, September, 1966, the U.S. Bureau of Commercial Fisheries.

Milner B. Schaefer is the co-author of another contribution to this volume: "The Ocean as a Receptacle" (Ch. 41).

rather better advanced than the analytical aspects, but large and rapid advances have been made in both since the end of the last great war, and particularly during the past decade. During this period we have obtained a vastly increased store of observational data, and there have been large increases in our understanding of the basic physics, chemistry, and biology of the oceans, and of the ecology and behaviour of populations of harvestable living organisms. The oceanographers' increasing capabilities to provide the information and understanding on which to base fisheries development is due in no small part to new developments in precise, rapid and sophisticated instrumentation and methods of observation. Observational coverage of the ocean has become more extensive and more intensive, both by the employment of many more research vessels, and by development of improved systems of data acquisition from the fishing fleets, merchant fleets, weather satellites, and so forth. Finally, we are enabled quickly to digest vast quantities of new information because of the development of rapid data processing systems, using high speed computers.

Oceanographic knowledge assists in increasing the harvest of the sea in five ways: (1) Location of new highly productive fishing areas. (2) Identification and location of promising unutilized fishery resources. (3) Providing the fisherman information which he can use to improve his tactical scouting and catching operations. (4) Forecasting space and time variations in the abundance and catchability of fish populations. (5) Providing the scientific basis of rational management of the heavily exploited fisheries. I will deal here with the first four of these topics, passing over the fifth, despite its very great importance, because of the limited time allotted for this presentation, and because it is a subject with which I am sure you are already very familiar.

LOCATION OF NEW PRODUCTIVE FISHING AREAS

Until 10 or 15 years ago, new fishing grounds were, with few exceptions, discovered by venturesome fishermen, and occasionally by governmental fishery explorations, trying out new areas, with little or no help from physical or biological oceanography. Following the discovery of new fishing areas by such exploratory fishing, the oceanographers came along and found out why these areas were highly productive. In each case, they found that the rich fisheries occur at or near those locations where large quantities of organic matter are produced by the phytoplankton, due to fertilization of the sunlit upper layer of the sea by upwelling, mixing along current boundaries, winter overturn, stirring of nutrients up from shallow bottoms, or other physical processes. With increased capabilities for studying the ocean circulation, for directly measuring phytoplankton productivity, for assessing abundance of larger organisms using underwater sound and other techniques, and with increased understanding of why the fertile ocean areas are fertile and the desert areas are desert, the oceanographers have become of more use in pioneering in the location of promising new fishing areas.

For example, the northwest coast of Africa has long been known to be a region of strong coastal upwelling, and measurements of basic productivity and standing crops of phytoplankton indicated that there should be abundant populations of organisms which might be harvestable by the commercial fisheries. This led to exploratory expeditions by the Russians, and more recently by others, including some from the United States, to examine into the fishery potential of this area in relation to oceanographic factors. In consequence, there have been discovered sizeable populations of tunas, of *Sardinella*, and of various demersal species as well.

Investigations of the physical and biological oceanography of the equatorial Pacific, in advance of and along with exploratory fishing operations, have greatly accelerated the development of the pelagic fisheries for tunas and spearfishes, conducted mostly by Japanese fishermen.

The most recent example is the incipient development of a large new fishery on the western side of the Indian Ocean which, I am sure, will be of major importance. Studies of this area carried out cooperatively during the Indian Ocean Expedition by oceanographers of the United States, England, Russia, and other countries demonstrate that this is a region of high basic productivity, associated with vertical circulation related to the monsoon winds, and there have been observed sizeable populations of sardines, mackerels, tunas, and other fishes.

Other examples of the utility of oceanography in the location and development of rich new fishing areas are the fisheries developments which are just commencing off the coasts of Chile and Argentina.

IDENTIFICATION AND LOCATION OF UNUSED RESOURCES

Even in those areas of the sea which have been long exploited by the commercial fisheries, systematic scientific observations may lead to the identification of important latent resources. For example, the systematic studies of the California Current, which have been going on for a number of years, and which had as their initial motivations the investigation of the ecology and fishery dynamics of the California sardine, have led to important discoveries of unused resources. One of the techniques of these investigations is systemtic surveys of the occurrence of sardine larvae and other fish larvae. One dominant element in the catches of fish larvae is the Pacific hake, from which it was inferred that there is a large latent resource of this species which might prove to be commercially exploitable. Following this lead, systematic explorations by echo sounding and by experimental trawling, have revealed large commercially exploitable concentrations along the coast of Washington, Oregon and northern California. It appears that this species moves south and somewhat offshore to spawn, and moves north on a feeding migration, although many of the details remain to be worked out. Whether the stocks are commercially exploitable, not only off Washington and Oregon, but also to the south in the vicinity of the spawning grounds remains to be investigated. These systematic surveys of fish larvae have also revealed that, with the decline of the sardine population, its close competitor, the anchovy, has increased very greatly in abundance. Scientists of the California Cooperative Fishery Investigations estimate that there is off California and Baja California a standing stock of some two to four million tons of anchovies, that could sustain a harvest of perhaps half a million tons per year, or more, and they believe that the reduction of the anchovy population might, at the same time, accelerate the recovery of the sardine population. These investigations have also indicated that the stock of jack mackerel, of which only some 40 to 50 thousand tons per year are currently harvested, extends westward over a vast region of the Pacific and could support a much larger fishery.

Another example of systematic observations revealing an unrealized resource is the recent development of the expanded fishery for swordfish in the northwest Atlantic, employing floating longlines at night. This was discovered, almost accidentally, by our colleagues at Woods Hole Oceanographic Institution in the course of their studies related to the bluefin and yellowfin tuna.

FISH BEHAVIOUR IN RELATION TO CATCHING OPERATIONS

The foregoing kinds of information are helpful to the fishing industry in indicating those sea areas, and often also the particular seasons, where abundant exploitable populations occur. The fisherman has, however, additional problems of locating fish shoals within a general area and then of catching them rapidly and efficiently.

Knowledge of the local distribution of the fish in relation to the properties of their environment, and knowledge of their behaviour, especially as it may vary in relation to measurable properties of the environment, can be useful to the fisherman in his tactical operations. If the oceanographer can indicate to the fisherman what measurements he himself can take at sea in order to guide his scouting and catching operations, this can increase his efficiency and cut down his cost of production. Some success has been achieved in these matters, but I am sure that we can do a good deal better as we learn more.

One of the things that both scientists and fishermen have known how easily to measure for a great many years is water temperature, both surface and subsurface. Also, the surface temperature of the ocean is the one physical measurement that is, and has been for many years, routinely observed as part of the merchant ship weather reporting system. Consequently, we have been able to learn a good deal about the local distributions of some kinds of fish in relation to temperature, and this knowledge can be of some tactical advantage to the fishermen. A few examples:

The North Pacific albacore, which are summer visitors to waters off the west coast of the United States, prefer water of temperature 60 to 66°F, about two-thirds of the total catch being made in waters of these temperatures. In directing their scouting operations, therefore, it is useful to the fishermen to consult the sea-surface temperature charts which are published by the Bureau of Commercial Fisheries at two-week intervals during the summer, and to take their own temperature measurements while searching for the albacore schools.

At the northern and southern extremes of their ranges, the distributions of the tropical tunas, yellowfin and skipjack, vary in relation to the water temperature, being limited by the lowest temperatures in which these species occur in commercial concentrations. Within the range of tolerable temperatures, however, the location of fish concentrations appears to be related to the food supply. All along Baja California there are large crops of forage organisms at all times of the year, yet the yellowfin tuna are found in there in commercial quantities only in waters of about 19°C and warmer, while skipjack occur in somewhat cooler water, down to about 17°C. These temperatures also limit the distributions of these species at the southern end of the range, off Peru and Chile. This knowledge of relationship between water temperature and occurrence of commercial concentrations of tropical tunas is not of great utility to California tuna fishermen at the northern end of the range, since the vessels must traverse these waters in any event to get to the fishing areas to the south. However, off Peru and Chile, the fishermen can benefit both from consulting the temperature charts which are issued at monthly intervals, and also by using their own thermometers as an aid in their scouting operations.

Investigations of the distributions of cod in relation to temperature in the vicinity of Bear Island, between Norway and Spitzbergen, by English scientists, have revealed useful relationships between the bottom temperatures and the location of paying concentrations of cod. It has been shown that paying quantities are rarely caught in water colder than 1.75°C, except in summer when the fish are feeding heavily to the east of Bear Island and may be found down to —0.5°C. In early summer and autumn, on grounds west of Bear Island, Atlantic water touching the Bear Island banks can give good cod catches with bottom temperature between 3° and 5°C. Thus, measurements of bottom water temperature can be useful to the trawlers in searching for concentrations of cod in this area.

Another relationship of tuna to their environment which appears to be of tactical value to tuna fishermen is the distribution and behaviour of the tropical tuna (in the eastern Pacific at least) in relation to the depth of the mixed layer and the structure of the underlying thermocline. The schools of tropical tuna occur in the upper mixed layer of warmer, low density water, which may vary from 10 to 80 meters deep, and which is underlain by colder water, the sharpness of transition (from the upper mixed layer to the underlying water), called the thermocline, being variable. Data respecting the percentage of successful purse-seine sets on tuna schools in relation to these factors indicate that the schools escape through the bottom of the net less frequently when the mixed layer is shallow, especially when it is shallower than the depth to which the net fishes, and when the gradient of temperature in the thermocline is very sharp. By measuring the vertical distribution of temperature, by bathythermographs or other means, the fishermen may, therefore, assist themselves in selecting situations where the escape rate is minimized.

A local phenomenon which often corresponds to fish concentrations is the occurrence of fronts, which are boundaries between water masses. Along such boundaries, which can often be located by sharp temperature transitions, differences in water color, and occurrence of floating debris, the associated vertical circulation often concentrates the plankton organism, which in turn leads to concentration of forage fishes and of the predatory fishes which prey upon them. Japanese long-line fishermen, for example, find that laying their gear along and across such fronts, which the Japanese call "siome", improves their fishing success. Similarly, the near-surface schools of pelagic fishes are frequently found more abundant near these features.

It is also well known that tunas, as well as some other marine fish species, tend to be more concentrated in the vicinity of sea-mounts, which the fishermen refer to as "banks". The discovery of new seamounts, both by the fishermen and by our submarine geologists have, therefore, led to the discovery of increasing numbers of good fishing spots. Bottom topography charts, together with echo sounders, thus can be used by the fishermen to good advantage.

The relationships of the harvestable fish to aggregations of their food organisms is also a potentially useful tool which fishermen may sometimes use to improve their own fishing operations, although this is not as yet very well developed. For example, the relationship between herring and the copepod *Calanus* on which it feeds is sufficiently close to assist the fishermen in locating herring by their own plankton collections in at least some situations in the North Sea and in the Barents Sea. Such simple instruments as the Hardy plankton indicator have been developed for the use of the fishermen in these situations.

FORECASTING SPACE AND TIME VARIATIONS

What both fishermen and fish processors would most like to have from oceanographers are reliable future forecasts of fishing locations and expected catches of particular kinds of fish.

To make such forecasts for any kind of fish, we need to have useful estimates of the magnitude of the exploitable fish populations, understanding of the distribution and behaviour of the fish in relation to measurable properties of the ocean (such as temperature, salinity, depth of mixed layer, strength of currents and upwelling), and means of predicting the space and time changes in the oceanic properties and processes. Considerable progress has been made on all of these, and in some instances useful forecasts a few to several weeks hence are possible. But we have yet a long way to go.

Through the compilation and analysis of statistics on catch and effort, and age composition of catches, supplemented in some instances by estimates of abundance of young fish prior to their entry into the stock of commercial sizes, methods have been developed for forecasting the magnitude of fish populations which will be available to the fishery. Well known examples are the New England haddock, Bristol Bay red salmon, sockeye and pink salmon of the Frazer River, yellowfin tuna of the Eastern Pacific, California sardines and anchovies.

As already noted, we have also some useful, but primitive, understanding of the relationships of some kinds of fish to environmental factors, usually temperature. One example not yet mentioned is the skipjack population of the Central Pacific near the Hawaiian Islands, a large component of which inhabits the waters of the California Current Extension, identifiable by temperature and salinity. As these waters shift northerly through the vicinity of Hawaii each summer, the "season" skipjack appear, their availability varying with the time and extent of the shift in the boundary between the California Current Extension and the water mass to the north. Another well known, large scale phenomenon is the "El Niño" off northern South America, which, at irregular intervals, averaging about seven years, brings abnormally warm surface waters to the coast of Peru, resulting in great shifts in the populations of anchovies, bonito, tuna, etc., and catastrophic effects on the guano birds.

Forecasting of ocean conditions, and hence of effects on the fisheries, is presently mostly what might be called "pattern and persistence" forecasting, supplemented to a limited extent by knowledge of the dynamic processes of the atmosphere and the sea. This is rather similar to much local weather forecasting, and is not very satisfactory. We rely on the facts that changes in the upper layer of the ocean, which are fundamentally due to the wind-driven circulation and the water and heat exchanges between sea and atmosphere, tend to occur in repetitive patterns, and that anomalies tend to persist for some weeks. The ocean is considerably more sluggish in its changes than is the atmosphere; it has been said that a week in the ocean is comparable to a day in the atmosphere.

This type of forecasting has enabled oceanographers to make useful predictions in the early spring of the success of the skipjack fishery near Hawaii during the summer. Similarly, from temperature and salinity distributions and trends off the United States west coast, forecasts are made each year of the expected catch of the albacore and bluefin tuna, and of the most probable areas of good albacore fishing. From the trends of temperature, which affect growth of kelp, it is possible to make some very general estimates of the expected kelp harvest along southern California. Upwelling in the Gulf of Panama, which influences the abundance of pink shrimp in shallower waters during the winter months, can be forecast somewhat better than chance. The continuing monitoring of the Peru Current by the Instituto del Mar der Peru has enabled short-term forecasting of success of anchovy fishing there.

We are, I believe, on the threshold of being able to do much better, through monitoring of atmospheric circulation and heat exchange between sea and atmosphere. As I have noted above, these are the principal driving forces on the upper layers of the sea, and the dynamic relationships between them and the ocean circulation are becoming increasingly better understood. It should soon be possible, given an adequate network of stations for observations of the atmosphere over the sea and of the upper layer of the ocean, by automatic unmanned stations (meteorological and oceanographic buoys) both to keep track of what the ocean is doing, in real time, and to forecast changes which will affect the fisheries.

To enable a really large advance in oceanographic forecasting, the observational net must be sufficient to describe the entire physical system, consisting of the atmosphere and the upper mixed layer of the sea for the whole globe, or at least a hemisphere. The cost of such a data acquisition system, and associated processing by computers, will be large, much larger than can be supported for fisheries alone. Fortunately, the same kind of ocean forecasting that is needed by the fisheries interests is also needed for other purposes, such as weather forecasting, ship routing, and several aspects of military ocean operations. We may hope to have such a system of data acquisition, and processing in real time, which is now within our technical capability, in operation within the coming decade.

~~~~~~~~~~~~~~~

Frank P. Rossi:

59.   *SEAQUAKES: SHAKERS OF SHIPS**

The Navy communications research ship *Belmont* left Callao, Peru, at 1300 GMT on October 17, 1966, proceeding at 5 kt. in good weather. Sometime later, shortly before 2143 GMT, the captain

* From *Mariners Weather Log*, Vol. 11, No. 5, September, 1967. Reprinted by permission of the author.

The editor of *Mariners Weather Log*, Frank P. Rossi is a commissioned officer of the Environmental Science Services Administration.

ordered a course change and the speed increased to 10 kt. Suddenly, the vessel began to shake.

The *Belmont* has a critical speed of 9 kt. and at first the skipper, Cdr. Scappini, thought the vibration was due to the ship's passing through this speed. But the vibration continued and became worse. The ship's mast whipped and so did her many antennas. Down on the mess deck crockery was smashed. Everything that wasn't tied down came adrift. After an estimated 12 to 18 sec. the vibration ended, just as suddenly as it had begun.

Cdr. Scappini ordered the engines stopped and general quarters sounded. "I knew we weren't aground," he later reported. "The Exec said we had 62 fathoms beneath the keel." After it was determined that there was no damage or fouling, the engines were again started and a speed of 10 kt. ordered. Only a slight shudder was felt when the critical speed of 9 kt. was reached—as normally expected.

The *Belmont* had experienced a seaquake. "I don't think there was a man aboard who wasn't scared," Cdr. Scappini commented. "I've been caught in typhoons and even the eye of a hurricane, but I've never before gone through anything like this, and I hope never to again."

On vessels at sea, earthquake shocks produce effects which vary but little, except in intensity. A rumbling sound is first heard, quickly followed by a series of shocks under which the ship either trembles or is so suddenly arrested in its course that it produces the impression of grounding upon a rock. A number of such shock series may be received in succession, after which the ship appears to slide over the "shoal" and continue its course as before. The intensity of shipboard seismic effects varies greatly, but an analysis of ship reports describing seaquakes, considered with respect to local geological conditions and available instrumental data, reveals several generalities that are in line with facts known about landquakes.

The principal seismic effect aboard ship is the jackhammering vibrations induced on the hull by the arrival of the P wave (primary wave, longitudinal). Upon entering the less dense water from the sedimentary covering on the ocean floor this compressional-type wave is bent by refraction and deflected almost vertically to the sea surface at 0.8 mi. per second. Frequently, the first P waves to arrive on the surface of the sea are not strong enough to be felt aboard ship and will pass into the atmosphere above the sea to create a sound wave. When the frequency of the sound wave is high enough to be audible a loud "booming" noise will immediately precede the actual vibrations. Sound is not heard in all earth-quakes, and it is possible under certain conditions to have the sound without the vibrations.

The duration of the vibrations may vary from a fraction of a second to several minutes. Ship reports indicate a usual duration of between 15 and 60 sec. When the P wave arrives at the sea surface its period is short and amplitude very low. Normally, the amplitude is so small there is no indication of a disturbance in the appearance of the sea surface. Yet this wave front simultaneously striking the complete underwater portion of the hull produces enough energy to cause severe vibrations. Rarely have these vibrations damaged ships, but a report from a ship near 18°03'N., 103°19'W., on April 15, 1941, stated that earthquake vibrations caused "a large deckload of steel assembly, some pieces weighing 6 tons, to shift about 6 in. and to jump as much as 5 to 6 in. up and down from its blocks." Also on June 15, 1966, the MV *Ninghai* at 10°35'S., 161°05'E., in the Solomon Islands, reported the following damage after being shaken repeatedly at various intervals for about 2 hr. "The cathode ray tube shattered, the capillary tube in the barometer (was) smashed, valves were shaken out of their sockets in the wireless transmitter, the suspension wire on the gyro snapped and the azimuth mirror on the monkey island gyro repeater fell off. In addition we made some water in No. 3 double bottoms and after peak; also the main engine fuel line was broken and the sanitary tank on the monkey island was holed. No water was made after the tremors, which suggests that as the ship was being shaken water was entering these tanks through various rivets and seams which had started and opened, but only for the duration of these tremors. The masts whipped about a great deal, and the funnel rattled alarmingly."

Occasionally, there is a weaker but definitely distinguishable second set of vibrations closely following the original jolt. This is not a twin quake but the arrival of part of the energy from the slower S wave (secondary wave, transverse). When this sheer wave strikes the density discontinuity at the ocean floor, part of the energy is reflected back into the earth and part of the energy is transformed into a compressional-type wave and deflected almost vertically into the less dense water. There is an energy loss in this transformation, but the arrival of the S wave under the hull is quite perceptible under proper conditions. If a vessel is in the immediate epicentral area of a shallow quake, the arrival of the second group will only tend to intensify the original vibrations and may not be detected. When the epicentral distance is too great the arrival of a weak second group may be imperceptible. However, there is a definite area between the two extremes in which the arrival of the S wave group is easily distinguishable.

The intensity of shipboard vibrations is determined by internal as well as external variables. Internal factors include the type and construction of the ship, the nature and amount of cargo on board—as well as the manner in which it is stowed—and under certain conditions, the position in which the cargo-handling gear or other heavy equipment is secured. Among the external variables the magnitude of the earthquake (determining the amount of energy released) and the depth of the original fracture (hypocenter) are very important. Frequently, the perpendicular distance to the fault along which the original fracture occurred may be more important than the epicentral distance. The earthquake energy tends to travel great distances down or parallel to the fault with little loss of intensity, but the perceptibility tends to fall off rather rapidly as the perpendicular distance from the fault increases. Although weather has no bearing on the origin of an earthquake, the effects (vibrations) on a ship may be magnified by unfavorable weather conditions.

An excellent example of the varied manner in which individual ships, located at random about the epicenter of an earthquake are affected, is available from a review of the ship reports describing experiences during the large shallow Mexican earthquake of June 3, 1932. Although slight motions were felt throughout the early morning hours in the mountainous area behind Manzanillo, it was not until 1037 GMT that the principal shock occurred. The epicenter, located about 30 mi. inland near 19.5°N., 104.3°W., fell in the chain of volcanic mountains that traverse Mexico in an east-west trend and are, probably, a continental continuation of the long straight Clarion Fracture Zone that originates in the Central Pacific and passes through the volcanic Revilla Gigedo Islands before emerging on the Mexican coast.

During the early morning hours of June 3, 1932, the SS *Solana* was steaming through a smooth sea with light variable winds near 18°30′N., 104°08′W. At 1037 GMT she was violently shaken for about 7 sec. The ship was then about 60 mi. (170°) from the epicenter in approximately 800 fathoms of water and did not detect any change in the state of the sea. The perpendicular distance to the fault zone was also about 60 mi.

A few miles to the southwest at 18°20′N., 104°32′W., the MV *Sevenor* experienced, at the same time, vibrations that were less severe but of longer duration (1 min.). The *Sevenor* was approximately 70 mi. (191°) from the epicenter and the perpendicular distance to the fault zone was between 65 and 70 mi. The ship reported a calm sea and slight westerly swells and detected no noticeable change in the surface of the sea.

Conditions aboard the MV *Northern Sun* at 19°56′N., 106°14′W. were entirely different. Although the vessel was 115 mi. (285°) from the epicenter, the perpendicular distance to the probable fault zone was probably not more than 10 mi. Vibrations, commencing at 1029 GMT, continued for 3 min. and became so violent that the engines were stopped. Before the earthquake, the sea had been smooth with a slight westerly swell, but by 1046 GMT the swell pattern had changed and the sea was confused.

Farther to the north at 20°28′N., 106°20′W., the SS *Arizona* commenced to vibrate at 1039 GMT and continued to do so for about 75 sec. The ship was about 130 mi. (297°) from the epicenter with a slight southwesterly sea and did not notice any change in the state of the sea. The perpendicular distance to the fault was probably somewhat over 40 mi.

The after shocks continued for many days. Ship reports indicate that during the next 36 hr. several strong underwater disturbances were experienced in the area. The MV *Silverwillow* at 18°45′N., 104°34′W. began to vibrate dangerously in every part and at the same time began an uneven short pitching motion followed by heavy rolling. The disturbances commenced at 0530 GMT on June 4, and the rolling continued for 15 min. Seven hours later at 1245 GMT in 19°31′N., 105°45′W. the crew aboard the SS *Talamanca* heard a loud noise like distant gunfire, then experienced severe vibrations, and at 1337 GMT two similar reports were heard about 10 sec. apart but there were no apparent vibrations. However, 20 min. later the sea surface was littered for 5 or 6 mi. with small white oval objects, presumably dead fish. Several hours later near 19°28′N., 106°06′W., the SS *Hanover* reported at 1205 ship's time (probably 1905 GMT) violent shocks that rocked the ship as a nearby explosion might. Fifteen minutes later 2 more shocks were experienced with only slight vibrations.

The main quake caused considerable damage throughout the countryside inland of Manzanillo and inundated the immediate coastal area with a minor tsunami. Tide gauges in Hawaii recorded a 2½-ft. wave and 12 hr. after the earthquake the boxlike harbor of Pago Pago, over 4,400 mi. southwest of the epicenter, experienced a series of sea level fluctuations on the order of 8 ft. for over an hour.

It is a quite general but not universal observation that the surface of the sea shows no indication of the seismic disturbance. Though the sea may have been without a ripple and as smooth as a surface

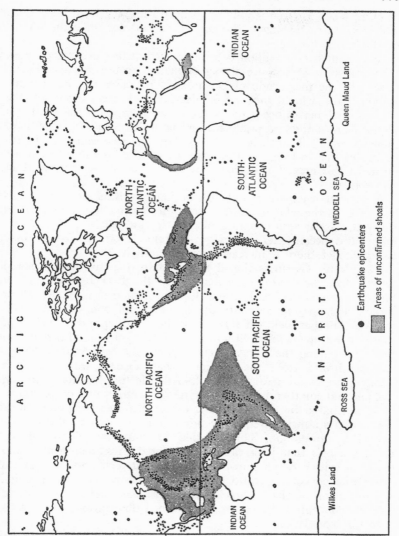

Fig. 59–1. The world distribution of seismic activity is depicted by the earthquake epicenters. There is a good correlation between seismic activity and reports of unconfirmed shoals.

of glass, a shock severe enough to startle the crew from deep sleep and bring them rushing to the deck often will not ruffle the surface of the water.

At present over 1 million detectable earthquakes occur each year, of which at least 700 are strong enough to cause damage. Fortunately, as the magnitude of earthquakes increases the relative frequency with which they occur decreases. Three-quarters of the world's earthquakes occur under the ocean floor, with the Northern Hemisphere more susceptible to seismic activity than the Southern Hemisphere. The area below 30°S. latitude represents one-fourth of the earth's surface, yet less than 10 percent of our earthquakes occur in this area. Earthquakes are unknown on the continent of Antarctica.

A chart showing the world distribution of seismic activity reveals that the earthquake epicenters occur in narrow belts and zones easily correlated with certain geological features such as high mountain chains, oceanic trenches, ridges, and rises. Normally, where there is high relief there is increased seismic activity.

The Pacific Ocean is ringed by a system of active volcanic and seismic belts and a branch extends into the East Indies. Another branch extends eastward across Central America into the West Indies. This system accounts for four-fifths of the world's earthquakes. Another belt extends from the Mediterranean region of southern Europe across southern Asia. Active belts are also found in the oceans along the Tonga Trench, down the Mid-Atlantic Ridge, and southward from the central Indian Ocean, with a branch swinging westward across the South Atlantic towards the Sandwich Trench and another branch swinging eastward south of Australia.

As illustrated by the comments of the *Belmont's* captain, vibrations from seaquakes frequently produce a sensation similar to that caused by grounding. This has led to numerous reports of uncharted shoals that later cannot be located. A similar relationship seems to exist between ship reports of distant reefs and rocks awash and those concerning early stages of submarine volcanic activity. A comparison of charts showing the earthquake belts of the world and the concentrated areas of unconfirmed observations reveal a remarkable correlation.

Observers should always include the precise time (GMT) of observation when reporting a suspected obstruction so that in its evaluation, the possibility of a seismic disturbance can be explored.

~~~~~~~~~~~~~~~~~~~~~~

Willard J. Pierson, Jr.:

60.   UNDERSTANDING AND FORECASTING
PHENOMENA AT THE AIR-SEA
INTERFACE*

Not very long ago, NASA released a photograph showing the whole earth. The New York *Daily News* had both a story with the caption "The Earth says 'Cheese'!" and also a cartoon showing a spacecraft, with a robotlike appearance, snapping a picture of a smiling earth.

The tenth anniversary of the launching of Sputnik occurred in September 1967, and since then, our planet has been photographed by spacecraft from altitudes varying from several hundred miles to 220,000 miles. Photographs, really often television images, from the Gemini series (NASA 1967), the Tiros series, the two Nimbus spacecraft, the ESSA spacecraft, the Applied Technology satellite, and Lunar Orbiter 5 have been made. Some are in the visible band of electromagnetic radiation, and others are in various portions of the infrared.

At the mean distance of the earth from the sun, approximately 93 million miles, each square centimeter of the disk of the earth[1] receives 2 langleys of solar radiation per minute at the top of the atmosphere. The total radiation reaching the top of the atmosphere in one minute equals 2.54×10^{18} langleys. Of this total, approximately 30 to 35 per cent on a global annual average is returned to space more or less unaltered, and a part of it reaches the spacecraft and is used to make the photographs.

Each time such a photograph is taken, valuable scientific data are obtained. The light that reaches the spacecraft to form the

---

*From a paper presented at the Governor's Conference on Oceanography at the Rockefeller University, New York, N.Y. October 12, 1967. Reprinted by permission of the author.

Dr. Willard J. Pierson, Jr. is professor of Oceanography at New York University. He is the co-author (with G. Neumann) of PRINCIPLES OF PHYSICAL OCEANOGRAPHY, published in 1966.

[1] i.e., a circle with the earth's radius in a plane normal to the rays of the sun.

image that makes the photograph can be analyzed to determine the local instantaneous and the space and time averaged albedo of the earth. To the eyes of scientists, these photographs, and other methods that sense radiation in the visible and infrared, present a wealth of information as in the work of Widger, Rogers, and Sherr (1966); Winston and Rao (1963); Rasool and Prabhakara (1966); and Arking and Levine (1967). For example, Rasool and Prabhakara used Tiros VII data to determine the amount of solar radiation absorbed by the atmosphere, oceans and land as a function of the time of the year and the latitude, and Arking and Levine have determined the albedo of the earth as a function of latitude and month.

That part of the solar radiation that is not returned to space mostly travels through the atmosphere and is absorbed at the surface of the earth. Were one langley to be completely absorbed by one cubic centimeter of water, the temperature of the water would go up one degree Celsius, and since 71 per cent of the surface of our planet is water, a very large fraction of that 2.54×10^{18} langleys per minute is being absorbed at the surface of the ocean. The amount of radiation actually being absorbed by the oceans, or the land, at a particular minute of the day depends on the position of the sun in the sky, on the clarity of the atmosphere, and on the clouds. Some new facts and a better understanding of this part of the problem has been provided in work by Hollman (1968). Scientifically calibrated images that can also be presented in the form of photographs provide a way to measure the amount of solar radiation that enters into the heat and radiation budget of the earth on a day-to-day global basis.

Both the ocean and land surfaces radiate in the infrared to heat the atmosphere. The infrared radiation from the sea surface and evaporation from the sea surface are important effects so that actually not very much solar radiation is used to warm the oceans. The atmospheric and surface infrared radiation eventually returns to space. For a grand average over many years over the whole earth, the total of the outgoing short wave and infrared radiation must equal the incoming solar radiation.

The incoming short wave radiation exceeds the outgoing long wave radiation in equatorial regions and the outgoing long wave radiation exceeds the incoming short wave radiation in the polar regions. This difference both causes, in one sense, and is due to, in another sense, the winds and storms of the atmosphere and the currents in the ocean. The infrared radiation to space of the large continents of the northern hemisphere during the northern hemisphere winter is part of a total system in which the atmosphere and the oceans transport heat northward from as far south as 30°S, to overcome this heat loss and keep the northern hemisphere winters from being even colder than they are, as shown by Rasool and Prabhakara (1966). This work, though based on spacecraft data, required an oceanographic input to provide the final results shown here.

Many phenomena occur at the air-sea interface. Storm surges driven by the winds of the atmosphere pile up water along coasts; the winds over the ocean in the planetary boundary layer raise mountainous storm seas that travel thousands of miles as swell across the oceans. The moving air in the planetary boundary layer is relatively dry as it moves out from a continent over the oceans and evaporates vast quantities of water vapor from the ocean surface. The winds of the atmosphere and the density differences in the oceans due to variations in salinity and temperature bring about the currents in the ocean that circulate in ocean scale gyres producing strong western boundary currents such as the Gulf Stream. The Gulf Stream carries warm water poleward in a narrow band bordering on colder coastal waters.

The air-sea interface, as the modern generation would say, is where the action is. It is the region where some of the solar radiation is transformed to sensible heat to raise the temperature of the air and the water. At this interface, latent heat, carried by water vapor evaporated by the winds from the oceans, which is a physical phenomenon one step removed from solar radiation, is supplied to the atmosphere to fuel the intertropical front, the hurricanes and typhoons that are spawned in the tropics, and the cyclones of middle latitudes. The waves and currents generated by the winds act as momentum sinks for the atmosphere, and the currents carry heat poleward to warm the polar regions.

When the details of the entire system are studied, the energy fluxes, that is radiation, latent, and sensible heat, at the air-sea interface prove to be of a magnitude comparable to the incoming solar radiation and the radiation fluxes in the troposphere. Much of the energy that drives the atmosphere and oceans is first made available at the air-sea interface.

The surface of the earth is the dominant domain of mankind. The floods, droughts, high winds, and blizzards that plague him on land ultimately tie back to this radiation budget, and the intercontinental commerce of the globe, except for a miniscule amount, is carried by merchant ships on the surface of the sea, often tossed by mountainous waves forty feet high, or higher.

The phenomena that occur at the air-sea boundary have been traditionally studied by oceanographers and meteorologists by means of ships. A long history of scientific work, going back before the days of Benjamin Franklin, has led to an understanding of them by means of laborious processing of ship reports and other oceanographic data. This work, of necessity, had to be limited in scope. Wave generation and propagation have been studied, given the winds over the water. Seasonal averages were computed for energy budgets. Features of the ocean circulation have been measured by many different means, but always only in part and rarely on a synoptic basis.

Numerous people have inquired whether or not it would be possible to study the oceans from space. The fact of the matter is that even now the oceans are being studied from space—or, at least, data of importance to oceanography are being gathered from spacecraft. The technology is still under development, and ways to measure wave properties, storm surges, sea surface temperatures, and surface currents are under study as described in a recent report by the National Council on Marine Resources and Engineering Development.

A most important long-range goal of meteorologists and oceanographers is to predict the future state of the atmosphere, the oceans, and the phenomena at the air-sea boundary. Were nearly perfect predictions available for one week into the future, there would be those who would want predictions for two weeks into the future, and thus the goal will never be met. Nevertheless, a stated goal of the Environmental Science Services Administration is to provide meteorological predictions up to ten days into the future as documented most recently in a NAS-NRC report.

Meteorologists have come a long way since the work of Richardson (1922) as reviewed recently by Platzman (1967). For example, computer programs developed by Dr. Joseph Smagorinski are now in existence that make good five-day predictions of the northern hemisphere weather patterns. These programs are not operational because it takes too long to make the computations. The knowledge is there, however; only the technology of computers lags. Computer programs to forecast oceanographic changes do not exist but programs to model ocean circulations, such as those of Bryan and Cox (1967) show great promise.

Computer programs to forecast waves are under development as described by Pierson et al (1966), given a prediction of the wind field over the oceans in the planetary boundary layer. The task of providing a wave climatology for the North Pacific for one year should be completed in a few more months. Also, the computer program and procedures being developed will be a part of a system capable of using data from a spacecraft to provide, from knowledge of waves, an improved analysis of the surface wind field over the oceans. From an improved concept of the winds in the planetary boundary layer, the computation of the energy transfer from the ocean surface to the atmosphere could be done as an extension of the developments in this research program given additional input material on radiation.

In the first few hundred meters of the ocean, the changes exhibit responses to the longer period anomalies of the atmosphere and to annual variations. Anomalistic conditions in both the North Atlantic and North Pacific Oceans have been associated by Namias[2] with droughts and floods in terms of how the upper air circulation is modified. Deeper down changes in oceanic conditions between the observations of the *Meteor* Expedition in the 1920's and the recent re-survey made by Woods Hole ships are undetectable. To predict the changes of the conditions of the upper ocean will require keeping track of the energy exchanges across the air-sea interface.

The problem of prediction involves both time and space scales. To predict the wind pattern at 20,000 feet one day into the future for the northern hemisphere requires only knowledge of atmospheric parameters near 20,000 feet over the northern hemisphere. Were the deep ocean North Atlantic circulation known as an initial value problem, much of it could be predicted several weeks into the future without reference to any effects from upper layers. Forecasts even for a day into the future for the air-sea boundary are, in contrast, a much more difficult problem because—just for one of many reasons—the clouds throughout the whole atmosphere must be predicted to compute the solar radiation reaching the sea surface, and these cloud patterns are continuously forming, changing and moving.

However, as the time span of the forecast computation is increased, more and more of the total physics of the system must be included and more and more of the globe must be observed to provide initial conditions just as the present five-day northern hemisphere forecasts of Dr. Smagorinski require many atmospheric levels and many grid points. It therefore becomes increasingly evident that to push to the ten-day and beyond forecast interval, it will be necessary to obtain data about the entire globe for all

[2] A seminar at New York University.

levels of the atmosphere, for the surface of the oceans, and for the upper layers of the oceans in order to establish the initial conditions for a forecast computation. Then all of these initially observed quantities must be forecasted numerically so as to predict any one of the variables of interest.

The goals of better weather predictions and of forecasts for what occurs on the surface of the oceans and in the oceans are thus inextricably intertwined. Any one goal is not possible without the others, and the final solution must consist of a global data gathering network obtaining observations in the atmosphere, on the surface of the land, at the air-sea interface, and at various depths in the ocean so as to provide the initial data. These observations need not be of the same spatial density and frequency in time, but they will all be needed. It may, for example, be possible to use computations of changes below the ocean surface that will be spot-checked at just a few points and then used in generating longer-range predictions.

It is difficult to predict just when this goal will be achieved because economic factors will strongly affect the rate of progress. The economic benefits of better forecasts, at times, are documented in strange ways, but the value of better forecasts will increase, in my opinion, in proportion to the pressures for increasing efficiency in transportation and food production as the world tries to cope with its overexpanding population.

From the scientific point of view, it is much less difficult for me to describe what I envision to be the form of a numerical global meteorological and oceanic forecasting system. Data to provide information for a computer forecast will be gathered by the present methods for the atmosphere such as surface and radiosonde observations. However, spacecraft will play an increasingly important role in terms of the number of parameters they measure, which will grow to include the full point by point radiation budget and information on the temperature variations in the troposphere, on the thickness of the clouds, and on areas and amounts of rainfall. Spacecraft will also be used, in conjunction with ship reports and oceanographic buoys, to make measurements that will yield information on the surface temperatures of the oceans, on the wind waves and winds over the oceans, on storm surges, and on ocean currents.

A recent paper by Saunders (1967) shows, for example, that by looking in the infrared window at the sea surface from two different directions, the effects of the atmosphere and the oceans can be separated so as to obtain a more nearly correct sea surface temperature. By looking at the sea surface from a number of different directions, such information can be made even more accurate by virtue of the redundancy of the data. Oceanographic information below the surface will be obtained from strategically located buoy systems. However, the amount of subsurface data needed will be considerably reduced by the global coverage of surface conditions made possible by spacecraft because what occurs within the ocean is completely determined by what occurs at the surface, in principle, at least.

As these methods are developed, it seems to me that there will be a major change in the present methods of preparing numerical predictions. Computer models will be developed whose sole task is that of describing the present state of the atmosphere, the air-sea interface, the oceans, and the land surface as completely as possible. The atmospheric and oceanic parameters stored in the computer at a given time will describe the conditions as they actually existed, say, an hour or so ago over the whole earth. The information in the computer memory will result from a combination of present numerical prediction techniques and of present data analysis techniques running on a real time basis such that what the computer has computed to be the conditions will be compared with the observations as soon as they become available from any source and the data in the computer will be corrected, as needed, by the observations. In a sense, the computer will predict what the observations from a particular pass of each of many spacecraft will be, compare the observations with what was predicted, and correct its stored data in as many ways as necessary to bring the two into agreement. Oceanographic buoys and ships and land stations will transmit data to be processed in the same way, and there will no longer be the need to collect all required data simultaneously over the whole earth every six hours.

One advantage of such a system is that information on areas where observations are missing, due to data transmission breakdowns, gaps in orbit coverage, or any other reasons is filled in by the best available computation of the present state.

This same basic computer program will then be used to make the forecasts. Once a day or so, as needed, the present state of the atmosphere and the oceans will be fed into a second computer and forecasts for the required number of days into the future will be generated simply by bypassing all of the observed data input steps and by computing changes at a faster rate.

REFERENCES

Arking, A., and J. S. Levine (1967): Earth albedo measurements: July 1963 to June 1964. Institute for Space Studies, Goddard Space Flight Center, NASA.

Bryan, K., and M. D. Cox (1967): A numerical investigation of the oceanic general circulation. *Tellus*, vol. 19, no. 1, pp. 54–80.

Hollman, R. (1968): Studies on the albedo of the sea surface. (Ph.D. Dissertation, New York University, GSL Report TR-68-5 School of Engineering and Science.)

National Academy of Sciences-National Research Council Oceanography 1966— Achievements and opportunities.

National Council on Marine Resources and Engineering Development, United States Activities in Spacecraft Oceanography (Oct. 1, 1967).

National Aeronautics and Space Administration (1967): Earth Photographs from Gemini III, IV and V. NASA SP-129, Science and Technical Information Division.

Neumann, G., and W. J. Pierson (1966): *Principles of Physical Oceanography*, Prentice-Hall, Inc., Englewood Cliffs, N.J., XII + 545 pp.

Pierson, W. J., L. J. Tick, and L. Baer (1966): Computer based procedures for preparing global wave forecasts and wind field analyses capable of using wave data obtained by a spacecraft. (Preprint 6th Symposium Naval Hydrodynamics, 2-1-42, Office of Naval Research and Stevens Institute of Technology.)

Platzman, G. W. (1967): A retrospective view of Richardson's book on weather prediction. *Bull. Amer. Meteor. Soc.*, vol. 48, no. 8, pp. 514–550.

Rasool, S. I., and C. Prabhakara (1966): Heat budget of the Southern Hemisphere. *Problems of Atmospheric Circulation*. Edited by T. F. Malone and R. V. Garcia, Spartan Publishing Co., Washington, D.C.

Richardson, L. F. (1922): *Weather Prediction by Numerical Process*. Cambridge University Press. Reprinted 1965 by Dover Publ.

Saunders, P. M. (1967): Aerial measurements of sea surface temperature in the infrared. *J. Geophys. Res.*, vol. 72, no. 16, pp. 4101–4108.

Widger, W. K., C. W. C. Rogers, and P. E. Sherr (1966): Looking down on spirals in the sky. *American Scientist*, Sept. 1966, pp. 288–315.

Winston, J. S., and P. K. Rao (1963): Temporal and spectral variations in the planetary-scale outgoing long-wave radiation as observed from TIROS II measurements. Wexler Memorial Issue, *Mo. Wea. Rev.*, Oct.-Dec.

Duncan C. Blanchard:

61.   A VISIT TO SURTSEY*

After some hours we came in sight of a solitary rock in the
ocean, forming a mighty vault, through which the foaming waves
poured with intense fury. The islets of Westman appeared to leap
from the ocean, being so low in the water as scarcely to be
seen until you were right upon them. From that moment the
schooner was steered to the westward in order to round Cape
Reykjaness, the western point of Iceland.[1]

Jules Verne's Professor Von Hardwigg and the professor's nephew
Harry were clearing the tiny Westman[2] Islands, just off the southern
shore of Iceland. The great adventure lay ahead of them. Their
destination was the glacier-capped volcano of Snaefells, perched on
the end of a long peninsula on the western side of Iceland, 150
miles northwest of the Westman Islands. The crater of Snaefells
was to be their gateway to the center of the earth.

It is unlikely that even the imagination of Jules Verne could
have foreseen that some day the Westman Islands would be witness
to a real-world spectacle to rival any of the fictional ones which
flowed from his pen. When he wrote, "The islets of Westman
appeared to leap from the ocean . . ." he was only using a de-
lightful metaphor to indicate the smallness of the islands. But
the passage of years has turned that metaphor into a fact. An
islet of Westman has indeed leaped from the ocean. In November
of 1963, without preliminary rumblings, a volcano suddenly burst

* Excerpted from FROM RAINDROPS TO VOLCANOES by D. C. Blanchard, where
the unabridged version appeared under the chapter heading, "A Volcano at the
Surface of the Sea". Copyright © 1966, 1967 by Doubleday & Company, New
York. Reprinted by permission of the publisher.

Duncan C. Blanchard is an atmospheric Physicist who is presently affiliated
with the Atmospheric Sciences Research Center at the State University of New
York at Albany.

[1] From the novel by Jules Verne, A Journey to the Centre of the Earth. Cape
Reykjanes is now spelled with a single "s" at the end.

[2] The proper spelling is Vestmannaeyjar, but you'll also see it spelled Vestmann or Westman.

through the surface of the sea. A new islet of Westman had been born.

THE BIRTH OF SURTSEY

It was early in the morning. The fishermen had just finished laying their lines a few miles west of the southernmost of the Westman Islands. These men of the fishing boat *Isleifur II* had done this many times before, and there was nothing different on this morning of November 14, 1963 to suggest that it would be anything but another normal, uneventful day of fishing.

The lines in place, the crew went below for a well-earned cup of coffee. At five minutes before seven, Árni Gudmundsson, the engineer, wandered out on deck. That's curious, what's that smell? He peered around, found nothing unusual, and went back below. At about the same time the captain, Gudmar Tomasson, came topside and he, too, had the same experience. It was a strange smell but nothing to get alarmed about. He went below to his bunk.

At seven-thirty he was suddenly awakened by the cook, Olafur Vestmann. Olafur had been on watch, and a few minutes before had had the peculiar feeling that the boat was moving as if caught in a whirlpool. In the distance, through the early morning haze, he could make out a dark object. A rock? It can't be a rock; there are no rocks around here. He looked again, and realized it was smoke. It was then that he hurried below to wake the captain. Maybe a ship was on fire.

The captain called the Westman Islands radio station. Had they received any S.O.S. calls? They had not. If it's not a rock or a burning ship, what is it? He trained his binoculars on the smoke and soon was able to make out dark columns of ash and cloud that were rising up through the surface of the sea. For the first time he realized that they were watching a volcano erupt from the sea.

They moved toward it for a better look, but increasing turbulence in the sea prevented them from approaching any closer than about a half mile. This was close enough; the eruption was increasing in intensity. Huge columns of ash, stones, and cloud were being hurled upward from the sea. A plume of cloud continued to rise high in the sky like smoke from a giant fire in the sea. By mid-morning the plume had reached a height of about 12,000 feet, and by late afternoon about 20,000 feet, almost four miles above the sea. It became visible to the inhabitants of Reykjavik, the capital city of Iceland, seventy miles to the northwest. High in the atmosphere and caught in the rays of the setting sun, it was vividly and beautifully etched against the evening sky.

As darkness descended on that first day, the explosions went on, and rocks and ash-streaked clouds continued to be thrust violently into the atmosphere. And yet there was no island or volcanic crater to be seen at the surface of the sea. The events of that day were only birth pangs; sometime in the night the volcanic island of Surtsey[3] was born.

In the cold light of morning the new island was seen for the first time. For many days, it had been building itself up unseen from the floor of the ocean, more than 400 feet below, and now it had finally burst through the surface of the sea to thrust itself thirty feet into the air. The sea was pouring into a large fissure and presumably was striking the molten lava. Explosions shook the new volcano, and fountains of ash and cloud rocketed skyward. The island grew rapidly under a rain of ash; four days later it was about 200 feet high and 2000 feet in length.

The Westman Islanders could lay claim to a new addition to their island group. Surtsey lay about twelve miles southwest of their main island of Heimaey, but only about three miles west-southwest of the pinpoint-sized island of Geirfuglasker. In addition to being the newest piece of land in Iceland, Surtsey had the honor of being the southernmost. Iceland now extended south to a latitude of 63°18′.

Surtsey continued to grow. Within two weeks after birth the island was larger, with the exception of Heimaey, than any of the other Westman Islands. The eruptions showed no sign of stopping, and by that time the story of the birth of this amazing volcanic island had spread around the world.[4]

A TRIP TO ICELAND

Icelandic scientists began their studies of Surtsey on the very day that it came into being. By eleven o'clock of that day several of them were flying overhead to make the first of a long series of detailed observations on the nature of the eruptions, and on the growth of Surtsey.

[3] This name was derived from *Surtur*, a giant who appears in Norse mythology.
[4] My account of the birth of Surtsey is based on the book, *Surtsey*, by Sigurdur Thorarinsson. Published in 1964, it may be obtained from Almenna Bókafélagid, Reykjavik, Iceland.

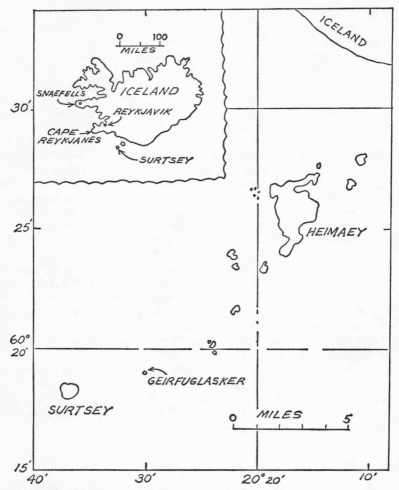

Fig. 61–1. Volcanic island of Surtsey lies off southern coast of Iceland. (From D. C. Blanchard, *From Raindrops to Volcanoes*, Doubleday & Company, New York, 1966, 1967.)

One of the first United States scientists to visit Surtsey was Paul Bauer, of American University. On the twenty-eighth of November 1963 he saw Surtsey in full eruption. When he returned from his trip he reported on what he and the Icelandic scientists had seen. They had seen, in addition to the explosions and the violent ejection of ash and cloud, something else; the ejection plumes were occasionally ablaze with numerous short, zig-zag flashes of lightning. The products of the eruption clearly were charged with electricity. But where the charge came from and what sign it was, no one knew.

THE VISIT TO SURTESY

The *Haraldur* rocked slowly as she moved through the ocean swell, and small waves smacked against her sides. At times the box dipped deep, and necklaces of water sparkled in the air before breaking on the foredeck. Overhead, the sea birds swooped and soared in long, graceful spirals. On the distant horizon we could see that Surtsey was ejecting vertical pillars of ash and cloud. We were in luck; the wind was out of the southeast; it would be possible to get close to the active vent on the southwest side of Surtsey and not have the eruption cloud blown over us.

The potential gradient was positive, holding steady, and appeared to be what one might normally find near the surface of the sea in clear weather. We had been out for about half an hour and Surtsey still loomed on the horizon, but now the island began to grow slowly and take shape. The dark shadows took on detail. High up on the slopes of ash the surface was smooth but pock-marked with craters made by falling rocks. Around the perimeter of Surtsey, where storm waves had earlier taken huge bites from the island, the smooth slopes gave way to short steep cliffs.

Every few seconds dark clouds rose from the vent on the other side of the island. The wind spread them out to form a huge dark vertical wall, which ran from the island to as far as we could see on our right, and from the sea upward to nearly the zenith. On the left we saw clear air, sea birds, and sunlight; on the right, a curtain of ash and the near darkness of night. Here and there vertical pillars of cloud broke the curtain; from far above, long fingers of ash (and maybe water) streamed downward to the sea.

By now we had expected to hear the roar of the volcano, but an eerie silence prevailed. Surtsey seemed to be performing in pantomime. Then every so often a sudden sharp crack, like a rifle shot, shattered the silence. We were mystified, and for a while thought the sound might be caused by rocks falling on the island. We looked more closely but could see no large rocks crashing into the island.

The *Haraldur* was now closer to the curtain of darkness, and every minute or so a flash of lightning darted out from the lower part of the clouds. A few seconds later the mysterious crack was heard, but now it was no longer mysterious. It was clear that it was thunder. None of us had ever heard thunder like this before; we were familiar with the type that booms and reverberates for many seconds, like the sound of a hundred cannon áll going off at slightly different times. Surtsey's thunder did not sound like this, probably because the lightning strokes were only a thousand feet or so in length. Thus the sound from every point in the lightning channel arrived at the *Haraldur* at about the same time, producing the sharp crack. A thunderstorm lightning stroke, on the other hand, may be 10,000 feet or more in length, and the time interval between the arrival of the first sound waves and those from the far end of the lightning channel may be several seconds.[5] This difference in path length of the sound waves produces the long drawn-out booming that we usually associate with thunder.

We were still to the east of the island but now turned left to pass by the southern side of Surtsey and approach the very throat of the volcano. Soon we could see it, and, as if to welcome us, Surtsey put on a grand display of the forces at its command. The sea had found its way through a large gaping V-shaped opening that was clearly visible in the seaward side of the crater. Tons of sea water presumably came into contact with the molten lava that was surging upward through the throat of the crater. There were violent explosions and upheavals that belched ash, cloud, rocks, and sea water in one vast mixture. Sometimes the eruption continued for a minute or more, while an immense fountain was spraying a black, ash-covered jet 1000 feet into the air. The jet would change from black to a black-and-white striped appearance, and, near the top where great cauliflower masses of cloud were forming from the condensing steam, the jet became almost completely white. At times the eruptions would cease, as if Surtsey were resting from its strenuous exercises. The bottom of the crater filled completely with sea water, and sea birds swooped low over the now quiet surface. Only a gentle steaming disturbed the surface, and we approached to within 300 feet of the crater. But no closer, for the giant was only slumbering.

Surtsey would awaken suddenly, the water in the center of the crater beginning to bubble, and within a second or two, ash and cloud would be hurled upward and outward at speeds of up to

[5] The speed of sound in air is about 1100 feet per second.

200 miles per hour. Like a huge black and white balloon being inflated, the outpouring swelled quickly until its top had reached a height of over 2000 feet. From the surface of these clouds secondary explosions hurled huge feathered spears of cloud and ash that fanned outward and finally arched earthward in long exquisite streamers silhouetted against the clear blue sky. Surely man, for all his genius, could never compete with nature in composing such splendor and beauty in violent upheaval.

Lightning and Surtsey-type thunder occurred during all these eruptions, but most exciting to us were the traces drawn on the chart by the pens automatically recording the potential gradient and the flow of electricity through the sharp point atop the mast. At the start of an eruption the potential gradient was not much more than +100 volts per meter, a normal value to find at sea. But as the clouds billowed upward, the gradient rose rapidly to several thousand volts per meter. And then, simultaneous with a lightning stroke, the gradient would fall back to nearly 100 volts per meter. This reversal occurred repeatedly, and the pen traced a sawtooth curve. A similar curve was traced by the pen recording the current flow between the air and the sharp point. The stronger the positive potential gradient, the stronger was the positive current that flowed from the air to the point.[6]

It looked as if a positive charge was being carried up from the crater by the eruption clouds. The increase in potential gradient and the point discharge current reflected the buildup of the charge. Finally, like a water-filled paper bag about to burst, the surrounding air could stand no more increase in potential gradient and broke down. A lightning stroke occurred, and the charge poured down through the lightning channel to the ground.

At about half-past one the eruption ceased and all was quiet. This was the intermission before the grand finale. At three o'clock Surtsey came to life again with eruptions that were far more intense and continuous than any heretofore. Great fountains played continuously and the immense curtain of ash and cloud columns loomed above us again. Looking up at it from the *Haraldur* bobbing offshore, we felt as if we were at the base of a thousand-foot-high Niagara Falls. Torrents of ash were cascading downward, and rocks plunging into the sea sent up white geysers of water. Al-

[6] This type of current is known by several names—point discharge current, corona current, or St. Elmo's fire. The last is especially well known to sailors as the flame-like glow that is sometimes seen from exposed points on a ship's rigging during a thunderstorm or stormy weather.

though we were upwind of this spectacle some ash did reach us, but it was very fine and barely noticeable.

Amid frequent flashes of lightning and cracks of thunder, the pen moved rapidly back and forth recording the now familiar saw-tooth changes in the potential gradient. I remember running into the cabin to observe these sudden changes while the eruption was at its height. The pen snapped back with every lightning flash that I could see, and sometimes when I saw no flash. When this happened I began to count off the seconds—1001, 1002—and then, crack! the thunder reached us. The lightning flash must have occurred hidden from view deep in that dark curtain.

At the height of the eruption there were so many exciting and wondrous things going on that we were like children at a great circus trying to watch the action in all three rings at the same time. Colossal jets streaking upward into the blue and the vast waterfall of ash tumbling down to the island and the sea shared the center ring. High above the far ring the aerialists held forth, beautiful mushroom clouds turning themselves inside out as they sprang upward. Here and there spinning smoke rings of cloud could be seen, and descending from some of the clouds, like long, sinewy, twisting ropes, were whirlwinds. In the near ring the thunder and lightning dominated the scene, while clouds rushed down the sides of the crater and rolled out over the sea. There was too much going on at once for our senses to absorb, and we hoped that our movie cameras were capturing on film this magnificent spectacle.

The afternoon shadows were lengthening and it was time for us to return to Heimaey. Surtsey was still in vigorous eruption as we steamed away. The potential gradient decreased slowly until, when Surtsey's cloud was low on the horizon and glowing red in the setting sun, it reached and maintained the low value it had had at the start of the trip.

We wondered just what this potential gradient record would finally tell us, whether it would agree with the findings of those who had flown around Surtsey all week, and with what Bernard Vonnegut had found in his visit to Surtsey the week before. We were to wait more than a month before learning that all the measurements appeared to point to one conclusion: the clouds rising from Surtsey's crater were highly charged with positive electricity. The flow of this charge from the crater constituted a positive current of about 0.03 ampere. Though only about 3 per cent of the current generated in a thunderstorm, the 0.03 ampere was sufficient to produce the electrical effects we had observed.

THE FLOW OF LAVA TO THE SEA

Everyone involved in the Surtsey expedition came away satisfied. The scientists who had worked from the airplane were satisfied because their instruments had worked so well, Vonnegut and Moore because the lightning was generated without the formation of heavy rain and hail, Hughes because the expedition he organized had worked so well, and I because we had found a positive charge in the Surtsey clouds.

With the background of some of the experiments we discussed in the last chapter, where the splashing of sea water on hot lava produced positively charged clouds, you might jump to the conclusion that the positively charged clouds at Surtsey were generated by sea water pouring into the crater and striking molten lava. Well, I'd like to jump to that conclusion also, but one really shouldn't.

Are we quite sure that the sea water struck the lava? I saw it pour into the crater, but how do I know it wasn't vaporized in the intense heat? And if it did strike the lava (which I am inclined to believe) why wasn't the equal and opposite negative charge carried into the air by the lava when it exploded into ash? Could it somehow have flowed away to ground? And how about other mechanisms of charge generation? Questions like these must be answered before we can conclude, firmly and definitely, that Surtsey's electricity was the direct result of sea water striking hot lava.

A conclusive proof of the capacity of sea water to generate charge upon striking hot lava probably could be obtained by making potential gradient measurements near the clouds that are produced when molten lava flows off the land and into the sea.

THE FUTURE OF SURTSEY

In late May of 1965, after a year and a half of activity, Surtsey became quiet. The powerful forces within the earth which had spawned Surtsey looked for another outlet, and in early June the sea began to boil about a third of a mile northeast of Surtsey. The familiar fountains of ash and cloud rocketed skyward and Syrtlingur was born.

On the seventeenth of October Syrtlingur was about 1600 feet in diameter and 160 feet high, but then it, too, became quiet. A week later, under the ceaseless pounding of the ocean waves, its slopes of ash were eaten away and it disappeared into the depths of the sea. Surtsey had been spared that fate because a protective armor of hard lava covered nearly half of its vulnerable interior.

More was yet to come. The day after Christmas the eruptions started again, but this time about a half mile to the southwest of Surtsey. Heavy winter storms prevented Christmas Island from growing very rapidly, but it continued in eruption until August 1966. Then all activity ceased.

A week later a fissure opened on the southeast coast of Surtsey. The island came to life once again as fountains of lava played from four craters to heights of about 450 feet. The volcanic activity had come full circle.

Man has learned much from Surtsey and its eruptions. The new knowledge extends far, far beyond what we had the good fortune to obtain in our study of the electricity in the volcanic clouds. Many other scientists have visited Surtsey; their interests have ranged from chemical changes in the sea to biological studies of life on the new volcanic soil.

A number of research trails have met and are crossing at Surtsey, and those of us involved would be foolish indeed if we did not take cognizance of this fact. At one of these junctions a new and exciting research trail may have been found. The signpost pointing the way does not say volcanic electricity, types of lava, fissure eruptions in the sea, heat flow through volcanic ash, or sea water and electricity. It says, "A key to the past."

The birth of Surtsey and the formation of the volcanic clouds, the struggle with the sea and the coming of life to the new island, are a re-enactment of what must have happened hundreds of times in the distant past. In this event, capsuled in space and time, may be a key that will enable man to open yet another of the doors that obscure our view down that long corridor through which he and the world have evolved.

Johannes A. Kylstra:

62.   LIQUID BREATHING: AN EXPERIMENTAL
APPROACH TO DEEP DIVING*

Decompression sickness and "inert" gas narcosis are due, directly or indirectly, to the compressibility of gases. The properties of water hardly change at all with pressure, and liquids could be truly inert respiratory gas diluents at any depth in the ocean. Moreover, no excessive amounts of inert gas would dissolve in the blood and tissues of a diver with liquid-filled lungs so that he would be free to come to the surface at any time and as rapidly as he desired without fear of bubble formation. Experimental evidence indicating that mammalian lungs can function as gills was presented for the first time five years ago (1). In retrospect, this is not too surprising since respiration in water or air is essentially very similar in spite of the apparent differences between the respiratory media. Oxygen dissolved in inspired nitrogen or water is exchanged for carbon dioxide dissolved in blood by diffusion across a thin membrane which separates the blood from the gas or liquid in lungs or gills. A mechanical pumping device delivers fresh air or water to the gas exchange area, and carbon dioxide produced in the tissues is eliminated from the body in exhaled air or water leaving the gills.

In a physical sense, air and water are both fluids. Qualitatively it makes little difference whether a breathing mixture consists of water or air, but there are large quantitative differences in physical properties between these two fluids. These differences are reflected in the anatomical characteristics of respiratory organs of aerobic organisms such as lungs and gills.

* From *Review of Subaquatic Physiology and Hyperbaric Medicine*, Tome 1, March, April, May, 1968, No. 1, pp. 45–49. Reprinted by permission of the publisher and the author.

Johannes A. Kylstra is a pioneer researcher in the physiological process of liquid breathing. Studies in this respiratory process began at the University of Leiden in the Netherlands and are being continued at Duke University where Dr. Kylstra has been affiliated.

For instance, the diffusion of oxygen and carbon dioxide in water is approximately 6,000 times slower than in air under similar conditions. A volume of water at 37°C contains 44 times less oxygen and 1.8 times less carbon dioxide than a similar volume of air at a given partial pressure. The force required for laminar flow of water through a system of tubes such as the trachea and bronchi is approximately 36 times greater than for a similar flow of air. Turbulence, which greatly increases the pressure required for a given flow, occurs in water at flow velocities that are approximately 27 times smaller than in air.

All animal life is believed to have originated in water, and the ancestors of air-breathing animals, including man, are presumed to have been water-breathing creatures. This implies that, in the past, some water-breathing animals must have converted to air breathing. In many respects such an evolutionary transition from aquatic to aerial respiration would seem to be advantageous, in particular as far as gas exchange of the individual with his environment is concerned (2). Yet, in spite of the apparent advantages of air over water as a respiratory medium, most fish do not survive when taken out of their natural habitat. For one thing, they cannot conserve body water in an essentially dry environment, and the acquisition of this faculty must have been one of the major adaptations required for animal life on land. In addition, most fish face serious respiratory problems when taken out of the water, and suffocate despite the relatively high oxygen content of air. This apparent paradox is a result of the delicate structure of gills which are not mechanically stable in air and tend to collapse and stick together so that not enough area remains available for gas exchange and the delicate balance of ventilation and perfusion is disrupted.

Mammals submerged in water usually also die from lack of oxygen but for different reasons. The oxygen content of water at sea level is approximately the same as that of air at an altitude of more than 70,000 feet. In addition, drowning mammals may inhale water, and the transfer of water and solutes across the alveolar membrane can damage the lung tissues, and cause fatal alterations in the volume and composition of the body fluids. This is due to the fact that water inhaled by a drowning individual usually has a composition quite different from that of blood. However, no significant net transfer of either water or solutes occurs across the blood-air barrier and no harm results from filling a lung with a solution containing salts in concentrations similar to the ones normally found in blood plasma (3).

According to Henry's Law, the amount of gas dissolved in a liquid is directly proportional to the partial gas pressure on the gas-liquid interface, at equilibrium. A volume of isotonic salt solution equilibrated with oxygen at a pressure of eight atmospheres absolute contains an approximately equal number of oxygen molecules as the same volume of air at sea level. On the basis of such considerations I wondered whether submerged mammals would not survive if they were able to breathe a suitable pressure-oxygenated salt solution instead of air. The first crucial experiments along these lines were performed on mice in a small pressure chamber (1).

The survival of these submerged mammals (that is, the interval between submersion and the last visible respiratory movement) varied with the oxygen pressure, the temperature and the chemical composition of the liquid. One mouse continued to breathe for 18 hours in a balanced salt solution to which a carbon dioxide buffer, 0.1% Tris-hydroxymethyl aminomethane, had been added, at 20°C equilibrated with oxygen at a pressure of eight atmospheres absolute.

However, it was by no means certain to what extent carbon dioxide was retained, whether the arterial blood was adequately oxygenated, or how much oxygen was actually taken up by the lungs rather than through the skin and mucous membranes. A mouse in a small pressure chamber is a very poor subject for such studies. For this reason, similar experiments were carried out on dogs in a pressure chamber large enough to also accommodate the investigator (breathing air), together with all the necessary equipment (4).

The dog was suspended over a tub that was partly filled with salt solution. The dog and the tub were covered with a transparent flexible hood to protect the observer from oxygen poisoning. The chamber was pressurized with air. Oxygen was then bubbled through the water (the space under the cover being vented into the main chamber exhaust) and after sufficient time had elapsed for oxygen to dissolve in the water, the bubbling was discontinued and the dog was lowered into the tub until completely submerged. Jets of exhaled liquid breaking the surface were clearly visible so that there was no doubt that the dog was pumping the liquid in and out of its lungs. At the end of the experiment the dog was lifted out of the tub. Water was drained from the lungs which were then reinflated with air. The experiments were done at a pressure of five atmospheres absolute, and the animals had been anesthetized and cooled to approximately 32°C so that their oxygen requirements were less than normal. One out of six dogs survived.

During the period of liquid breathing, the animal's blood pressure was slightly lower than normal but it remained stable. His heart rate and respiration were slow but regular. The arterial blood remained fully saturated with oxygen but the arterial carbon dioxide content increased, indicating that in spite of what appeared to be vigorous respiratory efforts, the resulting ventilation of the lungs with water was insufficient to eliminate adequate amounts of carbon dioxide from the body. The dog was resuscitated after having breathed water for 24 minutes. The animal recovered fully.

In the next series of experiments, the actual gas exchange in the lungs of water-breathing dogs was measured by determining the amount of oxygen and carbon dioxide in the inhaled salt solution and the volume and gas contents of subsequently exhaled liquid. The amount of oxygen taken up from the fluid in the lungs and the amount of carbon dioxide eliminated from the body through the liquid-filled lungs was computed simply by subtraction. The experimental procedure was, in essence, very similar to ordinary artificial respiration with air, except that the breathing mixture consisted of a pressure-oxygenated salt solution and inspiration and expiration were caused by gravity instead of by the movements of a piston in a mechanical pump (5).

The saline solution was oxygenated in advance in a reservoir outside the chamber by bubbling oxygen at a pressure of four atmospheres above atmospheric pressure through the fluid which was kept at a temperature of 37°C. The dogs were anesthetized and a rubber tube with an inflatable cuff at the tip was positioned in the trachea. The endotracheal tube was connected to a motor-driven valve system. During inspiration fresh oxygenated saline flowed by gravity into the lungs. During expiration liquid simply drained from the lungs into a receptacle on the floor of the chamber underneath the dog. It was found that the amount of oxygen extracted per minute from the water in the lungs of the liquid-breathing dogs was of the same order of magnitude as would have been the case under similar conditions in air-breathing dogs. However, as was expected, the amount of carbon dioxide dissolved in the exhaled water was not sufficient to prevent a gradual increase in the carbon dioxide content of the blood. The experiments were terminated as soon as a sufficient amount of information had been obtained, to minimize the risk of decompression sickness in the air-breathing investigators and not because the condition of the water-breathing dogs would have required this.

The oxygen consumption ranged from 31 to 93 ml/min. The respiratory exchange ratio varied from 0.3 to 0.7 at arterial carbon dioxide tensions from 43 to 80 mm/Hg. At inspired oxygen tensions ranging from 3,310 to 3,640 mm/Hg the arterial oxygen tensions ranged from 32 to 1,790 mm/Hg at expired minutes volumes ranging from 1 to 3.5 liters and respiratory frequencies ranging from 6 to 12 min. Mixed expired oxygen tensions ranged from 2,240 to 3,080 mm/Hg and mixed expired carbon dioxide tensions from 6 to 18 mm/Hg.

No particular emphasis was placed on resuscitation of the animals after the experiment: water was simply drained by gravity from the lungs through a hose connected with the endotracheal tube, and afterwards the lungs were forcefully inflated several times with air by mouth. Apart from this, the animals received no treatment. Even so, six out of 16 dogs survived the water breathing experiments which lasted up to three-quarters of an hour and subsequently returned to normal air breathing without many apparent ill after-effects. This indicates, that under certain conditions, water breathing can be a relatively harmless procedure in dogs and, possibly, also in man. Of more theoretical importance, however, is the fact that, on the basis of a careful analysis of the experimental data, it was now possible to formulate, in mathematical terms, some of the intuitively recognized relationships between the functional requirements, the structure of respiratory organs, and the physical properties of the ambient environment in mammals as well as in fish.

In the saline-ventilated dogs, the partial pressures of oxygen in liquid exhaled into a long sampling tube were progressively higher and the carbon dioxide tensions were progressively lower at increasing distances from the lung. It was postulated that the gas exchange units of the lung were filling and emptying concentrically so that liquid expelled first from the lungs had been located at a greater distance from the alveolar wall than subsequently exhaled liquid. Thus it appeared that the overall gas exchange in the liquid-filled lungs was diffusion limited, and that remarkably large gas tension gradients persisted within the exchange units as a result of the slow rate of oxygen and carbon dioxide diffusion in water.

Interestingly enough, these gas tension gradients turned out to be similar to the ones that can be computed for gas diffusion in a sphere. Thus the pulmonary gas exchange in water-breathing dogs appeared to be very similar to the gas exchange in a mathematical lung model consisting of roughly half a million identical spherical gas exchange units with a diameter of 1 mm in which gas transfer occurs by diffusion only. The computed number and size of these units agree closely with the overall size and number of primary lung lobules, which therefore would seem to be the smallest functional units of the lung.

Our lung model is composed of a great number of identical spherical exchange units. The spheres are assumed to have an initially uniform oxygen concentration and oxygen is removed by the blood from the surface at a constant rate. The spheres initially do not contain carbon dioxide and carbon dioxide concentration at the surface is assumed to remain constant. The gas tensions at the surface of the spheres are assumed to be equal to the gas tensions in the arterial blood. The partial pressures of oxygen and carbon dioxide existing within each exchange unit at the end of a respiratory cycle at a certain distance from the center can be computed from appropriate solutions to the diffusion equation. The partial pressure of carbon dioxide within the exchange unit is directly proportionate to the time of diffusion and the diffusion coefficient but inversely proportionate to the square of the distance from the center. The partial pressure of oxygen at a given distance from the center of an exchange unit depends upon the initial oxygen tension in the sphere, upon the oxygen flux at the surface, the radius of the sphere, the diffusion coefficient of oxygen, and the time of diffusion.

It is of considerable interest to compare the size and shape of the elementary gas exchange units in the mammalian lung with the geometry of such units in the gills of fish. Based on actual anatomical measurements and by analogy, the gas exchange in gills can be compared with gas transfer in a diffusion model containing a large number of identical exchange units which consist of flat parallel planes.

Evidently, to consider complex anatomical structures such as lungs and gills as if they were simple mathematical models can be no more than a first approximation to reality. Nevertheless, this turns out to be conceptually very useful and an analysis of diffusion in these lung and gill models clearly reveals the importance of geometry in the adaptation of an individual to his environment. For instance, the relationship between the oxygen tension in the arterial blood, the partial pressure, diffusion coefficient, and solubility of oxygen in the ambient environment, the volume of air or water inhaled, the number and dimensions of the gas exchange units, and the amount of oxygen taken up by these units, can be expressed in a fairly simple equation. However, the equation for diffusion in the lung model and the equation applicable to diffusion in the gill model are different (6).

If known normal values are substituted in these equations to compute the oxygen tension in the blood of two hypothetical fish, one with model gills and the other with model lungs, it turns out that the arterial oxygen tension in the fish with model gills is very similar to the ones actually found in a real fish, but that the blood of the hypothetical fish with model lungs would not contain any oxygen whatsoever so that this fish could not exist in water, merely because of the spherical shape of his gas exchange units. It is now easier to understand why most of the animals living in water have gills and why only a few water-breathing species, such as the sea-cucumber, have lung-like respiratory organs in an aqueous environment at normal barometric partial oxygen pressures.

Increasing the ambient oxygen partial pressure can, as we have demonstrated, help to partly overcome the intrinsic deficiencies of the lung as an aquatic gas exchanger. There are, however, other intrinsic deficiencies which cannot be overcome that easily. As we have seen before, large diffusion gradients for oxygen and carbon dioxide persist within the individual gas exchange units of the lung during liquid breathing so that there are large differences in mean gas tensions between the contents of the exchange units and the arterial blood. Such differences can be expressed in terms of respiratory dead space defined as the actual or virtual volume of inhaled air or water which, after leaving the respiratory organ, has failed to reach gas tension equilibrium with arterial blood.

From a mechanical point of view, dead space implies inefficiency since energy is wasted in propelling larger volumes of water or air through the respiratory organs than would be required in terms of actual inhaled oxygen content and optimal exhaled carbon dioxide content.

In a high-pressure environment it is not difficult to provide a submerged mammal with enough oxygen no matter how small the alveolar ventilation, since the partial oxygen pressure in the liquid can be raised at will to meet almost any metabolic demands under most circumstances. The amount of carbon dioxide exhaled with each breath, however, depends primarily on the partial pressure of carbon dioxide in the blood flowing through the alveolar capillaries and the solubility of carbon dioxide in the liquid present in the air spaces of the lung. The carbon dioxide partial pressure in blood represents the balance between the rate of production in the tissues and the rate of elimination through the lungs. Neither of these factors is affected by an increased oxygen pressure in the environment. An isotonic salt solution equilibrated with carbon dioxide at a pressure of 40 mm/Hg, such as normally exists in arterial blood, contains approximately 30 ml of dissolved CO_2 per liter at 37°C. One liter of exhaled air normally contains approximately 50 ml of carbon dioxide. One might expect, therefore, that approximately twice as much water as air would have to be exhaled each minute to dispose of equal amounts of CO_2. This implies that a water-breathing mammal would have to expend at least 60 times more energy in filling and emptying his lungs than an air-breathing mammal, since in the absence of turbulence, it requires approximately 36 times more work to propel equal volumes of water instead of air through trachea and bronchi. If flow were turbulent, even more breathing work would be required. The presence of a diffusion dead space for carbon dioxide necessitates even larger minute volumes of liquid ventilation than required for adequate alveolar ventilation in the absence of diffusion limitation. Unfortunately, however, trachea and bronchi collapse during expiration at minute volumes of ventilation theoretically required for adequate carbon dioxide elimination.

The viscosity of water is roughly 40 times greater than of air. Consequently, if flow remains laminar, saline flow through the airways at a given pressure difference between the alveoli and the mouth will be roughly 40 times slower than flow of air. It is a well known fact that, normally, bronchi collapse when during expiration a given flow rate is exceeded. It is reasonable, therefore, to expect airway collapse to occur at saline flow rates of approximately 1/40th of the maximum expiratory air flow, and to predict that the minute ventilation breathing saline would, maximally, be five liters per minute in a diver with a maximum voluntary ventilation of 200 l/sec while breathing air. Leith and Mead have measured maximum expiratory flow rates in excised lungs of mice, rats, and dogs and, by extrapolation, have estimated a maximum saline ventilation in man of about 3.5 l/min (7). I have recently measured a flow of 500 ml of saline in 8 seconds from the left lung of a woman who underwent lung lavage for bronchiectasis. Such a flow rate would correspond to a maximum minute ventilation of 3.7 liters, assuming equal time for inspiration and expiration.

Assuming that all problems of carbon dioxide retention could be overcome, for instance by intravenous administration of THAM (8), what inspiratory oxygen tensions will be required to provide for adequate arterial oxygenation at greatly reduced rates of ventilation? I would like to venture a fairly educated guess, based on the lung model discussed previously, and some anatomical measurements reported in the literature. According to von Hayek (9), the human lungs are made up of approximately 150,000 primary gas exchange units with a radius of 1 mm. Assuming that these values correspond to the number and dimensions of gas exchange units in our lung model, one can compute the inspired oxygen tension required to obtain an end-expiratory arterial oxygen tension of 100 mm/Hg at various rates of alveolar ventilation and oxygen consumption.

The result of such computation suggests that a saline-breathing diver at a depth of approximately 1,000 feet would be capable of performing moderate amounts of work. We must not forget, however, that the model used to compute these data is no more than a first approximation, and that the values used for the number and radius of the exchange units are based on anatomical, not functional measurements.

The liquid studied most extensively as an inert gas substitute thus far has been saline. Recently, Clark and Gollan have introduced synthetic liquids for this purpose (10). Some of the physical properties of synthetic liquids would seem to offer advantages over those of saline as a respiratory medium, and may well be suitable for use in human underwater activities.

The problems of liquid breathing in mammals are formidable, and the chances of success seem slim. But how many of us, 10 years ago, would have been willing to seriously consider the possibility of sending a diver with liquid-filled lungs down to the continental shelf or beyond to work for 20 minutes at the bottom and return to the surface within half an hour?

Conclusion: Gas exchange in water-filled lungs is diffusion limited, and resulting diffusion dead spaces impose various limitations on gas exchange. Maximal minute ventilation is severely restricted by airway collapse during expiration. As a result, carbon dioxide elimination is grossly deficient, even under basal conditions. In human underwater activities, liquid breathing will be possible only if the untoward effects of carbon dioxide retention can be minimized effectively.

REFERENCES

(1) Kylstra, J. A., M. O. Tissing, and A. Van Der Maen.—Of mice as fish. Trans. Amer. Soc. Artif. Internal Organs 8: 378–383, 1962.

(2) Hughes, G. M., and J. A. Kylstra.—Breathing in water. *New Scientist.* (419), 26 November 1964, pp. 566–569.

(3) Kylstra, J. A.—Lavage of the lung II. *Acta Physiol. Pharmacol. Neerl.* 8: 326–336, 1959.

(4) Kylstra, J. A., and M. O. Tissing.—Fluid breathing. In *Clinical Application*

of *Hyperbaric Oxygen,* Proc. 1st Intern. Congr., Amsterdam: Elsevier, 1963, pp. 371–379.

(5) Kylstra, J. A., C. V. Paganelli, and E. H. Lanphier.—Pulmonary gas exchange in dogs ventilated with hyperbarically oxygenated liquid. *J. Appl. Physiol.,* 21: 177–184, 1966.

(6) Kylstra, J. A., C. V. Paganelli, and H. Rahn.—Some implications of the dynamics of gas transfer in water-breathing dogs. Ciba Foundation Symposium *Development of the Lung.* London: Churchill, 1966, pp. 34–58.

(7) Leith, D. E., and J. Mead.—Maximum expiratory flow in liquid-filled lungs. *Fed. Proc.,* 25: 506, 1966.

(8) Nahas, G. G., and E. C. Jordan.—CO_2 elimination by the kidney during hypercapnia and administration of a buffer amine. Trans. Amer. Soc. Artif. Internal Organs, 5: 90, 1959.

(9) Von Hayek H.—Die Menschliche Lunge. Berlin, Springer, 1953.

(10) Clark, L. C., and F. Gollan.—Survival of mammals breathing organic liquids equilibrated with oxygen at atmospheric pressure. *Science* 152: 1755, 1966.

~~~~~~~~~~~~~~~~

Donald G. Snyder:

63.   *FISH PROTEIN CONCENTRATE**

Marine biologists tell us that only 15 percent of the annual marine fish potential is presently harvested. We are told by many fishermen that nearly 50 percent of their catch is discarded at sea. We also are told that there are enough fish in the sea to supply the total animal protein needs of between 5 and 30 billion people.

There is certainly no question that food, specifically animal protein, is desperately needed. Protein malnutrition presently stunts the health, vigor, and mental capacity of over one-half of the world's population. And we know that the world population will double during the next 40 years.

We also know that agriculture alone cannot be counted on to fill the gap between food needs and supply. In 40 out of 60 developing countries, there is a continuing decrease in per capita production of agricultural products. For only a few of these countries is

* From a Paper presented at the Governor's Symposium on Fish Protein Concentrate held at the dedication ceremonies for the opening of the new fish protein concentrate plant at New Bedford, Mass., April 29, 1968. By permission of the author.

Donald G. Snyder is Director of the U.S. Bureau of Commercial Fisheries Technological Laboratory in College Park, Md.

there any evidence that this trend will be reversed. And vegetable produce, the world's principal source of proteins and calories, is generally acknowledged to require supplementation with animal protein to ensure adequate human nutrition.

What is needed, then, is an animal protein available in large quantities and at low cost. The product needed must be stable at room temperature and retain its high nutritional value. Also, the product must be available in a form that can be readily incorporated in a wide variety of traditional food products to ensure that it will actually find its way into the diets of the peoples who need it.

Unexploited fish from the sea, in the form of fish protein concentrate (FPC), meets these requirements. By way of definition, FPC is any inexpensive stable, wholesome product of high nutritive quality, hygienically prepared from fish, in which the protein and other nutrient materials are more concentrated than they were in the fresh fish. This definition includes FPC products of varying characteristics ranging from tasteless, odorless, light-colored, flour-like materials, through coarse meals having a fishy taste and odor, to highly flavored, dark-colored pastes or powders resembling meat extracts.

Let's first look at the history of FPC and then at efforts toward commercialization that promise the growth of a significant, financially rewarding new industry with humanitarian overtones beyond the reaches of the imagination.

HISTORY OF FPC

Past History

To produce concentrates from fish for human consumption is not a new idea, although it has never been universally applied.

The earliest history of FPC is found in Arrian's account of the voyage of Nearchus along the eastern shore of the Persian Gulf in 325 B.C.

"Below the Gadrosians . . . dwell the people called 'The Fish Eaters.' . . . Thinking here to seize corn by force Nearchus attacked the town, but the natives showed freely their flour, ground down from dried fish; but only a small quantity of corn and barley . . . Only a few of them fish, for few have proper boats or any skill; for the most part it is the receding tide which leaves fish in pools which provide their catch. The more tender ones they eat raw, the larger and tougher ones they dry in the sun until quite sere

and then pound then and make flour and a bread of them . . .
Even their flocks are fed on dried fish so that the mutton has a
fishy taste like the flesh of sea birds."

The cookbook of Apicius from Roman days (the first century
A.D.) has been translated and published in 1958 by B. Flower and
E. Rosenbaum, *The Roman Cookery Book*, published by Peter
Nevill, Ltd., London and New York. Apicius describes in detail
the recipes of the upper- and middle-class families of Rome. He
indicates the method of manufacture of liquamen, a product that
can be considered as being a prototype FPC.

The manufacture of liquamen was one of the few large-scale food
processing industries in Rome. We have some idea of the technology
that was used for the manufacture of this supplement, which may
well have supplied a significant proportion of essential amino acids
to the diets of the average Roman. The method of manufacture is
described by Apicius as follows:

"Take fish entrails and small fish, such as small red mullet or
sprats or anchovy, and salt all this together, leave it to dry in the
sun, shaking the mixture frequently. When it has become dry from
the heat, extract the garum [the Greek word for liquamen] with a
fine meshed basket."

Although the fishing industry was big in Europe, we find no fish
concentrate manufacture or utilization there. Not so in Asia, however. The manufacture from fish of FPC in the form of fish
sauces and pastes developed very early all over the Far East.

As for the New World, we believe that the first commercial
fishery in the United States was established in Medford, Massachusetts, on April 17, 1629. On that date, the colonists were given
instructions to "let the fish be well saved with salt, packed up in
hog's heads" to be sent home to England. We have to wait for
another 250 years, however, for new developments in FPC.

We read in an article published by the U. S. Commission of
Fish and Fisheries in 1880 that the Honorable S. L. Goodale of
Saco, Maine, invented a process by which the juices of the flesh
of fish could be extracted to form a food that promised to be of
much commercial value. The readers of the article are told, "No
one needs less than yourself to be told how great are the possibilities for this new project. From each barrel of menhaden you can
get three pounds of extract when the flesh alone is used and four
pounds if the spine is retained in dressing." And further on, "I
cannot avoid the conclusion that a new source of food is within
reach which, at no distant day, may contribute materially to human
welfare."

The same article also describes biscuits made with "fish flour," and it was called such. These biscuits were exhibited by the Norwegian Department of Agriculture at an International Exhibition in 1876. In spite of the fact that they had been kept for a year in unsealed jars, the biscuits were said to be in perfect condition.

So we note that producing concentrated protein from fish is not new. However, only in the last twenty-five years—largely due to the untiring efforts of such organizations as UNICEF and FAO of the United Nations—have extensive endeavors been made in this direction. And only in the last several years has full recognition and world-wide serious interest been accorded FPC as a protein supplement of superior quality.

Recent History

Let's look at some more recent history in the manufacture of FPC. We must here report that three distinct methods are used to remove most of the fat and water from the fish. And this is what we do to concentrate the fish nutrients—remove fat and water. We must remove them, however, in an economical manner, yet end with a product of excellent quality and stability. There's the rub. Making such a product is not easy. We remove water, of course, to stabilize the product and prevent spoilage and to make it easily usable and economically transportable. We remove fat because the fats or lipids in fish are highly reactive—oxidize easily—and give flavor and taste to the product. The fats, too, might lower the nutritive quality of the protein if permitted to remain in the product during processing.

The three methods used to remove fat and water are classified as chemical, biological, and physical.

Chemical methods use solvent extraction to remove water and lipids from the fish—solvents such as alcohol.

Among chemical methods developed in various parts of the world before this decade are those of the following organizations: VioBin Corporation, General Foods Corporation, Lever Brothers Company, United Nations, Canada, Fishery Industry Research Institute of South Africa, and Astra of Sweden.

Biological methods use enzymes or proteolytic microorganisms to release tissue components, protein (or their breakdown products) from the oil and water. The oil and water are then separated from the protein by conventional means—such as centrifugation.

In the Far East, this type of process results in the manufacture of vast quantities of condiments in the form of pastes or sauces. However, aside from the fact that these fermentation processes are time consuming and the products often have poor quality protein, salt is added to the fermentation mixture as a preservative, which makes the product unsuitable for very small children. Workers in India and Canada have used specific isolated enzymes to produce FPC. One process has been devised of quite some note that I believe represents perhaps the only biological process near commercialization. This outstanding process is the work of Dr. Victor Bertullo of the University of Uruguay in Montevideo. It uses a unique proteolytic yeast. Incidentally, the biological methods result in products that are flavorful, differing from the solvent-extracted products, which are usually bland in taste.

Physical methods remove oil and water by physical means, such as by means of presses. This method is the one used to make fish meal. Physical processes have not been used exclusively for FPC manufacture thus far.

Such was the situation we found when we started work on FPC at the Bureau of Commercial Fisheries Technological Laboratory at College Park, Maryland, in 1960. A need existed for animal protein, fish was available in huge quantities to fill this need, and apparently early technological work had been conducted in translating fish into a usable FPC. Why then, no thriving industry? And when would commercialization occur?

COMMERCIALIZATION OF FPC

In my opinion, four problems hindered commercialization of FPC. The first problem demanded a change in concept for use of fish. The second centered around an existing FDA ruling preventing the use of whole fish in the manufacture of FPC—thus, making the product prohibitively expensive. The third was the lack of technical and engineering information available. And the final one was the lack of markets and market information.

Concept

Fish spoil more rapidly than do other protein foods, such as meat. Also, procedures developed to save fish have been limited in number; with one or two important exceptions, as I earlier discussed, drying, smoking, salting, pickling, cooling, freezing, and canning nearly complete the list. These processes reflect an effort to preserve the fish in a form closely resembling that of the original raw material.

The utilization of other, more stable foods has not been similarly restricted. Corn, for instance, is processed into cereal; and dried eggs and milk, by losing their original identity, have become utilizable in a large variety of foods. Many similar examples could be given. In the case of fish, however, the desire has, with few exceptions, almost always been to utilize it in the form of fish.

Faced with growing populations and attendant increasing shortages of protein, we had to conceive the use of fish as a rich additive to other foods. I think that the recent upswell and interest, nationally and internationally, in FPC means that the idea is not generally established and accepted of using fish as a concentrate of protein suitable for incorporation into foods of incomplete value.

FDA

When our studies on FPC started in 1961, our program was a broadly based research one designed to investigate simultaneously the three different methods of FPC manufacture I earlier mentioned. At this time, I must point out, research was in progress at several different locations around the world. All these programs, however, suffered from one or more deficiencies. All were inadequately financed, some were poorly designed, most were inadequately advised. In our work, we soon found that we were not rapidly completing our job of getting FPC to the people who needed it. The FDA problem had to be solved.

Secretary Udall, recognizing that the major importance of the FDA problem, directed us subsequently to drop our broadly based research program and develop one commercial method of FPC products that are flavorful, differing from the solvent-extracted product by this method, exhaustively test the product, and apply for FDA approval of the product as a food additive.

The next year was a hectic one. Eventually, based on experimental results obtained and on-engineering analyses performed, a scheme was proposed for the large-scale manufacture of FPC, using red hake as the raw material and isopropyl alcohol as the solvent.

The process was a three-stage countercurrent batch extraction that would yield a finished product with a residual lipid content of less than 0.5 percent. A test product prepared from whole fish by a method approximating the proposed commercial process was considered highly nutritious, safe and wholesome, and entirely satisfactory as a dietary supplement for human consumption.

A food additive petition was submitted to FDA in February of 1966. On February 2, 1967, the FDA approved the use of whole fish, in this case fish of the hake family, for FPC manufacture. They imposed several restrictions. They limited the level of IPA to 250 ppm and fluoride to 100 ppm. In addition, they permitted sale of FPC only directly to the consumer in pound or less packages. In other words, it could not be incorporated into other

other foods, such as bread, and sold to the consumer by the food manufacturer. Nevertheless, a victory.

Commercial Engineering Data

We earlier had recognized the eventual need for engineering information to permit potential manufacturers to build large-scale industrial plants. We recognized the fact that even with FDA approval American industry would not spend the millions in pre-engineering design studies and pilot-plant construction that were necessary preliminaries before a commercial-sized plant could be constructed with a reasonable probability of yielding a profit. Principally, they would not risk their capital because of the uncertainty of markets if they got into commercial production.

To remove this roadblock, Senators Magnuson of Washington and Bartlett of Alaska introduced a bill into Congress to authorize the construction of pilot plants. The bill also anticipated and provided for future food research and feasibility studies on the introduction of FPC into developing communities.

On November 2, 1966, President Johnson signed PL 89-701 which authorized the construction of one FPC pilot demonstration plant and the leasing of another. As a result of this law, pre-engineering design research was initiated to provide contractors information upon which a pilot plant could be built having a raw-fish capacity of 50 tons per day.

The pre-engineering design date should be completed in about 6 months. A contractor, soon to be selected, will then design, construct, and operate the plant, which Secretary Udall had indicated will be erected in the Pacific Northwest. Data obtained from the plant design, construction, and operation will be sufficient to provide industry with adequate engineering and technical data to construct commercial plants.

Rough estimates suggest that the pilot plant will cost about $1.5 million. Since this is an experimental demonstration plant, however, designed to work out engineering problems on a pilot basis, the product produced may be somewhat expensive.

My engineering colleagues assure me, however, that a truly commercial plant of about 200 tons per day of raw-fish input will result in a product costing no more than 25¢ per pound. This price includes a nickel profit on each pound.

Markets

There remains, of course, the last, and major, step of introducing this product to sale and creating a market for it. FPC produced in the pilot plant will be used to conduct market feasibility studies in the United States and in selected countries of the world. These market studies are in progress of being designed by the AID group responsible for overseas application of FPC. This is the Food From the Sea Division in the Office of the War on Hunger.

~~~~~~~~~~~~

Ursula B. Marvin:

64.   CONTINENTAL DRIFT*

Continental drift is an old concept that first acquired a large scientific following when it was proposed in 1912 by Alfred Wegener and expanded upon by Alexander Du Toit through the 1930's. Wegener postulated that, at the end of Mesozoic time, blocks of light, continental sial (silica-alumina) had broken from a former protocontinent and drifted apart through the heavier, oceanic sima (silica-magnesia). His theory attracted many geologists, particularly those who were puzzling over the distribution of sedimentary deposits and organisms in the Southern Hemisphere, but it was opposed by others, including many who clung to the belief that all oceans except the Pacific had sialic floors, an assumption that was finally disproved after World War II.

In 1928 as a result of a symposium held by the American Association of Petroleum Geologists, the drift hypothesis suffered a loss of credibility and ceased to be an acceptable subject of geological investigation in many universities. A rereading of the papers of the symposium makes it difficult to understand this overwhelmingly negative reaction, particularly as the chairman, W. A. J. van Waterschoot van der Gracht, favored drift. The reaction was, however, preconditioned in large part by the opposition to continental drift expressed earlier by Harold Jeffreys, whose enormous prestige as a

* From *Geo Science News*, Vol. 1, No. 4, March, April 1968. Copyright 1968 by the Neumann-Wall Corp., Pasadena. Reprinted by permission of the author.

Ursula B. Marvin has spent several years doing fieldwork in the U.S., South America and Africa. She is now engaged in full time research on the petrology of extraterrestrial materials at the Smithsonian Astrophysical Observatory in Cambridge, Massachusetts.

geophysicist proved decisive with many geologists. Jeffreys argued that the force of gravity is greater than any known tangential force acting within the earth, that the continental and oceanic crusts are strong enough to maintain topographic features such as Mt. Everest and the deep ocean trenches without slowly spreading out under the pull of gravity, and that they are therefore too strong to permit the horizontal drifting of sialic blocks through the sima. He concluded that the mantle is also too strong to yield to short-term horizontal stresses as it preserves the disequilibrium figure of the earth.

Jeffreys expanded upon his arguments through five editions of his book *The Earth*, and he is still, today, one of the strongest opponents of continental drift.

Over the past decade, however, the theory of continental drift has gained new vigor and new adherents as a result of advances in the studies of geochronology, paleomagnetism, and oceanography. Although many different configurations of ancient landmasses have been proposed, they all require a Mesozoic date for the breaking up and drifting apart of the present continents. Wegener believed the breakup was initiated about 70 million years ago, but current estimates range from about 250 to 150 million years ago.

Continental drift is postulated to explain certain geological phenomena, including the apparent fit of continents and of truncated structural trends separated by oceans—particularly the Atlantic; the bizzare pattern of climatic zones in the late Paleozoic, as shown by the distribution of glacial deposits and fossil plants and animals; the apparent migration of the magnetic poles along paths that differ for different continents, as indicated by remnant magnetism in rocks older than mid-Tertiary; the youth and topography of the ocean floors, and the linear patterns of magnetic anomalies paralleling the oceanic ridges.

The Atlantic shorelines of Africa and South America look like complementary pieces of a fractured block, and when they are matched along the 500-fathom line of the continental slopes, their fit is even better. North America and Europe are not so obviously paired, but a good fit can be made in the northern latitudes from Baffin Island to Greenland and Scandinavia. The northern and southen continents can then be joined so that the northwestern coast of Africa lies adjacent to North America from Florida to the Grand Banks (see Figure 64-1). This configuration requires the rotation of Spain into the Bay of Biscay, and the omission of Iceland, the Caribbean Islands, and most of Mexico and Central America.

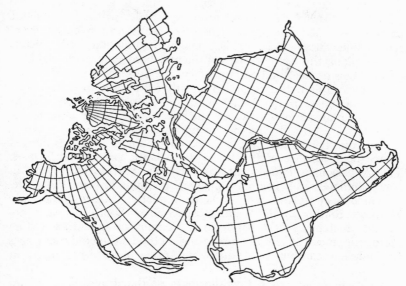

Fig. 64–1. Fit of the continents around the Atlantic as computed by Sir Edward Bullard and his colleagues.

As paleozoic rocks are known in Oaxaca, Mexico, however, adjustments must be made to include this area.

The eastern continents and Antarctica have been fitted by various schemes. Wegener assembled all the continents into a single large mass, which he called Pangaea. Alexander Du Toit believed there had been two primeval continents, Laurasia in the Northern Hemisphere and Gondwanaland in the Southern. Others have postulated at least four early landmasses. The majority of investigators agree that, if continental separation has occurred, it has been mainly associated with the Atlantic and Indian Oceans, where the geological formations are abruptly truncated at the continental margins. The Pacific Ocean is rimmed by deep trenches, island arcs, thrust faults dipping steeply beneath the continents, volcanism, and seismic activity, a pattern that suggests underthrusting of the Pacific floor.

Although the pattern shown in Figure 64–1 requires some distortions and omissions, it is nevertheless so remarkably good a fit that some investigators see it as a compelling argument that these continents were formerly part of a massive block. Others maintain that continents could not possibly fit so well if they had been through a catastrophic event powerful enough to split open the crust and upper mantle and set seven continents drifting to different parts of the planet. Judging from the faults and folds of every geosyncline, they would predict major deformation and igneous activity along the newly rifted continental borders and the slabbing off of shoals of small sialic islands (like the Seychelles and Madagascar). A close fit is thus regarded as either favorable or unfavorable to continental drift depending upon one's point of view. The fit of continental margins, however, unconfirmed by other evidence, is accepted as a critical criterion by no one.

Orogenic belts and lithologic contacts are abruptly truncated across their strike on both sides of the Atlantic and Indian Oceans. The Appalachian folded belt, for example, strikes out to sea in Newfoundland and has an apparent continuation in the Caledonian belt of Ireland and Scotland. Similarly, Paleozoic and early Mesozoic folding in the Cape geosyncline of South Africa is apparently matched in the Santa de la Ventana of Argentina. Before the development of radiometric dating methods, the equivalent ages and implied continuity of these and other units were often in question.

A current project of dating the rocks of Brazil and West Africa by both the K/Ar and the Rb/Sr methods is being carried on jointly by the geochronology laboratories directed by Prof. Patrick Hurley at MIT, and Dr. Geraldo Melcher at the University of Sao Paulo. The results are beginning to demonstrate a matching of rock provinces and contacts across the Atlantic to a degree well beyond anything likely to occur by coincidence. With the use of Bullard, Everett, and Smith's reconstruction of the two continents (Figure 64–1), a mapped contact, striking toward the Atlantic in Ghana, between rock provinces 2000 million and 500 million years old was extended westward to a predicted location near Sao Luis in northeastern Brazil. Subsequent sampling and dating of the basement rocks around Sao Luis have established the presence of this contact where it was predicted.

Farther south along the Brazilian coast a second belt of 2000-million-year-old rocks matches another one in West Africa. Each of these series of rocks is similar to its counterpart across the Atlantic in lithology and ore deposits, as well as in age. The elegant fit of these contacts, in addition to that of the continental margins, makes a persuasive case for the former continuity of Africa and South America in the Precambrian and early Paleozoic. That this continuity persisted through the Triassic is suggested by the apparent matching of the late Paleozoic sedimentary sections and the structural trends of

Triassic dike systems in each continent. Furthermore, the oldest marine embayments, demonstrating the presence of an ocean, along th Atlantic coastlines of Africa and South America are Jurassic, less than 180 million years old.

The distribution of glacial tillites of Permocarboniferous age is so irregular as to force a choice between stationary continents with major climatic fluctuations independent of latitude, or climatic zoning of the earth by latitude with migrating continents.

Permocarboniferous tillites have been mapped in Brazil, Uruguay, Argentina, the Falkland Islands, Africa from the equator to the Cape of Good Hope, Madagascar, India, Australia, and Antarctica (see Figure 64–2). Unlike the Pleistocene glaciers, which were confined to high latitudes and mountain ranges, Permian glaciers apparently occurred in the tropics at sea level. They are, in part, interbedded with marine deposits and coal seams. Except for India and a mountain range in Alaska, the Northern Hemisphere was evidently glacier-free, and warm and humid enough for the large-scale development of coal swamps in the same period. (The Permian tillite at Squantum, Massachusetts, was reclassified as a turbidite by R. H. Dott in 1961.)

With the retreat of the ice, the glaciated areas were covered by *Glossopteris*, a distinctive genus of seed fern found nowhere else. The uniqueness and strange distribution of tillites and the glossopteris flora led Du Toit to postulate that all areas bearing them had been grouped together in one continental mass, Gondwanaland, which was close to the South Pole in the Permocarboniferous. Other evidences for Gondwanaland include fossils of Mesosaurus, a small reptile found in beds deposited in brackish water immediately above the tillite in South America and South Africa, the presence of foreign boulders in the tillites of the Falkland Islands, and the distinctive similarity in each of these separate continents of the whole Permocarboniferous section, which everyone includes thousands of feet of continental sediments and basaltic lava flows. Without doubt, five continental regions and two groups of islands now widely separated by oceans had a strikingly similar history from the Carboniferous through the Permian.

Opponents of continental drift point out that an area may undergo violent changes of climate without changes of latitude. The Pleistocene to Recent history of the northern United States and Canada stands as an example. Jeffreys suggested that the Permocarboniferous tillites, in spite of their strange distribution close to and on both sides of the equator, should be taken as a lesson in meteorology rather than changes in the weather being cited as

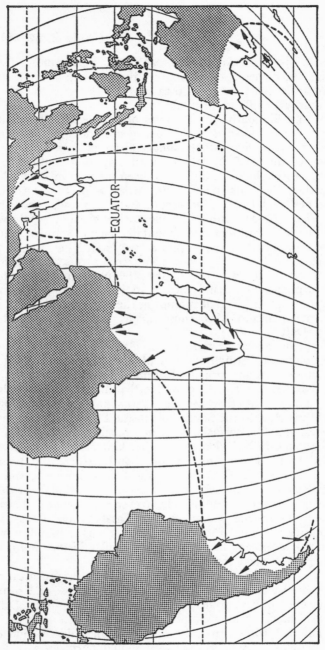

Fig. 64-2. A map by Arthur Holmes shows the distribution of the late Carboniferous glaciations of Gondwanaland with the continents in their present position, the arrows.

evidence for continental drift. The overseas distribution of *Glossopteris* has been ascribed to winged spores. The foreign boulders on the Falkland Islands have been attributed to iceberg rafting, a well-known mechanism for transport of materials at least as feasible as rafting continents, and Mesosaurus has been credited with crossing the Atlantic during periods of low water resulting from the large ice caps.

Attempts to map the distribution of late Paleozoic climates have been made on the basis of desert formations, evaporites, red beds, coal beds, and coral reefs. The evidence in every case displays anomalies and is ambiguous enough to cause differences of opinion among specialists. In the realm of paleoclimates, the most compelling evidence is that seven landmasses in the Southern Hemisphere have thick, distinctive Permocarboniferous deposits, including glacial tillites; the distribution of these deposits has not been adequately explained in terms other than continental drift.

Measurements of the fossil magnetism in unweathered rock samples from several continents show that for the past 20 million years, from the Miocene to the present, the locations of the earth's magnetic poles have remained essentially unchanged. Before the Miocene, the position of the magnetic pole, as determined by S. K. Runcorn of Newcastle-upon-Tyne, apparently moved at least 21,000 kilometers over a long curving path from western North America in the late Precambrian, through the present Pacific Ocean to northern Asia in the Mesozoic, and to the Arctic in the mid-Tertiary. If rocks of the same age in all continents were to point to the same pole throughout a long migration, this phenomenon could be ascribed to polar wandering. Polar wandering has two meanings. At one time it implied that the magnetic poles departed radically from the axis of rotation and swiveled independently within the earth. Such a mechanism, were it possible, would leave a record in magnetized rocks but would not involve climate changes, since the coldest regions of the planet, which behaves like a spinning gyroscope relative to the ecliptic, are always associated with the poles of the rotation axis.

At present, polar wandering is generally understood to mean that, while the magnetic poles remain fixed, an outer shell of the earth, including the crust and part or all of the mantle, becomes decoupled and moves as a unit over the interior—as though the skin of an orange could be loosened and moved over the fruit. Polar wandering of this type would allow the rocks of continents that are stationary, relative to each other, to record a simultaneous migration of the magnetic poles and of climatic zones. The actual evidence from rock magnetism, however, permits no such simple solution.

Rocks older than the Miocene from different continents point to different pole positions and describe systematically divergent paths of migration. This suggests that landmasses that were once joined have rifted and moved relative to one another and that their former positions can be reconstructed by superimposing their polar-migration curves. Many investigations have been carried out that purport to show that continental reconstructions based on paleomagnetism coincide well with the requirements of the fit of continental blocks and the pattern of paleoclimates. For example, paleomagnetically determined latitudes of Australia show an apparent migration of over 50° from the tropics in the Devonian toward the South Pole in the Carboniferous. During the same period Australian coral reefs died out and glaciation began. Correlations of this kind constitute impressive evidence in favor of continental drift.

Criticisms of paleomagnetism are based on its fundamental assumptions, on the rock sampling, and on the interpretations of results. The implicit assumption of a permanently dipolar magnetic field is challenged by those who believe the earth may well have been multipolar earlier in its history. If so, movements or rearrangements of pole positions could theoretically be recorded as separate curves from fixed landmasses. Various authorities, feeling that the sampling and mineralogical studies have been inadequate, are reserving judgment on paleomagnetic results until suites of samples of known age and mineralogy have been collected from larger areas of the continents. It is well known that pieces of continents move relative to each other, but these authorities feel that the case is less clear for continents as a whole. Paleomagnetic measurements record only the former latitudes of rock samples and give no indication of longitude, a situation that, to some, seems to allow too much freedom in plotting reconstructions, although in practice this freedom is severely limited by the necessity of fitting continental outlines and of presuming reasonable rates of drift.

Paleomagnetism is a rapidly developing branch of earth science. Major contributions have been made by Drs. Doell, Cox, and Dalrymple of the U.S. Geological Survey, Dr. Edward Irving of Australian National University, and Drs. Runcorn, Collinson, and Creer at Newcastle-upon-Tyne, to name but a few. Every year more measurements are made and duplicated by different investigators. The results seem increasingly reliable and appear to be far more solidly based than the objections to the method cited above. On balance, paleomagnetism confronts earth scientists with an impressive body of evidence that, to date, lacks an explanation other than continental drift.

Repeated reversals of the north and south magnetic poles are another phenomenon recorded by fossil-rock magnetism. Pole reversals are world-wide in effect and are, therefore, attributable to an alternation in polarity of the geomagnetic field. So-called self-reversals also occur, owing to special physical or chemical factors in rock units of limited extent.

Pole reversals are not ascribed to the moving of rock masses north and south of the equator and would, therefore, seem to have no relevance to continental drift. They do, however, constitute evidence of fundamental importance to the new concept of sea-floor spreading, which seeks to explain the youth, topography, and dynamics of the ocean floor, and is viewed by an increasing number of investigators as the mechanism by which continental drift is initiated and maintained.

Researches in oceanography during the past 15 years have resulted in many new data on the youth of the ocean basins and the complexity of submarine topography dominated by seamounts, guyots, trenches, and midocean ridges. In comparison with the continents, the ocean floors are geologically young. Continents include rock of all ages back to sediments that were metamorphosed about 3600 million years ago. Thus, continents were in existence and undergoing erosion and sedimentation within a few hundred million years after the formation of the solar system 4500 million years ago. Up to the present time, however, the ocean basins have yielded no rocks of Precambrian or even Paleozoic age. The oldest sediments in dredge or core samples from any ocean are late Jurassic, about 140 million years old. The unconsolidated red clays and globigerina oozes of the deep oceans are everywhere so thin that they could have accumulated within the past 100 million years beginning in the late Cretaceous. Dated basalt samples from oceanic ridges and seamounts range in age from less than 1 to about 60 million years, but interpretations of seismic profiles of the ocean floors suggest that the bedrock may date as far back as the early Mesozoic (225 million years) or even the mid-Paleozoic (400 million years). Given this earliest estimate, however, the ocean floors still appear to be significantly younger than the continents, from which they also differ in having a less siliceous composition and a greater density. One can only conclude that the earth has no "crust" in the sense of a continuous earth shell but that its surface consists of two provinces, the continents and the ocean floors, which are fundamentally different in lithology and geologic history. It seems that the bedrock of the ocean floors would be constantly renewed by its spreading away from the ridges, as on a system of opposed conveyor belts. As a result, the bedrock of the ocean floor would indeed be young and its cover of sediments thin.

If movement of this type occurs in the upper mantle, sialic continental blocks will presumably be floated passively away from the flanks of active ridges and centered over or between descending currents. If a ridge is initiated beneath a continent, the eventual result is visualized as a linear uplift followed by tensional necking and rifting and, finally, the symmetrical drifting apart of opposite continental blocks. Something like this may have caused the development of the Atlantic Ocean, beginning in the Mesozoic, and may be in initial stages today along the East African rift zone and in western North America. An alternative view of the latter region is that the North American continent, in its westward drifting, has partially overridden the East Pacific Rise, which was initiated not beneath a continent but in an ocean basin. This circumstance might help to explain some of the features of the Cordilleran region, including the uplift, tensional faulting, and belts of serpentinization.

Sea-floor spreading has been credited not only with continental drift but also with continental growth by accretion. Harry Hess and Robert Deitz have suggested that as the ocean floors approach the continents they are partially rolled downward and transformed by a loss of water from serpentine back to peridotite and partially crushed against the barrier until a prism of shelf and oceanic sediments and volcanics is welded to the continental margin by orogenic processes. Thus, the continents could show marginal belts of successively younger materials of apparent geosynclinal origin. The folds and thrusts of these belts, however—far from recording crustal shortening, as is generally assumed—would occur in formations that had been added to the continents. Sea-floor spreading has presumably occurred in different parts of the world during various geological periods, and J. Tuzo Wilson of the University of Toronto has suggested that oceans such as the Atlantic may have opened and closed more than once.

Of the several types of evidence advanced in support of sea-floor spreading, the newest and most dramatic are long, linear belts of magnetic anomalies that record reversals of the earth's magnetic poles. These belts are symmetrically distributed in alternate strips along either side of several oceanic ridges. Continental rocks record five periods of normal (north-seeking) polarity alternating with five of reversed polarity within the past four million years. Oceanic rocks should respond to the same reversals and, if it is assumed that these rocks acquire their magnetism as they cool on the ridges, the widths of the anomaly belts indicate how far oceanic rocks have spread laterally during the past one million to four million years and, by extrapolation, over much longer periods.

The rates of separation, as calculated by F. J. Vine of Princeton University, across several active ridges range from 1.9 centimeters per year for the Reykjanes Ridge south of Iceland, through 3 centimeters per year on the mid-Atlantic Ridge at latitude 38°S, 3 centimeters per year for the Carlsberg Ridge at latitude 5°N in the Indian Ocean, 5.8 centimeters per year at the Juan de Fuca Ridge south of Vancouver Island, to a maximum of 8.8 centimeters per year over the East Pacific Rise at latitude 51°S.

Assuming these rates of spreading, extrapolation of oceanic history have been attempted not only for the past four million years but for the past 11 million years and for much longer periods. Indeed, Dr. Vine suggests that the entire history of the ocean basins, in terms of sea-floor spreading, is frozen into the oceanic crust. His present projections of early Tertiary history, however, are not consistent with those made on the basis of heat-flow data in the Atlantic and Pacific.

Heat-flow values on the East Pacific Rise, as measured by scientists at the Lamont Geological Observatory, indicate that this is indeed an area of active upwelling and spreading, but at a rate of only about 1 centimeter per year. On the mid-Atlantic Ridge, however, the rate of heat flow is so low, excepting for a narrow zone along the crest, that continuous sea-floor spreading during the Cenozoic appears to be precluded. The Lamont investigators suggest that the mid-Atlantic Ridge may have generated floor spreading and continental drift during the Jurassic and Cretaceous and then lain dormant through the Tertiary until active spreading was renewed within the past 10 million years. This interpretation would allow for the formation of the Atlantic Ocean by spreading at the rate of 2 centimeters per year (and continental separation at 4 centimeters per year) for the first 100 million years, followed by cooling of the ridge until the recent rejuvenation, which accounts for the high heat flow along the axis and the bands of magnetic anomalies recording pole reversals over the past 4 to 11 million years.

In the seven years since sea-floor spreading was proposed by Dr. Hess, most of its supporters have seen in it the mechanism for causing continental drift. Efforts to accommodate sea-floor spreading without continental drift by postulating rapid expansion of the earth or a compensatory compression of the continents have proved untenable. The conclusion seems most reasonable that by sea-floor spreading the continents are slowly moved over the earth's surface in response to changes in the strength and distribution of convection currents in the upper mantle and in its surface expression, the ocean floors.

All variations of the continental drift theory depend for their driving force upon convection in the earth's mantle. Some of the most powerful and persuasive arguments against continental drift come from those geophysicists who are convinced on both theoretical and observational grounds that convection currents do not occur in the mantle. They argue that the upper mantle is too inhomogeneous for convection to have been significant; that the lower mantle is too rigid to convect, and that mantle-wide convection, from the core to the crust, is improbable in any case because the currents would not be sustained across the major transition zone separating the upper and lower mantles.

The inhomogeneous nature of the upper mantle is indicated by seismic, gravity, and heat-flow data collected over the past decade. These data show several discontinuities caused by phase or chemical layering and they also show that the mantle directly beneath the continents differs in density and composition from that under the ocean. Continental granodiorites are at least six times more radioactive than oceanic basalts. Nevertheless, contrary to all predictions, the rate of heat flow from the ocean floors is, on the average (although not in detail), equal to that from continents and mountain ranges. If, as many geophysicists believe, the heat is generated by radioactivity, then the mantle beneath the continents must be severely depleted in radioactive elements relative to that beneath the oceans, and according to Dr. Gordon J. F. MacDonald, the difference must persist to depths of several hundred kilometers. This suggests that continents are differentiated from the mantle rock directly beneath them, and such a deep-rooted genetic relationship argues against both rotating convection cells and continental drift.

The rigidity of the lower mantle is deduced from the fact that the nonequilibrium figure of the earth must be maintained by a strong earth shell that is unresponsive to short-term stress. As the upper mantle is plastic enough to respond to the loading and unloading of icecaps within periods of a few thousand years, the lower mantle remains the only layer that can have the requisite strength.

Most objections to convection currents are aimed largely at the classical conception of paired cells rotating in a viscous mantle. If the objections are valid, crustal tectonics result from some other type of mantle motion. Several variations on the convection theory have been proposed.

Dr. Orowan of MIT points out that, as the mantle is a crystalline solid, it is not subject to Newtonian viscous flow but that it is plastic at moderate temperatures and displays Andradean viscosity (hot creep with no strain hardening) at high temperatures. In such a mantle, deformation tends to concentrate in thin layers, and rising materials take the long, narrow dike-like forms of the oceanic ridges. From a consideration of movement on the mid-Atlantic Ridge and of the mean annual seismic energy release along our Pacific margin, he calculates that the Americas are moving westward and overriding the Pacific floor at the rate of 1 centimeter per year. Given movement as slow as this, no complete overturn of mantle rock as in a convection cell would have occurred since the Mesozoic. Minerals migrating at this rate may pass through phase changes en route and thus preserve mantle inhomogeneities.

Dr. Ramberg, of Copenhagen, suggests that the chemical differentiation of light, continental sial at a given site produces a heavier residue at depth that slowly sinks as the sial rises. The sinking material drags the surrounding mantle towards itself, subjecting the sial to horizontal compression from all sides and causing circumferential tension (oceanic ridges) some distance away from the sial. His hypotheses go far toward explaining many aspects of crustal tectonics without calling upon systematically totating currents in the mantle.

Serious objections are raised to all proposed patterns of convection, and the fact remains that we have no satisfactory theory of the forces governing the earth's interior. The restrictions on any dynamic model of the mantle are, today, more stringent than they were in 1924, when Jeffreys pronounced against continental drift without any knowledge of equal heat flow or mantle inhomogeneity. Nevertheless, evidence from both geology and geophysics indicates that massive movements of the ocean floors and continents are occurring and, therefore, that they must be described and measured with or without an adequate explanation of the energy sources motivating them.

During the past decade a great many very long fault planes have been recognized, with apparent offsets, along the strike, of a few hundred to over 1000 kilometers. These faults border the Pacific basin partly on land, partly in the ocean floor. A series of them cuts east to west across the crests of the East Pacific Rise and mid-Atlantic Ridge, and across the Carlsberg Ridge in the Indian Ocean.

The significance of these faults with respect to continental drift has been hotly debated. Some investigators see the movement of crustal blocks along these faults as living proof of drift. Others maintain that transcurrent faults would tear a continent to pieces and that, if they had been important in the movement of landmasses, no subsequent fit of continental margins would be possible.

Until the past year or so, there appeared to be no doubt that these were authentic strike-slip faults. However, the probability is now being examined that most of them are in fact transform faults, a type recently described by J. Tuzo Wilson. Transform faults occur at the sites of primary dislocations in the continuity of a feature such as an oceanic ridge. They involve horizontal movement of rigid materials but not on the scale that would be indicated if they were conventional transcurrent faults. They are a natural consequence of sea-floor spreading.

Of the many lines of evidence offered in support of continental drift, the most compelling in themselves and the most difficult to explain in the absence of drift are the following:

A. The divergent paths of continental migration, as indicated by paleomagnetism.

B. The symmetrical distribution of belts of ocean floor, showing evidence of alternate pole reversals along either side of the oceanic ridges.

C. The matching of truncated contacts between dated-rock provinces in West Africa and Brazil.

Evidence inconclusive in itself but favorable to drift in combination with the evidence cited includes the following:

A. The close fit of continental margins.

B. The distribution of paleoclimates, as indicated by the Permocarboniferous tillites and numerous other organic and inorganic deposits.

Evidence unfavorable to continental drift is the inhomogeneous nature of the upper mantle, as shown by heat-flow and seismic data.

My own conclusion is that the weight of evidence, much of which has been developed within the past ten years, indeed within the past two years, favors continental drift. The general concept has changed, within the same period, from one of moving continents through yielding ocean floors to that of moving ocean floors and, incidentally, moving continents and possibly related segments of upper mantle along with them.

The ultimate solution to the continental drift problem may come from satellite geodesy. Until very recently no site upon the earth's surface was pinpointed to an accuracy of more than 30 meters.

At present, each station in a worldwide network established by the Smithsonian Astrophysical Observatory for optical tracking of satellites is located to an accuracy of 10 meters. The substitution of laser for optical techniques will soon reduce the error to about 10 centimeters. Such precision will make possible the measurement of continental drift if it is occurring at the estimated rates of one to ten centimeters per year. Repeated determinations will be essential over several decades, with special care taken to detect and correct for local crustal movement. In the end, a negative answer would prove little; present stability does not disprove past drift.

If, however, the results were to show a definitive change in mean latitude or longitude of any landmass as a whole, these measurements would resolve one of the most spirited controversies in earth science.

John D. Isaacs:

65.   THE BIRTHPLACE OF WEATHER*

In the 1930's, a great drought turned a normally luxuriant part of the United States into what came to be known as the "Dust Bowl"; again in 1953, the southwestern part of the nation experienced a disastrous dry season; recently, an abnormal lack of rainfall in the Northeast dried up streams and ponds and seriously threatened even the supply of drinking water of many communities, while normally drier areas of the country were soaked by downpours; periodically, after intervals lasting a decade or longer, bank-to-bank floods have been known to sweep down the canyons and arroyos of the Southwest.

What factors are responsible for these phenomena? Could they be predicted?

The answers to these intriguing questions may lie in the little-understood large-scale temperature fluctuations in the surface layers of the waters of the North Pacific Ocean. It is in these vast ocean

*From *Naval Research Reviews*, Volume 21, November, December 1968, pp. 1–13. Reprinted by permission of the author.

John D. Isaacs is professor of oceanography at Scripps Institution of Oceanography and Director of Scripps' Marine Life Research.

reaches that many of the features of the North American weather receive their final identity.

The centers of strongly abnormal surface-water temperatures occur most frequently in the region of 35° to 45° N and 150° W and 150° E. These "abnormal" or anomalous conditions are large in area and persist for long periods of time. They are known to be associated with changes in the propagation of underwater sound, shifts of ocean and atmospheric circulations, changes in the migration patterns of important commercial fishes, alterations in the distribution of pelagic organisms (including members of the sound-scattering layers), and with unusual weather over the North Pacific Ocean and the continental United States and perhaps the entire northern hemisphere.

The University of California's Scripps Institution of Oceanography (SIO), under contract to the Office of Naval Research, has initiated a long-term study in the North Pacific. This study is designed to understand the nature of the relationship between the large-scale sea-surface temperature anomalies, and the subsurface events, and both of these as they relate to meteorological events in the atmosphere.

Data now available from the North Pacific indicates that:

The departure of the sea-surface temperature from the normal is the rule rather than the exception.

• The average dimension of the temperature anomaly is about one fifth of the width of the North Pacific Ocean. Larger anomalies frequently occupy one third to one half or more of the North Pacific.

• Large-scale anomalies usually persist for longer than three months and sometimes as long as 30 months.

• Anomalous areas often appear to progress from west to east over a period of two to three years at an apparent speed of about 200 miles per month (or seven miles per day).

• The intensities of the warm and cold sea-surface temperature anomalies range as high as 10° to 12°F. Cold anomalies tend to be less intense than the warm ones. As an example, in the central North Pacific, anomalous temperatures less than 3.5°F are more often cold than warm, whereas warm anomalies are more frequent than cold ones for temperature differences above 3.5°F.

• The monthly mean temperature gradient, that is, the mean spacing between isotherms, is most closely associated with the gradient of the more intense anomalies. In other words, the areas that display the greatest departure from normal temperatures surprisingly show the most slavish adherence to the long-term mean temperature gradients.

• Warm anomalies may be the result of shallow stability, whereas cold anomalies may be the result of mixing. There is thus an anisotropy of heating and cooling processes. By a suitable succession of events, an anomalously warm layer can form on an anomalously cool one and the conditions can persist for months, with the cold water eventually reappearing at the surface.

• The normal seasonal temperature changes of the central North Pacific very closely follow the apparent north-south seasonal solar cycle.

The records of the weather of the Pacific Coast reveal almost continuous fluctuations since their inception. Variations in the temperatures at such coastal stations were long thought to be very local effects, but in the last decade or so they have been shown to be correlated over dimensions of 1000 km or more. Further, some years ago, it was noted that the more extreme departures from the mean ocean temperatures were roughly synchronous at such widely-separated regions as Peru, Japan and California. These extreme fluctuations were sometimes in the same sense and sometimes in the inverse sense; that is, the intensity was correlated, but not the phase. Considered as a correlation of widely separated local changes, these were thought to be cases of teleconnection. However, it now appears that these correlations are very often simply an expression of the great spatial extent of the ocean-atmosphere variations.

Perhaps a brief review of the case history of a well-studied variation in the Pacific will bring some of these matters into focus. The mean sea-surface temperature over the North Pacific during the years 1955 to 1958 underwent an intense change. During this period a great warm anomaly appeared to progress across the Pacific from Japan to the west coast of North America. This was associated with at least two periods of highly anomalous surface-wind patterns. In the winter seasons of 1956–57 and 1957–58 anomalous low-pressure areas were centered roughly over the warm surface waters. Qualitatively this should have the effect of propagating and intensifying the warm anomaly toward the north and east, by advection and simple thermal exchange at least. The 1957–58 winter season was typified by an intense development of a low pressure area over the eastern North Pacific. The effects of these anomalous southerly winds off the Pacific coast were marked. The southerly-directed California Current weakened and swung offshore, warm subtropical water invaded the coast as far as British Columbia, and

Central Pacific water moved strongly to the east. In this change abnormal advection from abnormal winds has been implicated. Indeed, it appears that simple advection is partially successful in explaining these events and several scientists have developed and tested a series of increasingly sophisticated weather models based on this process.

In order to understand better the nature of the fluctuations in weather, it is necessary to know and to relate the weather behavior in the past to the known characteristics of today.

Scientists at Scripps have been accumulating much of the continuous and fragmentary data on the Pacific Coast conditions. This data consists of Spanish mission rainfall records, observations contained in whalers' logs, logs of Spanish galleons, letters of pioneers, *etc.* Data showing years when snow fell on the southern California and Mexican offshore islands, years of floods and displacements of tropical or northern fauna may eventually be fitted into a more thorough knowledge of the climatic variations in the Pacific and their etiology. Little-known expeditions to the Pacific have provided some very useful information. The logs of the Malaspina expeditions of 1786–94, which have long languished in Spanish archives, will soon be examined. These remarkable documents, which contain hundreds of excellent large color drawings of marine and terrestrial animals and plants, are a treasure trove of information. More ancient data has been gleaned from observations of what are the remnants of social habits of the inhabitants of Pacific coasts. Studies of the kitchen middens of coastal Indians have shown that the winds and currents must, in general, now be of the same nature as for the last four or more millennia.

At Scripps another and inexhaustive source of data on past variations in the Pacific is being developed. These are the rare and curious varved sediments laid down in certain coastal basins extending from British Columbia to Peru. These sediments are deposited at depths under water that is essentially devoid of oxygen. The sediments are not reworked by either currents or benthic organisms and are preserved as layers representing the annual fall of detritus from the overlying waters. These sediments, therefore, are virtually annual pages in the history book of the ocean-atmosphere system, that provide an extremely valuable entree into an understanding of the nature of oceanic fluctuations of the past, the frequency, the nature of the changing circulation, the relationships with rainfall, and the synchrony of changes between widely-separated areas. To decipher the message, we must know the range of distribution of the organisms whose remains contribute to the sediments. For example, the presence of a subarctic pteropod, the microscopic pelagic mollusc *Limacina helicina*, in the sediments of the Santa Barbara Basin must be a measure of the strength of the California Current.

Diatoms and foraminifera are also being tabulated. The results should give a great insight into the history and conditions of short- and long-term fluctuations in the Pacific, extending through the historical period for several thousand years before the present with a high time resolution. An attempt will be made to correlate this data with that of other basins and also with data from glaciers, tree rings, the historical record and other sources. Just the qualitative correlations of this pteropod data with known climatic change is intriguing. For example, periods of glacial advance in British Columbia appear to be associated with rapidly increasing numbers of *Limacina* and presumably with increasing strength in the California Current.

The information gathered this way, intriguing as it may be, is often empirical in nature and difficult to quantify; it gives only a vague insight into the nature of the sea-surface temperature anomalies and can only attempt to explain, in general terms, the atmospheric interaction of these features. To begin to understand the phenomenon, more accurate, extensive and synoptic measurements are needed. At the present, the only synoptic information on ocean temperature fluctuations is of the surface temperatures. We need to know more than this. We need to know what is transpiring below the surface of the sea during these fluctuations, so that we can determine such critical aspects as the fluctuation in heat content, the relationships of the large-scale changes and high-frequency events, the nature of diurnal heating and cooling, *etc.* Also needed is a better quantification of the insolation, wind drag, humidity and other atmospheric conditions associated with large-scale sea-surface temperature fluctuations. A new phase of study to gather accurate and extensive information is needed.

STUDY ENTERS NEW PHASE

To obtain a clear picture of nature of the processes, Scripps is turning to deep-moored, unmanned, catamaran-type floating instrument (buoy) stations to study the physical changes of the waters of the North Pacific. In this new phase of the study, the buoys will remain on location for a year or longer. The area under observation will be a vast expanse four million square miles in area and extending some 1000 miles south of the Aleutian Islands. In this area Scripps scientists have installed one cluster of four of these buoys north of Hawaii at 43° N. In the center of the cluster is a 40-foot "Monster Buoy" developed for the Office of Naval Research by the Convair Division of General Dynamics (see *Naval Research Reviews* of February, 1967). Other SIO buoys are anchored in other areas of the North Central Pacific. A second Convair buoy is to be anchored soon. Scripps and Convair buoys have both been tested extensively in the ocean and have survived at least 100-mile winds and 45-foot waves.

In addition to the data collected by the deep-moored buoys, scientists will collect other information such as satellite photographs of cloud cover from NASA and ESSA weather satellites, and hydrographic casts from sources such as ESSA, Bureau of Commerical Fisheries, U.S. Coast Guard, University of Washington, National Oceanographic Data Center, Oregon State University, University of Hawaii, Navy Oceanographic Office, Canadian ship observations, observations made by other countries and Scripps expeditions and mooring servicing cruises.

The Scripps-developed catamaran buoys, moored in water 12,000 to 18,000 feet deep, will record near-surface wind speeds and directions, and water temperatures at depths extending to 1000 and 1500 feet below the surface. A separate station in the cluster will monitor near-surface ocean currents. The buoys will also record barometric pressure, solar radiation and relative humidity.

THE FIRST QUESTION

Advection will be measured in four independent ways. The ships' hydro-casts will provide data for the analysis of geostropic currents. Since the abnormal currents may not be in geostropic balance, catamaran buoys will provide measurements for comparison with the known water masses to observe changes in water masses and to provide indication of their direction of motion. The current meters will directly record the advective motion in the surface layers. The plankton samples will provide critical evidence on the sources of water masses even though they may have undergone considerable temperature changes. The measurements associated with thermal energy will be used to ascertain the nature of the changes in the thermal reservoir and to obtain knowledge of the nature of the fluxes that give rise to the changes. Data about changes in the general circulation will provide information about the possible feedback effects on the atmospheric conditions. Such data will be gathered from the general weather maps, from the wind direction measurements at the moored buoys, and from the changes in cloud cover noted from satellite photographs and quantified by the insolation measurements at the moored stations. These various sources of data will also provide information on secondary changes in the conditions of the atmosphere, such as humidity, stability, and precipitation.

Although many descriptive and quantitative analyses and comparisons will be involved, much effort will be devoted to ascertain whether changes in ocean conditions lag or lead the related changes in the atmosphere as an indication of the source of primary excitation and the nature of feedback. This will involve a comparison of the atmospheric pressure distribution, averaged over different periods of time, with the observed changes in ocean conditions.

All data collected for the first question can be used to analyze the second one—what large-scale initial instabilities or oscillations of the ocean appear to occur in the North Pacific? The moored temperature profiling stations that make continuous records of temperatures from the surface to 1500 feet will be essential in detecting large-scale instabilities.

It is suspected that three mechanisms may be involved in the possible occurrence of initial instabilities or oscillations. There is first the possibility that large-scale Rossby-type waves, similar to the planetary waves in the atmosphere, may occur along the West Drift Current and, second, that large-scale long-period internal oscillations of the entire North Pacific thermal structure may occur. A third possibility is that energetic internal waves from some distant generating source contribute to the thermal mixing of the North Pacific. This would result from the instability of these waves as they encounter the discontinuity of thermal structure at about 42° N latitude. This region may be a sort of "internal wave surf zone." In this case, changes in the intensity of incident internal waves generated by remote events elsewhere could result in the production of abnormal sea-surface temperatures.

Although the primary objective of the North Pacific Study is to answer these vital questions, it is expected that the study by-products will undoubtedly be of general importance in furthering knowledge of ocean processes such as heating-cooling cycles, response of layer thickness to low and high-pressure areas, effect of turbidity on radiant energy absorption, and distribution of certain plankton organisms.

Heating-Cooling Cycles

From previous moored-station data, we learned that the diurnal heating of a thin surface layer is a characteristic of relatively calm weather and an increasing general stability of the water column. In the present study, we will further understand the nature of this diurnally-heated layer and the manner in which it is dissipated by winds and at night. We will also understand the rates at which these processes take place. Diurnal cooling of the surface layers is probably associated with periodic convergence and sinking. We will be able to understand this process and the distribution of the convergence cells in space.

Response of Layer Thickness to Low and High Pressure Areas

The moored-station data will shed light on the rate of response of the surface layer thickness to meteorological pressure changes, of differing derivations of these changes and their velocity of motion. For example, certain critical velocities of motion of high or low-pressure features may result in a high coupling with internal motions and lead to high internal "bow" waves and wakes that are propagated within the density structure. These may be propagated and cause sea-surface temperatures changes elsewhere.

Effect of Turbidity on Radiant Energy Absorption

Upwelling and mixing processes give rise to increased light absorption because of plankton growth. In some cases, this then profoundly alters the depth at which radiant energy is absorbed and, hence, the depth over which solar heating is distributed and increase the rate of heating of the upper layer. In opposed fashion, convergence and downwelling suppress turbidity, increase the layer of heating, and decrease the rate of upper-layer heating. It is quite possible that such processes are important feedback mechanisms in the air-sea interaction processes. Absorption measurements will be conducted during the ship surveys.

Distribution of Certain Plankton Organisms

The presence or absence of certain planktonic organisms is frequently one of the best water-mass indicators. We will thus obtain plankton samples as the fourth entree into the determination of abnormal advection. In addition, this information is one of the few keys to the nature of past fluctuations, through the special sediment deposits, and, hence, a key for the establishment of the past ranges of conditions.

The first to benefit from the North Pacific Study will be the Navy. The data gathered will be of great importance in its program of oceanographic research and its Anti-Submarine Warfare Environmental Prediction System (ASWEPS) program. Since ASWEPS forecasts are largely based on up-to-date oceanographic information, the development of a system of highly-reliable deep-moored buoys that could provide real-time data on the ocean is vital. The data will also aid in the development of a more effective detection and weapon systems. Included among the other beneficiaries are U.S. Weather Bureau forecasters, the U.S. Bureau of Commercial Fisheries, the World Weather Watch, expected to go into effect in the 1970's, commercial fishermen, farmers, ship operators and other people whose livelihood and lives may be affected by the climatic changes associated with profound fluctuations in ocean conditions.

And these fluctuations in the conditions of the world oceans have often drastically affected the lives of many people. Fisheries have appeared and disappeared; hurricanes have visited coasts during some periods and shunned them at others; great quasi-cyclical alterations of rainfall and drought have successively stimulated and destroyed agriculture. The fluctuations of the conditions of the ocean and atmosphere cover broad spacial and temporal scales ranging from local changes lasting only minutes to changes that involve time periods of months to decades and affect large parts of the earth. While man adjusts to seasonal changes and to the long-term changes in climate, his resources and habits are frequently incapable of accommodating the intensity and duration of changes of the intermediate time scale. Agriculture and fisheries, for instance, cannot survive successive years of drought or dearth, nor can the food reserves of many societies be stretched across long periods. The biblical tale of the seven fat and seven lean years predicted by Joseph emphasize the vital nature of changes of such duration. (Joseph's prediction may well be considered the longest long-range weather forecast—a forecast covering 14 years!)

But there is no need to go back so far in time and place to illustrate the effects of shifts in ocean conditions. The great American drought of the 1930's caused incalculable loss throughout a vast area of the United States. The economic catastrophe and human tragedy caused by that event are well illustrated in Steinbeck's *Grapes of Wrath*. Again in 1953 a drought of disaster proportion occurred throughout Arkansas, Kansas, Colorado, Oklahoma, Missouri, Texas and New Mexico. We may now safely surmise that these droughts are related to persistent sea-surface temperature anomalies.

There are also many maritime expressions of these anomalies. From the middle of 1957 through about 1960, over much of the eastern North Pacific, water temperatures were much higher than the long-term mean. As a result, tropical and subtropical fishes migrated as far as southern Alaska. A related phenomenon is presented by El Niño of the Peruvian coast. Here masses of warm water periodically and inexplicably flow over the cold coastal current, with considerable changes in the fisheries and disastrous results to the birds and sometimes to the local inhabitants. On the Pacific coasts of North America the effects of past shifts in ocean conditions are conspicuous in guise of verdant forests of eucalypti planted at the 1913 onset of wet period, and abandoned remains of large agricultural colonies in Baja California stimulated by similar periods.

Ignorance or disregard of these repetitive effects results in activities fraught with potential for disaster. An example of such activities is the [building of] new housing developments on potential slide areas and particularly in the canyons and arroyos of the Southwest. Here, in the last twenty years, civic conscience has not taken into account the danger of bank-to-bank floods, though such floods occurred once in a decade in the first half of this century.

Someday, data similar to that to be collected by the North Pacific Study will enable scientists to predict the recurrence of drastic long-term weather and climate fluctuations and anticipate their effects. In the not-too-distant future a large network of buoys could supply simultaneously information about hundreds of oceanographic factors throughout the oceans. Land-based scientists could interrogate these buoys and receive an hour-by-hour picture of what is going on throughout the total marine environment. Unlike Joseph, who must have had divine assistance to make his prediction, once the basic mechanisms of change are understood, they will only have to analyze this data to make accurate and long-term predictions of fat and lean years—rainfall or drought, or other vital changes in the weather and climate.

Jacques Piccard:

66.   *THE PROMISE OF THE UNDERWATER
        WORLD**

The underwater world holds promise and importance for all of mankind. In my estimation, it is as vital to the Australian sheep rancher or European housewife as it is to the Gloucester fisherman or Louisiana wildcatter. The sea affects all our lives in a variety of ways, and better understanding of the seas and their mechanics can only make the lot of all mankind easier, more productive, and more satisfying.

The theme of my remarks, then, is to be the need, by whatever means you gentlemen of the Congress ultimately decide upon, for speeding the orderly exploitation and development of the riches of the Continental Shelf and the oceans, which, rather than separating the United States from its Asian, European, or African neighbors, rather provides a ready and convenient link with them.

The vastness of the subject almost makes it impossible to know where to begin. Allow me to start with some of the more familiar uses and products of the oceans and proceed to some of the more exotic, esoteric fields where today we are just piercing the surface, so to speak.

For as long as man has lived on the shores of the oceans, rivers and lakes, he has been nourished by the fish he has been able to lure, trap, snare, spear, or net from the beach or a boat. It is amazing to note that the methods of catching fish are practically the same today as they were in the earliest dawn of mankind, and certainly not much more sophisticated than those in the days 2,000 years ago when men drew their precious food from the Sea of Galilee in straining nets and bobbing boats.

* From *Commercial Fisheries Review* December, 1968.

This article is nearly all of Dr. Piccard's testimony before a subcommittee of the House Committee on the Judiciary, July 24, 1968. Among his many accomplishments, oceanographic engineer Jacques Piccard designed and operated (with his father, Auguste Piccard) the first deep diving vessel. His book, SEVEN MILES DOWN, which he co-authored with Robert S. Dietz, was published in 1961.

The processing and marketing of seafood have developed along technological lines, but we are still in the Dark Ages when considering the search for fish, knowledge of their habits, spawning grounds and their nutritional value. Recent developments have been made in the production of fish protein concentrate, thanks to great encouragement and financial support by the U.S. Government, and a great deal more must be done to produce and merchandise this dietary supplement for Americans and, perhaps more importantly, for those millions of undernourished people whose protein supply is inadequate.

Better organized fishing methods will not only increase the catches and yields of the commercial fisherman, but will also help guard against the annihilation and disappearance of certain species of food fish—a sad fact which has already seen the reduction to dangerous limits in some areas of halibut, salmon, lobster, and shrimp.

Finally, it should be mentioned that while every maritime nation of the world has shown substantial increases in fish production and consumption, the United States has been at a virtual standstill, with fish imports rising to the point where Americans now eat more imported fish than that caught and processed domestically. Surely this is an area which deserves more attention and support.

Linked to the food-from-the-sea activity is the problem of pollution of the sea. This is a thorny problem, but because it is man-made, it admits of a solution. We have already seen great quantities of shellfish from large areas declared unfit for human consumption because of polluted waters—in the Raritan Bay area of New Jersey, for example.

We must guard against increasing destruction of the species and upsetment of the marine environment too by dumping, radioactive waste discharging, drainage from industrial plants and even the introduction of the heated water used for cooling powerplants to normally cool fish feeding grounds. A problem such as this which transcends State borders seems to call for the attention of, if not the regulation by the Federal Government.

My father once said that exploration is the sport of the scientist, and it is in exploration that much of oceanographic activity is found today.

Gentlemen, we are standing not at a single threshold, but before a long corridor marked by a series of doors. Behind each is a new and exciting field of opportunity awaiting the imaginative, the daring, the enterprising men who are blessed with both vision and the means to exploit these riches.

Besides food, the oceans contain, or more precisely, separate man from rich mineral deposits. One authority has calculated that the seas contain 30,000 trillion tons of chlorine—that is 30 followed by 15 zeros—2,000 trillion tons of magnesium, and similarly staggering quantities of sodium, sulphur, potassium, bromide, and carbon, and so on. The interesting point is that these minerals are not found only in minute quantities in the water itself. Off the California coast, phosphorous nodules resembling large pebbles are scattered around the seafloor at depths from 200 to 8,000 feet at least. Best known are the manganese deposits, confirmed to exist in the Atlantic, Pacific, and Indian Oceans.

While sufficient quantities of these various elements are obtainable on land, their exploitation from the seabed will receive low priority. When poorer strata are mined on land, raising production costs there, greater attention can be expected for offshore mining development. Such was the case in the petroleum industry, which is by far the leading developer of offshore resources.

Today some 70 countries are involved in the quest for oil and gas beneath the Continental Shelf. Twenty countries are producing these products, by recent estimate.

Like every general statistic about the seas the figures regarding petroleum production and reserves defy the imagination. About one-fifth of the world's total known oil reserves of 425 billion barrels is found offshore. Currently about 5½ million barrels are produced each day from wells sunk offshore. This is about 16 percent of the world total. In another 10 years perhaps 33 percent will come from offshore—all this to meet a demand which is increasing at a rate of 7 percent a year. No need to belabor the importance of offshore oil and gas production. It is, after all, the very raison d'etre of the legislation you are considering.

We must also acknowledge, too, that the water-starved areas of the globe see in the salty surface of the oceans, their first source of potable water, as desalinization techniques grow and hold out promise of abundant fresh water everywhere in the world. If we could theoretically separate all the minerals from all the water in the oceans, we would have, on one hand, enough salts to fill a freight train stretching back and forth between the earth and the sun 300,000 times and, on the other, about 1,500,000 trillion tons of fresh water. I apologize for having to resort to these big numbers, but I know you gentlemen want to know the facts.

We are only beginning to fully appreciate the preeminent role of the oceans in the origin and influence of weather. If man is to accurately predict the weather, to guard against destructive waves, prepare for hurricanes and typhoons, and some day exercise a degree of control over the elements, he must learn a great deal more of the dynamics that go on where sea meets sky, and the massive movements of ocean waters from one region to another.

While these remarks have dealt with, let us say, peaceful or materially productive uses of the seas, we cannot overlook the strategic importance of the undersea world in defensive and possibly offensive warfare. Greater knowledge of the terrain, not only along the Continental Shelves, but in midocean as well, is needed to assure the safe transit of military submarines. And we must understand the acoustic phenomenon better if effective defense measures are to be prepared.

The very immensity of the seas, which, as you know, cover about 70 percent of the earth's surface, makes a concise and specific summary of ocean-related activities difficult, if not impossible. Likewise, the fledgling efforts of governments and private industry are as diverse as the problems and challenges themselves.

Many, many American industrial firms have been attracted beyond the water's edge, so to speak. And they have invested sizable sums of their own money in the oceanography market. I would like to take just a minute to describe one of these programs, the oceanographic activities in which I am presently engaged with the Grumman Aircraft Engineering Corp. in Bethpage, N.Y.

Already a leader in the design and construction of military and private aircraft and sophisticated space vehicles, Grumman in 1965 appraised the oceanographic field and, rightly, I believe, saw there great potential.

In order to contribute to solving these problems of offshore mining, fish study, national defense, and the study of basic physical phenomena, it was decided to turn the vast engineering talent of the company to the development of a submersible vehicle, a work submarine which could bring man into the undersea environment to observe and perform useful tasks there.

About this time I became an exclusive consultant to Grumman, and after several studies, it was decided to build a mesoscaph or middle-depth submarine (from the Greek words for "middle"-"meso" and "ship"-"scaph"). It was to be based on a design I had prepared for an earlier submarine, the first mesoscaph, the *Auguste Piccard*, named for my father.

Subsequently, the PX-15, as the Grumman submersible was called, was built in Switzerland at the same factory which constructed the first vessel. In about 1 year the PX-15 was practically fully completed. In early March it was partially disassembled—to allow it to pass by railroad through our Swiss tunnels to Antwerp, where it was loaded on a merchant ship and transported to the Grumman facility in West Palm Beach, Fla.

Grumman engineers and several of my staff have been engaged since April in the final outfitting of this unique research submarine. The vehicle is built of high-strength steel and is about 50 feet long and about 130 tons in weight, making it the largest research submarine in the world. It can dive to 4,500 feet before collapsing, but we shall limit its operation to 2,000 feet. The live support system can sustain six men for 6 weeks, giving us a great deal more submerged endurance than any other research vehicle.

And 29 portholes, a closed-circuit television system as well as fixed external cameras and recording devices assure that we can observe and document the underwater secrets we uncover.

The various unique features of the Grumman-Piccard PX-15 admirably suit it for our first major undertaking, a kind of undersea adventure, with "science nonfiction" objectives.

Early next year the submarine with six men, including myself, on board will submerge off the Florida coast and drift in midwater at depths of 300 to 2,000 feet, propelled northward for 4 to 6 weeks only by the current of the Gulf Stream.

The scientists will conduct a series of long- and short-duration experiments concerning the mysterious Deep Scattering Layer, which "tricks" navigators by sending back false echoes on their fathometers and has implications in fish-feeding and marine-life cycles, on bottom topography, acoustics, marine biology, and fish habits, as well as analysis of the water's chemical properties, temperature, and speed.

The program is to be a cooperative enterprise with the U.S. Naval Oceanographic Office providing the all-important surface support ship (to give us navigational information) and two of the scientific observers on board the submarine.

When the Gulf Stream Drift Mission is terminated, probably 1,000 miles later off the coast of Massachusetts, the people at Grumman will make the submersible available on a lease basis to those who can best utilize its special depth, endurance, and large payload capabilities.

Just 2 weeks ago here in Washington, at a convention, we announced that the PX-15 henceforth will be known as the *Ben Franklin*, honoring your early American scientist-statesman, the man who first recognized the practical advantages of knowing and defining the limits of the Gulf Stream.

Franklin, as head of the U.S. Post Office, learned that British mail packets sailing from England, took 2 or 3 weeks longer to cross the Atlantic than Nantucket whalers returning from Europe. A conversation with some of the Yankee skippers brought the fact that they avoided the Gulf Stream while the English "bucked" the current much of the way.

Franklin then asked several of the New England whalers to make temperature readings throughout the North Atlantic and from these reports he charted the first map of the Gulf Stream. He turned it over to the British General Post Office, and we can assume that a substantial decrease in the London-to-Philadelphia mailing time followed shortly.

Just this week at the West Palm Beach facility we will begin dockside tests of the *Ben Franklin,* and on August 21 we will hold the formal christening ceremonies.

This Grumman program will involve more than $4 million of company funds, and it is just one of many pioneering efforts, some supported wholly or in part by Federal money, others purely company sponsored.

The important point, however, is that basic research into the workings of the world beneath the waves is moving forward. The Naval Oceanographic Office and the Office of Naval Research are spearheading this assault on the unknown, and scientists the world over acknowledge the preeminent position these agencies along with ESSA, the Bureau of Commercial Fisheries, and others occupy in the advancement of man's understanding of the oceans.

~~~~~~~~~~~~~~

Richard J. Pothier:

67.   *DEEP SEA DRILLING RECORD**

The 400-FOOT research ship *Glomar Challenger* may not look like much these days. It is caked with dirt and grime, encrusted with salt spray, and an unwieldy 150-foot derrick juts skyward from its crowded deck. But the *Glomar Challenger,* today drilling its way

* From *Sea Frontiers,* November, December, 1968, pp. 322–331. Copyright 1968 by the International Oceanographic Foundation, 10 Rickenbacker Causeway, Virginia Key, Miami, Florida 33149. Reprinted by permission.

Richard J. Pothier is Science editor of the *Miami Herald.* In 1965, upon receiving his M.S. from Columbia University Graduate School of Journalism, Mr. Pothier was awarded a Pulitzer Traveling Fellowship.

toward Dakar, West Africa, is the culmination of a decade of dreams and possibly the most important oceanographic research ship on the oceans of the world.

Glomar Challenger, a 10,000-ton deep-sea drilling vessel, is the key to the world's most ambitious deep-ocean drilling project. Ten years of planning, preliminary deep-sea sampling projects, and groundwork have already been done. Now JOIDES—for Joint Oceanographic Institutions Deep Earth Sampling—is bringing home the results, thanks to the enthusiastic support of the National Science Foundation. The results are indisputably significant. They include scientific triumphs, confirmation of older theories, and more than a few major surprises.

For a total project cost of about $12.5 million, JOIDES is learning more about this earth than the $25 billion Project Apollo will learn about the moon. Apollo will merely scratch the lunar surface, but JOIDES is sampling the very history of the world— the sediments that have been accumulating on the ocean floors through most of the earth's history.

The *Glomar Challenger* recently returned from the first two-month leg of its planned eighteen month circumnavigation of the world. Chosen by JOIDES to manage the project was Scripps Institution of Oceanography, which has successfully managed a major organizational feat. If the first leg's results are any indication of what the future of JOIDES holds, the *Glomar Challenger* could well become the most important vessel science has ever sent to sea.

THREE MAJOR SURPRISES

Its major findings were utterly unexpected, but they could be just the beginning of a long list of scientific successes for JOIDES.

First, the marine geologists aboard discovered unmistakable traces of oil and gas in the middle of the Gulf of Mexico. This is the first time oil has ever been found in a deep-ocean area away from the coast. This does not mean that the world's deep-ocean bottoms contain vast untapped reservoirs of commercially valuable oil, geologists hasten to point out, but the finding could have commercial significance and will almost certainly spur future research in deep-ocean areas previously ruled off the list of likely drilling sites.

Even more important, however, is the scientific significance of the oil traces, which are under nearly 12,000 feet of water and 500 feet of prehistoric sediment of the Gulf's floor about midway between Louisiana and the Yucatan Peninsula. Because hydrocarbon formation is generally associated with land-based biological processes, the discovery of oil lends credence to the theory that a long-lost continent once existed in the Gulf of Mexico.

The continent, Llanoria, is believed by some to have slowly sunk in the Gulf more than 100 million years ago, long before the age of man. Until now, little evidence for its existence has been uncovered. But the *Glomar Challenger's* core samples could result in intensified research about Llanoria.

ATLANTIC FAR OLDER THAN BELIEVED

Another unexpected finding came later in the JOIDES mission. A national scientific team aboard the ship turned up startling evidence that the Atlantic Ocean near the Bahamas is at least 50 million years older than it was generally believed to be. The finding came from drill cores in about 17,500 feet of water off San Salvador, one of the Bahama Islands.

The deep-sea sediments recovered several hundred feet down dated from at least 150 million years ago, the team reported. The determination of age was made by the core's fossil content—preserved evidence from long-dead organisms whose exact place in the long span of biological history is well-known. Quite simply, the cores mean that an ocean existed in the Atlantic basin for at least 150 million years and possibly much longer. This may call for a revision of current theories of continental drift (See *Sea Frontiers,* Vol. 13, No. 2, March-April, 1967).

When the JOIDES mission is completed, its alternating scientific teams will have drilled up to sixty holes deep into the ocean's floor, the deepest penetrations man has ever made into the crust of the earth.

THE FIRST DEEP SEA PROBES

JOIDES originated, in another form, at the University of Miami's Institute of Marine Sciences about eight years ago. Its predecessor was called LOCO—for LOng COres, and involved a cooperating team made up of the IMS, the Lamont Geological Observatory, the Woods Hole Oceanographic Institution, and the Scripps Institution of Oceanography (See *Sea Frontiers,* Vol. 8, No. 5, December, 1962).

In June, 1962, Dr. Cesare Emiliani of the IMS initated deep-sea drilling as a project to obtain long, continuous sections of deep-sea sediments. For the marine geologist, a long sediment core can be read almost as meaningfully as a historian reads old manuscripts.

The core represents a vertical history of the area in which the core was taken. Properly preserved and correctly interpreted, a good core sample can be an unassailable record of virtually every geological and biological process in the area's past.

LOCO was just a beginning and, next to JOIDES, it was a mere rehearsal. But in its time, it was a pioneering and revolutionary approach to the earth's history. In 1962, the drilling vessel *Submarex*, from the Global Marine Exploration Company of Los Angeles, chartered by the University of Miami with National Science Foundation funds, was used for a limited drilling/coring venture on the Nicaragua Rise southwest of Jamaica in about 2,000 feet of water. Global Marine, builder of the current *Glomar Challenger*, puts its vast oil-drilling experience to work for marine geology.

Submarex used a skid-mounted drilling rig that operated over the side. At one point, the drill string and bit were powered 185 feet into the sea floor. A total of 68 feet of core was recovered. Later study showed that a much longer and deeper core could be retained with a bigger ship and more advanced techniques.

DEEPER HOLES IN THE OCEAN FLOOR

That is where JOIDES came in. It was organized in May, 1964, by the same institutions that participated in LOCO. JOIDES initiated the first of its joint drilling efforts in December, 1964, when the Pan American Oil Company's drilling vessel *Caldrill I* successfully explored the Blake Plateau, off the east coast of Florida. During this month-long operation one hole was drilled in 3,500 feet of water and another penetrated 1,050 feet below the ocean floor. Sediments 70 million years old were recovered and, 22 miles offshore, the drilling pipes gushed fresh water, indicating beds usually associated with land formations (see *Sea Frontiers*, Vol. 11, No. 6, November-December, 1965).

Through the intervening years, planning and preparation went ahead. Global Marine built the *Glomar Challenger* and, in mid-July, JOIDES began drilling at two-mile-deep sites in the Gulf. The vessel took core samples off Florida and up the coast to New Jersey, where it docked for the first time in its two-month first leg. By the time its 40,000 mile circumnavigation is ended, its earlier results might lead to further specialized research in specific areas.

Since JOIDES called for drilling in up to 20,000 feet of water, an entirely new drilling technology had to be created. For instance, the ship must be kept almost exactly over the site miles below. If the ship drifts just a bit too much, either from wind or current, the heavy drill string could be broken or ripped from the bottom of the ship.

For an answer to this problem, JOIDES planners turned to the electronic computer. Before beginning to drill, the crew lowers a set of transponders or "sonar beacons" to the ocean floor around the site of the hole to be drilled. These beacons transmit sonar pings back up to the *Glomar Challenger,* and underwater microphones on the ship pick up the sounds.

If the ship moves beyond a small "safety area" of drift, the microphones and computer instantaneously sense the difference in location from the changed arrival times of the "pings." Within a second, the *Glomar Challenger's* computer sends correction orders to the ship's engines. Propellers mounted in the ship's side-thrust hull tunnels are able to power the ship back to its desired location. Thus, the ship's location is self-correcting. Before the forces of wind or current can move the *Glomar Challenger* dangerously far away from its position over the drill site, the engines are ordered to power it back.

After the new ship was sea-tested in trials from its Texas port, the first targets were a series of mysterious domelike knolls (the Sigsbee Knolls) on the Gulf of Mexico's floor. Some scientists thought these might be ocean-floor versions of the salt domes that often mean oil on land. But virtually no one thought oil would be found so deep in an ocean and so far away from the nearest land.

In the series of holes to be drilled across the Atlantic on the ship's second leg to Dakar, the scientific team will be looking for evidence about the formation of the world's continents and oceans. Since the earth's crust is much thinner beneath the oceans than it is under the continents, the deep-sea floor is the obvious place to look for this evidence.

DO CONTINENTS DRIFT?

The team will be particularly alert for evidence that could apply to the continental-drift theory being adopted by an increasing number of geologists. "Drifters," as holders of this theory are often called, believe that the world's continents were originally joined and made up two "super-continents." Millions of years ago, according to the drift theory, these continents broke up and the pieces began spreading apart as a result of huge, slow, convective overturnings deep in the earth. These convective "cells" emerge on the deep-ocean floor and are still pushing the continents even farther apart, the theory says.

The *Glomar Challenger* team hopes to find hard evidence—one way or the other—at drill sites along the vast Mid-Atlantic Ridge that stretches from north to south.

Chief scientists on the first leg were Dr. Maurice Ewing and Dr. J. Lamar Worzel, both of Columbia's Lamont Geological Observatory. On later legs in the Atlantic and Pacific, other scientists from the cooperating oceanographic institutions will take turns leading the *Glomar Challenger*'s scientific staff.

~~~~~~~~~~~~~~~~

Edward P. Clancy:

68.   *THE POWER PLANT AT LA RANCE**

At the time of this writing only one large-scale tidal power plant exists. So far as the author is aware, no other is even under construction, though some proposals are being vigorously pushed. The existing plant, newly completed, is in a barrier built across the mouth of La Rance estuary in Brittany.

The estuary, shown in Figure 68–1 lies between the towns of St. Malo and Dinard. It has an area of about nine square miles, and is located in a region of exceptional tidal range. The basin extends inland some thirteen miles.

Calculations show that usable tidal energy is proportional to the area of the basin involved and to the square of the amplitude of the tide. The maximum tidal range at La Rance is 44 feet. For these equinoctial tides, water flows in or out of the estuary at the maximum rate of 630,000 cubic feet per second. (This is three times the flow of the Rhone River in flood.) A useful volume of over six billion cubic feet is created.

The barrier was built at a point where the channel is 2500 feet wide. Rocks two miles downstream at the mouth of the estuary protect the works from ocean storm waves.

The installation consists of four main parts: the dam, the power plant, locks for navigation, and a barrage of sluice gates to accelerate the filling and emptying of the basin. Much geological reconnaissance was done beforehand. Borings revealed a substratum chiefly

Fig. 68–1. Tidal power plant across the mouth of La Rance estuary in Brittany. (From E. P. Clancy, *The Tides*, Doubleday & Company, New York, 1968)

of gneiss, covered in places by thin layers of sand and gravel. The deepest water encountered was 39 feet at lowest tide, and 83 feet at maximum tide. The engineering difficulties faced were substantial but not formidable. Design of the dam involved an unusual factor, of course—the structure must be able to withstand pressure from both directions!

Before construction was started, hydraulic engineers built a working model of the whole estuary. Everything—the basin with all its contours, the proposed dam and associated works, and the tides themselves—was reproduced with the greatest fidelity. The model showed the intensity and direction of currents to be expected, and helped enormously with various aspects of the planning.

To get a "dry field" so that foundations of the different structures could be placed on bedrock, the working areas were surrounded by a string of caissons. The caissons were linked with watertight joints, and the enclosure they formed was then pumped dry. An engineering operation of this magnitude is not done quickly; some six years were needed for completion of the whole enterprise.

Vanes 33 feet high and 49 feet wide control water flow through the sluices. They, too, must resist pressure from both directions. Unlike gates in ordinary dams, which are moved only a few times a year, the vanes at La Rance are in almost constant motion. The reason: for the most efficient generation of power there must be a continuous and very close control over the water level within the basin.

The power plant, of reinforced concrete, looks inside like a vast tunnel 1200 feet long. It contains all the control equipment. The arched roof gives the structure rigidity to resist water pressure from either side. Traveling cranes within the tunnel service the generating units. Each unit lies in its individual conduit beneath the floor; the bottom of the conduit is some 33 feet below the lowest water level. Figure 68–2 shows the structure in cross-section. It is interesting that at high water an observer outside and at some distance sees only a thin white line projecting above the surface of the bay. This is the roof of the power plant; everything else is submerged! To give some idea of scale: each conduit is 174 feet long, and its cross-sectional area at either end is some 1000 square feet. There are twenty-four of these conduits.

Construction of a project such as this had to wait upon design and development of a most unusual and ingenious device—the "bulb-type" turbine-generator unit which can also act as a pump. The device resembles, on an enormous scale, a short, fat torpedo. It is entirely surrounded by water. The body of the torpedo contains the electric generator, and the propeller exactly fits the constricted throat of the conduit (see Figure 68–2). Struts projecting radially inward from the walls of the conduit support the unit. One of the struts is hollow, and large enough for a man to climb down a ladder from the control room into the interior of the bulb to perform servicing.

Design studies on the device were started in 1952. Smaller models of differing characteristics were installed in existing dams, and hydraulic circuits were constructed so that the units could be tested with water going both ways. In 1955 sizable units were set up in an abandoned lock system at St. Malo in order to test under actual tidal conditions.

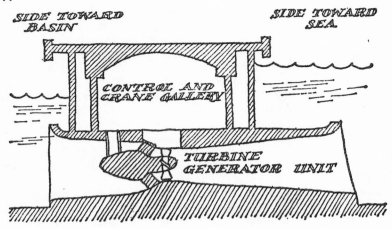

SIDE TOWARD BASIN

SIDE TOWARD SEA

CONTROL AND CRANE GALLERY

TURBINE GENERATOR UNIT

Fig. 68–2. Cross-section of the tidal power plant. (From E. P. Clancy, *The Tides*, Doubleday & Company, New York, 1968)

The machines which evolved and which are now installed at La Rance each have a generating capacity of 10,000 kilowatts. The propellers, with a diameter of 17.5 feet, turn at 94 revolutions per minute. Inside the bulb, air pressure is kept double that of the normal atmosphere. The result: better cooling of the generator. At atmospheric pressure the output is limited to 7500 kilowatts, showing the great importance of proper temperature control.

The units generate power at 3.5 kilovolts. Step-up transformers increase this voltage to 225 kilovolts; the current then enters three transmission lines which leave in different directions to link with the French national power grid.

So much for the technical details of construction. A most fascinating question remains: How can the whole complex be managed for most efficient power output? Figure 68–3 shows the sequence of various phases of operation when no pumping is done. Sea level is denoted by the solid line; it is essentially a sine curve. Level within the basin is shown by the dashed line. A crucial aspect is the vertical difference in height of these two curves, i.e., the head of water. When it is appreciable, power generation is possible. The cross-hatched sections represent the times of turbine operation.

The sequence is as follows: as the ocean starts to rise from its minimum level and the head decreases to the point where efficient generation is no longer possible, the turbines are shut down, but the sluice gates open to allow continuing outflow from the basin.

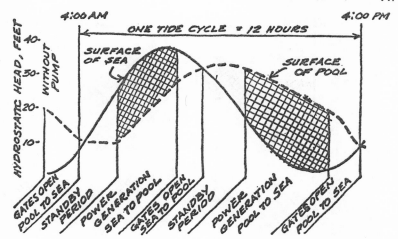

Fig. 68–3. Phases of operation of tidal power plant without pumping. (From E. P. Clancy, *The Tides*, Doubleday & Company, New York, 1968)

When basin and sea are at the same level, all gates are closed and there is a waiting period until sufficient head builds up. Then power generation begins, and continues until the combination of decreasing sea level and increasing level in the basin results in too little head. The turbines are stopped, but the sluice gates allow further filling of the basin. When levels within and without are equal the gates are closed and there is a waiting period until sea level falls sufficiently to create a new head—this time in the opposite direction. Meanwhile the blades of the turbines have been reversed and a new cycle of power generation begins, continuing until the head is again no longer adequate.

We have referred to the fact that the bulb units can also act as pumps. If power from outside the plant is fed into the generator, it is no longer a generator but a motor! It can then drive the turbine blades to act as a pump forcing water through the conduit, just as the motor of an electric fan turns the blades to create a stream of air.

But under the circumstances, what is the advantage of pumping? The answer is a little subtle but not too hard to see. Figure 68–4 is like Figure 68–3, but with the superposition of a dotted line which shows the basin level as it can be managed if pumping is done. We see that the cross-hatched area, and therefore the amount of power generated, is appreciably increased. Part of each waiting

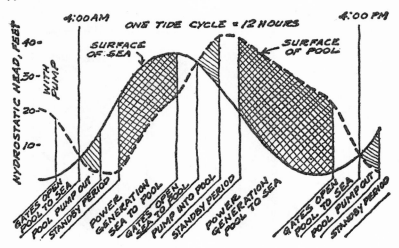

Fig. 68–4. Phases of operation of tidal power plant with pumping. (From E. P. Clancy, *The Tides*, Doubleday & Company, New York, 1968)

period is used for pumping—in one part of the cycle for building up the basin level, in the other part for lowering it. In both cases the available head is increased.

You can't get something for nothing, though. Since the efficiency of any machine is less than 100 percent, don't you end up with a net *loss* of energy? No, for the following reason. As you can see from the graph, one always pumps against a small head. The water pumped will later be used at a much greater head, however. Here we have the key to the worth of pumping. Another, and not altogether minor, factor is that electric energy has different monetary values at different times of day. During hours of low usage, extra power is available at reduced rates. (You already know this if your home has a clock-operated electric water heater on a separate meter.) When a waiting period at a tidal plant occurs in these hours, pumping becomes particularly rewarding.

There are several variables, as you see: basin level, sea level, value from hour to hour of energy generated and of energy bought for pumping. Proper operation of a tidal plant for maximum efficiency requires a constant and rather complicated calculation of all factors involved. The result of this running calculation must be continuously translated into control of the various components: the vanes of the sluice gates, the pitch of the turbine propeller blades, the starting and stopping of generating or pumping cycles. The whole situation calls for a computer-controlled operation, and in the plant there is indeed a computer programmed not only to perform the necessary calculations but also to control all components according to the results of the calculations.

In each of the 24 conduits at La Rance is a turbo-generator of 10,000 kilowatts capacity. Maximum power output is therefore 240,000 kilowatts. An ordinary hydroelectric plant running continuously at this capacity would produce 2100 million kilowatt-hours per year. The annual energy output at La Rance is about 540 million kilowatt-hours without pumping, and an additional 130 million with pumping. The figures starkly underline the nonconstant output of a tidal power plant. Note well, however! This is an *assured production*. There are no dry years for a tidal installation! And no worries about damage from disastrous floods.

~~~~~~~~~~~~~~~~~~~

John E. Bardach:

69.   *AQUACULTURE**

Optimistic forecasters of the world food supply in the year 2000 predict that serious regional food shortages will exist; pessimists warn of widespread famine as populations in many countries increase more rapidly than agricultural production. The one bright spot in this otherwise gloomy picture is the rate of growth of 8 percent per year of the world fish harvest during the last decade (1). The annual harvest now amounts to 53 million metric tons (2) and is expected to increase for some time to come, though estimates of the possible total sustained yield differ widely, ranging from 120 to 2000 million metric tons. All are based on extrapolations from scanty data on primary productivity throughout the world's seas and on incomplete knowledge of the food relations of many harvested organisms.

* From *Science*, Vol. 161, pp. 1098–1106, September 13, 1968. Copyright 1968 by the American Association for the Advancement of Science. Reprinted by permission of the publisher and author.

John E. Bardach is a professor of zoology in the Department of Fisheries at the University of Michigan, Ann Arbor.

Aquatic harvests supply almost nothing but proteins, since the bulk of aquatic plants are plankton algae that are uneconomical to harvest (4) and hold no promise for furnishing carbohydrate staples. A breakdown of the total yield from aquatic ecosystems into marine, fresh, and brackish water moieties shows that the yields from fresh and brackish water make up about 14 percent of the tonnage (2). Much of man's fishing has been in estuaries and bays of the sea, and in ponds, lakes, reservoirs, and streams, where he has long practiced aquaculture (5).

Aquaculture resembles agriculture rather than fisheries in that it does not rely on a common property resource but presumes ownership or leased rights to such bases of production as ponds or portions of, or sites in, bays or other large bodies of water. Products of aquaculture must compete successfully with those of fisheries and of animal husbandry; in Western food economy, aquaculture products such as trout, oysters, and shrimp bring good returns because they fall in the luxury class, whereas in developing countries various kinds of raised fish command a high price (6), since animal protein, including that derived from marine catches, is generally scarce. Although subsidized small home or village ponds may be justified in certain underdeveloped areas to help alleviate malnutrition, aquaculture, wherever it is practiced, should be examined primarily as a commercial enterprise that must compete with other protein supplies to be successful.

The organisms now being raised in aquaculture comprise several bivalve mollusks (mainly oysters of the genera *Ostrea* and *Crassostrea*), a few crustaceans (predominantly shrimp, in particular *Peneus japonicus*), and a limited number of fish species (6). Among the fish species, the carp, *Cyprinus carpio*, and selected other members of the same family, Cyprinidae (minnows), are the most important. Trout and salmon are also important in aquaculture, especially the rainbow trout, *Salmo gairdneri*, as are the Southeast Asian milkfish (*Chanos chanos*), and mullets, especially *Mugil cephalus*, and yellowtail (*Seriola quinqueradiata*), in Japan. Also noteworthy are the channel catfish industry (*Ictalurus punctatus*) in the southern United States and the use of *Tilapia* as pondfish, mainly in Africa (6). Most of these species are adjusted to life in fresh or brackish water, but the culturing of some marine fishes is being attempted, notably in Great Britain with plaice (*Pleuronectes platessa*) and sole (*Solea solea*) (7) and with pelagic (high seas) schooling species in Japan and the United States, among them the Pacific sardine and mackerel (*Sardinops caerula, Pneumatophorus diego*) (8) and the pompano (*Trachinotus carolinus*)

(9). Some attached algae are also produced under semi-cultivation, both in temperate and tropical waters and certain phytoplankton species are cultured as food for oyster and shrimp larvae. These represent a special crop and are of minor or indirect nutritive value; they are omitted from this article, in which the potential of aquaculture for supplying high-quality protein is assessed.

Aquaculture furnishes the world with over 2 million metric tons, mainly fish. Mainland China alone reports annual production of 1.5 million metric tons of carp and carplike fishes (6). Two million metric tons represent nearly 4 percent of the total world catch and far exceed the United States' food fish harvest, although they are produced from a fraction of 1 percent of the world's waters.

Aquaculture ranges in intensity from simple weeding of natural stands of algae to complete husbandry of domesticated fish like trout or carp. It is sometimes difficult to distinguish intensive management from culture. The term, as used here, comprises practices that subject organisms to at least one, and usually more than one, manipulation before harvest. In addition, as in agriculture, the harvest in aquaculture takes most, if not all, the organisms tended. Most often only one species is raised, although a few to several compatible species may be cultured simultaneously.

To be productive for husbandry, aquatic animals should have the following characteristics. (i) They should reproduce in captivity or semi-confinement (for example, trout) to make selective breeding possible or yield easily to manipulations that result in the production of their offspring (for example, carp). Failing ease of breeding, their larvae or young should be easily available for gathering (for example, oysters). (ii) Their eggs or larvae or both should be fairly hardy and capable of being hatched or reared under controlled conditions. (iii) The larvae or young should have food habits that can be satisfied by operations to increase their natural foods, or they should be able to take extraneous feeds from their early stages. (iv) They should gain weight fast and nourish themselves entirely or in part from abundantly available food that can be supplied cheaply, or that can be readily produced or increased in the area where the cultured species lives.

Few aquatic organisms have all these attributes, and substantial expansion of the aquacultural crop depends in part on how biological and engineering skills can make the missing characteristics less crucial; other constraints are economic. I discuss here several operations and problems common to the raising of aquatic organisms (10), and I attempt to appraise realistically the potential of aquaculture on a world scale.

SELECTIVE BREEDING OF AQUATIC STOCK

Even before Jacob tended Laban's flocks, livestock had been subjected by man to selection for one or another desirable attribute, and breeding of domestic birds and animals has produced spectacular results. The first treatise on fish culture was written in China by Fan Li in 475 B.C. (11), but there are still only two aquatic animals over which genetic control has been exercised. These are carp and several species of trout; trout has a shorter and less varied history of breeding than carp. No true breeding programs exist with invertebrates, though oyster culture is advancing so rapidly that experiments in oyster genetics are likely to begin soon.

The breeding of aquatic animals, compared with terrestrial animals, has peculiar problems. Spawning habits often make the isolation of pairs difficult; isolation of numerous offspring requires many replicate ponds (aquariums are too unlike nature); and there is rarely more than one mating a year. Moreover, the environment has an overriding influence on the growth of poikilothermous animals; consequently, many different-sized animals of the same age are found together. Many aquatic animals require special environmental or social conditions for mating and reproduction, which are not easily duplicated under human control. Manipulations of water temperature or flow have triggered spawning; however, the development during the last two decades of the practice of hypophyzation, or treatment with pituitary hormone (12), to make some fishes spawn helps alleviate constraints on breeding for some species. This practice has influenced fish culture all over the world, from catfish growers in the southern United States and sturgeon breeders in the Ukraine, to the fishpond cooperatives of mainland China, where it is of paramount importance in making common carp produce eggs three times a year and in facilitating the propagation of its cyprinid pond mates, whose eggs were difficult to collect in rivers before the process of hypophyzation was developed. Use of pituitary material may also produce advances with the breeding of two species of fish important in brackish water culture—the milkfish and the gray mullet. Aquatic animals have one advantage over terrestrial animals from the breeder's point of view—a pair have large numbers of offspring, which permit mass selection.

Carp are readily adaptable to selective breeding because their eggs are large for fish eggs; they are not too delicate; and they are easily secured. Carp have been bred for fast growth, a body shape with more flesh than is found on the wild type, reduction of scale cover for greater ease in preparing the fish for the table, resistance to disease, and resistance to crowding and to low temperature (13). With such breeding practices as progeny testing (selection of parents according to the performance of their offspring) and diallele analysis (a system of mating that determines separately the genotypes of each parent) (14), further improvements on already well-domesticated strains may be expected. It is necessary to prevent reversions to the wild type. That these can occur rapidly is illustrated by the fate of carp introduced to America. After being brought to the New World in 1877 (15), carp was allowed to escape into lakes and rivers where indiscriminate mixtures of its prolific stock resulted in bony and scaly fish which soon became a nuisance in waters used for game fishing. There was no incentive for carp culture in the United States, where protein was abundant from land livestock. However, since carp has become a prized angling trophy in Western Europe, and because of the rapid eutrophication of American lakes and rivers (a process which favors carp) and the predicted narrowing of the gap, even in America, between the supply of terrestrial protein and the demand, it is not farfetched to think that carp may be cultured in the United States.

Trout, at least in America, were until recently raised mostly for stream stocking; consequently, disease resistance was the main concern in hatcheries not equipped for experiments in fish genetics. Demonstration of what may reside in the trout's gene pool has come mainly from two sources: the Danish table trout industry (16) and the experimental trout and salmon breeding program of the University of Washington in Seattle (17), where specially fed rainbow trout stock, continuously graded by selection during 30 years, grows to as much as 3 kilograms in 18 months while a wild rainbow trout in a lake at that age rarely weighs 200 grams (18); these fish tolerate higher temperatures than their wild congeners.

Trout and salmon eggs are larger than those of the carp; they develop slowly and are hardy, combining several advantageous properties. Salmon permit the establishment of hatcheries on suitable streams because they return to spawn to the stream with the odor of which they were imprinted as fry. In such hatcheries inadvertent selection from the spawning run of the largest—fastest growing —brood fish has produced strains that returned to the hatchery 1 year earlier than the offspring of their wild congeners. Salmonid fishes can be selected for higher fecundity, larger egg size, and better survival and faster growth of fry, and for exact timing of their return to the parent stream (19). These breeding potentials should be used to increase the abundance of salmon especially since improved techniques now feasible in United States salmon hatcheries could produce about ten times as many young fish as are now released (20).

Salmon-fishing regulations are still based on propagation potentials in natural streams and require that 50 percent of the run be allowed to escape the fishery. Salmon runs will increasingly depend on hatcheries that program their fish to return for stripping and the raising of a well-protected progeny whose rate of survival at the time of release is many times greater than that attained in nature, where maximum fish mortality takes place during the first few months of life. Thus, the salmon harvest of certain river mouths may almost be doubled in view of the fact that hatchery-dependent runs need only a few fish to supply the next generation. Salmon are highly valuable fish [$65 million for the United States catch in 1965 (21)], and it may be worthwhile to press for regional revision of escapement regulations and to examine the economic requirements and consequences of hatchery improvements.

Another advantage of breeding fishes is the ease with which many of them hybridize (22). At the University of Washington at Seattle, male steelhead (that is, seagoing rainbow) trout were crossed with fast-growing freshwater rainbow females. The growth rate of the offspring was intermediate between that of the parents, their shape was more fusiform than that of the female, and they migrated to sea. They had a voracious appetite and adopted parent streams to which they returned as 2-year-olds, weighing 2 to 3 kilograms on the average and occasionally as much as 5 kilograms (23). They would probably not breed true in the second generation, and they should therefore be hatchery-produced, but they represent an interesting use of the sea's unused fish food.

Difficult as it may be to raise the progeny of one pair of parents of carp and trout, to do so with oysters is still more complicated. Mass spawning is usually done on oyster beds, and although the female of the genus *Crassostrea*, to which the American oyster belongs, retains the eggs inside her shells until after fertilization, paternity on the oyster bed is impossible to ascertain. Although there are thousands of eggs for each carp or trout, there can be up to 100 million for each female oyster (24). This fact, however, has aided in mass selection. Progressive growers of Long Island oysters raise the larvae in warmed water and use cultured algal food. They also give proper attention to stirring and other manipulations simulating planktonic conditions. The many eggs and improved survival of free-floating larvae permit a filter screen to be used to select only 20 percent of the largest, most rapidly growing early larvae. These larvae exhibit good growth throughout life (6). But to achieve true selective breeding, growers of Long Island oysters now plan to rear single oyster progeny; since oysters reverse their sex from male to female halfway through their adult lives, the possibility of freezing sperm from a functional male is being tested, and it may be possible to use it to fertilize the same oyster later when it becomes a female (25).

THE RAISING OF AQUATIC LARVAE

Many aquatic animals go through larval stages which do not resemble their adult phase; some larvae, including those of shrimp or oysters, and of many fishes, are planktonic and minute and feed on the smallest organisms. More than with domestic birds or mammals, nursing them through their early lives poses difficult technical and nutritional problems to growers. In British experiments with raising plaice and sole larvae in captivity, as much as 66 percent survival through the stage of metamorphosis has been accomplished. Ultraviolet radiation of the water decreased the danger of bacterial infection; tanks without corners minimized encounters with solid obstacles; and salinity, temperature, and pH were controlled. The size of the first food offered was geared to the tiny mouthparts of the larvae, but was increased with their capacity to take larger live food. Nauplii of the barnacle (*Balanus balanoides*) were used at first; they were replaced by nauplii of the brine shrimp (*Artemia*) with subsequent admixtures of small oligochaetes (*Enchytrea*) when the small fishes had metamorphosed and were resting on the bottom. Finally, chopped mussels (*Mytilus*) were used. Since plaice larvae, just before settling, consume 200 brine shrimp nauplii per day, the production of several hundred thousand young plaice posed serious technical problems in continuous food culture (7).

Obtaining and correctly supplying food was a significant part of the experiments at the U.S. Bureau of Fisheries at La Jolla, California, with larvae of high seas schooling species such as Pacific sardines and mackerels. In these experiments very small food organisms had to be supplied at the precise time of complete yolk absorption, and in sufficient quantities to allow larvae of limited mobility to find food in all parts of the aquarium. Because sardine larvae search in only about 1 cubic centimeter of water per hour, at the onset of feeding, but require a minimum of four food organisms per hour to replace energy lost in swimming and body functions, the rearing of 2000 larvae in 1,800,000 cubic centimeters of water (500 gallons) meant replacing 7,200,000 food organisms removed by larval predation each hour or approximately 86,400,000 food organisms during a 12-hour day.

The large quantities of food organisms in varying sizes needed for these experiments were collected mostly at night. A 1000-watt underwater lamp connected to a submersible pump was suspended several feet below the surface of the sea. Copepods were attracted from a wide distance and concentrated near the pump where they were sucked up with water and transported to the surface. Plankton-enriched water was then passed through a series of filters, which further concentrated food organisms, and the highly enriched filtrate was piped to a 760 liter storage tank. Organisms with a cross-sectional diameter of 0.028 millimeter and larger were thereby collected. Before being fed to fish larvae, concentrated plankton was graded by filters to remove organisms larger than 0.1 millimeter. The portion containing large copepods, crab larvae, chaetognaths, and the like was fed to advanced fish fry and juveniles (6, 8).

Comparable techniques may help to achieve survival, after forced spawning in captivity, of milkfish and mullet. Inasmuch as these two species of economic importance in Asia are now raised from fry collected on the shores and as the fry are becoming scarce regionally, domestication of the two species, including manipulations ensuring high survival of fry will be an important advance for fish culture.

Although fish larvae are recognizable as fish even though they are not like the adults, invertebrates undergo more profound transformations from egg to adult. Oysters spend their first 2 weeks before they "set" as ciliated trochophores and veliger larvae needing flagellate algae for food. About 2000 cells of two or more species, for instance *Isochrysis galbana, Monochrysis lutheri,* and *Rhodomonas* and *Nannochloris* species, have to be available for each larva per day, and larger species are required to replace the smaller species as the larvae grow. Algae must be cultured en masse when oyster larvae are raised indoors, an innovation largely developed at the U.S. Bureau of Commercial Fisheries Biological Laboratory at Milford, Connecticut (26), and now expanded by progressive growers of Long Island oysters.

In shrimp raising, which is successful on a commercial scale only in Japan, there are problems with the larval stages before the animals can be fed chopped trashfish and shellfish. The operation, initiated by M. Fujinaga in 1934, begins in the spring with the collection of "berried" (egg carrying) females ready to release the stored spermatophores from their seminal receptacles; raising the water temperature speeds this and subsequent processes. After three distinctly different planktonic stages and 12 molts in about as many days, the postlarvae begin to crawl on the bottom; they still have to undergo some transformations and another 20 molts before they become adults. The early part of the life cycle of the cultured shrimp takes place indoors in ceramic tile-lined wooden tanks and in water heated to between 26° and 30°C. Diatom —mainly *Skeletonema costatum*—and flagellate cultures are maintained for feeding the early larvae, which are later given finely chopped mussel or clam flesh. When they have reached a length of between 15 and 20 millimeters or a weight of about 10 milligrams, they are stocked in outside ponds with arrangements for aeration and circulation.

In October or November, the shrimp, though not fully grown, are ready for market. They are about 10 centimeters long and weigh 20 grams having been fed once daily, converting 10 to 12 kilograms of food into 1 kilogram of shrimp. When the water later cools down to below 15°C, the animals no longer feed, but many of them may be retained without feeding for a later more favorable market (6).

The oldest shrimp-farming enterprise is now located near Takamatsu on Shikoku. It covers almost 10 hectares and has a staff of 30 men, including some in management research. Ten million shrimp were produced there in 1967, a quarter of which were raised to adult size; the rest were sold for stocking. The cost of production of cultured shrimp is certainly higher than that in any other aquacultural enterprise, but the wholesale price in Japan for tempura-sized shrimp of 6 to 10 centimeters is between $12 and $13 per kilogram, and the supply does not meet the demand. Shrimp farming of this type in a country whose material or labor costs are less favorable than those of Japan would not be possible (6). There are, however, opportunities for greater mechanization and for feeding innovations that will simplify the most laborious parts of culture operations for larval as well as postlarval shrimp. The use of the most improved shrimp-culturing methods with fast-growing species may hold some promise for a number of regions in the world (27).

MAKING FULL USE OF THE WATER

Aside from selecting the best suited strains, a practice not yet widely followed in aquatic husbandry, aquaculture should make use of the entire water column where possible and be three-dimensional, as it is in China and other Asian countries, where common carp is stocked with other species of the minnow family (Cyprinidae) such as the grass carp (*Ctenopharyngodon idella*), the silver carp

(*Hypothalmichthys molitrix*), and the bighead carp (*Aristichthys nobilis*) (28). The success of this method is based on the different food habits of the respective species; the carp is a bottom feeder; the grass carp and the silver carp feed on plants (banana leaves, even) and beanmeal or rice bran supplied to them from outside the ponds; and the bighead carp uses the plankton surplus in the well-fertilized water. Thus, the various water layers and all potential food sources are used (29).

The culture of oysters in Japan's best oyster-growing district, Hiroshima Bay, also is an illustration of the use of the entire water column (6). Seed oysters are collected on scallop shells suspended on wires from a bamboo framework driven into the bottom. Biologists from the prefectural and municipal laboratories monitor the plankton during the spawning period and advise the growers on the best time for spat collection. It is not uncommon to collect several thousand spat per scallop shell, although the average is about 200. The shells are removed from the collecting frames after one month when the surviving oysters have reached a size of about 12 millimeters. They are then cleaned, culled, and restrung on heavier wires separated by bamboo (and more recently by plastic) spacers. These wire rens are suspended from bamboo rafts, buoyed by floats of various kinds, and extend to a depth of 10 to 15 meters. Floats are added as the oysters grow, and before harvest require several times the support they needed at the beginning of the growing season. Long lines instead of rafts are an innovation in the method of suspension, but they are still only a variant on the hanging-culture technique, which uses the water column efficiently and which protects the oyster from its bottom-living predators, such as starfish and oyster drills.

A typical raft, about 20 by 25 meters carries 600 rens and produces more than 4 metric tons of shucked oyster meat per year. On a per-hectare basis, this harvest amounts to 20 metric tons, if it is assumed that only one-fourth of a certain area of intensive cultivation is covered by rafts, as is the current practice. Such yields result from intensive care and high primary productivity in the water that is dependent on tidal exchange and fertile terrestrial runoff. By comparison, the average is 5 metric tons per hectare of well-managed, leased oyster ground in the United States and the peak harvest of 300 metric tons per hectare of mussels (*Mytilus edulis*) also grown with hanging culture in the bays of Galicia in Spain. On public oyster grounds in the United States, where the mollusks are a minimally managed common property resource, the average per hectare is only 10 kilograms (0.001 metric ton) or less (6).

Fertilization of bays, fjords, or enclosures has led to increases in phyto- and zooplanktons, but favorable cost-benefit ratios for use with fish have not been proved (30). In ponds (including brackish ones) organic and inorganic fertilization has been efficacious. In Israel, fertilized carp ponds, some with admixtures of *Tilapia* and mullet, produce twice the tonnage per hectare of unfertilized ponds, and fertilization and additional feeding doubles the yield again (31). Fertilized *Tilapia* ponds in which the fish were also fed have yielded as much as ten times the crop of unenriched ones (32).

Many kinds of inorganic or organic fertilizers can be used, but sewage which produces dense invertebrate populations certainly works well. Munich sewage ponds with a slow exchange of water produce 500 kilograms of carp per hectare per year and a profit for their operator, the Bavarian Hydropower Company; the method requires large tracts of land, however; under temperate conditions rising land values threaten to make it obsolete (6).

In a much warmer, rapidly flowing stream in West Java, with a high sewage content, carp, confined in bamboo cages to graze on the dense carpet of worms and insect larvae in the sandy substrate, grow rapidly to yield 50 or more kilograms of fish per square meter of cage surface, or 500 metric tons per hectare (33). Even with allowances made for only partial use of the stream surfaces, this practice clearly represents an extremely efficient and ecologically sound use of sewage, especially in warm waters. The main drawbacks to this practice arise because the fish are not always well cooked before they are eaten.

In addition to the fertility of the water, its temperature, especially in a colder climate, is also very important. The most spectacular use of naturally warmed water for fish culture is in Idaho's Snake River valley trout-farming district, where springs of an even 16°C (optimum temperature for trout) gush forth from the canyon wall year in and year out. A thousand tons of trout can be raised in a year on every 2830 liters per second (100 cubic feet per second) that flow from these springs. Such unprecedented results in fish husbandry depend on high-density stocking, fast growth, mechanization, and cheap feed—the latter being locally procurable since the Snake River valley is also a stock feed-growing area (34). Most of all, however, the high yield depends on the flushing of growth-inhibiting wastes from the trout raceways. Hence, it is more appropriate to relate weight gain to water flow rather than to water surface or volume. By such a measurement, production would be around 170 kilograms per liter per second.

Naturally warmed water is not prevalent, but man-made heated effluents occur with increasing frequency. In fact, thermal pollution may become a threat to some natural waters because it hastens eutrophication. Heated power plant effluents, however, can also be used to the advantage of the aquaculturist. At the atomic energy plant at Hunterston, Scotland, cooling water, ascertained to be nontoxic to fish, was fed into cement troughs for sole and plaice raising. Both species were grown to marketable sizes in 6 to 8 months at between 15° and 20°C, as compared with the 3 or 4 years needed for the same growth under natural conditions (35).

A progressive grower of Long Island shellfish used about 57,000 liters per minute of cooling water discharge of the Long Island Lighting Company. The cooling water is taken from a deep section of the bay and has a high nutrient content, which favors oyster growth as does its warmth. Year-round production in a near 3-hectare lagoon of both oysters and hard clams (*Mercenaria mercenaria*) has been achieved and seed oyster production in the heated lagoon promises to be highly successful. Summer water temperatures above 30°C, first feared to arrest growth or to be lethal, in fact, promoted exceptionally rapid growth (6, 25). At the atomic plant at Turkey Point (Florida), replicate feeding trials by the University of Miami with shrimp (*Peneus duorarum*) and pompano (*Trachinotus carolinus*) are in progress to compare the effects of different levels of water temperature and consequently of different levels of heated water admixture (9). Heated waste water is also used for freshwater fish culture in the Soviet Union (36).

TABLE 1. SELECTED RANGES OF AQUACULTURALS YIELDS (6) PER YEAR. RESULTS ARE GIVEN IN KILOGRAMS PER HECTARE EXCEPT AS NOTED. THE VALUE IS IN DOLLARS PER HECTARE EXCEPT AS NOTED.

Type of cultivation	Location	Yield	Approximate wholesale value of annual crop
Oyster			
Common property resource (public grounds)	U.S.	9	38
Intensive cultivation, heated hatchery, larval feeding	U.S.	5,000	21,000
Intensive care, hanging culture	Japan*	20,000	23,000

Type of cultivation		Location	Yield	Approximate wholesale value of annual crop
	Mussels			
Intensive care, hanging culture		Spain*	300,000	49,000
	Shrimp			
Extensive, no fertilization, no feeding		S.E. Asia	1,000	1,200
Very intensive, complete feeding		Japan	6,000	43,000
	Carp			
Fertilized ponds, sewage ponds		Israel	500	600
		S. Germany	500	
Fertilized ponds, accessory feeding		Israel	2,100	
Sewage streams, fast running		Indonesia*	125,000	
Recirculating water, intensive feeding		Japan	100†	114†
	Catfish			
Ponds, no fertilization or feeding		Southern U.S.	200	70
With fertilization and feeding in slowly flowing water			3,400	2,400 (net profit 300)
	Milkfish			
Brackish ponds, extensive management		Indonesia	400	
With fertilization and intensive care			2,000	600
	Trout			
Cement raceways, intensive feeding, rapid flow		U.S.	170†	168†

* Values for raft culture and comparable intensive practices based on 25 percent of the area being occupied.

† Per liter per second.

STATUS AND POTENTIAL OF AQUACULTURE

Aquaculture, practiced with a far wider range of species than mentioned here, is found in most of the world. In many areas it occurs at a subsistence level, and its potential contribution to the food supply has not been assessed (37). Village ponds, once a hopeful development in Africa, for instance, are now in disrepair and their potential is not being realized (32). Local fish ponds can be important, however, as has been demonstrated in Taiwan, mainland China, and Indonesia (6).

Husbandry of aquatic animals brings increasing financial returns as it is practiced on a larger scale. Culture intensities vary, as do the fixed and variable costs of the operations and the yields (Table 1). From a commercial point of view, the return on the investment is of most interest; in milkfish culture the annual return ranges from 10 to 20 percent or more, and increases with the intensity of cultivation. Malayan mixed pig and fish farms yield 30 percent, and similar returns are noted in the oyster business (6).

Aquaculture can be not only a lucrative business but it may even produce yields high compared with the harvest of comparably sized land surfaces. The relative scarcity of such peaks in aquacultural production, especially in the tropics, is caused by a lack of bio-technical engineering and managerial skills, the absence of suitable credit or seed capital for even low-cost installations, and the absence of transport and marketing facilities that might encourage the development of a product for a certain market, and so forth.

This is well illustrated by a comparison of Indonesian and Taiwanese milkfish culture in brackish water. Milkfish feed predominantly on bluegreen algae and are raised in pond complexes on land cleared of mangroves. Canals permit the control of water level and salinity by means of sluices, which regulate tidal or freshwater flow (38). Average Indonesian and Philippine annual harvests are 300 to 400 kilograms per hectare, whereas Taiwanese milkfish raisers attain nearly 2000 kilograms on the average, in spite of a cooler climate (39). Cooperatives, rural reconstruction agencies, a good layout of the farms, control of predators of the fry, some fertilization, and prevention of siltation of ponds and connecting water bodies are some of the secrets of successful milkfish farming in Taiwan. For similar reasons there occur in mollusk culture the aforementioned wide range of yields, from nearly 10 kilograms per hectare on public oyster grounds in the United States to the 58,000 kilograms per hectare in Hiroshima Bay.

Filter feeding mollusks and milkfish are brackish water plankton-

or algae-feeders, respectively. These hold more promise for protein-deficient regions than do the carnivores of the same environment because it is more sound to increase the fertility of the water than to produce extraneous feed, let alone to raise one aquatic animal with scrap from another, which is perhaps already being used, or could be used, directly for human consumption.

Most products of aquaculture could be called luxury foods, whether they are sold as high-priced items in a food economy with wide consumer choice (for example, shrimp in Japan, trout in the United States) or boost the scant animal protein supply of developing nations (for example, milkfish in Southeast Asia), where they also bring a good return to the producer. It might seem unrealistic, therefore, to expect aquaculture to help alleviate the world protein deficiency, but such is not necessarily the case. Luxury foods stop being a luxury when they can be mass produced, a case well exemplified by the broiler chicken industry in the United States and Western Europe.

Differences in biology between chickens and aquatic animals notwithstanding, some of the latter could well become mass-produced cheap and abundant foods at conversion rates of two parts of dry feed to one part of fish flesh. Among fresh and brackish water fish, especially trout, carp, and catfish can be raised with pellets. Chinese carp and certain tilapias eat leaves and stems of leafy plants; other fish feed on algae. In Southeast Asia well over 200,000 hectares of ponds now lie in former mangrove areas; there are in the tropics vast unused mangrove regions, some of which could be turned into pond complexes for the culture of fish. Mollusk production, though limited eventually by the suitability of grounds, could be expanded, and above all intensified in the areas where it is now prevalent. Aquaculture is only beginning to develop such practices as manipulation of the temperature regime to achieve best growth, devising simple automated feeders that fish can learn to activate themselves, and building machines that simplify harvesting. Several disciplines are expected to contribute to the development of aquaculture. Since intensive husbandry alters the conditions of nature, a knowledge of the ecology of the cultured organisms in both natural and artificial states is essential. Engineering can also make increasingly important contributions to aquaculture development as it has in the successful pilot-scale raising of plaice and sole by the British White-Authority (40). It was the basis for the as yet theoretical calculation that "the annual British catch of plaice could be housed in shallow ponds covering 1¼ square miles in extent" (7).

Japanese yellowtail fish are now raised at high density, and with sequential cropping have already achieved yields of 28 kilograms per square meter (280 metric tons per hectare) and shown that it is economical to use small portions of the sea under very intensive management. The success with this oceanic schooling species and the fact that other species of similar habits had become adapted to confinement led to the speculation that still others, such as tuna, might behave similarly and that their mass culture under controlled conditions might become possible. In fact, Inoue of the Fisheries Research Laboratory, Tokyo University, Japan, urged that Japan take the initiative in launching a tuna-rearing project in the equatorial Pacific, where atolls and lagoons could be used as sea farms (8).

Such projections say nothing of the problems of translating small to modest enterprises into much vaster ones—the main one likely to be the procurement of many millions of tons of suitable food. Trashfish, in part now used for fish meal, krill and other marine organisms lower in the food chain than the highly prized fish to be cultured have been thought suitable, provided that they can be produced at a low enough cost. The theoretical potential of marine fish culture also rests on the assumption that marine fish can be induced to function sexually under artificial conditions, as have many freshwater fish. Hormone stimulation is expected to be one of the solutions to this problem along with rearing an initial breeding stock born and adjusted to life in artificial environments.

But even without further advances through research, a considerable increase of aquacultural yields appears attainable soon by consistent application of already known techniques on inefficiently managed fresh and brackish water bodies. It has been advocated (4) that millions of hectares of ponds be constructed in Asia, Latin America, and Africa to help satisfy the protein needs of these areas. If local economic and socio-political constraints were removed, these new waters and the upgrading of presently existing ones could yield by the year 2000 a harvest of 30 to 40 million metric tons (3, 41) produced near areas of need, which are still likely to lack refrigeration.

Long-term and large-scale projections of yields attainable through practicing aquaculture with marine animals, outside the brackish water zone, can hardly be attempted; true mariculture is in its infancy. However, experiments in several locations have established that it is technically feasible, and no doubt the intensive development and success of brackish water aquaculture will lead to further efforts to develop mariculture on a large scale. It is too early, however, to tell where or under what conditions such efforts could become economically sound.

SUMMARY

The role of aquaculture in producing high-grade animal proteins for human nutrition is discussed. Raising and tending aquatic animals is mainly practiced in fresh and brackish waters although there are promising pilot experiments and a few commercial applications of true mariculture. Yields vary with the organisms under culture and the intensity of the husbanding care bestowed on them. The products are now mainly luxury foods, but there are some indications that upgrading of the frequently primitive culture methods now in use could lead to increasing yields per unit of effort and to reduced production costs per unit of weight. Under favorable conditions, production of animal flesh from a unit volume of water far exceeds that attained from a unit surface of ground. With high-density stocking of aquatic animals flushing is important, and flowing water or tidal exchange is essential. Combinations of biological and engineering skills are necessary for full exploitation of aquacultural potentials; these are only partially realized because economic incentives may be lacking to tend aquatic organisms rather than to secure them from wild stocks, because of social, cultural, and political constraints. Nevertheless, a substantial development of aquaculture should occur in the next three decades and with it a severalfold increase in total yield.

REFERENCES AND NOTES

1. W. M. Chapman, *Food Technol.* **20**, 895 (1966).
2. Editorial, *Yearb. Fish. Stat.* **20** (1965).
3. President's Science Advisory Council, *The World Food Problem* (U.S. Government Printing Office, Washington, D.C., 1967), vol. 2, pp. 345–361.
4. L. A. Walford, *Living Resources of the Sea* (Ronald, New York, 1958), pp. 121–132.
5. I prefer the spelling aquaculture to aquiculture because the former is etymologically more correct.
6. In 1970, 23,000 metric tons of channel catfish are expected to be harvested in the lower Mississippi River states, and this production will double again in 1972 [editorial, *Comm. Fish. Rev.* **30** (5), 18 (1968)]; J. E. Bardach and J. H. Ryther, *The Status and Potential of Aquaculture, Particularly Fish Culture,* prepared for National Council on Marine Resources and Engineering Development 1967, PB 177768 (Clearinghouse Fed. Sci. Tech. Info., Springfield, Va., 1968); J. H. Ryther and J. E. Bardach, *The Status and Potential of Aquaculture, Particularly Invertebrate and Algae Culture,* prepared for National Council on Marine Resources and Engineering Development, PB 177767 (Clearinghouse Fed. Sci. Tech. Info., Springfield, Va., 1968).

7. J. E. Shelbourne, *Advan. Mar. Biol.* **2**, 1 (1964).
8. G. O. Schumann, personal communication.
9. C. P. Idyll, personal communication.
10. The study of the status and potential of aquaculture was financed by a contract with the National Council on Marine Research and Engineering Development, Executive Office of the President.
11. W. A. Dill, *Proc. World Symp. Warm Water Pond Fish Culture, Fish. Rep.* **44** (1), i (1967).
12. H. P. Clemens and K. E. Sneed, *Bioassay and Use of Pituitary Materials to Spawn Warm-Water Fishes*, Res. Rept. 61 (U.S. Fish and Wildlife Service, Washington, D.C., 1962), 30 pp.
13. W. Steffens, *Verh. int. Ver. Limmol.* **16** (3), 1441 (1967).
14. R. Moav and G. Wohlfarth, *Bamidgeh* **12**, 5 (1960).
15. Departments of Commerce and Labor, *Fisheries of the U.S. 1908; Special Report* (U.S. Government Printing Office, Washington, D.C., 1911), p. 49.
16. F. Bregnballe *Progr. Fish. Culturist* **25** (3), 115 (1963).
17. L. R. Donaldson and D. Manasveta, *Trans. Amer. Fish. Soc.* **90**, 160 (1961).
18. K. D. Carlander, *Handbook of Freshwater Fishery Biology* (Brown, Dubuque, Iowa, 1950), pp. 30–36.
19. L. R. Donaldson, *Proc. Pac. Sci. Congr. Tokyo Sci. Counc. 11th* **7**, 4 (1966).
20. N. Fredin, personal communication.
21. *Fishery Statistics of the United States 1965*, Statistical Digest No. 59 (U.S. Department of Interior, Washington, D.C., 1967), pp. 541–547.
22. C. L. Hubbs, in *Vertebrate Speciation*, W. F. Blair, Ed. (Univ. of Texas Press, Austin, 1961), pp. 5–23.
23. L. R. Donaldson, personal communication.
24. P. S. Galtsoff, "The American oyster fish," *U.S. Dept. Interior Bull.* **64**. 297–323 (1964).
25. J. H. Ryther, personal communication.
26. V. L. Loosanoff and H. C. Davis, *Adv Mar. Biol.* **1**, 1 (1963).
27. Research on shrimp rearing in the United States is carried on at the Laboratory of the Bureau of Commercial Fisheries in Galveston, at the Bears Bluff Laboratory of the South Carolina Wildlife Resources Commission, and at the Institute of Marine Sciences of the University of Miami in Florida.
28. S. L. Hora and T. V. R. Pillay, *Handbook on Fish Culture in the Indo-Pacific Region*, FAO Fish. Biol. Tech. Paper No. 14 (Foreign Agriculture Office, Rome, 1962), pp. 124–132.
29. Yun-An Tang, personal communication.
30. F. Gross, S. M. Marshall, A. P. Orr, J. E. G. Raymont, *Proc. Roy. Soc., Edinburgh Ser. B* **63**, 1 (1947); F. Gross, S. R. Nutman, D. T. Gauld, J. E. G. Raymont, *ibid.* **64**, 1 (1950).
31. A. Yashouv, *Bamidgeh* **17** (3), 55 (1965); A. Yashouv, personal communication.
32. M. Huet, *Rech. Eaux Forêts Groenendaal-Hoeilaart Belgique, Trans. Ser. D* **22**, 1–109 (1957).
33. K. F. Vaas and M. Sachlan, *Proc. Indopacif. Fish Counc. 6th* (1956), pp. 187–196.
34. Th. Rangen, personal communication.
35. Whitefish Authority, *Annual Report and Accounts 1967* (Her Majesty's Stationery Office, London, 1967).
36. L. V. Gribanov, *Use of Thermal Waters for Commercial Production of*

Carp in Floats in the U.S.S.R., Working MS 44060. World Symposium on Warm Water Pondfish Culture (Foreign Agriculture Office, Rome, 1966).
37. T. V. R. Pillay, personal communication.
38. W. H. Schuster, *Fish Culture in Salt-Water Ponds on Java* (Dept. of Agriculture and Fisheries, Div. of Inland Fisheries, publ. 2, Bandung, 1949), 277 pp.
39. Yun-An Tang, *Philippines Fish. Yearb.* (1966), p. 82.
40. The U.S. Atomic Energy Commission Laboratory at Oak Ridge studies the feasibility of agronuclear complexes as shore installations in arid regions to produce cheap power, fresh water, and fertilizer; see New York *Times*, 10 Mar. 1968, p. 74. The agronuclear complexes will furnish ideal conditions for advanced aquaculture on a large scale.
41. S. J. Holt, in *The Biological Basis of Freshwater Fish Production* (Wiley, New York, 1967), pp. 455–467.
42. I thank for assistance and information J. H. Ryther, G. O. Schumann, L. R. Donaldson, S. J. Holt, T. V. R. Pillay, W. Beckman, Th. Rangen, M. Fujiya, A. Yashouv, F. Bregnballe, E. Bertelsen, C. Mozzi, K. Kuronuma, S. Y. Lin, S. W. Ling, Y. A. Tang, M. Ovchynnyk, C. F. Hickling, I. Richardson, S. H. Swingle, R. V. Pantulu, F. P. Meyer, J. Donahue, M. Bohl, M. Delmendo, H. H. Reichenbach-Klinke, and D. E. Thackrey.

David A. Ross, Egon T. Degens, John M. Hunt, and Earl E. Hays:

70.   *THE HOT BRINE DEEPS OF THE RED SEA**

HISTORY OF EXPLORATION

The Red Sea has been investigated by oceanographic research vessels since the late nineteenth century; however, it was not until the late 1940s that the hot brine area was discovered. The Swedish *Albatross* Expedition of 1947–48 first noted small anomolous increases in salinity and temperature in the deep waters of the central

* Woods Hole Oceanographic Institution Contribution No. 2225. (This is an original contribution to this volume.)

David A. Ross is an assistant scientist at Woods Hole Oceanographic Institution and an associate professor at Cape Cod Community College.

Egon T. Degens is also associated with Woods Hole Oceanographic Institution as Senior Scientist in the Department of Chemistry.

John M. Hunt is Chairman of the Department of Chemistry at Woods Hole.

Earl E. Hays, formerly Chairman of the Geophysics Department at Woods Hole, is now Deputy Director of Saclant ASW Research Center for N.A.T.O.

part of the Red Sea (Bruneau et al. 1953). They measured salinities of 45⁰/₀₀ and temperatures of 24.5°C at a depth of 1,930 meters; normal conditions at this depth are about 40⁰/₀₀ and 20–22°C. The *Atlantis* and *Atlantis II* of the Woods Hole Oceanographic Institution and the British research vessel *Discovery* in subsequent years confirmed the findings of the *Albatross*. The *Discovery* returned to the area in 1964 and measured, much to their surprise, water having a temperature of 44°C and a salinity* of about 255⁰/₀₀ (Swallow and Crease, 1965). In 1965 the *Atlantis II* returned to the area and measured bottom temperatures of 56°C and salinities of also 255⁰/₀₀ (Miller et al., 1966). The German vessel *Meteor* also visited the area in 1966.

THE CHAIN EXPEDITION

Considering the results of these previous investigations the Woods Hole Oceanographic Institution applied and received a research grant from the National Science Foundation to make a detailed investigation of the area. In 1966 the R.V. *Chain* spent six weeks studying all oceanographic aspects of the area. The remainder of this paper summarizes some of the results of the cruise.

The first objective of the cruise was to survey the area. This survey showed that the areas initially explored by *Discovery* and *Atlantis* were separate and distinct areas (Figure 70–1). These areas have been named for the ships that first discovered them; a new deep, the *Chain* Deep was also found (Ross and Hunt, 1967) that had a temperature of 34°C and a salinity of 47⁰/₀₀. The deepest part of the *Chain* Deep was not sampled so these values are probably not the maximum values.

GEOLOGIC SETTING

The brine area is located in the middle of the central rift valley of the Red Sea, an area of intensive tectonic activity. The patterns of magnetic anomalies from this area had been interpreted as indicating a recent spreading or rifting apart of the sea floor along this central rift. The rate of spreading is estimated as about 1.5 cm/year. As the sea floor spreads apart new ocean floor is added along the rift valley; this is accompanied by folding, faulting, and volca-

---

* These salinities are not true salinities, since the ratio of the major ions are different from that of sea water. The values presented here are the total solids after evaporation of the water (heated to 200°C).

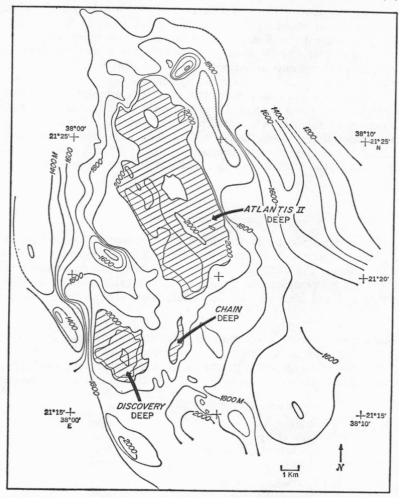

Fig. 70–1. General bathymetry of the hot brine region of the Red Sea (from Hunt et al., 1967).

nism. This process is strongly related to the discharge of the hot brine into the deeps.

The *Atlantis II* and *Discovery* Deeps are connected by a small narrow channel that has a sill high enough to prevent present mixing of the hot saline waters of the different deeps. The deeps are irregular in shape. The *Atlantis II* Deep is the largest; it is an elongate basin about 14 km long and 5 km wide at the 2000 m contour interval. Its flanks slope from a maximum of about 35° on part of the eastern flank to 5 to 15°. The *Discovery* Deep is circular in shape and as defined at the 2000 m contour interval is about 4 km long and 2.5 km wide. Its flanks slope 15° or less. *Chain* Deep is very narrow and elongated; its slopes are about 20°. This deep is only 3 km long and 0.7 km wide. The maximum depth observed in the *Atlantis II* Deep is 2170 m, the *Discovery* Deep 2220 m, and the *Chain* Deep 2066 m. The total area of the three basins below the 2000 m contour is about 70 km², about 0.016 per cent of the total area of the Red Sea (Emery, Hunt and Hays, 1969).

WATER STRUCTURE

The water structure in the deeps was measured by conventional hydrocasts using reversing thermometers and by a temperature measuring pinger. The latter device gave a continuous measurement of the water temperature and showed a distinct water structure for the *Atlantis II* and *Discovery* Deeps (Table 70–1). It can be seen from

TABLE 70–1. WATER STRUCTURE IN THE *Atlantis II* AND *Discovery* DEEPS (DEPTHS IN CORRECTED METERS BUT NO CORRECTION FOR THE SPEED OF SOUND IN THE BRINE, DATA FROM ROSS, (1969).

Atlantis II Deep	*Depth meters*
Start of hot water	1984
Top of 44° water	2009
Bottom of 44° water	2037
Top of 56° water	2042
Discovery Deep	
Start of hot water	1986
Top of 36° water	2023
Bottom of 36° water	2027
Top of 44° water	2042

this table that several different layers of anomalous water were found. The different layers may result from periodic discharges of brine or, as laboratory experiments indicate, may result from heating from below. The available evidence suggests that the source of the hot brine is the *Atlantis II* Deep; the hot water apparently at times in the past has overflowed into the *Discovery* and *Chain* Deeps.

The main chemical components of the brine are shown in Table 70–2. One especially interesting property of these brines is their

TABLE 70–2. CHEMICAL COMPOSITION (G/KG) OF THE BRINES OF *Atlantis II*,
Discovery AND *Chain* DEEPS (DATA FROM BREWER AND SPENCER, 1969).

Element	Atlantis II	Discovery	Chain	Normal sea water
Cl	156.03	155.3	41.9	19.35
Br	0.128	0.119	0.084	0.066
$SO_4^=$	0.840	0.695	2.81	2.71
Si	0.0276	0.003	—	0.004
Na	92.60	93.05	24.0	10.76
K	1.87	2.14	0.78	0.39
Ca	5.15	5.12	1.18	0.41
Mg	0.764	0.810	1.42	1.29
Sr	4.8×10^{-2}	0.046	0.012	0.008
Fe	8.1×10^{-2}	2.7×10^{-4}	—	2×10^{-5}
Mn	8.2×10^{-2}	5.46×10^{-4}	0.005	1×10^{-5}
Zn	5.4×10^{-3}	7.7×10^{-4}	—	5×10^{-6}
Cu	2.6×10^{-4}	7.5×10^{-5}	—	1×10^{-5}
Co	1.6×10^{-4}	1.29×10^{-4}	—	—
Ni	—	3.42×10^{-4}	—	4×10^{-6}
Pb	6.3×10^{-4}	1.65×10^{-4}	—	1×10^{-7}
Temperature (°C)	56.5°	44.7°	29.1°	—
Salinity (‰)	257.7	257.3	72.2	35.7

content of heavy metals. The brines are enriched, sometimes as much as 50,000 times over normal sea water, in metals like iron, manganese, zinc, lead, copper, silver, and gold. The value of these waters, because of their contained amounts of heavy metals, is over 10 million dollars.

SEDIMENTS

The most surprising thing about this area is the sediments underlying these hot brines. These sediments are the most spectacularly colored sediments obtained from the deep sea. A detailed analysis (Bischoff, 1969) has shown that three main facies or sediment types are dominant:

1) Iron—Montmorillonite—mostly iron oxides with some sphalerite
2) Goethite—Amorphous—mainly goethite
3) Sulfide—mainly sulfide minerals

All these sediments are enriched in the same heavy metals found in the overlying water. The thickness of these sediments is at least 10 meters; in some isolated areas 100 meters may be present.

The metalliferous sediments are precipitated from the brine when it comes in contact with sulfide ions and oxygen in the overlying waters. The sediments settle out forming a blanket deposit over the area. These deposits are somewhat similar to the sulfide deposits of Illinois and Missouri.

ECONOMIC POTENTIAL

Bischoff and Manheim, 1969, have made an economic evaluation of upper 10 meters of sediment in the *Atlantis II* Deep. Their estimate based on numerous chemical analyses of the sediment is that at current smelter prices (December, 1967) the zinc, copper, lead, silver, and gold, are worth 2.3 billion dollars (Table 70–3).

TABLE 70–3. VALUE OF METALS IN THE SEDIMENTS OF THE
Atlantis II DEEP
(DATA FROM BISCHOFF AND MANHEIM, 1969).

Metals	Average Assay (%)	tons in top 10 meters (in millions)	value (in millions of dollars)
Iron	29.	24.3	—
Zinc	3.4	2.9	780
Copper	1.3	1.06	1170
Lead	0.1	0.08	20
Silver	.0054	0.0045	280
Gold	.00005	0.000045	50
			2,300

This is the *in situ* value at the ocean bottom and does not consider the cost of raising and refining the material. The total amount of sediment, on a brine free basis, exceeds 80 million tons. The value of the deposit raises another question—who owns it? According to the Geneva Convention the deposit belongs to Sudan, however, several alternative points can be presented to this very confusing legal problem. The economic history of this area will probably be one of complex legal maneuvers for the next few years.

This short paper has only discussed a few of the interesting aspects of the Red Sea brine area. A full account of the research on this problem has been published in a symposium volume: *Hot Brines and Recent Heavy Metal Deposits in the Red Sea*, edited by E. T. Degens and D. A. Ross, and published by Springer Verlag Inc., New York, 1969.

REFERENCES

Bischoff, J. L., 1969, Red Sea geothermal brine deposits: their mineralogy, chemistry, and genesis, in: *Hot Brines and Recent Heavy Metal Deposits in the Red Sea*, edited by E. T. Degens and D. A. Ross, Springer Verlag Inc., New York.

Bischoff, J. L., and F. T. Manheim, 1969, Economic potential of the Red Sea metal deposits, in: *Hot Brines and Recent Heavy Metal Deposits in the Red Sea*, edited by E. T. Degens and D. A. Ross, Springer Verlag Inc., New York.

Brewer, P. G., and D. W. Spencer, 1969, A note on the chemical composition of the Red Sea brines, in: *Hot Brines and Recent Heavy Metal Deposits in the Red Sea*, edited by E. T. Degens and D. A. Ross, Springer Verlag Inc., New York.

Bruneau, L., N. G. Jerlov, and F. F. Koczy, 1953, Reports of the Swedish Deep Sea Expedition, V. 3, Physics and Chemistry, Fasc. II, Appendix 29.

Emery, K. O., J. M. Hunt, and E. E. Hays, 1969, Summary of hot brines and heavy metal deposits in the Red Sea, in: *Hot Brines and Recent Heavy Metal Deposits in the Red Sea*, edited by E. T. Degens and D. A. Ross, Springer Verlag Inc., New York.

Hunt, J. M., E. E. Hays, E. T. Degens, and D. A. Ross, 1967, Red Sea: detailed survey of hot-brine areas, Science, 156, 514–516.

Miller, A. R., C. D. Densmore, E. T. Degens, J. C. Hathaway, F. T. Manheim, P. F. McFarlin, R. Pocklington, and A. Jokela, 1966, Hot brines and recent iron deposits in deeps of the Red Sea, Geochimica et Cosmochimica Acta, 30, 341–359.

Ross, D. A., 1969, Temperature structure of the Red Sea brines, in: *Hot Brines and Recent Heavy Metal Deposits in the Red Sea*, edited by E. T. Degens and D. A. Ross, Springer Verlag Inc., New York.

Ross, D. A., and J. M. Hunt, 1967, Third brine pool in the Red Sea, Nature, 213, 687–688.

Swallow, J. C. and J. Crease, 1965, Hot salty water at the bottom of the Red Sea, Nature, 205, 165–166.

~~~~~~~~~~~~~~~~

Arthur C. Mathieson:

71.   THE PROMISE OF SEAWEED*

One of the major sources of potential food products in the sea is represented by the attached macroscopic marine algae commonly called "seaweeds."

About a decade ago it was estimated that 750,000 tons of seaweed—having a gross value of $30-million—were harvested annually in the Western world. Today's totals probably are double or more what they were.

Many species of seaweeds have been used as a direct source of food since ancient times. The most diversified dietary use of seaweed was developed in Hawaii where, during the 19th century, 75 different kinds were used regularly as food. In most cases, the algae, called "limu," were chopped up and used as a relish in combination with nuts, fish, octopus, squid, and other foods.

Each limu had a particular culinary use. Some species occurred in very small quantities, and were considered delicacies for the nobility. Indeed, certain limus were transplanted to royal gardens, where they were tended and harvested. Three of the most popular forms were limu ele-ele (black limu), limu kohu (red limu), and limu lipoa.

The first type is composed of two green algae (*Enteromorpha intestinalis* and *E. flexuosa*), the second is a red alga (*Asparagopsis sanfordiana*), and the third is a brown alga (*Haliseris plagiogramma*).

The Japanese made extensive use of seaweed as food. The red alga *Porphyra*, or purple laver as it also is called, has been harvested for food for centuries. At present, it is the basis of an industry that employs more than a half million people.

Porphyra is the only alga that is currently cultivated and harvested on a commercial scale. It has been "farmed" in Tokyo Bay and elsewhere in Japan since 1670.

* From *Oceanology International*, Vol. 4 No. 1, January/February, 1969, pp. 37–39. Copyright © 1969 by Industrial Research, Inc. Reprinted by permission of the publisher and author.

Arthur C. Mathieson is a professor in the department of Botany at the University of New Hampshire, in Durham.

Different grades of nori are determined by the purity of *Porphyra*. The final product is used in soups, sauces, sandwiches, macaroni, and various other commodities. The value of the nori industry has been estimated at over $17-million annually, and an average income-per-acre is said to be $350.

The larger brown algae (kelps) have been used extensively as a source of food (kombu and wakame) since before the Christian era. The stalks (stipes) and blades are dried and pressed into blocks, and then are sold. Thin slices are used for soups, sauces, and vegetables. They also are mixed with various meats, steeped in fresh water to make a drink, and eaten as a candy after being coated with sugar.

Many of the smaller brown and green algae are used by the Japanese, but they are not exported extensively. They are used in salads, as vegetables, as garnishes for meats and fish, in soups and sauces, and in jellies.

The red algae dulse (*Rhodymenia palmata*) and Irish moss (*Chondrus crispus*) are used as food in parts of Western Europe, the maritime provinces of Canada, and New England. Dulse is eaten raw, cooked with soups, eaten with fish and butter, and used in a variety of other ways. Irish moss is dried and eaten out-of-hand like popcorn or used in making blancmanges and soft jellies.

The jelling qualities of Irish moss are due to the colloidal material (carrageenan) found within its cells. A soft jelly bread also is made from Irish moss. The Indians in the Pacific Northwest used *Porphyra* and the common sea lettuce (*Ulva*) as a source of food and salt.

LITTLE NUTRITIVE VALUE

Seaweeds contained a high percentage of indigestible carbohydrates. They are comparable to lettuce and celery for the roughage they provide. Their greatest nutritional value lies in the various vitamins, minerals, and trace elements they contain.

The amount of vitamin C in some brown and red algae is equal to or greater than that in a lemon. Thiamine, niacin, and riboflavin also are abundant in brown algae. Most seaweeds are a good source of iodine, which aids in the normal functioning of the thyroid gland.

Marine algae long have been used as fodder in coastal areas (particularly near the North Sea). The livestock in these areas graze directly on the seaweeds at low tide, and during the winter harvested seaweed is used to supplement their diets. Dulse and kelps are favorite foods of goats, cows, and sheep.

Seaweed meals and powders made from the brown alga, *Asco-phyllum nodosum*, are used extensively as supplements to dried milk and other rations. They serve as a valuable source of vitamins and trace elements.

Seaweeds (particularly *Ascophyllum nodosum*) long have been used as green manures in maritime districts of Europe and North America. The fertilizing constituents in fresh seaweed are compara-ble to barnyard manures, but contain more potassium salts and less phosphorous.

Seaweed manures are particularly good for root crops (beets and potatoes). They are said to promote germination of certain seeds, to increase the resistance of plants to fungal and insect pests, and to impart a degree of frost resistance to tomatoes.

SEAWEED MEDICINAL USE

Seaweeds were considered of medicinal value in the Orient as long ago as 3000 B.C. The Chinese and Japanese used them in the treatment of goiter and other glandular troubles. Although the Ro-mans believed seaweeds to be useless, they did use them to heal wounds, burns, scurvy, and rashes. The British used *Porphyra* to prevent scurvy on long voyages.

Various red algae (particularly *Corallina officinalis, C. rubens,* and *Alsidium helminthocorton*) were employed as vermifuges in ancient times. Dulse is reported to be a laxative, and also to reduce fever. Several red algae (including *Chondrus crispus, Gracilaria, Gelidium,* and *Pterocladia*) have been used to treat various stomach and intestinal disorders. The algae apparently absorb enough water to relieve constipation and other associated discomforts. One Hawai-ian red alga, *Centroceras clavulatum*, was used extensively as a cathartic. The stipes of one large kelp (*Laminaria cloustoni*) have been used to aid in childbirth by distending the uterus during labor.

Recently, a number of species of marine algae have been found to have anticoagulant and antibiotic properties. The colloidal ex-tracts (carrageenan) of some red algae may be useful in ulcer therapy, while the colloidal materials of brown algae (alginates) are found to prolong the "rate of activity" of certain drugs.

The first industrial use of seaweed in Europe was begun during the 17th century. Various brown algae (particularly species of *Laminaria*) were burned to produce soda and potash, which was used in the production of soap, glass, porcelain, and alum.

The ash originally was referred to as kelp, and later the brown algae that produced the ash were designated as kelps. By 1800, over 20,000 tons of potash were produced in Scotland. This is even more impressive when you consider that kelps yield 4% soda.

The production of soda from seaweeds ended in about 1810, when a cheaper source was discovered. However, at about the same time, iodine was discovered in seaweed ash. It was used widely as an antiseptic, and later in dyestuffs and photography. Thus, kelp burning again was revived, and it continued at a high level until 1870, when an extensive source of iodate was found in Chilean nitrate deposits. At present, only Japan produces iodine from seaweeds.

During 1917–18, the wartime demands for potash and acetone brought about the rapid industrialization of giant kelps (particularly *Macrocystis*) on the Pacific Coast of North America. New methods of harvesting (mechanical) and drying were developed, and over 400,000 tons of seaweed were harvested annually.

After the war, it no longer was feasible to obtain potash from kelp, and its production was ceased. However, in 1926 a versatile kelp industry was established upon the organic constituents of seaweeds (phycocolloids).

Phycocolloids are naturally occurring storage products (polysaccharides) of seaweeds. They also are referred to as hydrocolloids, because they are able to form colloidal systems when dispersed in water. They are cell wall components of seaweeds, but are commercially extractable from the brown and red algae.

The principal phycocolloids are algin (from kelps and rockweeds), agar (from *Gelidium* and other related red algae), and carrageenan (from the red algae *Chondrus crispus*, *Gigartina*, and related species). Each phycocolloid has characteristics suiting it to particular uses, and each can be varied within relatively broad limits by extractive and chemical techniques.

PRIMARY SOURCE OF ALGIN

Algin or alginic acid is prominent in kelps. It is said to constitute about 2.5% of the total weight in *Macrocystis*. The latter has become the primary source of algin in the United States because of its ease of harvesting and high algin content.

Dense stands of the giant kelp are gathered along the California coastline by large motor-driven barges with mowers. The mechanical harvesters cut the kelp canopy just under 1 meter below the water surface, and transport the material to the barge. Several hundred tons of seaweed can be cut in a day. After being harvested, the material is washed and chopped, and the algin is extracted. The state of California carefully regulates the harvesting of *Macrocystis* because of its great economic value.

Several derivatives of alginic acid (calcium, sodium, ammonium, potassium, and propylene glycol alginates) have a wide variety of uses because of their viscosity and water-absorbing properties. Alginates commonly are used as emulsifiers and stabilizers in dairy products, such as sherbets, ice cream, chocolate milk, cheese, puddings, and toppings. They also are used in syrups, sauces, salad dressings, soaps, shampoos, toothpastes, shaving creams, medicines, lipsticks, paints, insecticides, plastics, fireproofing fabrics, and polishes.

Some surgical threads now are being made of alginates, because they will dissolve and do not have to be removed. A whole-blood substitute derived from seaweed has been used in emergency transfusions.

Carrageenan is another very important industrial colloid. It is obtained primarily from Irish moss and species of *Gigartina*, but it also can be extracted from at least 20 other species of red algae, many of which are found in different parts of the world.

At present, Irish moss is one of the major marine resources of New England and the maritime provinces of Canada, and it is the basis of an extensive colloid industry. Carrageenan resembles agar chemically (*i.e.* it is a carbohydrate ethereal sulphate), but it has a higher ash content and requires somewhat higher concentrations to form a gel.

As mentioned earlier, Irish moss first was harvested in Ireland and used in the preparation of blancmanges and molds. The early American colonists imported large quantities from France and Ireland to make the same favorite desserts. In 1835, extensive beds of Irish moss were found in Massachusetts, and a thriving industry soon was initiated at Scituate, Mass. In 1898, about 770,000 lbs. of the moss were harvested. Approximately 10-million lbs. of moss now are being processed from New England and the Canadian maritimes.

The moss usually is gathered by raking from a small boat or from the shore. Long-handled rakes (3 to 5 meters long) are used to scrape it from the rocks where it grows. A good raker will remove only the large blades and leave the others to be harvested at a later date.

More than one crop can be harvested per season (May to September) if a bed is properly raked. Excessive raking results in a large number of undesirable green and brown seaweeds and often ruins a commercial bed.

The raking of moss is limited in time to a few hours at low tide, and in area to waters shallow enough to be within effective reach of the rake. In some parts of Canada, Irish moss is gathered along beaches after storms. Mechanical harvesters now are being tested for gathering moss (particularly in deeper waters), but they have not been utilized commercially. When perfected, they will be a major boon to the industry. The harvested moss either is sold by the collector as wet weed, or it is cleaned and dried and then sold. Large mechanical dryers recently have been built in Maine and Canada in order to dry the wet weed.

The colloid extracted from Irish moss constitutes about half of the weight of the plants (dry weight basis). Irish moss is worth 12¢ to 13¢ per lb., dry weight, but the colloid, as extracted, standardized, and blended (*i.e.* with different carrageenans), costs well over $1 per lb. Despite this high cost, demand exceeds supply.

Carrageenan is widely used in the food and pharmaceutical industries because of its thickening, emulsifying, stabilizing, and suspending properties. It is used extensively in milk-based products because of its unique interaction and stabilizing effects with milk protein. Extracts find their way into hundreds of other common household items, such as toothpaste, diet foods (the carbohydrate is not metabolized in the human digestive system), hand creams, soups, confections, insect sprays, water-base paints, inks, shoe stains, shampoos, and cosmetics. Carrageenan also is applied in the sizing of cloth and thread, in certain printing processes, as a clarifying agent in the production of beer, and as a dental impression compound.

FIRST STABLE PRODUCT

Agar is a gel-forming substance found in certain species of red algae (*e.g. Gelidium, Gracilaria,* and *Pterocladia*). The name agar is an abbreviation for the Malayan or Ceylonese term agar-agar, which means jelly. A jelly is produced from these seaweeds when they are boiled and the resulting liquid is cooled.

Agar first was produced commercially by the Japanese in 1670, and it was the first seaweed product to become an important stable item of commerce. The Japanese still are the primary producers of agar. However, since World War II, agar has been produced by Britain, Denmark, Australia, United States, Soviet Union, New Zealand, India, and South Africa.

The harvesting of most agarophytes (*i.e.* agar-producing seaweeds) is done by hand, although various rakes, hooks, grapnels, and nets also are employed. Divers sometimes collect in deep locations.

Most of the seaweeds are obtained from natural beds, although the Japanese have had reasonable success propagating one genus (*Gracilaria*) in Tokyo Bay. Branches of the plant are placed at intervals in the twists of ropes and the ropes are suspended in the nutrient rich waters. Later they are pulled up and harvested. Agar constitutes about 30% to 35% of the total dry weight of most species.

When agar originally was discovered it was considered to be a novelty. It subsequently has become fundamental to microbiologists as a media for bacteriological cultures, as well as a basic component of medicines, foods, and a variety of other products. Robert Koch showed (in 1881) that agar was an effective culture medium because many microorganisms were unable to decompose it.

Agar was found to be useful for stomach and intestinal disorders. It is a nonirritant bulk producer that absorbs and holds water as well as serving as a mild laxative. It now is employed as a covering for various capsules (antibiotics, sulfa compound, and vitamins) when a slow release of the medicine is desired at a point beyond the stomach.

Agar preparations sometimes are used beneath bandages to heal wounds. In addition, it has a variety of other uses—the preservation of canned meats, fish, and other easily spoiled foodstuffs; the preparation of sizing for fabrics; an ingredient of waterproof paper, waterproof cloth, and glue; a cleaning medium; a clarifying agent in the manufacturing of wines, beers and coffee; and the preparation of special breads for diabetics, in which agar replaces the starch.

It is evident that agar, carrageenan, and algin have many similar uses. However, they have specific properties that restrict or enhance their use, depending on the circumstances.

The usage of seaweed products (especially phycocolloids) has increased substantially in recent years. In most cases, demand far exceeds supply. The potential for future growth of the seaweed industry is excellent, if adequate sources of raw materials are available. Thus, intelligent programs of conservation, cultivation, and harvesting of these valuable marine resources must be initiated.